ITALIAN PHYSICAL SOCIETY

PROCEEDINGS
OF THE
INTERNATIONAL SCHOOL OF PHYSICS « ENRICO FERMI »

COURSE XXXI

C. H. TOWNES
Director of the Course

VARENNA ON LAKE COMO
VILLA MONASTERO
19th - 31st AUGUST 1963

Quantum Electronics and Coherent Light

Proceedings edited by
P. A. MILES

1964

ACADEMIC PRESS · NEW YORK AND LONDON

SOCIETÀ ITALIANA DI FISICA

RENDICONTI

DELLA

SCUOLA INTERNAZIONALE DI FISICA «ENRICO FERMI»

XXXI CORSO

C. H. TOWNES
Direttore del Corso

VARENNA SUL LAGO DI COMO
VILLA MONASTERO
19-31 AGOSTO 1963

Elettronica quantistica e luce coerente

Rendiconti a cura di
P. A. MILES

1964

ACADEMIC PRESS • NEW YORK AND LONDON

ACADEMIC PRESS INC.
111 Fifth Avenue
New York 3, N. Y.

United Kingdom Edition
Published by
ACADEMIC PRESS INC. (London) Ltd.
Berkeley Square House, London W. 1

Library of Congress Catalog Card Number: 64-17798

PRINTED IN ITALY

INDICE

Maser Amplification and Coherent Light.
Introduction.

C. H. TOWNES
Massachusetts Institute of Technology - Cambridge, Mass.

The appearance of optical, infra-red and ultra-violet masers (or lasers) makes practical a wide variety of new physical experiments, and lends additional importance to the development of new aspects of the theory of radiation and its interaction with matter. Hence, the initiation by Professor GILBERTO BERNARDINI of the thirty-first Course of the Scuola Internazionale di Fisica « Enrico Fermi » on « Quantum Electronics and Coherent Light » was timely and welcomed. The present collection of papers results from lectures on this topic by the faculty of the Course and some of its guests and students, who assembled in late August 1963 in delightful Varenna on Lake Como. The Course itself was of record size, including over eighty participants.

Perfectly coherent light is a mathematical idealization and cannot exist physically. Yet the radiation generated by lasers represents a very large step from previously available light towards coherence, and hence can reasonably, though in approximation only, be referred to as coherent. Certain of its properties are, in fact, different numerically by many orders of magnitude from those of previously attainable optical and infra-red radiations. Prior to lasers, our light sources have largely been black-body radiators, and have hence usually been limited by fundamental thermodynamic laws and by the maximum temperatures (of the order of 10^4 °K) to which it is practical to raise a radiating mass of atoms or molecules without decomposing either them or their containers. Even certain special types of sources, such as fluorescent materials, have not radically increased this radiative temperature. Coherent amplification of light provided by maser techniques allows one in principle to produce light of an indefinitely large effective temperature, or with an indefinitely large number of quanta per electromagnetic mode. In practice, effective temperatures higher than 10^{20} °K are rather easily achieved. This may be regarded as the essence of the «breakthrough» provided by lasers, from which one obtains exceedingly large values for the energy or power per frequency interval per area per solid angle, or light in which any one of these parameters can take on striking values. In fact, firm limits to the characteristics of laser radiation are set only by the fundamental wave-particle properties of radiation.

Already, only a few years after the first efforts towards applying maser techniques to the amplification of light, lasers are available in many forms and such systems have been made to oscillate at hundreds of different frequencies over a wide spectral region from the near ultra-violet into the far infra-red. Extension of coherent oscillators further into the ultra-violet, and into the submillimeter region to join the microwave range, seems only to require a little more time. The broad principles and characteristics of these maser oscillators seem to be understood and, based on them, a large variety of techniques, devices, and applications have been either explored in a preliminary way or are on the verge of being developed. The field is already too large and diverse to be represented in any detail in one volume. Hence, the summer school called by the Società Italiana di Fisica, and this volume which are its proceedings, have paid attention almost exclusively to basic physical aspects of lasers, the «coherent» light which they generate, and interaction of such intense light with matter.

Material in this volume is arranged somewhat in the nature of a course, which was its basis. However, a few additional special topics, more of the nature of research papers, are also included. Furthermore, even the tutorial and summarizing papers include a considerable amount of material which was not previously published. Papers have been ordered in the following general arrangement of topics:

— Surveys of optically pumped and injection lasers.
— Examination of electromagnetic resonators which are useful in optical systems.
— Theory of oscillation of gaseous masers, and interaction between electromagnetic waves and matter within the maser.
— Special topics on the behavior of gaseous and solid-state masers.
— Techniques and theory of high-resolution interference spectroscopy.
— Excitation and states of certain impurities in crystals.
— General examination of nonlinear optical effects.
— Special topics on nonlinear optical effects in semiconductors.
— Quantum theory of Raman maser action.
— Coherent Raman and Brillouin effects.
— Special topics on laser devices, and on measurement of the velocity of light.

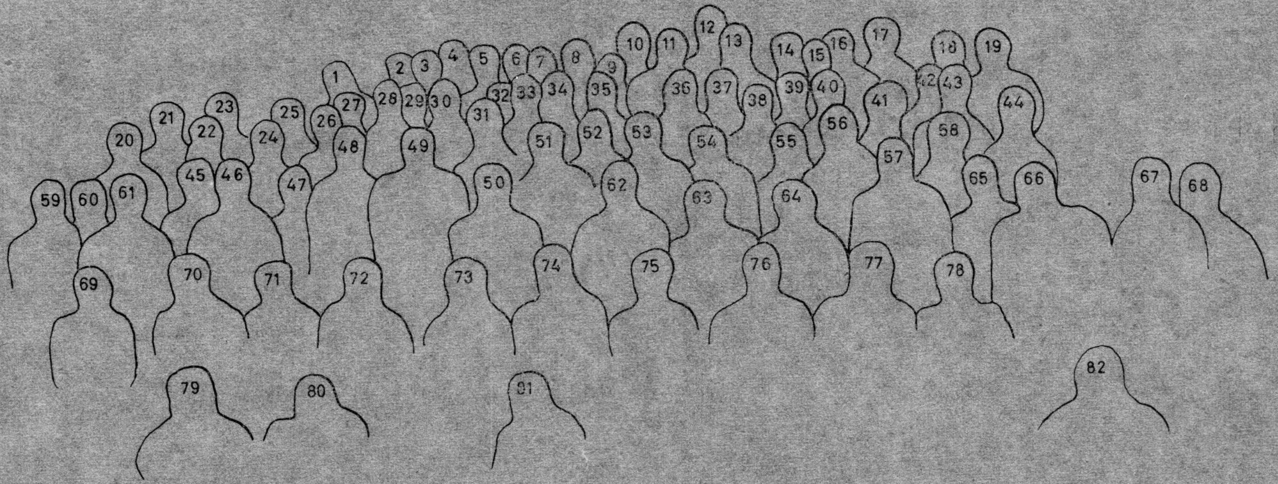

1. B. Kronast
2. J. Haisma
3. E. H. Frei
4. O. N. Krochin
5. V. Andresciani
6. L. R. Wilcox
7. S. Yatsiv
8. J. Emmett
9. R. Cappelletti
10. E. Panizza
11. P. Gordon
12. H. F. Vanheek
13. D. L. Falkoff
14. E. van der Voort
15. E. Polacco
16. A. Steinemann
17. H. Sauermann
18. H. Risken
19. A. Sona
20. A. H. Oraevski
21. Y. Merle d'Aubigné
22. L. Huldt
23. P. T. Bolwijn
24. W. Lukosz
25. J. E. Hansen
26. G. Magyar
27. A. Omont
28. H. Hora
29. J. F. Westerkamp
30. D. W. Goodwin
31. F. T. Arecchi
32. M. Mancini
33. T. P. McLean
34. J. L. Otto
35. J. M. Burch
36. H. S. Boyne
37. E. Patscheke
38. G. Tondello
39. H. Walther
40. O. Svelto
41. B. Elschner
42. W. Schneider
43. B. Daino
44. J. P. van der Ziel
45. B. Pajot
46. H. Gärtner
47. P. Lallemand
48. K. Shimoda
49. S. Chandra
50. G. Toraldo di Francia
51. D. Sette
52. M. Worlock
53. E. Zilli
54. G. E. Frigerio
55. F. Marinelli
56. F. De Martini
57. P. A. Miles
58. L. U. Hibbard
59. E. A. Triaille
60. A. Kahane
61. J.-C. Lehmann
62. E. Gatti
63. W. Low
64. B. Stoicheff
65. G. Wang
66. A. L. Schawlow
67. H. W. de Wijn
68. C. Patek
69. F. Grossetête
70. S. J. Lewandowski
71. M. Bertolotti
72. L. Ronchi Abbozzo
73. A. Javan
74. J. P. Gordon
75. W. E. Lamb jr.
76. C. H. Townes
77. P. Connes
78. N. Bloembergen
79. P. Toschek
80. R. Buisson
81. M. Iannuzzi
82. R. Pratesi

SOCIETÀ ITALIANA DI FISICA

SCUOLA INTERNAZIONALE DI FISICA « E. FERMI »

XXXI CORSO - VARENNA SUL LAGO DI COMO - VILLA MONASTERO - 19-31 Agosto 1963

Optically Pumped Masers and Solid-State Masers.

A. L. Schawlow

Department of Physics, Stanford University - Stanford, Cal.

I. Optically Pumped Masers.

Before we discuss optically pumped masers, let us derive, in a simplified manner, the threshold conditions for laser oscillation. The approach is essentially the rate-equation approximation, except that we are concerned only with threshold requirements and do not go as far as the rate equations. In other words, we will initially neglect the effects of stimulated emission on the population in the excited state. In this respect, the approximations are essentially those used in some of the earliest derivations of the requirements for laser operation [1].

We consider a long column of active medium terminated at the ends by mirrors having reflectivity R. For the moment, we consider only two energy levels, E_1 and E_2 with E_2 above E_1. If the length of the column is D, and the amplification constant (negative absorption constant) is α per cm, the threshold requirement for oscillation is that the gain during one pass is enough to compensate for the losses on reflection: losses in the medium are neglected. This is, a wave of unit intensity, after traversing the column and being reflected once, has its original intensity:

$$\exp\big[|\alpha| D\big] R \geqslant 1 . \tag{1}$$

If α is small

$$(1 + |\alpha| D) R \geqslant 1 \tag{2}$$

or

$$|\alpha| D \geqslant \frac{1-R}{R} . \tag{3}$$

If R is close to unity, then this becomes approximately

$$|\alpha| D \geqslant 1 - R \, . \tag{4}$$

For a Gaussian line shape, the absorption constant α, whether positive or negative, is related to the atomic constants by [3] (cgs units)

$$\alpha = \frac{2}{\Delta\nu} \sqrt{\frac{\ln 2}{\pi}} \frac{\pi e^2}{mc} \left(N_1 - \frac{g_1}{g_2} N_2 \right) f \, , \tag{5}$$

where $\Delta\nu$ is the line width,

e is the electron charge,

m is the electron mass,

f is the oscillator strength,

g_1 and g_2 are the degeneracy of the two states E_1 and E_2, respectively.

Numerically

$$\alpha = \frac{2.50 \cdot 10^{-2}}{\Delta\nu} \left(N_1 - \frac{g_1}{g_2} N_2 \right) f \, . \tag{6}$$

A Doppler-broadened line has a Gaussian shape, and an atomic line broadened by random strains in a solid approximates it.

For a Lorentzian line shape

$$\alpha = \frac{2}{\Delta\nu} \frac{1}{\pi} \frac{\pi e^2}{mc} \left(N_1 - \frac{g_1}{g_2} N_2 \right) f \, , \tag{7}$$

$$\alpha = \frac{1.69 \cdot 10^{-2}}{\Delta\nu} \left(N_1 - \frac{g_1}{g_2} N_2 \right) f \, . \tag{8}$$

A Lorentzian line shape is typical of a radiation-damping natural width, a pressure-broadened microwave spectral line, or a temperature-broadened line from an atom in a crystal.

For either case, f may be related to the radiative lifetime, τ_R, for spontaneous transitions from E_2 to E_1 by

$$f = \frac{mc}{8\pi^2 e^2} \frac{g_2}{g_1} \frac{\lambda_0^2}{\tau_R} \, , \tag{9}$$

where λ_0 is the wavelength.

If a fraction of the atoms, φ, decays radiatively in the desired mode, the actual lifetime is $\tau = \tau_R \varphi$.

Then for a Gaussian line

$$\alpha = \frac{2}{\Delta\nu}\sqrt{\frac{\ln 2}{\pi}}\,\frac{\pi e^2}{mc}\,\frac{mc}{8\pi\cdot\pi e^2}\,\frac{g_2}{g_1}\,\varphi\,\frac{\lambda_0^2}{\tau}\left(N_1 - \frac{g_1}{g_2}N_1\right), \tag{10}$$

$$\alpha = 3.74\cdot 10^{-2}\,\frac{\nu}{\Delta\nu}\,\varphi\,\frac{\lambda_0^3 g_1}{\tau c\, g_2}\left(N_1 - \frac{g_1}{g_2}N_2\right). \tag{11}$$

For laser action $-\alpha D \geqslant 1 - R$. If we also assume $N_1 = 0$ then for the threshold of oscillation

$$\frac{N_2}{\tau} = \frac{26.8}{\varphi}\,\frac{\Delta\nu}{\nu}\,\frac{c(1-R)}{\lambda_0^3 D}. \tag{12}$$

This is the number of atoms that must be supplied per second to E_2 if E_1 remains empty. Similarly, for a Lorentzian line, the threshold condition is

$$\frac{N_2}{\tau} = \frac{39.6}{\varphi}\,\frac{\Delta\nu}{\nu}\,\frac{c(1-R)}{\lambda_0^3 \mathrm{D}}. \tag{13}$$

In either case, the number of atoms which must be excited to E_2 during each second is proportional to the line width, $\Delta\nu$, and inversely proportional to φ. Thus we would look, in general, for materials whose fluorescence lines are fairly narrow lines and have good quantum efficiency. Other favorable factors, such as a good method for populating upper states, or a long operating wavelength, λ_0 may permit us to relax these requirements.

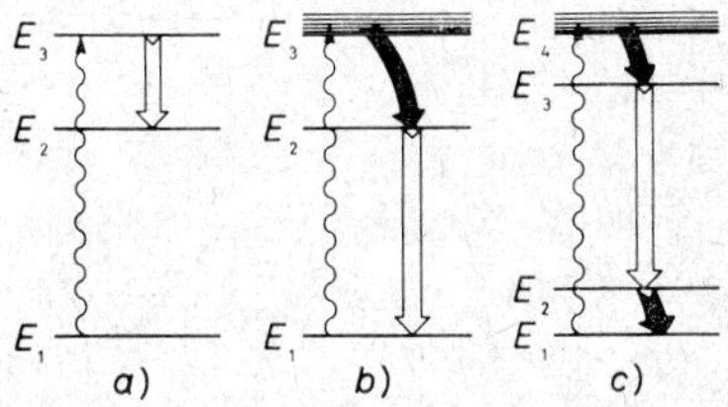

Fig. 1. – Three and four-level optically-pumped masers.

Figure 1 shows three distinct optical pumping schemes, each of which has been used for laser action in a different material. Each of these is a variant of the three-level radiofrequency pumping scheme originally proposed by BASOV and PROKHOROV and, for solids, by BLOEMBERGEN.

In Fig. 1*a*) the pumping light induces transitions from E_1 to E_3. E_3 is initially empty. E_2 will be empty if it can relax to the ground state, and $(E_2 - E_1)/h \gg kT$. Since at room temperature $kT \approx 200\ \text{cm}^{-1}$, this condition is often satisfied in the optical region, at least for low operating temperatures. The maser action takes place between levels E_3 and E_2. This arrangement has the advantage that E_2 is empty, so that any atoms excited to E_3 produce gain. It has the disadvantage that the width of the pumping transition $E_1 \to E_3$ is little more than that of the radiative transition, and thus a broad-band pumping source is not very useful. This is the arrangement used in the cesium-vapor infra-red maser. As with other alkali vapors, the pumping radiation could come from a filtered lamp of the same material. However, it is convenient to make use of an accidental coincidence of the absorption line in cesium with a strong emission line from a helium lamp [1, 4].

The scheme of Fig. 1*b*) is applicable if there is fast relaxation between levels E_3 and E_2. Then, if an atom is pumped from level E_1 to E_3 it immediately drops to E_2. Thus, we can continue pumping without equalizing the populations of levels E_1 and E_3 and can actually pump more than half of the atoms into E_2. Then maser action can take place between E_2 and E_1.

This is the arrangement of levels in pink ruby [5] (dilute Cr^{3+} in Al_2O_3), and in $CaF_2:T_m^{2+}$ [6]. It has the disadvantage that approximately half of the atoms must be transferred to the upper state before any gain at all is achieved. However, the functions of absorbing and emitting are separated. Thus, absorption may take place over a broad band of wavelenths, while the emitting level remains sharp.

The advantages of both Fig. 1*a*) and Fig. 1*b*) may be obtained if four levels are available as in Fig. 1*c*). This is indeed the arrangement of levels with many rare-earth ions, such as neodymium, proesodymium, etc.

Suitable materials may be found in the form of gases, or in condensed materials such as solids or liquids. Because it is usually easier to pump a gas maser by some electrical discharge mechanism, not much has been done on optically pumped gas masers. In solids, most of the suitable materials have used energy levels of rare-earth ions, but ruby is a very important example of a transition-metal ion in a crystal.

Rare-earth ions can be treated almost as if free. That is, the energy levels are identified as in free space by quantum numbers L, S and J. This is so, because the rare-earth ions have an unfilled shell of f electrons, which are fairly strongly localized in the radial direction. Thus, their wave functions do not extend out far enough to have much overlap with neighboring ions. The important optical transitions are between different states of the same f^n configuration, and those are not much affected by the electric fields of neighboring ions, or by lattice vibrations. Crystalline fields split these levels into at most $2J+1$ states, usually within a few hundred cm^{-1} of each other.

We may write the Hamiltonian of an ion, in a solid, in the form

$$H = -\frac{\hbar^2}{2m}\sum_i \nabla_i^2 - \sum_i \frac{Ze^2}{r_i} + \frac{1}{2}\sum_{i\neq j}\frac{e^2}{r_{ij}} + \sum_i \xi(r)\,\boldsymbol{l}_i\cdot\boldsymbol{s}_i + V\,.$$

(See, for example, Ballhausen [7], p. 58).

This is the Hamiltonian of a free atom, with Coulomb interaction (the third term), plus an additional term, V, representing the interaction with the crystalline field. We may distinguish three cases

$$V < \xi(r)\boldsymbol{l}\cdot\boldsymbol{s} \qquad \text{weak crystalline field},$$

$$\xi(r)\boldsymbol{l}\cdot\boldsymbol{s} < V < e^2/r_{ij} \qquad \text{intermediate crystalline field},$$

$$V > e^2/r_{ij} \qquad \text{strong crystalline field}.$$

The first case is appropriate for the rare-earth ions, which are most often trivalent. Their energy levels have been studied extensively by the groups of HELLWEGE, DIEKE, LOW and others [8].

The spectra of divalent rare-earth ions have been recently reviewed by DIEKE [8] and by KISS and MCCLURE (to be published). In some respects they resemble the spectrum of a neighboring trivalent ion, but f to d-electron transitions produce broad bands which can also be used for pumping.

Transition-metal ions in crystals are often closer to the strong-field case, and the energy levels are identified by new labels appropriate to that case. A common type of evironment finds the transition-metal ion at, or nearly at, the center of an octahedron of negatively charged ions, such as oxygen. If these ions produce a sufficiently strong cubic field, then the appropriate d-electron orbitals are those known as $d\varepsilon$ or t orbitals, and $d\gamma$ or e orbitals. The $d\varepsilon$ or t orbitals have xy, yz or zx symmetry (where the z axis joins the central ion to one of the relative ions), and avoid the region of these negative ions. The $d\gamma$ or e orbitals, on the other hand, are directed toward negative ions, so that their energy is raised by electrostatic repulsion.

The trivalent chromium ion has three d electrons. In the lowest strong field state, ${}^4A_2$, these electrons are all in t orbitals, with their spins parallel. In the lowest excited state, ${}^2E$, the electrons remain in t orbitals, but one of the electron spins is inverted. The energy is raised from the ground state, because of the spin-spin electrostatic interaction. This is not very sensitive to moderate changes in the crystalline field, and so the line is sharp. When the energy levels are further split by a trigonal component of crystal field, the transition between the ${}^2E$ and ${}^4A_2$ states gives rise to the familiar R lines of ruby, at 6934 and 6919 Å.

A transition in which one of the electrons changes from a t orbital to an e orbital, however, is more sensitive to the crystalline field. Thus, these transitions are strongly coupled to the lattice vibrations, and give rise to broad bands in the green and blue (${}^4A_2 \to {}^4F_1$ and ${}^4A_2 \to {}^4F_2$). These bands, and others in the ultra-violet, are broad and strong enough to be good absorbers for pumping radiation. Any atom excited through these bands drops very quickly (in less than 10^{-7} s) to the metastable ${}^2E$ level.

The radiative transition between the ${}^2E$ level and the ${}^4A_2$ ground state state is fairly strongly forbidden, since the total spin changes but the parity does not change. Indeed, for the same chromium ion in the strictly cubic crystal field of magnesium oxide (which has the NaCl crystal structure), the R line occurs only as a weak magnetic dipole transition (oscillator strength $\sim 10^{-8}$.)

In ruby, the ion is somewhat displaced from a center of symmetry, so that there is a hemihedral (odd symmetry) component of crystal field. This hemihedral field mixes in states of opposite parity and permits a weak electric dipole transition.

This picture is somewhat oversimplified, as it suggests that a strong electric field applied to the crystal could produce similar mixing and permit a detectable, though weak, electric dipole transition in MgO. The experiment has been tried recently by G. F. Imbusch at Stanford University, with a negative result. It appears, therefore, that the strength of the ruby R-line transitions is not explained by an electrostatic crystal field model, and depends strongly on the partial covalent character of the bonding.

Although the lines in ruby have an oscillator strength of the order of only 10^{-6}, these lines are quite sharp and therefore fairly strong. The line width ranges from about 10 cm^{-1} at room temperature to as narrow as 0.08 cm^{-1} at 77 °K. Moreover, the concentration of ions in even pink ruby (0.05% Cr_2O_3) is approximately 10^{19} per cm^3, which is as high as that of atoms in a gas at atmospheric pressure. Thus, the peak absorption constant in the R-line of pink ruby may be of the order of 20 cm^{-1} at 77 °K. When an appreciable excess fraction of the atoms is excited to the ^2E state, comparably large gains per unit length are achieved.

This small oscillator strength leads to a relatively long lifetime, 4.3 millisecond for dilute ruby at 77 °K. It should be noted, however, that the relation between oscillator strength and lifetime is complicated in a solid by the polarizability of the medium. Most of this can be taken into account by using for λ_0, in the equations, the wavelength in the medium. However, the usual difficulties in obtaining the electric field at a point in a dielectric will have to be faced if one ever tries to use these equations for exact calculations. It would be possible to study this question by measuring the lifetime τ, the quantum efficiency and the absorption oscillator strength for some spectral lines.

It will be noticed that the emitting level in ruby is at 14 400 cm^{-1}, while the levels giving rise to absorption are centered at 18 000 and 25 000 cm^{-1}. If there were a level at 28 800 cm^{-1}, it could interfere with amplification by stimulated absorption. Thus a photon of 14 400 cm^{-1} could cause an atom in the metastable state either to make a downward amplifying transition to the ground state, or an upward absorbing transition. In some other crystals containing chromium, there are absorption bands at these places, which prevent their use as maser matrices.

Upward absorption is only occasionally a problem in the infra-red. It becomes increasingly common and severe as we try to extend maser action to the blue and ultra-violet regions. This absorption can arise from upward transition to higher states of the same molecule, including states in which the excited electron is transferred to a neighboring atom. The upward absorption could also be one which excites nearby atoms or molecules or electronic states of the lost lattice. Such absorption is expecially troublesome in rare-earth chelates. In these, one uses an absorption band of the chelate molecule to receive pumping energy and transfer it to the rare-earth ion (9,10). However, the close coupling between ion and molecule also may permit upward absorption, so that many possible chelate-ion combinations which fluoresce strongly do not give maser action.

Another type of background absorption which can be quite troublesome is that due to scattering. If there is good mode selection, as with small plane parallel mirrors, even very small angle scattering can be serious. Thus, COLLINS and NELSON [11] found an effective loss of 30% per pass, in a ruby 5 cm long.

In some other crystals, or in better ruby samples, much smaller losses can be obtained [12].

Still another cause of background absorption can be that arising from the broad tails of strong absorption bands. If any of these causes of loss is present, it is not possible to use very long active media to overcome end losses.

Whatever the output wavelength, it is necessary to have a shorter wavelength for pumping. For the blue and ultra-violet regions, this requires strong sources of ultra-violet radiation. Recently EMMETT has shown that a flash lamp run at a very high current density gives a greatly enhanced ultra-violet output [13]. Lamps operated in this manner should permit operation of optically pumped masers with ions such as Tb^{+3} and possibly Gd^{3+}. His method will be described in another lecture at this course.

II. Solid-State Masers

1. – Masers for the far infra-red.

In the previous lecture, we had that for a Gaussian line and an empty lower state, the gain, $|\alpha|$ is given by

$$|\alpha| = \frac{2.50\cdot 10^{-2}\,Nf}{\Delta\nu} \tag{14}$$

provided all N of the atoms are in the excited state. If there is a strong background absorption, whether from scattering, from the tails of nearby broad bands, or from host-lattice absorption, the first requirement is that $|\alpha|$ be large enough to overcome the background absorption. Then there must be sufficient additional gain to compensate for the reflection losses at the ends.

The problem of background absorption from the host lattice becomes somewhat troublesome if one tries to make a solid maser for the middle or far infra-red. Background absorption is also a very serious difficulty confronting attempts to obtain maser action in the far ultra-violet or gamma-ray region.

In the far infra-red region, the lack of suitable sources has discouraged spectroscopy and prevented high-resolution spectroscopy. Thus, the transmission of some conceivable host materials, in the far infra-red region, has not been studied. Generally speaking, all materials do have strong absorption bands somewhere in the infra-red region, but many of them are quite transparent again by the time the microwave region is reached. At any chosen wavelength, at least a few materials are reasonably transparent.

Recently, it has been shown by several investigators that far infra-red absorption in several materials is much less at low temperatures than it is at room temperatures. In these cases the absorption seems to arise through transitions from states near the top of the acoustic bands to the optical phonon bands. Cooling the crystal depopulates the upper part of the acoustic phonon bands, and so prevents this kind of absorption [14].

Thus, in the far infra-red region, lattice absorption limits the choice of host materials for solid masers, but should not entirely prevent maser operation. Indeed, optically pumped solid microwave masers have been reported, with operating temperatures as high as 77 °K.

A potentially more serious difficulty is the widespread tendency for excited states to relax rapidly in the far infra-red region. This occurs because many kinds of lattice vibrations have frequencies in the region. The peak density of modes occurs somewhere near the Einstein or Debye frequency, typically a few hundred cm^{-1}. Above this, there are few lattice vibration modes, so that excited ion states with spacing in the visible and near infra-red can relax only by multiphonon processes. Below the Debye frequency, the density of modes within a line of given frequency interval is approximately proportional to ν^2, so that typically relaxation rates are also proportional to at least ν^2. Thus, relaxation times in the region around 100 cm^{-1} are likely to be so short that it will be difficult to maintain an excess population in an excited state. However, there may well be exceptions, and much more work is needed to understand and control relaxation times.

Moreover, it may also be possible to use the lattice vibrations themselves as the molecular resonances for masers. As YATSIV has pointed out at this Course, some molecular crystals have rather sharp molecular vibrations. These vibrational states are populated when an ion in the molecule is excited and fluoresces. Possibly the selection rules for this kind of excitation may produce a population inversion between vibrational states. The observed sharpness of the vibrational sidebands places an upper limit on the relaxation rate, although it remains to be seen whether the relaxation time is long enough for maser action. Actually, in the particular materials which YATSIV reported, the vibrational frequencies are in the near, rather than far infra-red. Far infra-red vibrational excitations may relax somewhat faster.

2. – Masers in the ultra-violet.

As we proceed to the other side of the visible region, into the ultra-violet, strong electronic absorptions become more common and troublesome. In ionic crystals these may be charge-transfer bands, corresponding to ionization of the active ions, or electronic excitations of the host crystal. Wherever there is a band of levels in the ion as far above the emitting level as the final level is below it, absorptive transitions to these levels will compete with stimulated emission. On the other hand, if there is an excited level of the host lattice at that position, it may or may not cause absorption.

If the ion is not at all coupled to the lattice, the ion and lattice are separate and distinct systems, each with its own energy levels. However, if they are at all coupled, then upward transitions from the metastable state of the ion to the excited band of the crystal can occur. It is quite possible that this sort of absorption will occur commonly wherever the first excited band of the crystal lies below twice the desired laser output quantum energy. Pure calcium fluoride is transparent to 1400 Å, so that it, at least, could be a suitable host crystal for operation at wavelengths down to 2800 Å. With loosely coupled ions, shorter wavelengths might be generated, as long as the crystal remains transparent.

Coherent radiation at selected wavelengths in the infra-red and ultra-violet regions can also be generated by combining lasers with nonlinear media. Thus, strong ultra-violet harmonics of ruby lasers have been observed at twice and three times the ruby output frequency. Resistive and reactive mixers can combine two coherent waves, or even coherent and incoherent waves, to produce sum and difference frequencies. Coherent Raman mixing provides powerful radiation at frequencies differing from the source by plus or minus one, two, three or more times a molecular vibrational frequency. Thus, it is already possible to get intense radiation at many wavelengths in the infra-red, visible, and near ultra-violet portions of the spectrum.

3. – Far ultra-violet and X-ray regions.

When one considers the possibility of making masers or other coherent sources in the far ultra-violet or X-ray regions, the difficulties are considerably greater. In fact, only Clogston's law provides much hope of success with this problem (Clogston's law, enunciated by A. M. CLOGSTON, states that any device you can think of can be built, unless it actually violates the laws of conservation of energy or momentum. It does not mention the second law of thermodynamics, which can always be evaded locally.)

In the far ultra-violet and soft X-ray regions, no material is transparent, and all solids absorb heavily. In this region, not only can the valence electrons be excited, but also those in inner shells closer to the nucleus. Thus, absorption can come from all the atomic electrons, while it is difficult to excite more than one of them at a time. If there is any hope at all for maser action in the region, it would use a light material with few electrons in inner shells.

In the ordinary X-ray region, around 1 Å, most materials are not quite so completely opaque, although they are by no means transparent. It has occured to several people that the narrow-line γ-rays from the Mössbauer effect might give a favorable ratio of stimulated to spontaneous emission. Let us see whether Clogston's law applies to this proposal. In particular, let us see whether sufficient energy can be supplied from the excited nuclei.

To take the most favorable case, assume that the crystal and the Mössbauer line narrowing are so perfect that the only source of line width is the radiative damping from the finite lifetime of the excited state.

That is,

$$\Delta\nu = \frac{1}{2\pi\tau}\,. \tag{15}$$

Also, we had

$$f\tau = 1.50\lambda^2\,, \tag{16}$$

so that

$$\frac{f}{\Delta\nu} = 9.42\lambda^2\,, \tag{17}$$

and from eq. (14)

$$|\alpha| = 0.24N\lambda^2\,. \tag{18}$$

If $\lambda = 1$ Å (10^{-8} cm), $|\alpha| = 2.4\cdot10^{-17}N$. For a medium atomic weight material, such as tin, the background absorption is 630 cm^{-1}. Thus, to overcome it, N must be $2.6\cdot10^{19}$ excited atoms per cm^3. Since tin contains $3.7\cdot10^{22}$ atoms per cm^3, this is not impossible — about 1 atom in 1400 must be excited at any time.

We are supposing that the excited atoms come from radioactivity, with the line narrowed by the Mössbauer effect. If the radioactive lifetime, τ, were 1 second (corresponding to $\Delta\nu/\nu = 5\cdot10^{-20}$), an initially undiluted supply of radioactive atoms would be reduced to this level in about 7 seconds. This not only assumes a crystal so perfect as to give such a narrow line, but also assumes no isotopic dilution. It would be necessary to prepare the crystal in a time comparable with this radioactive lifetime. This seems to offer some difficulty. Moreover, the fractional line width assumed is about 10^5 times narrower than that of any known Mössbauer emitter.

If we did have such an emitting crystal, for a true maser, it would be necessary to provide end mirrors. However, a useful directional device (although not a true maser) could also be obtained by making just a long column of the active material. This might be, say, a straight wire 1 cm long and 1 μm in diameter. Waves along the axis would be amplified much more than those inclined to the axis. The output would consist of monochromatic intense bursts of γ-rays along the axis, although successive bursts would not have phase coherence with each other. The properties of a long column of excited atoms, without reflectors, were first pointed out by DICKE, and have recently been examined for the X-ray region by CHIRIKOV [15].

While it would be very nice to have a crystal of radioactive atoms which need no pumping, one might also consider the energetics of a pumped X-ray maser. With external pumping, as by electron bombardment, the sample could be prepared in advance, and then subjected to a large burst of pumping energy. Assume then, that this pumping energy is all useful in raising atoms to the upper level for maser action. This is an extremely optimistic assumption. Again, if radiation damping is the only source of line broadening, to overcome the background absorption in tin, we require $2.6\cdot10^{19}$ excited atoms per cm^3. Since the photon at 1 Å is 1250 volt, at least $2.6\cdot10^{19}\cdot1.25\cdot10^4=3.25\cdot10^{23}$ electron volt $=2.0\cdot10^4$ joule must be supplied. If the volume of the sample is 10^{-8} cm^3, it would require $2.0\cdot10^{-4}$ joule to be supplied during the radiative lifetime. The higher the useful pumping power density that could be applied, the shorter the radiative lifetime that could be tolerated. At a pumping power level of 10^6 watt, a state with a radiative lifetime of 10^{-10} s could accumulate enough atoms for amplification by stimulated emission greater than the background absorption. With this kind of operation, one could reduce the threshold power by using a lighter material, with fewer electrons in inner shells.

Thus, it is not yet completely clear whether excitation energy can be supplied fast enough to operate an X-ray maser. Since the applicability of Clogston's law is not unequivocal, one might hope to avoid the consequences of the corollary. (The corollary to Clogston's law is: Since you know in advance that the device can be built, it is not very interesting to build it).

4. – Monochromatic solid-state masers.

It is commonly assumed that solid-state masers are not at all suitable for use as wavelength standards. It is true that most solid-state masers are intended to deliver a high power output, and are operated under violently pulsed conditions with considerable temperature rise during the pulse. Moreover, most emission lines from solids are broader than most emission lines from gases.

However, solids do have the important property that the lines can remain quite sharp despite large concentrations of active ions. For example, pink ruby with 0.05% Cr_2O_3, contains as great a density of active ions as a gas at atmospheric pressure. The emission line has components no broader than 0.08 cm^{-1} at low temperatures. It is, thus, possible to get a large amplification in a short distance, perhaps as much as 10 cm^{-1}. Then it is possible to construct a laser with a short, low-Q cavity resonator, so that the spectral line plays an important part in determining the exact output wavelength. One may hope to find lines so sharp and so strong that the line Q is much greater than the cavity Q. After all, the width of lines from ions in solids is not limited by Doppler effect, and so very sharp lines should exist.

To be sure, the ruby emission line is not always as sharp as 0.08 cm^{-1}. At room temperature, the line broadens to about 10 cm^{-1}, and shifts to the red by more than 15 cm^{-1} [16]. However, at low temperatures both the thermal broadening and shift decrease roughly as T^4, and are very small. The line width at the lowest temperatures is probably produced by internal strains in the crystal.

The ruby line is not ideal, even at low temperature, because of its complex structure (Fig. 2), but a ruby laser has been constructed using a ruby rod cooled to 77° K by immersion in liquid nitrogen. One end of the rod (which was 4 cm long) was uncoated, so that its reflectivity was only 8%. Under

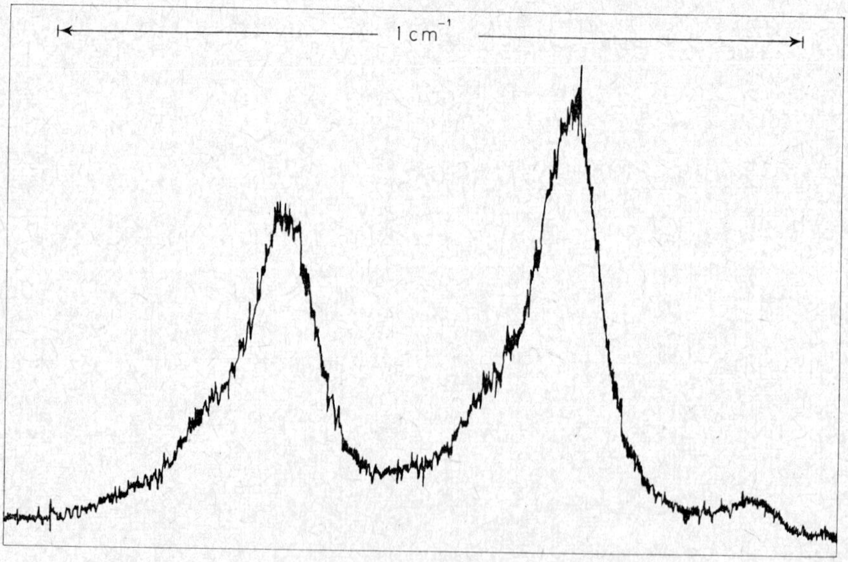

Fig. 2. – The ruby R_1 line at 4 °K, showing the two components due to the ground state splitting, and smaller components from chromium isotopes.

these conditions, the Q of the axial-mode resonances is about the same as that of the ruby emission line. However, with the low reflectivity, there is little discrimination against modes with propagation vectors very slightly inclined to the axis of the rod. At least one of these modes will be very close to the center of the spectral line, and so oscillation begins there without further adjustment. When this device is operated very close to the threshold of oscillation, a single line is obtained with fractional width and reproducibility better than $2 \cdot 10^{-7}$ [17].

The ruby line does shift to the red as the temperature is raised. To minimize wavelength shifts from heating during the pulse, a composite (clad) rod was used. This peculiarly solid-state device has as its core a ruby rod with a cylindrical sheath of clear sapphire, the whole being a single crystal. Since sapphire is a very good heat conductor, the sapphire sheath shares any heat introduced into the ruby, and provides some thermal ballast. This composite rod structure also reduces pumping power [18]. The theory and operation of the composite rod have been discussed by McKenna [19] and by Svelto [20], who also discussed a concentric spherical overlay.

Still narrower lines have been observed recently by Kiss and Duncan, from Dy^{2+} and Tm^{2+} ions in calcium fluoride [21]. These lines are certainly narrower than instrumental resolution of 0.03 cm^{-1} and may be ten times narrower. Both $CaF_2:Dy^{2+}$ and $CaF_2:Tm^{2+}$ have been used in continuous-wave lasers at low temperatures, and should make good wavelength standards. Although even these materials are probably not yet competitive in stability with the best gas masers, still better materials may be found.

5. – High-power solid optical masers.

Although pulsed gas masers have now produced peak powers of 100 watt, and may eventually go very much higher, solids have considerable advantages for high-power operation. The high density of ions, permits storage of large amounts of energy per unit volume. Moreover, many ions in solids have fairly long radiative lifetimes, ($\sim 10^{-3}$ s), so that excitation energy may be supplied for a millisecond or so, and then delivered in a short burst. Ruby is especially favorable for high-power operation, because it has several broad absorption bands to accept pumping radiation. Neodymium-doped glass permits higher ion concentrations, and can be obtained in large pieces of good optical quality. However, many glasses are damaged by ultra-violet radiation, so that only visible and near infra-red light can be used to pump them. This means that by raising the flash-lamp color temperatures, as by Emmett's double pulse method, the useful pumping light for neodymium in glass goes up only linearly with the absolute temperature of the discharge. If the ultra-violet can be used, as in ruby, the pumping power increases as the fourth power of the lamp temperature.

Really high-peak maser output powers are obtained by using the « Q-spoil » technique, first proposed by HELLWARTH [22]. In this method which is shown in Fig. 3, one mirror detached from the *amplifying* crystal, and a shutter is

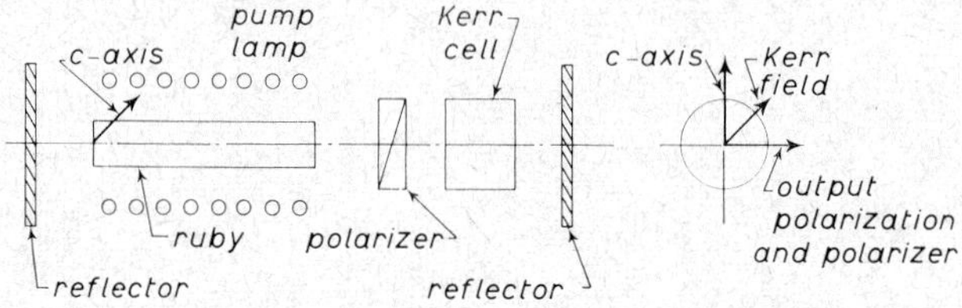

Fig. 3. – Giant pulse or Q-Spoil laser. The Kerr-cell and polarizer act as a shutter to prevent light from reaching the mirror until the laser rod has been fully excited.

placed between the mirror and the laser rod. To begin with, the shutter is closed, as the pumping light flash is applied. After a time of the order of 100 to 300 microsecond, a sufficient number of atoms have accumulated in the upper state to reach the threshold for laser action. However, laser action is prevented because the light path to the mirror is blocked. Thus, it is possible to continue accumulating atoms in the excited state, until these are many more than the minimum for laser oscillation. The gain is then much more than needed to make up for the losses at the two mirrors.

At this time, the shutter is suddenly opened, so that stimulated light can reach the second mirror. With such large amplification, the peak intensity builds up very rapidly, and the stored energy is delivered in one giant pulse.

Various kinds of shutters can be used, but for the largest output pulses the shutter should open very quickly. Several kinds of mechanical shutters have been used, but the fastest shutter is the combination of a Kerr effect electro-optical cell and a polarizer [23]. Such a shutter can open in a few nanoseconds. After a build-up interval of the order of 100 nanosecond, an output pulse lasting about 10 nanosecond is produced. During this giant pulse, the power output may be as high as 50 megawatt. Moreover, giant pulse lasers often give better collimated output beams than ordinary lasers, having a divergence of only 10^{-3} radian.

Still higher peak output powers can be obtained by using a second rod of the same active material as an amplifier after the giant pulse oscillator. The amplifier rod is pumped by its own flash lamp at the same time as the oscillator. It uses no reflectors, in fact it is usually best for the ends of the amplifier rod to be coated or cut at the Brewster angle to prevent reflection. Oscillator-amplifier combinations of this sort have produced well-collimated pulses of about 10^9 watt peak power, and substantially higher powers seem possible.

Rapid pumping is especially beneficial for giant pulse oscillators and travelling wave amplifiers. This is so because these devices operate with substantial population inversion, and with appreciable amplification per unit length. Thus, spontaneous radiation from these materials is amplified as it passes through to the surface. In so doing, the supply of excited atoms is reduced. In other words, the effective lifetime is reduced by internal amplification of spontaneous emission. Thus, the pumping radiation should be supplied in a time shorter than this reduced radiative lifetime of the excited states. This, also, can be accomplished by the double-pulse method of operating flash lamps.

The amount of energy that can be delivered in a giant pulse depends on what fraction of the atoms contribute to it. If the line is inhomogeneously broadened, as by strains, only those atoms with frequencies very close to the center of the line will contribute to the giant pulse. However, in a homogeneously broadened line, the frequency of an individual atom is only defined within the line width, and so all excited atoms can contribute to the output pulse. The Lorentzian shape of the ruby line at room temperature is an indication that it is homogeneously broadened.

More exactly, the cross-relaxation rate from one frequency to another within the line width determines the degree of homogeneity of a line. If this time were, for example, around 10^{-5} s, the line would be homogeneous for ordinary fluorescence, but inhomogeneous when stimulated to emit in less than a microsecond.

There is another kind of cross-relaxation. In an optical maser, there is a standing wave pattern, and excited atoms are depleted more rapidly at the nodes than at the loops. There are processes by which energy can diffuse from excited atoms at the nodes to atoms at the positions of the loops. This process may be fast or slow, depending on the concentration of ions.

6. – Conclusions.

By now it has been demonstrated that optically pumped solid-state masers can operate from 2.6 μm in the infra-red (U^{3+} in CaF_2, BaF_2 or SrF_2) to 0.61 μm in the visible (Eu^{3+} in Y_2O_3 and in plastics). Several of them have been operated continuously and delivered powers of the order of one watt. Peak powers have ranged from 100 kilowatt, in conventional operation, up to 10^9 watt from a giant pulse maser followed by an amplifier. Some considerable extension of the wavelength and power ranges may be anticipated.

Moreover, the interest in solid-state masers has stimulated much spectroscopy of these and related materials. This has already led to improved understanding of such matters as line widths and transition probabilities. It seems likely to give considerable information about the interaction of ions with each other and with their environment.

REFERENCES

[1] A. L. SCHAWLOW and C. H. TOWNES: *Phys. Rev.*, **112**, 1970 (1958).

[2] A. L. SCHAWLOW: *Solid State Journal*, **2**, No. 6, 21 (1961).

[3] A. C. G. MITCHELL and M. W. ZEMANSKY: *Resonance Radiation and Excited Atoms* (Cambridge, 1961).

4] P. RABINOWITZ, S. JACOBS and G. GOULD: *Appl. Op.*, **1**, 513 (1963).

[5] T. H. MAIMAN: *Nature*, **187**, 493 (1960).

[6] Z. KISS and R. C. DUNCAN, JR.: *Proc. I.R.E.*, **50**, 1531 (1962).

[7] C. J. BALLHAUSEN: *Ligand Field Theory* (New York, 1962).

[8] A recent compilation is given by G. H. DIEKE and H. M. CROSSWHITE: *Appl. Op.*, **2**, 657 (1963).

[9] A. LEMPICKI and H. SAMELSON: *Phys. Lett.*, **4**, 133 (1963).

[10] R. J. PRESSLEY and N. E. WOLFF: *Appl. Phys. Lett.*, **2**, 152 (1963).

[11] R. J. COLLINS and D. F. NELSON: *Proc. London Conference on Optical Instruments and Techniques* (London, 1961).

[12] W.KAISER and M. J. KECK: *Journ. Appl. Phys.*, **33**, 762 (1962).

[13] J. L. EMMETT and A. L. SCHAWLOW: *Appl. Phys. Lett.*, **2**, 204 (1963).

[14] B. WYNCKE and A. HADNÉ, and by W. S. C. CHANG and R. F. ROUNTREE at the Procedings of the *Paris Conference on Quantum Electronics* (February 1963) P. GRIVET and N. BLOEMBERGEN editors New (York, 1964).

[15] B. V. CHIRIKOV: *Žurn. Ėksp. Teor. Fiz.*, **44**, 2016 (1963).

[16] A. L. SCHAWLOW: in *Advances in Quantum Electronics*, J. R. SINGER, editor (New York, 1961); D. MCCUMBER and M. D. STURGE: *Journ. Appl. Phys.*, **34**, 1682 (1963).

[17] L. F. MOLLENAUER, G. F. IMBUSCH, H. W. MOOS, A. L. SCHAWLOW and A. D. MAY: published in *Proceedings of the Conference on Optical Masers*, sponsored by Polytechnic Institute of Brooklyn (New York, 1963).

[18] G. E. DEVLIN, J. MCKENNA, A. D. MAY and A. L. SCHAWLOW: *Appl. Op.*, **1**, 11 (1962).

[19] J. MCKENNA: *Appl. Op.*, **2**, 303 (1963).

[20] O. SVELTO: *Appl. Op.*, **1**, 743 (1962); O. SVELTO and M. DI DOMENICO: *Appl. Op.*, **2**, 431 (1963).

[21] Z. J. KISS: *Appl. Phys. Lett.*, **2**, 61 (1963); Z. J. KISS and R. C. DUNCAN, jr.: *Proc. I.R.E.*, **50**, 1531 (1962).

[22] R. W. HELLWARTH: in *Advances in Quantum Electronics*, J. R. SINGER, editor (New York, 1961).

[23] F. J. MCCLUNG and R. W. HELLWARTH: *Proc. I.E.E.E.*, **51**, 46 (1963).

Infra-Red Semiconductor Lasers.

B. LAX

Lincoln Laboratory (*), *Massachusetts Institute of Technology - Lexington, Mass.*

1. – Introduction.

It has been known for some time that semiconductors possessed unique properties which exhibited characteristic absorption and emission phenomena in the infra-red region of the electromagnetic spectrum. Infra-red absorption spectroscopy has been extensively used as a tool for studying the energy level structure in semiconductors [1]. The forbidden energy gap has been accurately determined by this technique in a number of semiconductors for a range of temperatures and absorption coefficients were studied as a function of wavelength. The latter has elucidated the band structures and provided information of the transitions involved. Impurity levels have been studied in such materials as silicon and germanium at longer wavelengths in the near and far infra-red. Perhaps the most detailed and informative measurements were those involving magnetic fields in which Zeeman effect of impurity levels, excitons and the magneto-absorption spectra of interband transition provided quantitative data on effective masses, g-factors and very accurate measurements of energy [2]. In addition to the absorption spectroscopy, a number of interesting phenomena have been observed in emission during the last decade. Optical and electrical excitation of such semiconductors as Si, Ge, SiC and some of the 3-5 compounds have exhibited luminescence which has been most useful in studying phonon spectra and interaction as well as exciton complexes in which impurities were involved [3]. Consequently with this important background it is not surprising that semiconductor physicists began to consider seriously the possibilities of using this knowledge for the development of various types of masers in the infra-red.

(*) Operated with support from the U. S. Air Force.

The possibility of realizing maser action in semiconductors in the infra-red was informally discussed among various groups as early as 1954, following the development of the microwave ammonia maser by GORDON, ZEIGER and TOWNES [4]. VON NEUMAN proposed an electrically pumped device very much like the present junction-diode laser about this time. AIGRAIN [5] entertained the use of point contact devices in 1958 and he and his group have been working on various schemes for electrical and optical pumping of masers in germanium and other semiconductors. The group at Lincoln Laboratory has also considered a number of devices such as the cyclotron-resonance maser [6], interband and impurity masers, some of which appeared feasible on theoretical grounds. Independently the group at Lebedev Institute under the direction of BASOV [7] has made a number of proposals for analogous systems in semiconductors. Many of these were discussed in their formative stage at the First Quantum Electronics Conference in September 1959. Subsequently some of these ideas were attempted experimentally but without any definitive results until 1962. At this time several groups began to observe unusual emission from GaAs. The most striking results were those of KEYES and QUIST [8] who discovered a tenfold increase in emission from a GaAs diode just below the energy gap at 77 °K with quantum efficiencies approaching unity. This immediately suggested that a maser could be built using such a diode with a proper resonant geometrical structure. Independently from theoretical considerations, DUMKE [9] predicted that a direct-transition maser in GaAs would be the most likely candidate as contrasted to an indirect-transition device. In the fall of 1962, the group at General Electric reported success and were shortly followed by the results of the I.B.M. and Lincoln groups [10]. Since then many laboratories have been engaged in this type of research on junction-diode masers. Many new developments have been reported since then. Diode lasers of alloys of $GaAs_xP_{1-x}$ [11] in the red, InAs [12], InP [13] and alloys of $In_{1-x}Ga_xAs$ [14] have been made to operate in the infra-red from 8400 Å to 3200 Å (3.2 μm). Some of these diodes have operated as CW devices and on a pulse basis as high as room temperature. Magnetic fields and pressure have been used to tune or alter the frequency.

2. – Fundamental concepts.

There are three basic types of masers that have been seriously considered theoretically and experimentally in the literature. These may be called the direct-transition masers, the indirect-transition or two-boson maser and a class of magneto-optical masers including the cyclotron-resonance maser. A fourth, involving impurity levels, has been briefly treated. However, this is still in a speculative stage and we shall not discuss it at this time since a clear cut idea or calculation has not been proposed. We shall restrict most of our discussion to the first three with the major emphasis on the direct-transition maser and some on the magneto-optical and less on the two-boson maser since no experimental results have been obtained on the latter.

In order to operate any maser there are three necessary requirements, 1) a scheme for inverting the electron population in a higher energy state relative to one below it, 2) sufficient power from the subsequent stimulated emission to overcome the losses, and 3) a resonant structure of some sort for confining the electromagnetic energy, thereby providing feedback and coherence of the resultant radiation. We shall consider each of these separately, first in a descriptive fashion, then quantitatively wherever it is possible.

2·1. *Direct transition.* – The simplest possible situation for creating an inverted population can be examined for a direct transition in an idealized model of a semiconductor shown in Fig. 1.

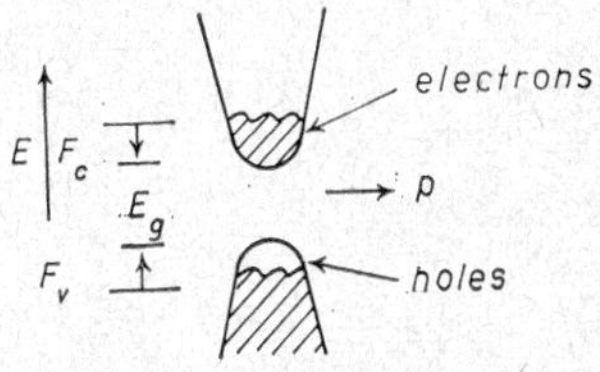

Fig. 1. – Inversion of carriers in intrinsic semiconductors.

The energy levels in a semiconductor are no longer discrete or narrow as in the case of atomic levels or impurities in a solid, but are broadened into bands with a forbidden region separated by an energy gap. The concept of an inverted population is not as apparent as in the case of the discrete levels since available levels are spread out in energy both in the conduction and valence bands. If a sudden electrical or optical pulse is applied such that electrons and holes are created in pairs in the conduction and valence bands respectively, and these are allowed to come into equilibrium in each band in a time small compared to the recombination time, then the degenerate population of electrons is inverted relative to the empty valence-band states represented by the degenerate population of holes. The allowed transitions of electrons for which $\Delta p = 0$ where p is the momentum gives a spectral distribution of photon emission in the range

$$E_g < h\nu < F_c \text{ and } F_v\,, \tag{1}$$

where F_v and F_c are the quasi-Fermi levels for the holes and electrons, respectively. In a steady-state process where the electron and hole pairs are produced continually, the electrons and holes are not in equilibrium with one another but they are in thermal equilibrium with the lattice. Hence, their distributions are described by Fermi functions corresponding to the temperature of the crystal and the Fermi energies F_v and F_c correspond accordingly to hole-electron concentrations.

In a *p-n* junction in which one side of the junction is more heavily doped than the other it is possible to inject holes or electrons into the side with the lower concentration of impurities. In either case the excess holes or electrons which are injected into the normally conducting n-type and p-type materials create empty states as shown in Fig. 2.

In Fig. 2a) the excess holes permit the inversion of the electrons near the bottom of the conduction band and thereby permit emission of a photon $h\nu$. In Fig. 2b) the injection of electrons into the conduction band for p-type material inverts them relative to the normally empty states near the top of the valence band. These electrons on recombination with holes of corresponding momentum $\Delta p = 0$ give rise to the emission of photons. In some of the actual p-n junctions in which both sides are highly degenerate it is believed that the emission comes from the junction region or the « depletion » layer where the material is compensated or « neutral ». Upon applying a forward voltage to the junction the energy bands are lowered as shown in Fig. 3 and n- and p-type regions overlap. This approximates the situation depicted for a bulk material in Fig. 1. Consequently, the overlap region becomes inverted and becomes a source for photon emission.

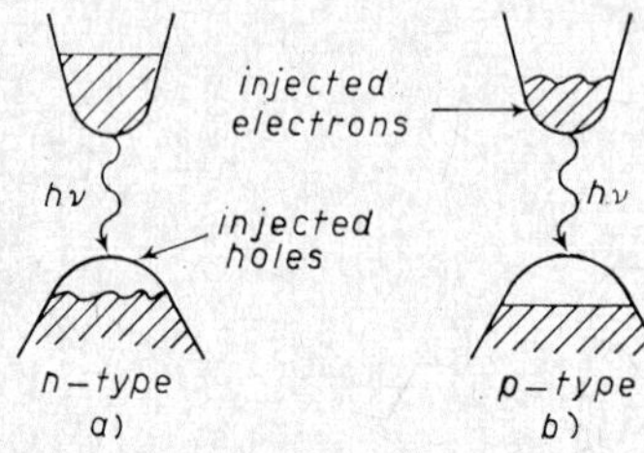

Fig. 2. – Inversion of carriers in intrinsic semiconductors.

In junction lasers the actual transitions of electrons do not occur between energy bands. Actually in Fig. 1 and Fig. 2 the allowed transitions would occur over a photon distribution which is quite wide and which would depend on the electron and hole concentration, *i.e.*,

$$\Delta\nu \approx \mathscr{E}_c + \mathscr{E}_v\,,$$

where $\mathscr{E}_c$ and $\mathscr{E}_v$ are the energies of the degenerate distribution above the bottom of the conduction band and below the top of the valence bands. From the form of the energy bands which are assumed to be parabolic and the density of states we can calculate at low temperatures that

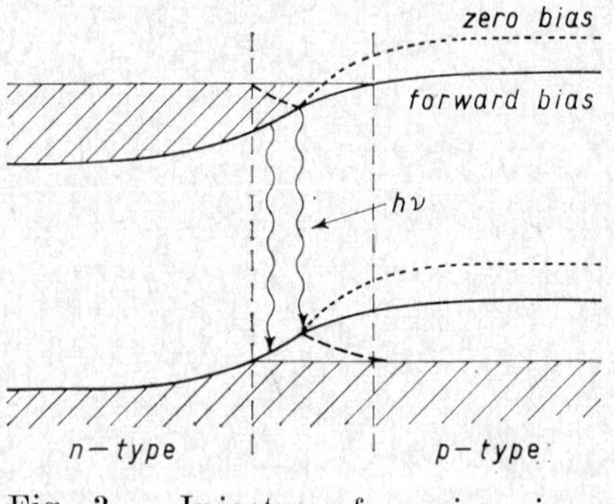

Fig. 3. – Injecton of carriers in a junction. Population inversion occurs in the overlap region.

$$\mathscr{E}_{v,c} = \frac{h^2}{2m_{v,c}}\left(\frac{3N_{v,c}}{8\pi}\right)^{\frac{2}{3}}, \tag{2}$$

where $m_{v,c}$ and $N_{v,c}$ are the effective masses and carrier concentrations of holes and electrons respectively. For values of $m_v \approx 0.3\,m_0$, $m_c \approx 0.1\,m_0$ and $N_v \approx \approx N_c \approx 10^{18}/\text{cm}^3$, we obtain $\mathscr{E}_v \approx 0.05$ eV and $\mathscr{E}_c \approx 0.01$ eV: thus the spread $\Delta\mathscr{E} \approx 0.06$ eV. Actually we find lines at 77 °K, where the degeneracy assumption is reasonable and corresponds to widths of (100 – 200) Å at the spontaneous emission peak of 8400 Å. At lower temperatures of 4.2 °K this may be as low as 50 Å. Consequently the observed spontaneous line width $\Delta\mathscr{E} < < 0.01$ eV would suggest that the interband emission is not the appropriate interpretation of the optical transition or else that the estimate of $10^{18}/\text{cm}^3$ carriers is too high. In addition the line shape associated with interband transition would have a different appearance than the apparent Lorentzian line which is actually observed. These conjectures are, however, not conclusive.

However, from the wavelength of the actual emission which we observed at 1.47 eV as compared to $E_g = 1.51$ eV we deduce that the transitions involve at least one set of impurity levels. Therefore in a crystal which is doped with impurities, energy levels are introduced in the energy gap below the conduction band or above the valence band as indicated schematically. The levels may appear as discrete or at higher concentration will smear out and appear contiguous with the normal bands.

The diagrams in Fig. 4 shown *a*) *n*-type material with injected holes, *b*) *p*-type material with injected electrons and *c*) compensated material with injected hole-electron pairs. In any event, there is an enhancement of the transition probability for impurity transitions as indicated by the diagram in Fig. 4 where $h\nu < E_g$. Consistent with this discussion, five models have been proposed for such transitions, namely 1) the interband, 2) donor to valence band, 3) conduction band to acceptor, 4) donor to acceptor, 5) exciton to acceptor. We have ruled out the first from energy considerations. Recent experiments with magnetic fields indicate that either of the last two are possibilities. Later we shall treat this problem in greater detail.

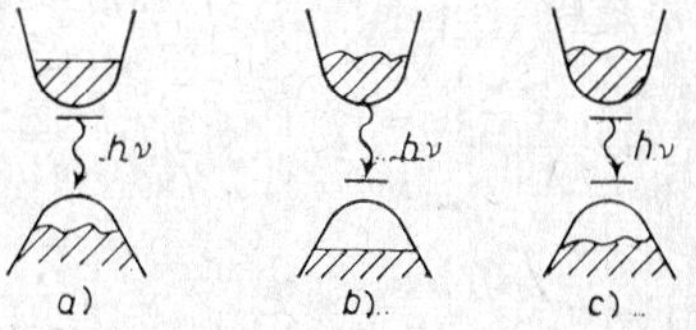

Fig. 4. – Emission from impurity states in doped semiconductors: *a*) *n*-type; *b*) *p*-type; *c*) compensated material.

2·2. *Indirect transition.* – The inversion of a direct transition is relatively simple since it involves transitions in which the valence and conduction bands are located at the same region of the energy-momentum diagram. Consequently transitions result in the emission of a photon alone when the electron and a hole recombine. However, in an indirect transition the two energy bands are displaced relatively to one another in momentum space as in Ge and Si. This is shown in Fig. 5 where the conduction band is at the edge of Brillouin zone along the [111] direction in Ge and near the edge along the [100] direction in Si. At low temperatures when the phonon population is negligible the indirect transition for an electron between the conduction and valence bands will result in the emission of a photon with little or no phonon absorption. Thus for an electron to be transferred from the valence band ($p=0$) to the conduction band ($p>0$) in order for the momentum to be conserved, the electron has to transfer this momentum to the lattice by exciting a phonon. Then the energy balance for the absorption of a photon in an indirect transition is given by

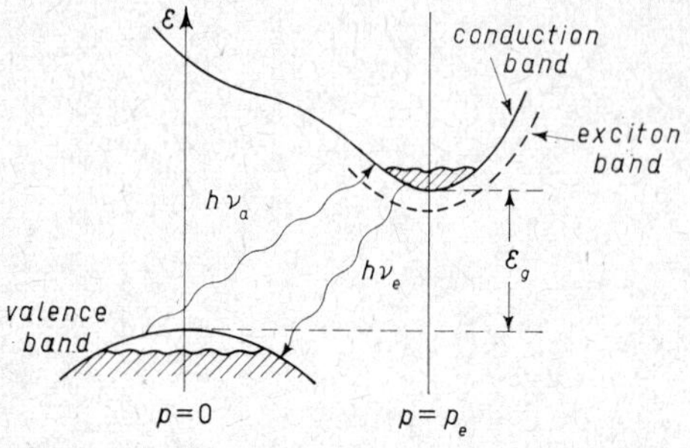

Fig. 5. – Indirect transitions in semiconductors $h\nu_a$ energy of absorbed photon, $h\nu_e$ emitted photon, $h\nu_a < h\nu_e$.

$$h\nu_a = E_g + h\nu_q \qquad \text{(absorption)}, \tag{3}$$

where $h\nu_a$ is the energy of the photon absorbed and $h\nu_q$ is the energy of the phonon. Similarly on induced emission wherein a photon $h\nu_e$ is created then the energy and momentum balance requires the creation of a phonon as well and the relation is summarized by

$$h\nu_e = E_g - h\nu_q \qquad \text{(emission)}. \tag{4}$$

The implications of the above relation are that the emitted photon and phonon do not have enough energy to be reabsorbed and cannot excite an electron from the valence band to the conduction band. However, the two in combination can induce another electron to make a downward transition to an empty state in the valence band. Thus an electron-hole pair at the bottom of the conduction band and top of the valence band, respectively, constitute inversion at low temperature. In actuality the hole-electron pair can trap one another by their Coulomb interaction in a hydrogen-like structure known as the exciton. This energy state is just below the conduction band and forms an exciton band since the bound pair have the momentum corresponding to that of the electron at or near the edge of zone. At low temperatures where the binding energy of the exciton $\mathscr{E}_{ex} \approx 0.0025\ \text{eV} \ll kT$, the radiation corresponding to the annihilation of the exciton shows up as sharp emission lines at the appropriate energies usually with one-phonon excitation favored. From absorption data the experimental evidence indicates that the transition probability at low temperatures for the exciton is larger, although it is still an indirect transition with the simultaneous emission of a phonon. The increased transition probability comes from the increased density of states which for Ge is of the order of $m_{ex} = (m_v + m_c)^{\frac{3}{2}} = (0.33\,m_0 + 0.11\,m_0)^{\frac{3}{2}} \approx (0.44)^{\frac{3}{2}} \approx 0.29\,m_0^{\frac{3}{2}}$

and for the free carrier recombination the appropriate density of states is that of the conduction band $m^{*\frac{3}{2}} = (m_t^2 me)^{\frac{1}{2}} = [(0.08)^2(1.6)]^{\frac{1}{2}} \approx 0.1\, m_0^{\frac{3}{2}}$. Hence the density of states is increased approximately by a factor of 3. The transition probability may possibly be enhanced by introducing impurities which result in exciton complexes. Another possibility is that of compensated donors and acceptors in which the recombination is between overlapping impurity centers.

2·3. *Condition for inversion* (*). – If the energy states of the electrons and holes are represented by expressions of the form $\mathscr{E}_v = h^2k^2/2m_v$ and $\mathscr{E}_c = h^2k^2/2m_c$, then under steady-state conditions the distribution of each of the two degenerate sets of carriers, following Shockley's representation for injected electrons, is given by

$$f_c = \frac{1}{1 + \exp[\mathscr{E}_c - F_c]/kT}, \tag{5}$$

$$f_v = \frac{1}{1 + \exp[\mathscr{E}_v - F_v]/kT}, \tag{6}$$

where F_c and F_v are the quasi-Fermi levels for electrons and holes in the conduction and valence bands, respectively.

The two energy states $\mathscr{E}_c$ and $\mathscr{E}_v$ for a direct transition are then related to the photon energies inducting the transition by

$$\mathscr{E}_c - \mathscr{E}_v = h\nu, \tag{7}$$

where momentum is conserved and $\Delta k = 0$, neglecting the momentum of the photon. Then if W_{cv} is the transition probability for an electron to go from the valence band to the conduction band by a radiative transition, in which the electron absorbs a photon energy and the radiation density P_ν then the number of photons absorbed per unit time

$$\frac{dN_a}{dt} = CW_{cv} f_v(1 - f_c) P_\nu. \tag{8}$$

The number of photons emitted per unit time by stimulated emission by the same photon field P_ν is given by

$$\frac{dN_e}{dt} = CW_{cv} f_c(1 - f_v) P_\nu, \tag{9}$$

(*) The condition for inverting the population for laser action was derived by BERNARD and DURAFFOURG [13]. We follow their development in this paper.

where C is the same constant for both processes depending on the reduced density of states for the valence and conduction bandsand $W_{cv}=W_{vc}$. Then if the rate of stimulated emission is to exceed that of absorption

$$\frac{dN_e}{dt}>\frac{dN_a}{dt}. \tag{10}$$

From eqs. (7) and (8) it then follows that

$$f_c(1-f_v)>f_v(1-f_c) \tag{11}$$

or

$$\exp[F_c-F_v]/kT>\exp[E_c-E_v]/kT. \tag{12}$$

From eq. (3) the necessary condition for amplification becomes

$$F_c-F_v>h\nu. \tag{13}$$

Another way of stating this is that the photon energies have an upper and a lower limit given by

$$E_g<h\nu<F_c-F_v. \tag{14}$$

The above condition can be generalized to the situations for transitions between impurity levels and energy bands, between two sets of impurity levels and also for the indirect or two-boson transitions. For the latter stimulated emission is given by the energy relation

$$h\nu_e=E_c-E_v\mp h\nu_q, \tag{15}$$

where $\mp h\nu_q$ represents the creation or the absorption of a phonon. At low temperatures the latter has a low probability. For absorption of a photon the relation is as follows:

$$h\nu_a=E_c-E_v\pm h\nu_q, \tag{16}$$

where $\pm h\nu_q$ represents the emission or absorption of a phonon, respectively. Thus for a given photon energy $h\nu$ to be stimulated, the substitution of the eqs. (9) and (10) into eq. (7) for either the phonon creation or annihilation results in the condition

$$F_c-F_v>h\nu\pm h\nu_q. \tag{17}$$

2·4. *Magneto-optical masers.* – Magnetic fields have played a unique and significant role in the study of the optical properties of semiconductors. A variety of new magneto-optical phenomena have been observed by absorption and reflection techniques not only on interband but also on intraband and impurity level transitions as well [2]. The band properties of a semiconductor are modified in the presence of a magnetic field, since the transverse co-ordinates are quantized. The effective-mass Hamiltonian of a Bloch electron can be written as

$$\frac{-h^2}{2m^*}\nabla^2\psi - \frac{h\omega_c}{2}\frac{\partial\psi}{\partial\varphi} + \frac{m^*\omega_c^2}{8}(x^2+y^2)\psi = \mathscr{E}\psi\,. \tag{18}$$

It has been shown that the solution of the above equation leads to eigenvalues given by the following for the valence and conduction bands:

$$\mathscr{E}_v = -\left(n+\frac{1}{2}\right)h\omega_v + \frac{h^2k_z^2}{2m_v}\,, \tag{19}$$

$$\mathscr{E}_c = \left(n+\frac{1}{2}\right)h\omega_c + \frac{h^2k_z^2}{2m_c} + \mathscr{E}_g\,, \tag{20}$$

where $\omega_c = eH/m_cC$, $\omega_v = eH/m_vC$ are cyclotron frequencies, m_v and m_c are the hole and electron effective masses respectively and H is the magnetic field along the z-direction. If for our purposes we ignore the co-ordinates along the

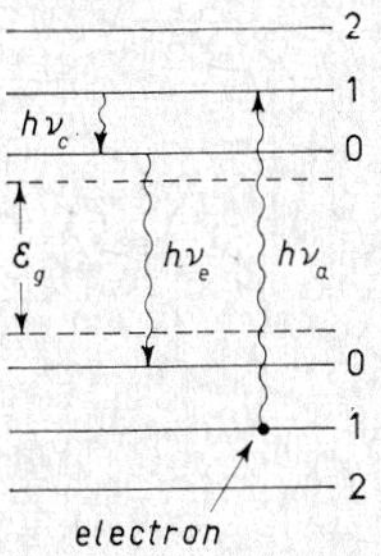

Fig. 6. – Interband transition in a semiconductor in a magnetic field. $h\nu_a$ absorbed photon, $h\nu_e$ emitted photon, $h\nu_c$ photon from induced cyclotron-resonance emission.

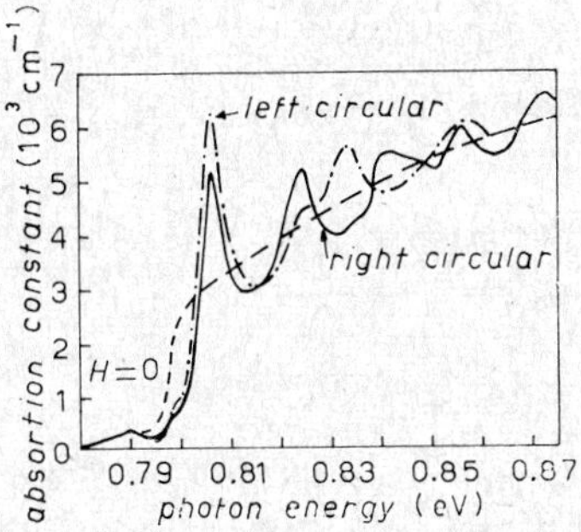

Fig. 7. – Circularly polarized magneto-absorption spectra of the direct transition in germanium. (After BURSTEIN, PICUS, WALLIS and BLATT: *Phys. Rev.*, **113**, 15 (1959).)

magnetic field then the energy levels are quantized in the transverse co-ordinates for both holes and electrons as shown in Fig. 6. It can be shown from perturbation treatment that the absorption coefficient α in the presence of a magnetic field is given by

$$\alpha = A \sum_n \frac{\omega_c^*}{\sqrt{\omega - (n+\frac{1}{2})\omega_c^* - \omega_g}}\,, \tag{21}$$

where $\omega_c^* = eH/\mu c$ and $\mu = m_c m_v/(m_c + m_v)$ is the reduced effective mass. The selection rules for a direct transition is $\Delta k_z = 0$ and $\Delta n = 0$. The singularity in the denominator for the absorption corresponds to the peaking of the density of states at the bottom of each magnetic sub-band given by eq. (21). Thus in a magnetic field the absorption across the energy gap is characterized by oscillatory peaks corresponding to the transitions between the quantized levels. These are indicated as absorption maxima in Ge in Fig. 7. This phenomenon has several interesting applications to semiconductor masers. The first and most obvious is that the energy gap is increased by the magnetic field and hence an emission of a photon across the gap corresponding to transition between levels for which $n = 0$ is given by

$$h\nu_e = \mathscr{E}_g + \tfrac{1}{2}(\hbar\omega_c + \hbar\omega_v)\,. \tag{22}$$

In addition the increased density of states gives rise to a peaking of the emission and hence the transition probability. This fact is the basis for the interband magneto-optical maser. A crude estimate shows that for a magnetic field of 100 kilogauss the total density of states associated with a single magnetic sub-band is in excess of 10^{18} cm^{-3}. Hence either by electrical or optical inversion of hole-electron pairs, enhanced stimulated emission should occur in a suitable semiconductor such as InSb or InAs to provide a magneto-optical maser. Obviously the radiation emitted by such a maser will be tunable by the magnetic field according to eq. (22). For InSb at 4 °K, where $m_c \approx \approx 0.015\, m_0$, for $H = 100$ kG, and $\mathscr{E}_g = 0.25$ eV, the energy gap is increased by $\Delta E \approx 0.03$ eV or about 12%. Comparable change can be achieved in InAs as we shall see from the emission in diodes and lasers in a magnetic field.

Another application of the quantization of levels in a magnetic field is the excitation of a cyclotron-resonance maser as indicated in Fig. 6. A strong optical source such as a laser is used to excite electrons from the valence band to a level in the conduction band creating an inverted population. Then in a resonant structure a transition is induced downward at the cyclotron frequency $h\omega_c$ between adjacent levels of the conduction band. This requires that the energy spacing between levels 0 and 1 are unique and differ from that between 1 and 2, thereby avoiding transitions upward which result in absorption. Such unique levels exist in a variety of semiconductors [6]. For continuous operation in this case it would be necessary to have simultaneous operation of an interband magneto-optical maser in order to deplete the electrons from level 0 in the conduction band and prevent electrons from piling up. A second possibility for pumping a cyclotron resonance maser would require a strong monochromatic source at longer wavelengths. This may be possible by a pulsed gas laser. In this case the electrons are excited to the magnetic levels in the conduction band from the ground state of the impurity level. The advantage in this case would be that the absorption of the pumping radiation would be in the bulk and would depend on the impurity concentration.

The cyclotron-resonance maser can also be pumped electrically as in a *p-n* junction. The conduction band can be inverted relative to the valence band on the *p*-side of a diode such that in a magnetic field the electrons are stimulated as in a magneto-optical maser between the magnetic sub-bands. In this case the level 0 of the valence band would be inverted relative to the empty level 1 of the valence as shown in Fig. 8. Cyclotron-resonance transition then would be stimulated by the appropriate resonant structure. Another possibility for electrical pumping of such a maser presents itself in a tunnel diode which is biased in the forward direction. Then if the magnetic field is along the direction of the current the tunneling of electrons from the conduction band to the valence band will obey the usual selection rules for electric-dipole transitions in a magnetic field, *i.e.*, $\Delta n = 0$. Hence again, level 0 will be inverted to level 1 in the valence band. A variation on this theme has been proposed for InSb in which the magnetic or Landau levels of eq. (21) exhibit large splitting associated with anomalous spin or g-factor. Thus in a tunneling transition as shown in Fig. 9 for an electric-dipole transition not only is n conserved but spin as well, so that in high magnetic field and low temperatures where $g\mu_\beta H > kT$ the plus $\frac{1}{2}$, $n = 0$ state becomes inverted relative to the minus $\frac{1}{2}$,

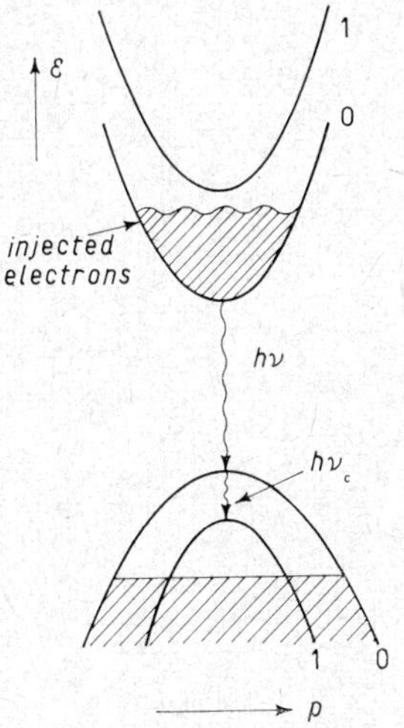

Fig. 8. – Interband transition between lowest magnetic levels with emission of photon $h\nu$. Induced emission between cyclotron states with photon $h\nu_c$.

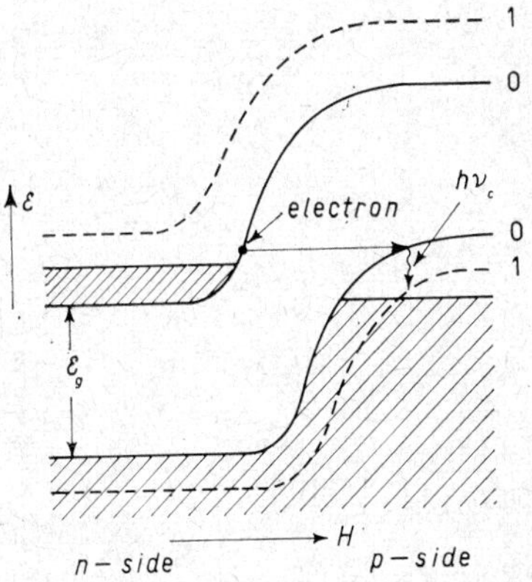

Fig. 9. – Energy diagram of a tunnel diode in a magnetic field. Electron tunnels electrically to the top of the valence band to level 0 and emits a photon of energy $h\nu_c$ at cyclotron frequency.

$n = 0$ state. (The spin quantum numbers are inverted for the conduction band and the light-hole valence band.) Then a magnetic-dipole transition can be induced downward instead of the cyclotron-resonance transition. Although the latter may have a somewhat large matrix element, the magnetic-dipole matrix is still quite large and in addition the relaxation for the spin transition is much longer than that for the cyclotron-resonance or electric-dipole transition.

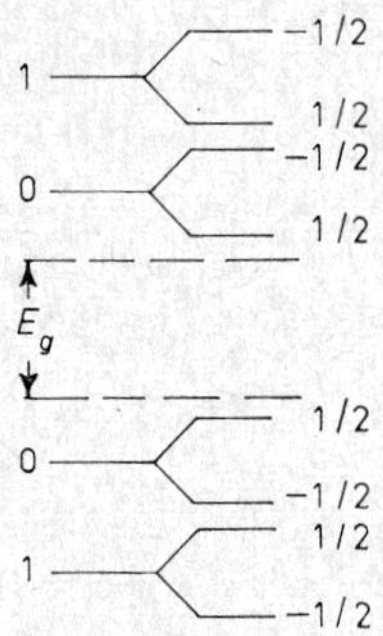

Fig. 10. – Energy levels in indium antimonide in a magnetic field. E_g is energy gap.

2'5. *Losses in the maser.* – In order to obtain amplification or oscillation in a maser it is necessary that the photon energy generated by stimulated emission overcomes the losses incurred in the device. The losses in a semiconductor maser may be of two classes namely those due to the bulk properties and those due to surface effects. Then the rate equation for the creation of loss of photons in a given mode can be written as

$$\frac{\mathrm{d}N_i}{\mathrm{d}t} = A(N_i + 1) - BN_i - CN_i = 0\,, \tag{23}$$

$$N_i = \frac{A}{B + C - A}\,, \tag{24}$$

where N_i is the number of photons in the i-th mode. The first term on the right is the creation term due to stimulated emission plus the spontaneous emission, the second term is the bulk loss and the third term is that due to surface losses. On the threshold for maser-operation steady state is reached and $\mathrm{d}N_i/dt = 0$. The losses are balanced by the creation process so that the denominator approaches zero and the number of photons increases exponentially

$$N_i = \frac{A}{A - B - C}\left[\exp[(A - B - C)t] - 1\right]. \tag{25}$$

Thus when $A > B + C$, the maser oscillates. This condition can be expressed in a more convenient form which is equivalent, namely,

$$\alpha_g > \alpha_B + \alpha_s\,, \tag{26}$$

where α_g is the growth per unit length due to photon creation, α_B the bulk attenuation and α_s that due to surface effects. In semiconductors the two most important loss mechanisms are those due to free carriers in the bulk and reflection or transmission losses. The latter can be readily expressed in terms of the reflection coefficient R:

$$\alpha_s = \frac{-\ln R}{L} \approx \frac{1-R}{L}, \tag{27}$$

where L is the length of the maser. For GaAs where the index of refraction is $n_0 = 3.6$ and $R = (n-1)^2/(n+1)^2 = 0.32$, $L = 1$ mm, $\alpha_s \approx 6\ \text{cm}^{-1}$. We can also calculate the free-carrier absorption in a bulk material from the conductivity which is given by the expression

$$\sigma = \frac{Ne^2\tau}{m^*(1+\omega^2\tau^2)} \approx \frac{Ne^2}{m^*\omega^2\tau}, \tag{28}$$

$$\alpha_B = \sigma\sqrt{\frac{\mu_0}{\varepsilon}}. \tag{29}$$

For the material used in the typical diodes the free-carrier concentration $N \approx (10^{17} \div 10^{18})/\text{cm}^3$. If we use representative values of the various parameters $m_c \approx 0.1 m_0$, $\tau \approx 10^{-13}$ s, $\omega = 2\pi \cdot 3.6 \cdot 10^{14} = 2.2 \cdot 10^{15}$ we find $\alpha_B \approx 1\ \text{cm}^{-1}$. Alternatively from experimental data at these wavelengths we find $\alpha_B \approx 5\ \text{cm}^{-1}$. This is of the right order of magnitude.

The value of the growth coefficient α_{gd} for the direct transition can be estimated from absorption experiments. It is known that the interband absorption is given by

$$\alpha_{gd} \approx A(h\nu - \mathscr{E}_g)^{\frac{1}{2}}. \tag{30}$$

For injection levels of inverted carriers of the order $N \approx (10^{16} \div 10^{18})/\text{cm}^3$ we find that $\alpha_{gd} \approx (300 \div 1500)\ \text{cm}^{-1}$. This is much greater than the losses due to free carriers and therefore the direct-transition maser appears quite favorable from this point of view. In an actual maser as we shall see, the inversion layer is very narrow of the order of about 1 μm and the electromagnetic wave is spread on either side to a total width of about 10 μm. Hence the growth coefficient is reduced by a factor of ten relative to the losses. Nevertheless its value is still considerably greater than that of the losses. Another consideration is that the actual stimulated transition is between bound donor or exciton states to bound acceptor states. The values for the absorption coefficient for such transitions have been measured or calculated theoretically and give $\alpha_g \approx 300\ \text{cm}^{-1}$ for free electron to acceptor concentration of $N \approx 10^{17}\ \text{cm}^3$. This is not too far from the actual situation.

A similar calculation can be made for the indirect transition. In this instance the interband absorption coefficient and hence the stimulated emission is given by:

$$\alpha = B(h\nu - E_g + h\nu_p)^2 . \tag{31}$$

For carrier concentrations of the order of 10^{18} cm³ the energy above the bottom of the band is $\Delta E \approx 0.01$ eV. Then $\alpha = 2\,400(\Delta E)^2 = 0.24$ cm^{-1}. Experimental results indicate $\alpha_{gi} \approx 1$ cm^{-1} at low temperatures for the exciton, which is of the right order of magnitude from the density-of-states ratio. If we compare this with the free-carrier absorption from experimental data we find that $\alpha_B \approx 5$ cm^{-1} at these concentrations. For concentrations of 10^{17} cm³ the exciton coefficient becomes comparable to the free-carrier absorption. Thus, if reflection losses can be reduced and the exciton absorption or emission coefficient increased as in Si or higher-gap semiconductors the number for maser conditions may become more favorable. In Si the free-carrier absorption at the gap energy is of ~ 1 μm, extrapolating to $\alpha \approx 0.3$ cm^{-1} for $N \approx 3\cdot 10^{17}$ cm³. This is less than $\alpha_g \approx 1$ cm^{-1} for the exciton. However, with additional reflection losses the indirect-exciton two-boson maser appears just marginal.

For the cyclotron-resonance maser the coefficient for stimulated emission is

$$\alpha_g = \sigma_r \sqrt{\frac{\mu_0}{E}} = \frac{Ne^2\tau}{m^*}\sqrt{\frac{\mu_0}{E}} . \tag{32}$$

The conductivity off-resonance for the free carriers to higher states which are absorbing the radiation can be expressed as

$$\sigma_f = \frac{Ne^2\tau}{m^*(1 + (\omega_t - \omega_r)^2\tau^2)} \approx \frac{Ne^2\tau}{m^*\omega_r\Delta\omega\tau^2} , \tag{33}$$

$$\frac{\alpha_g}{\alpha_b} = \frac{\sigma_r}{\sigma_f} = \omega_r\Delta\omega\tau^2 . \tag{34}$$

At low temperatures it has been shown that for concentration $N \approx 10^{16}$ cm³, $\tau > 10^{-13}$ s in InSb. This gives for $\alpha_g/\alpha_b \approx 30$ for a 100 kG field, $\omega_r \approx 10^{14}$, $\Delta\omega \approx 3\cdot 10^{13}$, which is quite adequate for maser oscillations.

3. – Experimental results.

3·1. *Gallium arsenide diodes.* – The early work on gallium arsenide diodes was made on thin wafers of n-type material into which are diffused zinc or cadmium impurities to provide a p-n junction. When current is passed through the junction, radiation is emitted through the n-region which is ~ 100 μm thick. When this radiation is examined at room temperature and at 77 °K there is a remarkable change in the character of the radiation. At 300 °K there are two dominant peaks, a broad one at ~1.0 eV and a narrower one at 1.35 eV with a line-width of about 0.050 eV at 300 °K. Translated into wavelength the peak occurs at 9200 Å, $\Delta\lambda \approx 300$ Å. At low temperatures of 77 °K the broad peak diminishes in amplitude as shown in Fig. 11. There are still two small peaks at 1.02 eV and 1.28 eV and a very intense peak at 1.47 eV or 8400 Å with a line width of 0.017 eV or $\Delta\lambda \approx 100$ Å. The peak intensity of the 1.47 eV radiation at 77 °K is about 20 times that of the corresponding one of 1.35 eV at room temperature. It was the observation of this highly efficient intense emission that suggested the possibility of attempting to achieve maser action in diodes.

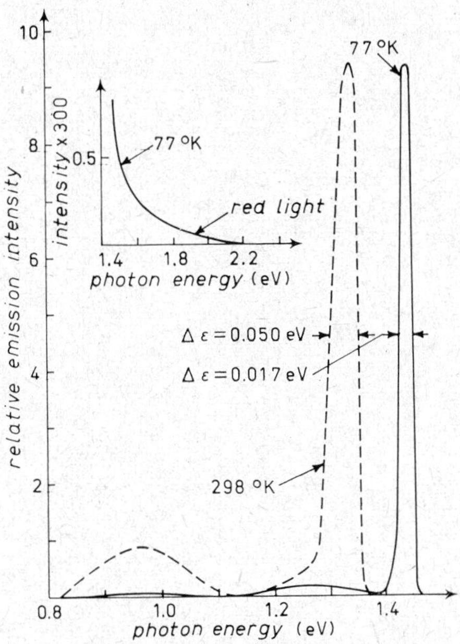

Fig. 11. – Emission spectra of GaAs diodes. (After KEYES and QUIST: *Proc. I.R.E.*, **50**, 1822 (1962).)

A diode maser is fabricated somewhat differently from the incoherent diodes. The wafers contain n-type impurities of the order of 10^{17} to 10^{18} cm^{-3}, into which is diffused Zn with a somewhat higher concentration, to a depth of approximately 10 to 100 μm, depending on a variety of factors. The diode dimensions may be of the order of (0.3 ÷ 1.0) mm in transverse dimension polished down to thicknesses of the order of (0.1 ÷ 0.3) mm. The wafers are rectangular in shape with two opposite faces cleaved or polished to provide flat parallel faces for the Fabry-Perot interferometric resonant modes. The n-side is gold-tin plated and alloyed to a molybdenum pad, while on the p-side silver-gold alloy is evaporated to make the other electrical contact. A sketch of the diode construction is shown in Fig. 12. The coherent infra-red radiation emerges from the cleaved parallel surfaces as indicated in the sketch. The masers are usually operated at low temperatures of 77 °K or 4.2 °K immersed in a bath of liquid nitrogen or liquid helium, respectively. In order to prevent heating, large voltage pulses of short duration are applied to the

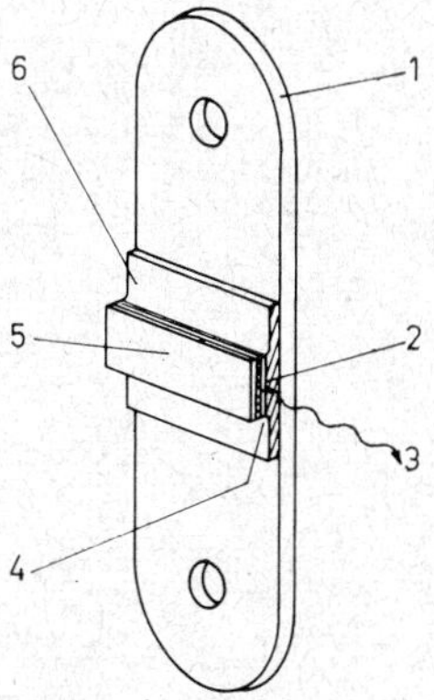

Fig. 12. – Sketch of GaAs laser.

diode from a fraction to a few microseconds. The repetition rate may vary from 1000 to 10 per s, respectively, depending on the pulse duration. The radiation may be observed by eye through an infra-red image converter called the snooperscope or may be detected by a silicon photo-diode or its spectrum observed by a monochromator. The radiation output of the diode has been studied as a function of current as shown in Fig. 13. At very low temperatures of 4 °K the radiation intensity begins to increase very rapidly at about 10 A corresponding to ~1000 A/cm². This corresponds approximately to the threshold for maser action. At 77 °K the threshold increases to approximately 100 A or ~ 10^4 A/cm². The measurement of threshold with temperature has been studied by the IBM group in diode lasers and shows variations with temperature for GaAs as indicated in Fig. 14. The threshold remains flat slightly below 100 A/cm² up to 20 °K. Then the threshold goes up to as high as 10^5 A/cm² at 300 °K. There are two reasons for the increase in the threshold. One is due to the increase in the free-carrier loss at higher temperatures, the other is the deviation from the degenerate distribution of the injected carriers. In the latter case the stimulated absorption for upward transitions begins to compete with the stimulated emission for downward transitions.

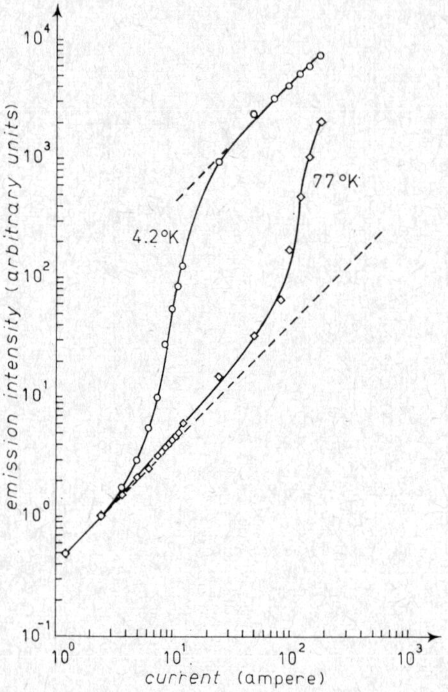

Fig. 13. – Characteristics of GaAs laser. (After QUIST, *et al.*: *Appl. Phys. Lett.*, **1**, 91 (1962).)

When a monochromator is used to study the output spectrum of a diode maser it is found that the line narrows from about 125 Å to a few ångström at 77 °K, as shown in Fig. 15. At 4.2 °K the lines become even narrower from about 100 Å for the incoherent emission to less than 1 Å for the coherent. This narrowing is of course another indication of maser action. Further studies by a high-resolution grating spectrometer in which the spectrum is recorded photographically [14] are indicated in Fig. 16*a*). Below threshold, at 15 A for this diode, the line width of the incoherent spontaneous emission exceeds the width of the exposed film. At 20 A, just above the threshold for maser action, a single line corresponding to a single mode of the interferometer appears. The width of this emission line is about 0.5 Å. When the current is

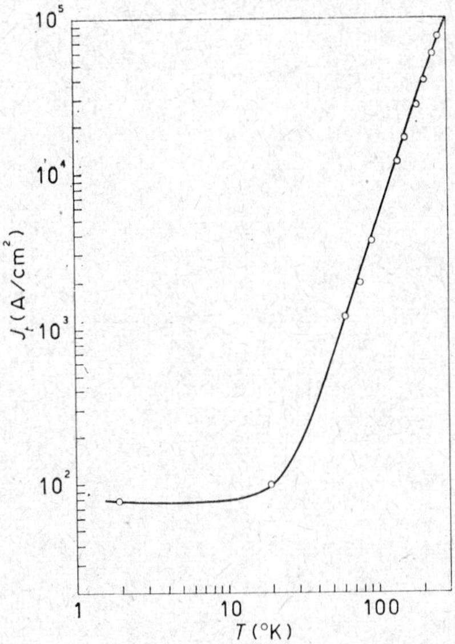

Fig. 14. – Threshold for stimulated emission *vs.* temperature in GaAs. (After BURNS, DILL and NATHAN: *Proc. I.E.E.E.*, **51**, 947 (1963).)

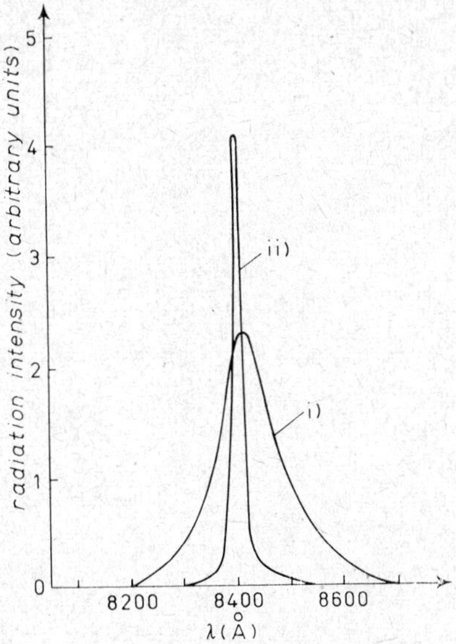

Fig. 15. – Spectrum of radiation as a function of wavelength at 77 °K in a typical gallium arsenide diode, i) below threshold current, and ii) above threshold current to operate as a maser.

increased well above the threshold to 40 A, many other modes of oscillation are excited. The additional resonant modes of the Fabry-Perot interferometer are conclusive evidence of the coherent nature of the emitted radiation. The results for this diode maser are more graphically illustrated by the densitometer trace of the photographic data. This is shown in Fig. 16*b*). From these data it is easily determined that the next nearest mode is about 1 Å away from its neighbor. This can be readily verified from the theoretical

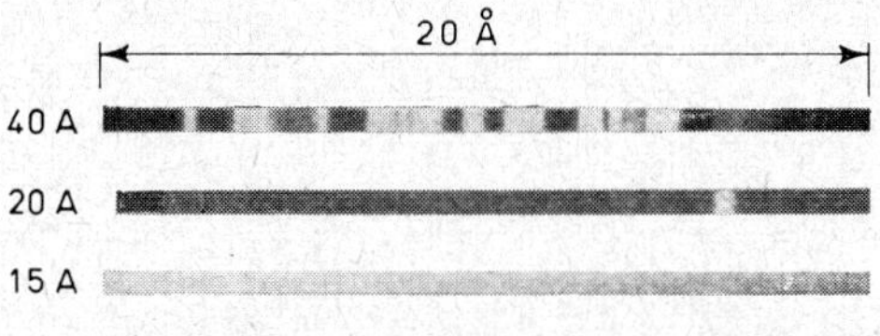

Fig. 16*a*. – Photographic film of emission spectrum of GaAs laser. (After QUIST, REDIKER, KEYES and KRAG: *Bull. Am. Phys. Soc.*, **8**, 88 (1963).

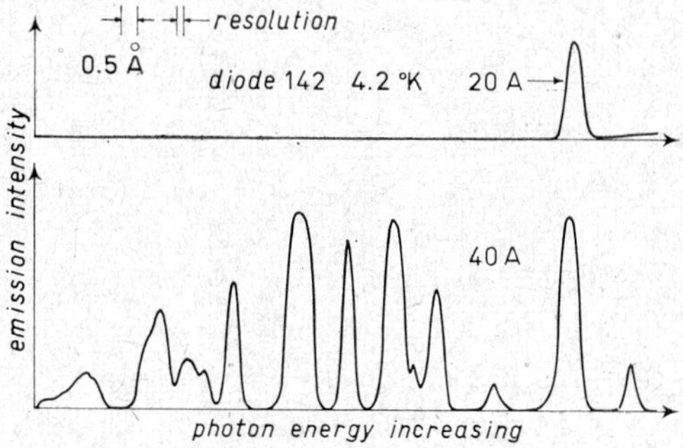

Fig. 16*b*. – Densitometer trace of spectrum. (After QUIST, REDIKER, KEYES and KRAG: *Bull. Am. Phys. Soc.*, **8**, 88 (1963).)

expression for the separation of the modes given by

$$\Delta\lambda = \frac{\lambda_0^2}{2L[n_0 - \lambda_0\, dn/d\lambda]} \approx \frac{\lambda_0^2}{2Ln_0}\,. \tag{35}$$

For gallium arsenide the index of refraction $n_0 = 3.6$, $\lambda_0 = 8\,400$ Å, for this diode $L \approx 1$ mm. If these numbers are substituted into the above equation we find that

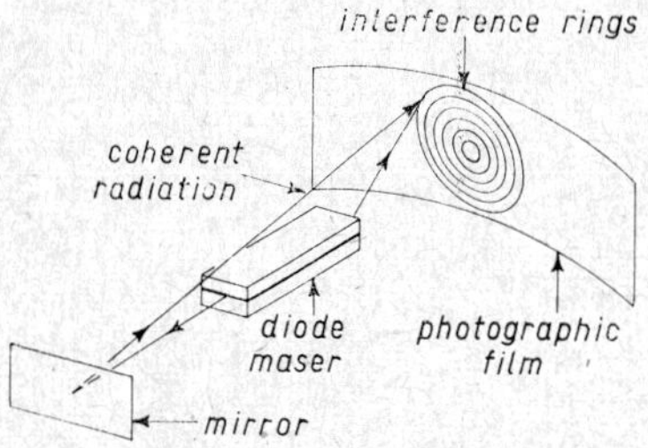

Fig. 17. – Interference rings of GaAs laser. (After WALKER and MICHEL: *Bull. Am. Phys. Soc.*, **8**, 202 (1963).)

$$\Delta\lambda = \frac{(0.84)^2 \cdot 10^8}{2 \cdot 10^7 \cdot 3.6} \approx 1\text{ Å}\,.$$

Other properties of the GaAs laser which have been observed experimentally that are intimately related to its coherent properties are the diffraction patterns, the polarization of the waves, the horizontal and vertical radiation patterns and demonstrations of the interference properties of the forward and backward radiation of the diodes. The diffraction patterns are those one would expect from a narrow horizontal slit of coherent source producing vertical striations on a photographic plate at a distance from the source. A more striking demonstration of the diode maser is that shown in Fig. 17 in which the radiation emitted from the opposite and parallel ends of the diode is combined by means of a mirror to produce interference rings [15]. Another set of measurements which shows the far field radiation pattern is shown in Fig. 18. The radiation was sampled by a monochromator and represents a high spectral and spatial sampling of one mode [16]. The main lobe is approximately 1° wide in the horizontal plane. This represents a filament width of $d = \lambda/\theta = 0.94 \cdot 57 \approx 50$ μm. In the vertical plane as shown in Fig. 19 the beam width is greater and of the

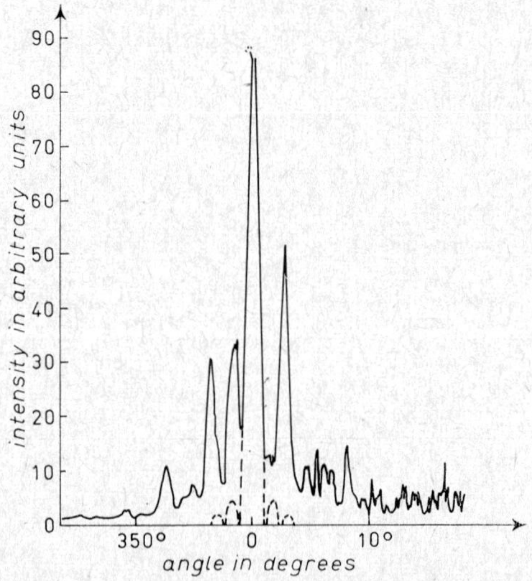

Fig. 18. – Radiation pattern of GaAs laser in horizontal plane, $\lambda = 8\,412$, $L = 64$. (After KINGSLEY and FINNER: *Bull. Am. Phys. Soc.*, **8**, 88 (1963).)

order of 6°. This corresponds to a filament height of $h = \lambda/\theta \approx 10$ μm. The filament height represents the half-width of the luminescent area, which of course is smaller than the active inverted region.

Diode masers as indicated have operated on a pulse basis as high as room temperature. However, at very low temperatures by pumping on the helium to 2 °K reducing the dimensions of the diode to about 0.1 mm × 0.5 mm and polishing all four sides the threshold was lowered to about 100 A/cm² and operated continuously [17]. Apparently by increasing the surface-volume ratio, the heat transfer properties of the diode were improved. At the same time the reflection losses of the diode were reduced because the mode of operation took advantage of the internal reflection at angles of 16° or greater with the normal. Thus by combining these effects the first continuous diode maser was achieved. Recently by improved design of diodes between molybdenum [18] or pure tungsten tabs as efficient heat sinks the average power delivered by a diode has been in excess of 1 W average. A recent unit has been able to operate continuously at this power level at an overall efficiency of 30 % [19]. The limiting factor in this case particularly at high peak currents is the series I^2R or ohmic loss in the bulk n- and p-regions of the diode. For high efficiencies these should be made as thin as possible.

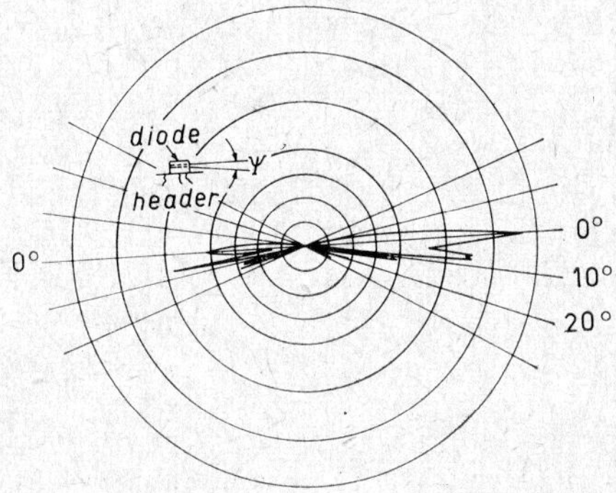

Fig. 19. – Radiation pattern of GaAs laser in vertical plane, $L = 188$. (After KINGSLEY and FENNER: *Bull. Am. Phys. Soc.*, **8**, 88 (1963).)

3·2. *New materials.* – In addition to the GaAs maser other materials have now been successfully made into semiconductor lasers. One of the first to be reported was $GaAs_{1-x}P_x$, an alloy of gallium arsenide phosphide [11]. The radiation at 77 °K showed line narrowing from 125 Å to 12 Å at a threshold of about 20 000 A/cm². Since the energy gap in this alloy is higher than that of GaAs it is not surprising that the emission occurred at 7 100 Å. Another interesting development has been that in InAs diodes [12], which emit at longer wavelength in the infra-red, namely, at 3.1 μm. These have been operated at 4.2 °K and 77 °K with cleaved surfaces along the (110) cleavage plane. The threshold for maser action at these two temperatures was of the order of 10^3 A/cm² and 10^4 A/cm², corresponding closely to the values obtained for GaAs. However, at these longer wavelengths the spontaneous emission line width of the incoherent diode was 1900 Å at 77 °K and narrowed down to about 40 Å or a factor of 50. This is shown in Fig. 20. Above the threshold additional modes were excited as indicated. At 4.2° the spontaneous emission line is 1100 Å wide and that of the coherent line was 70 Å. The angular dependence of the radiation pattern was measured and gave a horizontal beam angle of 5° and a vertical angle of 20°. These suggest a luminous filament of about 35 μm wide and ~10 μm high. By the use of a magnetic field the diode was operated continuously. It was also tuned by the magnetic field [20]. We shall discuss this more extensively later.

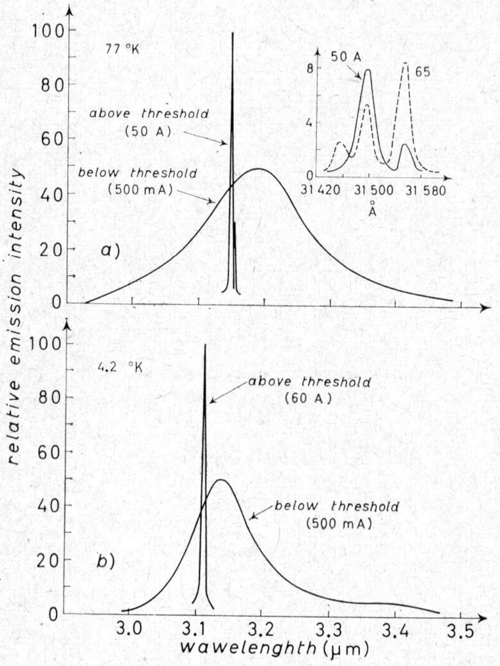

Fig. 20. – Emission spectrum of InAs laser. (After MELNGAILIS and REDIKER: *Appl. Phys. Lett.*, **2**, 202 (1963).)

Other materials which have also been developed into laser diodes include indium phosphide, InP [21], and alloys of gallium-indium arsenide $Ga_{1-x}In_xAs$ [22]. The former emitted radiation in the vicinity of 9000 Å at low temperatures with line widths of the order of 1 Å. In general the characteristics of thresholds *vs.* temperature and other properties of these diode masers closely repeated those of GaAs but at somewhat longer wavelengths. The ternary alloy masers of $In_xGa_{1-x}As$ represent another approach to extending the wavelength range of the semiconductor lasers in the infrared region. Actually two mixtures have been fabricated with $x=0.75$ operating at 2.07 μm and $x=0.65$ operating at 1.77 μm. The net donor concentration of the bulk materials was $3\cdot10^{17}$ cm^{-3} and $6\cdot10^{17}$ cm^{-3}, respectively. The threshold for these mixed crystals was somewhat higher than those of the binary compounds of GaAs and InAs. A magnetic field of the order of 14 kG was used to lower the threshold at 1.9 °K to $3\cdot10^4$ A/cm^2. The line width was observed to be about 6.5 Å for coherent emission.

3'3. *Magnetic effects of diodes and lasers.* – A number of problems associated with the basic phenomena of emission in the GaAs maser have puzzled investigators. Among these has been the identification of the nature of transition involved in the emission. A number of mechanisms have been proposed, namely 1) interband transition between free holes and electrons, 2) electron from donor to valence band, 3) electron to acceptor states, 4) between overlapping donor to acceptor, 5) exciton annihilation bound to an acceptor state. The use of magnetic-field effects on the variation of the energy spectrum with magnetic field has finally narrowed down the possibility to the last two [23]. The shift of the emission line of both a diode and a maser showed a quadratic dependence on magnetic field as indicated in Fig. 21. This shift can be readily correlated with the quadratic Zeeman effect of the ground state of a shallow donor or exciton as the initial state. The energy shift is given by

$$\Delta\varepsilon = \left(\frac{\hbar^2 e^2/m^2}{13.6}\right)\frac{K^2}{(m^*/m)^3}\frac{B^2}{8}. \tag{36}$$

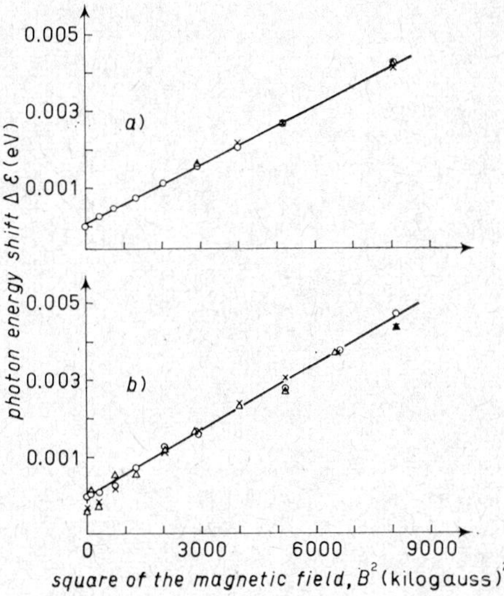

Fig. 21. – Zeeman effect of emission at 4.2 °K from *a*) GaAs laser, *b*) GaAs diode. (After GALEENER, WRIGHT, QUIST and ZEIGER: *Phys. Rev. Lett.*, **10**, 472 (1962).)

With a value of the dielectric constant $K=12.9$ maser data give mass ratios $m^*/m_0=0.074$, while for the diode data $m^*/m_0=0.071$. These correspond very closely to the measured value of the electron mass in GaAs. Consequently, the conclusion to be drawn is that the shift of the emission line is associated with a shallow level just below the conduction band. This, of course, can be accounted for either by a donor or an exciton state. However, it is known that the binding energy of these states is $\mathscr{E}_d = 13.6\, m^*/m_0 K^2 = 6\cdot 10^{-3}$ eV. This still leaves a discrepancy of approximately 0.03 eV between the emission line and the energy gap which can easily be accounted for by the binding energy of the acceptor since the hole mass $m_v^* \approx 0.4\, m_0$, then $\mathscr{E}_a \approx 13.6\cdot 0.4/(12.9)^2 \approx 0.033$ eV.

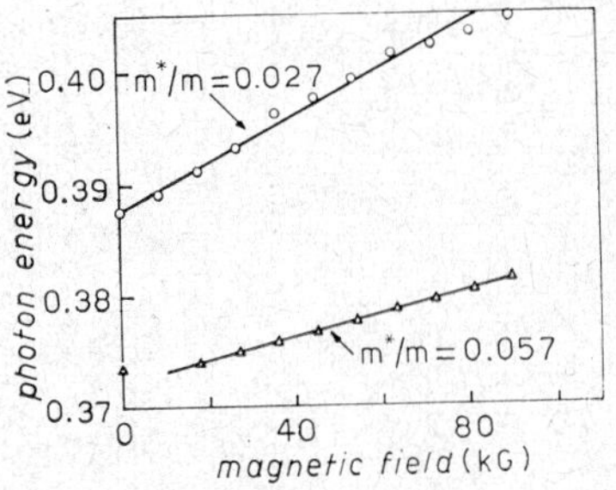

Fig. 22. – Zeeman effect of emission from InAs diodes at 77 °K: ○ $n=2\cdot 10^{16}$ cm^{-3} △ $n\approx 10^{19}$ cm^{-3}. (After MELNGAILIS: *Bull. Am. Phys. Soc.*, **8**, 202 (1963)).

Magnetic effects on the emission of InAs have now also been studied fairly extensively [24]. The initial measurements were made on incoherent diodes in which the energy shift of the emission lines showed large variations as a linear function of magnetic field as shown in Fig. 22. With relatively lightly doped diodes the shift was consistent with that predicted from eq. (22) for the increase of the energy gap with magnetic field from the known masses of the electron-hole pair. For the higher doping, the shift is still linear but is considerably less, the apparent effective mass deduced from these data is larger. This effect is associated with the overlap of donor wave functions, since the separation between centers is less than that of the radius of the donor ground state.

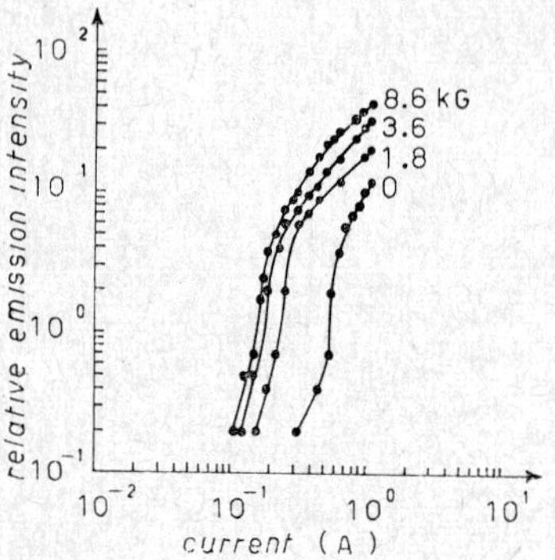

Fig. 23. – Threshold of InAs laser in a magnetic field. (After MELNGAILIS and REDIKER: *Appl. Phys. Lett.*, **2**, 202 (1963).)

In InAs masers, other interesting results were also observed as a function of magnetic field [20]. It was found that the threshold for maser oscillations was reduced by the magnetic field as shown in Fig. 23. The magnetic field was perpendicular to the current flow and in the plane of the junction. From this it can be seen that the threshold at 500 mA or approximately 4000 A/cm² is reduced to about 1000 A/cm² at fields of the order of 8000 G. The threshold reaches a limiting value as the magnetic field is increased beyond this range. The reduction in threshold is accounted for primarily by the effect of the magnetic field upon the diffusion of injected carriers across the junction. It is known that the diffusion length is reduced by the magnetic field according to the relation

$$L_D = \sqrt{D\tau_r} = \sqrt{\frac{D_0 \tau_r}{1 + \omega_c^2 \tau^2}} \approx \frac{\sqrt{D_0 \tau_r}}{\omega_c \tau}, \tag{37}$$

where D_0 is the diffusion coefficient in the absence of the magnetic field, τ_r is the recombination lifetime and τ is the collision frequency. In any event, from a qualitative argument it can be seen that the inversion layer is reduced by the magnetic field, but the electron-hole concentration is increased. This would tend to increase the stimulated emission and hence reduce the threshold current. The other aspect of the magnetic-field effect is shown in Fig. 24. As the field is increased, the frequency of the dominant mode shifts to shorter wavelengths. In addition, a mode of a given number is shifted to somewhat

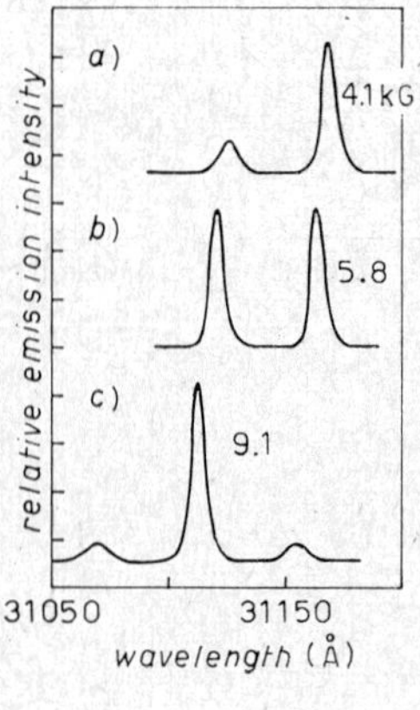

Fig. 24. – Mode spectrum of InAs laser in a magnetic field. (After MELNGAILIS and REDIKER: *Appl. Phys. Lett.*, **2**, 202 (1963).)

higher frequencies. This can be accounted for by the change in the index of refraction due to the magnetic field. It is known that the index of refraction decreases as the wavelength of the radiation approaches the energy gap. This is due to the peak in the dispersive component associated with the direct transition. The index of refraction in the absence of a magnetic field can be written as

$$n \approx n_0 + \frac{A}{\omega^2}\left[2\sqrt{\omega_g} - \sqrt{\omega_g + \omega} - \sqrt{\omega_g - \omega}\right], \tag{38}$$

where $A = e^2 M^2 (2\mu)^{\frac{3}{2}}/n_0 m^2 \hbar^3$, n_0 is the index of refraction, μ the reduced mass, M the momentum matrix element and ω_g is the frequency corresponding to the energy gap. It is possible to write an analogous expression for the magneto-dispersion. This is usually expressed in terms of a tensor, but in this case it can be readily shown that the diagonal component is the most important term. Then the expression becomes

$$n = n_0 + \sum \frac{A\omega_c}{2\omega^2}\left[-\frac{2}{\sqrt{\omega_n}} + \frac{1}{\sqrt{\omega_n + \omega}} + \frac{1}{\sqrt{\omega_n - \omega}}\right], \tag{39}$$

where ω_c is the reduced cyclotron frequency and $\omega_n = \omega_g + (n + \frac{1}{2})\omega_c$. It can be seen that the dispersion shows a singularity and also an increase with magnetic field. Hence, the magneto-dispersion effects are large and should be readily studied at high magnetic fields by observing the shift of the mode structure as well as the change in mode spacing with the magnetic fields.

3·4. *Theory of electromagnetic modes.* – From the emitted radiation of the junction maser, it is apparent that the electromagnetic energy is confined to a plane at or near the junction. This region is the inverted region indicated by ① as shown in Fig. 25 with a width of $2w$. Its dielectric properties are represented by $\varepsilon_1 = \varepsilon_1' - \sigma_1/j\omega$, where σ_1 is the negative conductivity associated with the inverted population, ε_1' is the real part of the dielectric constant and includes the dispersive component contributed by the inverted carriers as well. From the Kramers-Kronig relation this can be obtained from the analytical representation of σ_1. The region ① which is inverted is of the order of 1 μm which is considerably larger than the depletion layer of the p-n junction. Regions ② and ③ are the p- and n-regions containing free carriers, holes and electrons respectively and are characterized by complex

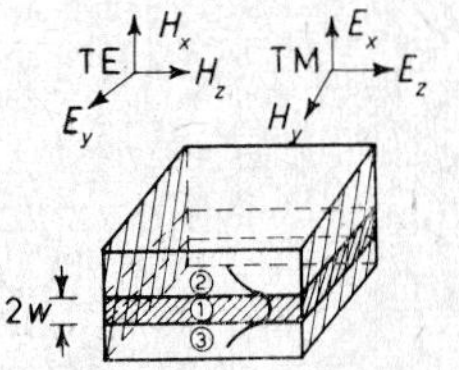

Fig. 25. – TE and TM modes of a diode laser. (After McWhorter, Zeiger and Lax: *Journ. Appl. Phys.*, **34**, 235 (1963).)

conductivities of the form

(40) $$\sigma_{2,3} = \frac{N_{2,3}e^2\tau_{2,3}}{m_{2,3}(1+j\omega\tau_{2,3})} \approx \frac{N_{2,3}e^2}{m_{2,3}}\left(\frac{1}{\omega^2\tau_{2,3}} - \frac{j}{\omega}\right),$$

since $\omega\tau_{2,3} \gg 1$ where the carrier concentrations differ and vary from about $(10^{17} \div 10^{18})/\text{cm}^{-3}$ in the usual diodes. τ_2 and τ_3 are also junctions of the carrier concentrations as well as the temperature. It is hard to predict the values *a priori*. However, these have been measured and can be estimated quite well for a given concentration and temperature from the experimental data. As we see from eq. (40) that the free carriers reduce the effective dielectric constant of the media in the p- and n-regions which are represented by

(41) $$\begin{cases} \varepsilon_2 = \varepsilon_2' + \dfrac{\sigma_2}{j\omega}, \\ \varepsilon_3 = \varepsilon_3' + \dfrac{\sigma_3}{j\omega}. \end{cases}$$

The electromagnetic problem follows the original development given by McWhorter, Zeiger and Lax [25]. The maser is idealized by the well-defined regions indicated in Fig. 25 and represents an extension of the dielectric-slab problem in which the electromagnetic field is concentrated in the slab of higher dielectric and decays exponentially into the neighboring regions normal to the plane of the slab. In the problem it is assumed that the slab is extended in the y-direction and hence independent of this co-ordinate. The direction of propagation is along the z-direction with variation $\exp[j\omega t - kz]$. In regions ② and ③ the waves have the form $\exp[jk_2x]$ and $\exp[-jk_3x]$, respectively, representing decaying exponentials. In region ① the x-variation is given by $A\cos k_1x + B\sin k_1x$. The modes in this configuration can be classified either as transverse electric (TE) or transverse magnetic (TM) modes depending on whether a single component of the electric or magnetic vector is present as shown in Fig. 25. Taking the appropriate relations for the field components from Maxwell's equations for either of the two modes and then satisfying the boundary conditions for the continuity of the transverse components of $\boldsymbol{E}$ and $\boldsymbol{H}$ at the interfaces between regions ① and ② and between ① and ③, a secular equation is obtained which then results in the complex transcendental equations of the form

(42) $$\text{tg}\, 2k_1 w = jk_1 \frac{k_2 + k_3}{k_1^2 + k_2k_3} \qquad \text{(TE mode)}$$

and

(43) $$\text{tg}\, 2k_1 w = j(k_1/t_1)\frac{(k_2/t_2) + (k_3/t_3)}{(k_1/t_1)^2 + (k_2k_3/t_2t_3)} \qquad \text{(TM mode)}.$$

These are generalized equations which have been obtained by McWhorter [26] and extend the original solutions which for simplicity assumed $k_2 = k_3$ and $\varepsilon_2 = \varepsilon_3$. In addition to the above condition from Maxwell's equations, we obtain dispersion relations for regions ①, ② and ③ of the form

$$k^2 + k_i^2 = \omega^2 \varepsilon_i \mu_0 \qquad (i = 1, 2, 3). \tag{44}$$

From the above equations it is not a simple matter to solve for the complex propagation constant. However, for the semiconductor diodes in question it is quite justified to assume that $(k_1 w)^2 \ll 1$. This allows the transcendental equations to be expanded in power series of this parameter or more specifically in terms of the differential quantity $\omega^2 \mu_0 (\varepsilon_1 - \varepsilon_2) w^2$ which is very small compared to unity. In addition to these conditions it can be readily shown that $\sigma_2, \sigma_3 \ll \sigma_1 \ll \omega\varepsilon$. The problem can then be readily solved for the complex propagation constant

$$k \approx k_0 (1 + j\eta/2), \tag{45}$$

where $k_0 = \sqrt{\varepsilon \mu_0}$ is the propagation constant in the pure semiconductor. The imaginary part of k is taken as positive, representing a growing wave and is given here as a dimensionless quantity. When the solution of η, the parameter for the power gain, is obtained the result is

$$\eta = \frac{\bar{\sigma}}{\omega\varepsilon} + 2(k_0 w)^2 \left(\frac{\varepsilon_1' - \bar{\varepsilon}'}{\varepsilon}\right) \frac{\sigma_1}{\omega\varepsilon} + \dots, \tag{46}$$

where $\bar{\sigma} = (\sigma_2 + \sigma_3)/2$ and $\bar{\varepsilon}' = (\varepsilon_2' + \varepsilon_3')/2$. This is of the same form as the solution obtained in the original treatment which assumed that regions ② and ③ were identical, *i.e.*, $\sigma_2 = \sigma_3$ and $\varepsilon_2' = \varepsilon_3'$. The above result represents the solution in terms of the mean of the two quantities. The first term on the right in eq. (46) is the loss due to the free-carrier absorption in regions ② and ③ and the second term is the positive term due to the inverted population. This term must exceed the first to give rise to a growing wave. Another quantity that can be obtained from the transcendental equations is the penetration of the waves into the lossy regions. These are given by

$$jk_2 = (k_0^2 w)\left(\frac{\varepsilon_1 - \bar{\varepsilon}}{\varepsilon}\right) + \frac{1}{4w}\left(\frac{\varepsilon_3 - \varepsilon_2}{\varepsilon_1 - \varepsilon}\right) + \dots . \tag{47}$$

A similar expression can be written for jk_3. The above result is rather interesting in that for a diode in which $\varepsilon_3 \approx \varepsilon_2$ the decay of the wave transversely is determined by the presence of a region of the high inverted conductivity. This is certainly true if $\sigma_1 \gg \sigma_2, \sigma_3$ and the decay or penetration depth under these conditions is given by

$$k_2 \approx k_0^2 \, w\sigma_1 \tag{48}$$

or

$$\sigma_2 \approx \frac{1}{\omega\mu_0\sigma_1 w}, \tag{49}$$

which on resonance for the inverted transition gives a value of a few μm, quite consistent with the values determined from the radiation patterns.

Actually the results of the transcendental equation for the case where it is assumed that $\varepsilon_2 = \varepsilon_3$ have been more extensively worked out then for the more general situation where $\varepsilon_2 \neq \varepsilon_3$. Without loss of great generality the more restricted case illustrates much of the electromagnetic phenomena of interest. In this approximation the transcendental equations for the two possible sets of modes become:

$$k_1 \operatorname{tg} k_1 w = jk_2 \qquad \text{(TE mode)}, \tag{50}$$

$$(k_1/\varepsilon_1) \operatorname{tg} k_1 w = (jk_2/\varepsilon_2) \qquad \text{(TM mode)}. \tag{51}$$

Again assuming $k_1 w \ll 1$ we find

$$jk_2 \approx k_1^2 w$$

and

$$jk_2 = \frac{\varepsilon_2}{\varepsilon_1} k_1^2 w \,. \tag{52}$$

Using the results of eq. (44) we can eliminate k_1^2 since $k_1^2 = k_2^2 + \omega^2(\varepsilon_1 - \varepsilon_2)$. This results in two sets of quadratic equations of the following form:

$$k_2^2 - \frac{jk_2}{w} + \omega^2(\varepsilon_1 - \varepsilon_2) = 0 \qquad \text{(TE mode)}, \tag{53}$$

$$k_2^2 - \frac{jk_2}{w}\frac{\varepsilon_1}{\varepsilon_2} + \varepsilon^2(\varepsilon_1 - \varepsilon_2) = 0 \qquad \text{(TM mode)}. \tag{54}$$

Upon solving the above equation for k_2 and then expanding the results as a power series in $(k_0 w)^2(\varepsilon_1 - \varepsilon_2)/\varepsilon$ the solutions for k^2 and hence for $k \approx k_0(1 + j\eta/2)$ are automatically obtained. These then become

$$k^2 = k_0^2 \left[\frac{\varepsilon_2}{\varepsilon} + (k_0 w)^2 \left(\frac{\varepsilon_1 - \varepsilon_2}{\varepsilon}\right)^2 - \frac{4}{3}(k_0 w)^2 \left(\frac{\varepsilon_1 - \varepsilon_2}{\varepsilon}\right)^3 + \ldots\right] \tag{55}$$

for the TE mode and for the TM mode

$$(56)\quad k^2 = k_0^2\frac{\varepsilon_2}{\varepsilon} + (k_0 w)^2\left(\frac{\varepsilon_1-\varepsilon_2}{\varepsilon}\right)\left(\frac{\varepsilon_2}{\varepsilon_1}\right)^2 - \frac{4}{3}(k_0 w)^4\left(\frac{\varepsilon_1-\varepsilon_2}{\varepsilon}\right)^3\left[-\frac{1}{2}+\frac{3}{2}\left(\frac{\varepsilon_2}{\varepsilon_1}\right)^2\right] + \dots .$$

Using the approximation of eq. (45) we then obtain the value of the growth coefficient:

$$(57)\quad \eta = -\frac{\sigma_2}{\omega\varepsilon} + 2(k_0 w)^2\left(\frac{\varepsilon_1^1-\varepsilon_2^1}{\varepsilon}\right)\frac{\sigma_1}{\omega\varepsilon} + \frac{4}{3}(k_0 w)^4\left[\left(\frac{\sigma_1}{\omega\varepsilon}\right)^3 - 3\left(\frac{\varepsilon_1^1-\varepsilon_2^1}{\varepsilon}\right)^2\frac{\sigma_1}{\omega\varepsilon}\right] \quad (\mathrm{TE}),$$

$$(58)\quad \eta = -\frac{\sigma_2}{\omega\varepsilon} + 2(k_0 w)^2\left(\frac{\varepsilon_1'-\varepsilon_2'}{\varepsilon}\right)\frac{\sigma_1}{\omega\varepsilon} +$$

$$+ [2(k_0 w)^2 + 4(k_0 w)^4]\left[\left(\frac{\sigma_1}{\omega\varepsilon}\right)^3 - 3\frac{(\varepsilon_1'-\varepsilon_2')^2}{\varepsilon}\frac{\sigma_1}{\omega\varepsilon}\right] \quad (\mathrm{TM}).$$

If the free carrier susceptibilities are neglected compared to the normal dielectric constant and at the spontaneous emission peak, then $\varepsilon_1'=\varepsilon_2'=\varepsilon$ and the above expressions simplify to

$$(59)\quad \eta = -\frac{\sigma^2}{\omega\varepsilon} + \frac{4}{3}(k_0 w)^4\left(\frac{\sigma_1}{\omega\varepsilon}\right)^3 \quad (\mathrm{TE}),$$

$$(60)\quad \eta = -\frac{\sigma^2}{\omega\varepsilon} + \left[2(k_0 w)^2 + \frac{4}{3}(k_0 w)^4\right]\left(\frac{\sigma_1}{\omega\varepsilon}\right)^3 \quad (\mathrm{TM}).$$

On the resonance peak of the spontaneous emission line the TM mode has a somewhat lower threshold as seen from eqs. (59) and (60) and at high $k_0 w \gg 1$ the two modes are nearly the same. However, returning to the previous set of eqs. (57) and (58) it can be seen that the dispersive component of ε_1' and the negative conductivity σ_1, can contribute to the growth of the wave. Assuming a Lorentzian line and maximizing the value of η the result for maser oscillation occurs on the high-frequency side of the spontaneous line where $t_1' > t$ at $\omega \approx \omega_0 + (\Delta\omega/2\sqrt{3})$ where $\Delta\omega$ is the half-power width and ω_0 is the peak frequency. The condition for growth is then given by the first two terms of eqs. (58) and (60) which are the same for the TE and TM modes, then η becomes:

$$(61)\quad \eta \approx -\frac{\sigma_2}{\omega_0\varepsilon} + \frac{3\sqrt{3}}{8}(k_0 w)^2\left(\frac{\sigma_{01}}{\omega_0\varepsilon}\right)^2,$$

where σ_{01} is the peak value of σ_1 at $\omega=\omega_0$. Under these conditions we can also calculate the complex value of k_2 which together with the condition that at threshold $\eta=0$ from eq. (61) becomes

$$k_2 \approx k_0 \left(\frac{\sqrt{3}}{2}\frac{\sigma_2}{\omega\varepsilon}\right)^{\frac{1}{2}}\left(1-\frac{J}{\sqrt{3}}\right). \tag{62}$$

Thus at threshold the penetration depth is dependent on σ_2 and to this approximation independent of w. From the above expression it is simple to calculate the penetration depth into the free-carrier region

$$\delta_2 \approx \operatorname{Re}\frac{1}{jk_2} = \frac{\sqrt{3}\lambda}{2\pi}\left(\frac{4\pi}{\sqrt{3}\alpha\lambda}\right)^{\frac{1}{2}}, \tag{63}$$

where δ_2 is the penetration depth, λ the wavelength of the radiation, $\alpha = k_0(\sigma_2/\omega\varepsilon)$ is the absorption coefficient in region ②. These have been measured to be about 1000 cm^{-1} to 10 cm^{-1} depending on the doping level. If we substitute these values into eq. (63) we find δ_2 varies from 2.5 μm to 25 μm. The mean value which is appropriate corresponds quite closely to the experimental measurements. From the result of eq. (63) it is possible to estimate the vertical half-power beam width of the diode maser. Its approximate value is given by

$$\theta \approx \frac{\lambda}{\delta_2} \approx \frac{0.85}{10} \approx 0.1 \text{ radian} \simeq 6^\circ . \tag{64}$$

This agrees well with the values quoted earlier in the experimental section.

So far we have balanced the growing wave with the losses due to free-carrier absorption. Another important contribution is the reflection due to the dielectric discontinuity at the cleaved or polished surfaces of the diodes. The transmission loss due to this effect has to be added to the expression for η given by eq. (61). This gives

$$\eta \approx -\frac{\sigma_2}{\omega\varepsilon} - \frac{1}{k_0 L}\log\frac{1}{R} + \frac{3\sqrt{3}}{8}(k_0 w)^2\left(\frac{\sigma_{01}}{\omega\varepsilon}\right)^2, \tag{65}$$

where R is the reflection coefficient determined by the dielectric constant $R = (\sqrt{\varepsilon}-1)^2/(\sqrt{\varepsilon}+1)^2$. For $\varepsilon \approx 13$, $R = 0.32$, if we solve for the threshold condition $\eta = 0$ we obtain that

$$\frac{\sigma_{c1}}{\omega\varepsilon} \approx \left(\frac{8}{3\sqrt{3}k_0}\right)^{\frac{1}{2}}\frac{1}{k_0 w}\left(\alpha + \frac{1}{L}\log\frac{1}{R}\right)^{\frac{1}{2}}. \tag{66}$$

For a diode of 1 mm length or less the reflection loss begins to compare with the absorption loss whose mean value $\bar{\alpha} \approx 100$ cm^{-1} whereas $\alpha_R = L^{-1}\log R^{-1} \approx 30$ cm^{-1} for $L = 0.3$ mm.

4. – Calculation of the negative conductivity.

The particular outstanding problem that has received attention recently is that of determining the nature of the transitions which are responsible for the stimulated emission in the semiconductor maser. There are two problems of interest: one is to calculate the negative conductivity in terms of the statistics or distribution functions which describe the population of the upper and lower states involved; the other is to identify the particular model for the transition and then calculate the matrix element for the transition in terms of the suitable wave function representing the upper and lower states. This problem has been considered by DUMKE [27] for the donor to valence band and conduction band to acceptor transitions. ZEIGER [28] has worked out a much more generalized treatment in which he has considered several possibilities including those of DUMKE and in addition the more likely one of donor to acceptor transition. In these notes we shall follow the treatment of ZEIGER.

From time-dependent perturbation theory we can write the net absorption rate per unit volume for photons of a given frequency ω as follows:

$$\frac{\mathrm{d}N(\omega)}{\mathrm{d}t} = \frac{2\pi}{\hbar}\int \varrho_u \varrho_l [(1-f_u)f_l - f_u(1-f_l)]\cdot M_{ul}^2 \frac{E^2}{2}\cdot \delta(\mathscr{E}_u - \mathscr{E}_l - \hbar\omega)\,\mathrm{d}\mathscr{E}_u\,\mathrm{d}\mathscr{E}_l\,, \tag{67}$$

where ϱ_u, ϱ_l, f_u and f_l are the density of states and distribution functions for electron occupation of the upper and lower energy states, respectively. Each of these is of course a function of the corresponding energies $\mathscr{E}_u$ and $\mathscr{E}_l$. M_{ul} is the momentum matrix element for an electric dipole transition and is of the form $ep/j\omega m$, where p is the momentum operator. The δ function is the usual requirement necessary for conserving energy in the transition.

From eq. (67) it is possible to obtain the suitable expression for the negative conductivity since by definition the net power created per unit volume is given by

$$P = \hbar\omega \frac{\mathrm{d}N}{\mathrm{d}t} = \frac{\sigma_1 E^2}{2}\,. \tag{68}$$

Then

$$\sigma_1 = \pi\omega \iint \varphi_u \varphi_l [f_l - f_u]\, M_{ul}^2\, \delta(\mathscr{E}_u - \mathscr{E}_l - \hbar\omega)\,\mathrm{d}\mathscr{E}_u\,\mathrm{d}\mathscr{E}_l\,. \tag{69}$$

By the Kramer-Kronig relation it is possible to obtain the dispersive part of the dielectric constant $\mathscr{E}'$, which is associated with σ_1. We can also obtain an expression for the spontaneous emission using the expression for the density of electromagnetic modes in angular frequency $k_0^3/\pi^2\omega$. The rate of spontaneous emission is given by

$$\frac{\mathrm{d}N_g}{\mathrm{d}t} = \frac{k_0^3}{\pi}\iint \varrho_u \varrho_l f_u(1-f_l) M_{ul}^2 \delta(\mathscr{E}_u - \mathscr{E}_l - \hbar\omega)\,\mathrm{d}\mathscr{E}_u\,\mathrm{d}\mathscr{E}_l\,. \tag{70}$$

From eqs. (69) and (70) it can be shown that the rate of spontaneous emission just below threshold exceeds that of the stimulated emission by the reabsorption term. Then we can relate the negative conductivity over the length of the diode, *i.e.*, the conductance by

$$\int \sigma_1\,\mathrm{d}x < \frac{\pi^2 \omega \mathscr{E}}{e k_0^3}\, j g(\omega)\,, \tag{71}$$

where $g(\omega)$ is the normalized shape of the spontaneous emission line. When we then express this in terms of the threshold criterion obtained for the growing wave from eq. (66), then

$$J_{\text{th}} > \left(\frac{8}{3\sqrt{3}}\right) e k_0^{\frac{3}{2}} \Delta\nu \left(\bar{\alpha} + \frac{1}{L}\log\frac{1}{R}\right)^{\frac{1}{2}}, \tag{72}$$

where $\Delta\nu$ is the line width of the spontaneous emission line. This is about $\Delta\nu = 100$ Å and gives $J_{\text{th}} \approx 2\,000$ A/cm² for $\bar{\alpha} \approx 500\ \text{cm}^{-1}$ which compares favorably with the experimental values obtained.

5. – Calculation of the matrix elements.

In calculating the momentum matrix elements for the transitions involved, we use the effective-mass approximation of the wave functions which we shall assume to be normalized in each of the three components given as follows:

$$\psi(\boldsymbol{r}) = C\,\mu_k(\boldsymbol{r}) \exp[i\,\boldsymbol{k}\cdot\boldsymbol{r}]\,F(\boldsymbol{r})\,, \tag{73}$$

where $\mu_k(\boldsymbol{r}) \exp[i\,\boldsymbol{k}\cdot\boldsymbol{r}]$ is the Bloch function of a band with u_k repeated over every unit cell and $\exp[i\,\boldsymbol{k}\cdot\boldsymbol{r}]$ is the slowly varying Bloch wave and $F(\boldsymbol{r})$ is the envelope function which describes the localized states of donors, acceptors, excitons etc. The matrix element when expressed in terms of these functions takes the form

$$M_{12} = C_N \int \mu_1^* \mu_2 (F_1 \boldsymbol{p} F_2)\,\mathrm{d}\boldsymbol{r} + C_N \int F_1^* F_2 (\mu_1 \exp[-j\boldsymbol{k}_1 \boldsymbol{r}]\,\boldsymbol{p}\mu_2 \exp[jk_2\boldsymbol{r}])\,\mathrm{d}\boldsymbol{r}\,, \tag{74}$$

where for a direct transition $k_1 = k_2$ $\boldsymbol{p}$ is the momentum operator. The above general expression in eq. (74) can be specialized. If we are considering transitions between impurity levels of the same band then the second integral is small since they are the same for the three states. For the present, we shall not consider this case but shall go on to the interband situation in which the functions $u_1 \neq u_2$ but are orthogonal to one another. In this case then the first integral vanishes. The second can be simplified by considering that the u_1, u_2 functions are rapidly varying and F_1, F_2 are slowly varying over many unit cells. Hence the integral can be broken up into a summation over many unit cells, in practice this sum can be replaced by an integral over the crystal volume. Thus

$$M_{12} = C_n \int_{\text{cell}} u_n^* \exp[-j\boldsymbol{k}_1\boldsymbol{r}]\boldsymbol{p}u_2 \exp[-j\boldsymbol{k}_2\boldsymbol{r}]\,\mathrm{d}\boldsymbol{r} \int_{\text{crystal}} F_1^* F_2\,\mathrm{d}\boldsymbol{r}\,. \tag{75}$$

We can then rewrite the result as a product of two integrals

$$M_{12} = C_n p_{12} O_{12}\,, \tag{76}$$

where these are given by

$$p_{12} = \int_{\text{cell}} u_1^* \exp[-j\boldsymbol{k}_1\boldsymbol{r}]\boldsymbol{p}u_2 \exp[j\boldsymbol{k}_2\boldsymbol{r}]\,\mathrm{d}\boldsymbol{r}\,, \tag{77}$$

$$O_{12} = \int_{\text{crystal}} F_1^* F_2\,\mathrm{d}\boldsymbol{r}\,, \tag{78}$$

where $\boldsymbol{p}_{12}$, the momentum matrix, can actually be determined from experiments by absorption measurements for interband transitions where we can take $F_1 = F_2 = 1$. The result of such calculations gives the well-known expression for the absorption coefficient α as the following:

$$\alpha = \frac{2e^2 p_{12}^2}{\sqrt{\pi}\, m^2 c\omega}\left(\frac{2u}{\hbar^2}\right)^{\frac{3}{2}} \sqrt{\omega - \omega_g}\,. \tag{79}$$

The principal problem left in this case is to determine the overlap integral for the suitable models under consideration, namely donor to valence band or conduction band to acceptor, donor to acceptor and exciton to acceptor. The final two have been done, the last has not been worked out. The integrals take the form:

$$\begin{cases} O_{12}\ (\text{donor-band}) = \left(\dfrac{1}{a}\right)^{\frac{3}{2}} \dfrac{1}{\sqrt{\pi}} \displaystyle\int \exp[j\boldsymbol{k}\cdot\boldsymbol{r}] \exp\left[-\dfrac{r}{a}\right] \mathrm{d}\boldsymbol{r}\,, \\ O_{12}\ (\text{donor-acceptor}) = \left(\dfrac{1}{ab}\right)^{\frac{3}{2}} \dfrac{1}{\pi} \displaystyle\int \exp\left[-\dfrac{r}{a}\right] \exp\left[-\dfrac{|\boldsymbol{r}-\boldsymbol{r}'|}{b}\right] \mathrm{d}\boldsymbol{r}\,. \end{cases} \tag{80}$$

The first is rather simple to evaluate and the second becomes more involved. In any event with some simple assumptions about the energy distributions of donors and acceptors, the conclusion known from these calculations is that the donor-acceptor transition is more favorable than the donor-band transition for acceptor concentrations $n_a > 1/b^3$ where $b = (m/m_v)\varkappa a_B$ is the acceptor radius, where m_v is the hole effective mass, $\varkappa$ the dielectric constant and a_B the Bohr radius. Thus for GaAs $m_v \approx 0.7\,m$, $\varkappa \approx 13$, $b \approx 200\,a_B$ or ~ 100 Å. Thus if the acceptor concentration exceeds $10^{18}/\text{cm}^3$ and if donors and acceptors are more closely paired than random, the donor-acceptor transition is favorable.

Another use of the overlap calculation that has been made by DUMKE [27] and MCWHORTER [26] has been to estimate the lifetime of electrons in an upper state due to spontaneous emission. The result for the minimum lifetime is given by DUMKE:

$$\tau_{\min} = \frac{C^3 \hbar m^2}{16 n_0\, e^2 \omega R_{12}^2 O_{12}^2}, \tag{81}$$

where n_0 is the index of refraction. The lifetime calculated gives a result which makes $\tau_{\min} \approx 0.3 \cdot 10^{-9}$ s for electrons.

ZEIGER has also calculated matrix elements and overlap integrals for indirect transitions as well.

6. – Discussion.

In addition to the results reported in the main body of the paper, several new developments have occurred during recent weeks, some of which are as yet not in the literature. The important feature of these recent results is that they demonstrate the use of semiconductor masers for the study of the physical prop-

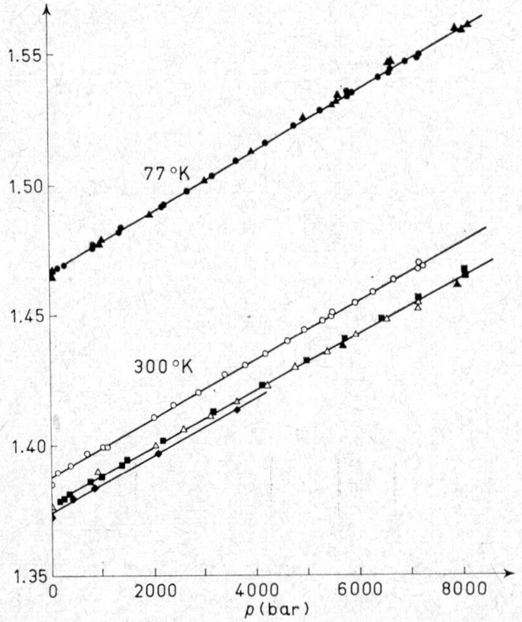

Fig. 26. – GaAs radiation *vs.* pressure: ● IBM 17-30-14, 10 mA, 0.001 eV; ▲ IBM 17-18-12, 10 mA, 0.04 eV; ○ Linc 44QK73, 10 mA, 0.006 eV; △ Linc 44QK73, 50 mA, 0.04 eV; ■ IBM 17-18-18, 10 mA, 0.006 eV; ◆ IBM 17-18-18, 10 mA, 0.02 eV. (After FEINLEIB, GROVES, PAUL and ZALLEN: *Phys. Rev.*, **131**, 2070 (1963).)

erties of the material itself. One of the interesting experiments of this type has been the operation of a GaAs laser at high pressure up to 8 000 bar by the group at Harvard [29]. They have measured the shift of the emission line of diodes and masers as a function of pressure and have found that it increases linearly with pressure as shown in Fig. 26. A change of 0.1 eV was achieved at the highest pressure. From this they can then determine the deformation potential directly since it is known that the shift is a measure of the change of the energy gap with pressure.

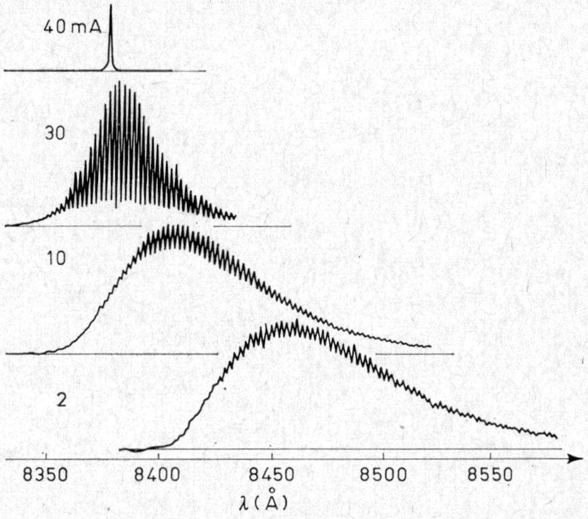

Fig. 27. – Mode spectra of GaAs diode below threshold at 2 °K. (After NATHAN, FOWLER and BURNS: *Phys. Rev. Lett.*, **11**, 152 (1962).)

Another very interesting experiment that has been carried out by the IBM groups [30] has been to study the dispersion of the index of refraction by the use of a diode of GaAs which is operating just below the threshold for maser oscillation. The results of the observation appear as shown in Fig. 27 and are rather striking in that they show the Fabry-Perot modes amplified by the reflected spontaneous emission. By studying the separation between successive modes and using the theoretical expression

$$n - \lambda \frac{\mathrm{d}n}{\mathrm{d}\lambda} = \frac{\lambda^2}{2L\Delta\lambda} \tag{82}$$

the above quantity on the left-hand side of the equation was plotted. The results are shown in Fig. 28, which shows a decided increase of this quantity as the wavelength approaches the energy gap. From the theory for the index of refraction near the energy gap this is predictable. As a matter of fact, when the quantity in eq. (82) is calculated and all but the singular terms are dropped, then the result becomes

$$\left(n - \lambda \frac{\mathrm{d}n}{\mathrm{d}\lambda}\right)_0 \approx \frac{A}{2\omega\sqrt{\omega_g - \omega}}\,. \tag{83}$$

When the above quantity is plotted as a function of the frequency quantity on the right-hand side of eq. (83) we find that indeed the results fit a straight line as shown in Fig. 29. From such a plot, the slope can be determined and hence the value of the coefficient A. This contains the dipole matrix and well-

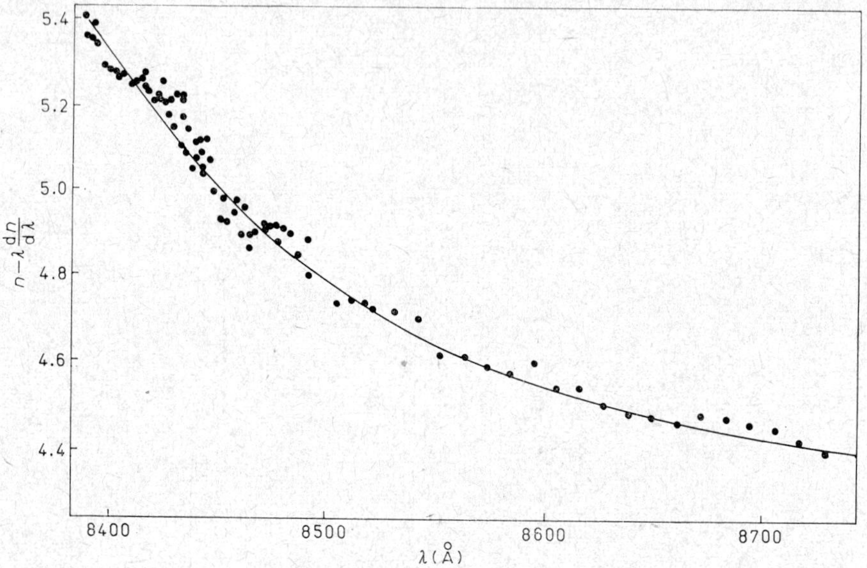

Fig. 28. – Dispersion of index of refraction in GaAs at 2 °K. (After NATHAN, FOWLER and BURNS: *Phys. Rev. Lett.*, **11**, 152 (1963).)

known constants given after eq. (38), from which we can then calculate the value of M, the matrix element. In addition, when the magnetic field is introduced, the magneto-dispersion, analogous to the expression given in eq. (83) becomes the following:

$$(84)\qquad \left(n - \lambda\frac{\mathrm{d}n}{\mathrm{d}\lambda}\right)_H \approx \sum \frac{A\omega_c}{4\omega^2}\cdot \cdot[2\omega(\omega_n - \omega)^{-\frac{3}{2}} - 2(\omega_n - \omega)^{-\frac{1}{2}}]\,.$$

This effect should be much larger than that at zero field and should provide additional information about the band parameters such as effective masses and g-factors of the conduction and valence bands.

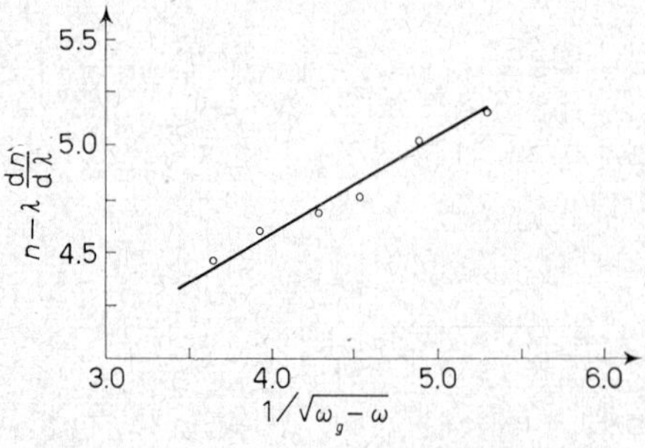

Fig. 29. – Second harmonic emission from GaAs laser.

One final experiment that should be mentioned in these notes are the nonlinear effects that are induced in the semiconductor diode masers themselves.

Recently at Lincoln Laboratory [31] and at IBM [32] second harmonic emission has been observed from the pulsed GaAs masers. From the work of BLOEMBERGEN and DUCUING [33], it is known that GaAs is nonlinear. Furthermore when a diode laser emits approximately 100 W distributed over an active region approximately 1 μm thick and 100 μm wide, then the electric field becomes $E \approx 10^5$ V/cm.

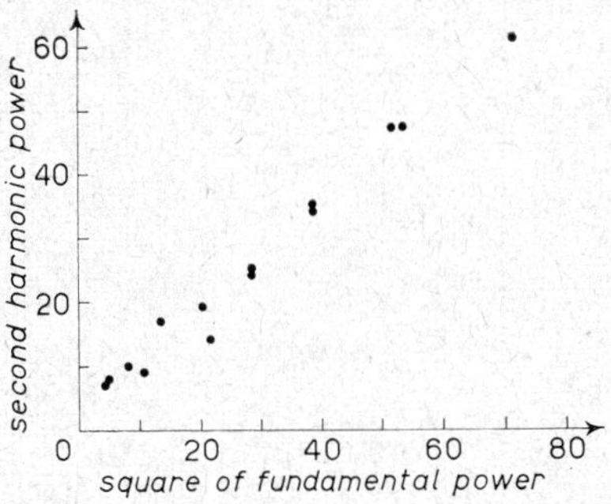

Fig. 30. – Second harmonic emission from GaAs laser. (After MALSTRON, SCHLICKMAN and KINGSTON: *Journ. Appl. Phys.*, **35**, 248 (1964).)

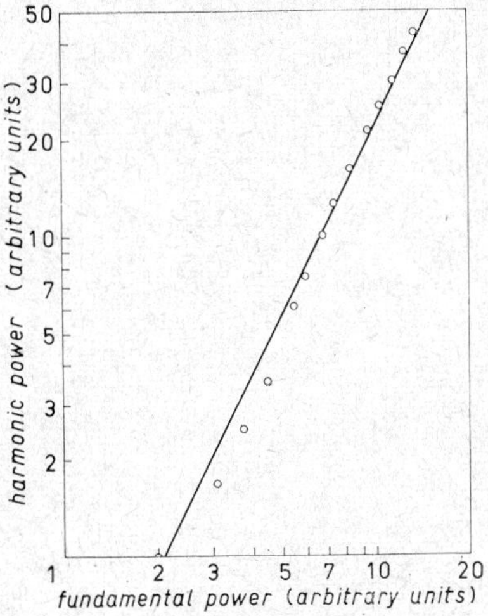

Fig. 31. – Second harmonic emission from GaAs laser. (After ARMSTRONG, NATHAN and SMITH: *Appl. Phys. Lett.*, **3**, 68 (1963).)

This is sufficient to produce harmonic generation. The results show that the power out at the second harmonic 4175 Å is proportional to the square of the fundamental power. This is indicated in Fig. 30 and Fig. 31 performed with pulsed operation and CW masers respectively.

REFERENCES

[1] N. B. HANNAY: *Semiconductors* (New York, 1959); R. A. SMITH: *Semiconductors* (New York, 1961).

[2] B. LAX and S. ZWERDLING: *Progress in Semiconductors*, vol. **5** (London, 1960).

[3] *Proc. of International Conf. on Physics of Semiconductors* (Exeter, July 1962).

[4] J. P. GORDON, H. J. ZEIGER and C. H. TOWNES: *Phys. Rev.*, **95**, 282 (1954).

[5] P. AIGRAIN: *Int. Conf. on Solid State Physics in Electronics and Telecommunications* (Brussels, 1958).

[6] B. LAX: *Quantum Electronics*, edited by C. H. TOWNES (New York, 1960), p. 428; *Advances in Quantum Electronics*, edited by J. R. SINGER (New York, 1961), p. 465.

[7] N. B. Basov, O. Krokhin and J. M. Popov: *Advances in Quantum Electronics*, edited by J. R. Singer (New York, 1961), p. 498.
[8] R. J. Keyes and T. M. Quist: *Proc. I.R.E.*, **50**, 1822 (1962).
[9] W. P. Dumke: *Phys. Rev.*, **127**, 1559 (1962).
[10] R. N. Hall, G. E. Fenner, J. D. Kingsley, T. J. Soltys and R. O. Carlson: *Phys. Rev. Lett.*, **9**, 366 (1962); M. I. Nathan, W. P. Dumke, G. Burns, F. H. Dill, jr. and G. Lasher: *Appl. Phys. Lett.*, **1**, 62 (1962); T. M. Quist, R. H. Rediker, R. J. Keyes, W. E. Krag, B. Lax, A. L. McWhorter and H. J. Zeiger: *Appl. Phys. Lett.*, **1**, 91 (1962).
[11] N. Holonyak, jr. and S. F. Bevacqua: *Appl. Phys. Lett.*, **1**, 82 (1962).
[12] I. Melngailis: *Appl. Phys. Lett.*, **2**, 176 (1963).
[13] M. G. A. Bernard and G. Duraffourg: *Physica Status Solidi*, **1**, 699 (1961).
[14] T. M. Quist, R. H. Rediker, R. J. Keyes and W. E. Krag: *Bull. Am. Phys. Soc.* (January 1963), p. 88.
[15] E. J. Walker and A. E. Michel: *Bull. Am. Phys. Soc.*, **8**, 202 (1963).
[16] I. D. Kingsley and G. E. Fenner: *Bull. Am. Phys. Soc.*, **8**, 88 (1963).
[17] W. E. Howard, F. F. Fang, F. H. Dill, jr., M. I. Nathan: *I.B.M. Journ. of Res. and Dev.*, **7**, 75 (1963).
[18] C. Hilsum: *Proc. of Third Quantum Electronics Conference* (Paris, 1963) (to be published).
[19] M. Garfinkel and W. E. Engeler: *1963 I.E.E.E. Solid State Device Research Conference*, Michigan State Univ. (June 1963).
[20] I. Melngailis and R. H. Rediker: *Appl. Phys. Lett.*, **2**, 202 (1963).
[21] K. Weiser and R. S. Levitt: *Appl. Phys. Lett.*, **2**, 178 (1963).
[22] I. Melngailis, A. J. Strauss and R. H. Rediker: *Proc. I.E.E.E.*, **51**, 1154 (1963).
[23] F. Galeener, G. B. Wright, T. M. Quist and H. J. Zeiger: *Phys. Rev. Lett.*, **10**, 472 (1963).
[24] I. Melngailis: *Bull. Amer. Phys. Soc.*, **8**, 202 (1963).
[25] A. L. McWhorter, H. J. Zeiger and B. Lax: *Journ. Appl. Phys.*, **34**, 235 (1963).
[26] A. L. McWhorter: *Solid State Electronics*, **6**, 417 (1963).
[27] W. P. Dumke: *Phys. Rev.*, **132**, 1998 (1963).
[28] H. J. Zeiger: (to be published).
[29] I. Feinleib, A. Groves, W. Paul and R. Zallen: *Phys. Rev.*, **131**, 2070 (1963).
[30] M. I. Nathan, A. B. Fowler and G. Burns: *Phys. Rev. Lett.*, **11**, 152 (1963).
[31] L. D. Malstron, J. J. Schlickman and R. H. Kingston: *Journ. Appl. Phys.*, **35**, 248 (1964).
[32] J. A. Armstrong, M. I. Nathan and A. W. Smith: *Appl. Phys. Lett.*, **3**, 68 (1963).
[33] J. Ducuing and N. Bloembergen: *Phys. Rev. Lett.*, **10**, 474 (1963).

Theory of Optical Resonators.

G. Toraldo di Francia
Istituto di Fisica Superiore dell'Università - Firenze

1. – The Fabry-Perot resonator.

1·1. *Waveguide theory.* – In a typical microwave maser an unstable ensemble of atomic or molecular systems is introduced into a cavity which would normally have one resonant mode near the frequency which corresponds to radiative transitions of these systems. In order to obtain oscillation, the minimum excess population of the atomic systems in the upper state which is necessary turns out to be inversely proportional to the quality factor of the cavity. It is therefore desirable for the Q of the mode of interest to have a high value.

As is well known, in order for a cavity to accept only a single mode within a small bandwidth, the linear dimensions of the cavity must be of the order of one wavelength. It is absolutely impossible to obtain this condition at optical frequencies. Hence, the cavity of an optical maser is necessarily very large compared to a wavelength and may support a large number of modes within the frequency range of the transition.

However, one can isolate one mode or a small number of modes of interest by making use of the directional properties of optical radiation.

This principle can be applied by making the radiation bounce back and forth between two parallel flat mirrors, as in a Fabry-Perot interferometer [1-3]. One or both end mirrors may be made slightly transparent, to provide coupling to external space.

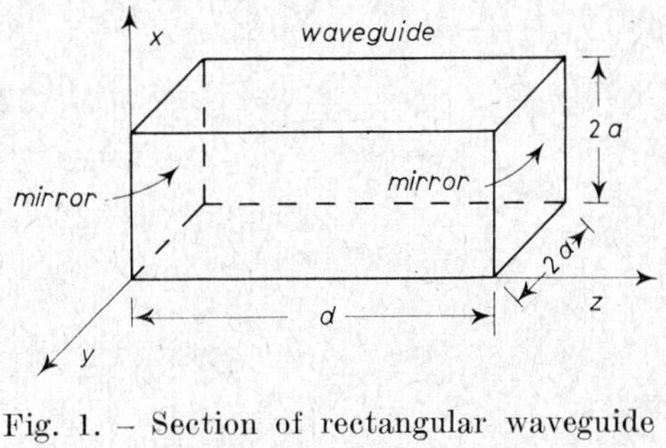

Fig. 1. – Section of rectangular waveguide with reflecting end walls.

An approximate theory of this multimode resonator was proposed by Schawlow and Townes [1] who started by considering the case when the two mirrors form the end bases of a section of a waveguide with metal walls (Fig. 1). Let the waveguide have length d (z-axis) and square cross-section of dimension $2a$ (xy-plane). As is well known, this rectangular cavity can oscillate in an infinite number of modes, with frequencies of the form

$$\nu = \frac{c}{2n}\left[\left(\frac{q}{d}\right)^2 + \left(\frac{r}{2a}\right)^2 + \left(\frac{s}{2a}\right)^2\right]^{\frac{1}{2}}, \tag{1.1-1}$$

where q, r, s are positive integers, c is the velocity of light and n is the refractive index of the medium. Each mode can be thought of as generated by a plane wave reflected back and forth by all the side walls [4], and characterized by the direction cosines $\pm r\lambda/4a$, $\pm s\lambda/4a$, $\pm q\lambda/2d$, where λ denotes the wavelength in the medium.

For our purpose only those waves are of interest which make a very small angle with the axis of the waveguide and radiate almost end-fire through the slightly transparent mirrors. For such waves, q practically represents the number of half-wavelengths comprised in the length d and has a very large value ($q = 10^5 \div 10^6$) while r and s are small. In this case, if the ratio $2a/d$ is not too small, (1.1-1) can be written as

$$\nu = \frac{c}{2n}\left(\frac{q}{d} + \frac{r^2 d}{8qa^2} + \frac{s^2 d}{8qa^2}\right). \tag{1.1-2}$$

If we denote by α the reflection coefficient of the mirrors, it is readily derived that the energy of a nearly axial wave will have a decay time t in the cavity given by

$$t = \frac{nd}{(1-\alpha)c} \tag{1.1-3}$$

or a quality factor

$$Q = 2\pi\nu t = \frac{2\pi d}{(1-\alpha)\lambda}. \tag{1.1-4}$$

By making α close to unity (*e.g.*, $\alpha = 0.98$), one obtains Q of the order of 10^7.

Now we have from (1.1-2) that two modes with successive values of q will practically be separated in frequency by

$$\Delta\nu_q = \frac{c}{2nd}. \tag{1.1 5}$$

If α is very close to unity, there follows from (1.1-3) $\Delta\nu_q \gg 1/t$. This means that successive axial modes are discrete. If the bandwidth of the transition is less than $c/2nd$, it is possible to set into oscillation only a single axial mode.

This can be achieved with the ordinary solid-state materials. Alternatively, discrimination against unwanted axial modes can be achieved by an extra reflecting surface suitably positioned outside the maser, as was proposed by KLEINMAN and KISLIUK [5]. However, modes with successive values of r and the same value of q are separated in frequency by the amount

$$\Delta\nu_r = \frac{c(r+\frac{1}{2})d}{8nqa^2} \tag{1.1-6}$$

and a corresponding result is found for s. A typical value of $d/2a$ for a solid-state laser is 10. Hence, with $\alpha = 0.98$ and r of the order of unity, we have $\Delta\nu_r < 1/t$. This means that the first lateral modes are almost degenerate and may merge in a continuum. Several lateral modes are liable to be set into laser oscillation at the same time.

However, SCHAWLOW and TOWNES pointed out that the lateral modes may be separated by their directional properties. First of all, it is easy to see that each mode will radiate into four directions having the first two direction cosines given by $\pm r\lambda/4a$, $\pm s\lambda/4a$. Hence the directions of radiation of all modes form a regular array and are equispaced by the amount $\lambda/4a$ in direction-cosine space. The finiteness of the end apertures will give rise to diffraction, each beam having the half-width at half-maximum approximately given by $\lambda/4a$. It is therefore possible to practically separate one single mode by focusing radiation from the end walls by means of a lens onto a black screen with a suitable small hole.

At this point we may remove the side walls and deal with the original Fabry-Perot resonator. Since the rigorous theory of such an open cavity is very difficult to work out, we will assume with SCHAWLOW and TOWNES that the modes of the closed cavity with small r and s still represent good approximations to the real modes, with the only difference that, due to the absence of the side walls, they continually spill energy into external space. This will reduce the Q of all modes, but the effect will be the more pronounced, the higher the values of r and s.

The decomposition of each mode into plane waves helps to understand the situation. There is a purely geometrical effect, by which the oblique waves reflected back and forth, gradually walk off the end mirrors. To this, of course, there is superimposed a diffraction effect.

The geometric effect is easy to evaluate. For instance, a wave with $r \neq 0$, $s = 0$, travels at an angle $r\lambda/4a$ with the axis and loses an additional fraction $(r\lambda/4a)(d/2a)$ of its energy at each reflection. There readily follows that the geometrical decay time t' is given by

$$t' = \frac{8na^2}{rc\lambda}. \tag{1.1-7}$$

This time is equal to the time t given by (1.1-3) when

$$r = \frac{8a^2(1-\alpha)}{\lambda d} . \tag{1.1-8}$$

For $\alpha = 0.98$, $d = 10$ cm, $2a = 0.5$ cm, $\lambda = 5 \cdot 10^{-5}$ cm, we obtain $r = 20$. Hence the modes with $r > 20$ have a Q which is less than half the Q of the fundamental mode. If the pump power is not too high, they are under threshold and do not oscillate.

More precise results can be derived only by taking into account diffraction, as will be done in the next Section. However we can conclude that, in an ordinary Fabry-Perot resonator, unless special measures are taken, a few tens or hundreds of lateral modes are likely to lase at the same time.

Here we have assumed for simplicity that the interferometer is embedded in an infinite homogeneous medium. The situation is much different in the case of a ruby rod because of reflection at the side walls. In this case one might expect that the off-axis modes should have higher Q than the axial modes. However, the experience shows that emission is still prevalent in nearly axial directions. This phenomenon has been discussed by COLLINS and GIORDMAINE [6], who attributed it to the interaction between different modes caused by small nonuniformities in surface reflectivity or volume gain. This interaction can give rise to new modes of higher Q and lower oscillation threshold.

1·2. *Physical-optics theory.* – The first satisfactory approach to the theory of the Fabry-Perot resonator is due to FOX and LI [7], who applied the technique of scalar wave optics. This approach is perfectly sound and can be justified by observing that 1) the sizes of both mirrors are very large with respect to the wavelength, and 2) all angles of interest are sufficiently small.

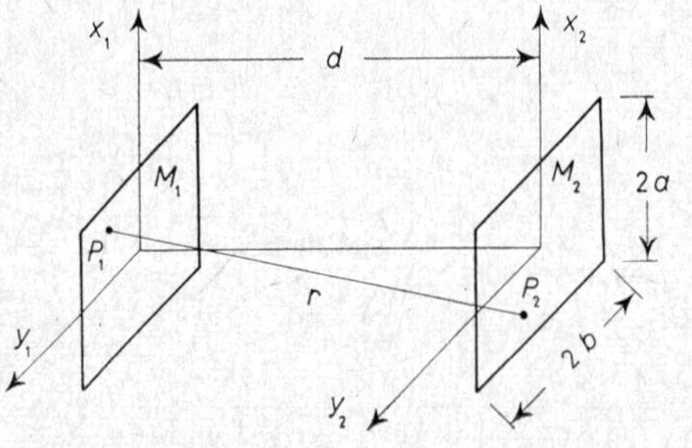

Fig. 2. – The Fabry-Perot interferometer.

For the sake of simplicity, let us assume the Fabry-Perot resonator to be in free space, or immersed in the active medium with no side-wall discontinuities. The two mirrors M_1, M_2 (Fig. 2) will be supposed to be identical.

According to the usual wave-optics approximation we shall assume the field to be very nearly transverse electromagnetic and uniformly polarized. A single scalar quantity u is sufficient to represent this field.

Let us start with a field distribution $u_1(P_1)$ across the first mirror M_1. By Huygens' principle this field will produce a distribution $u_2(P_2)$ across the second mirror M_2, given by

$$u_2(P_2) = -\frac{i}{\lambda}\int_{M_1} u_1(P_1)\,\frac{\exp[ikr]}{r}\cos\theta\,\mathrm{d}S_1\,. \tag{1.2-1}$$

where r is the distance P_1P_2, θ is the angle between P_1P_2 and the normal to the mirrors (*) and $k=2\pi/\lambda$. As is customary in physical optics the time factor (which is omitted) is $\exp[-i\omega t]$. In electronics the usual factor is $\exp[j\omega t]$, hence to make comparisons one has to substitute $i=-j$ in all formulas.

The normal modes or eigenfunctions of the resonator are obtained by requiring that the field distribution over M_1 reproduces itself within a constant factor over M_2, and thus $u_2=\sigma u_1$. As a result, we obtain the integral equation

$$\sigma u(x_2, y_2) = -\frac{i}{\lambda}\int_{M_1} u(x_1, y_1)\,\frac{\exp[ikr]}{r}\cos\theta\,\mathrm{d}x_1\,\mathrm{d}y_1\,. \tag{1.2-2}$$

This is a two-dimensional homogeneous linear equation of the second kind. Each eigenfunction u represents a mode of the resonator and the corresponding eigenvalue σ specifies both the attenuation and the phase change in going from one mirror to the other.

When the mirror separation is much larger than the mirror dimensions eq. (1.2-2) can take a more convenient form, namely,

$$\sigma u(x_2, y_2) = -\frac{i}{\lambda d}\int_{M_1} u(x_1, y_1)\exp\left[ik\,\frac{(x_1-x_2)^2+(y_1-y_2)^2}{2d}\right]\mathrm{d}x_1\,\mathrm{d}y_1\,. \tag{1.2 3}$$

A factor $\exp[ikd]$ corresponding to the normal optical path has been omitted on the right-hand side, or, what amounts to the same, a factor $\exp[-ikd]$ has been absorbed in σ. The argument of the complex number σ will be termed the phase shift.

More precisely eq. (1.2-3) is valid when $a^2/d\lambda$ is much less than d^2/a^2, where a is a typical dimension of the mirrors. We will introduce the Fresnel number

$$N = \frac{a^2}{d\lambda}\,, \tag{1.2-4}$$

(*) For an aperture in a plane screen and a point at a distance much greater than λ, (1.2-1) with the factor $\cos\theta$ is correct, provided $u_1(P_1)$ represents the actual amplitude distribution across the aperture. The formula often used, which contains the factor $(1+\cos\theta)/2$ is never rigorous in the case of a finite aperture and is inconsistent with the boundary values of u_1. See, for instance [8].

which is approximately equal to the number of Fresnel zones seen in one mirror from the center of the other mirror. Hence the condition for the validity of (1.2-3) becomes

$$N \ll \frac{d^2}{a^2}\,. \tag{1.2-5}$$

By introducing the dimensionless variables

$$\xi_{1,2} = \sqrt{N}\,\frac{x_{1,2}}{a}\,, \qquad \eta_{1,2} = \sqrt{N}\,\frac{y_{1,2}}{a}\,, \tag{1.2-6}$$

eq. (1.2-3) can be written as

$$\sigma u(\xi_2, \eta_2) = -i\int_{\mathscr{M}_1} u(\xi_1, \eta_1) \exp\left[i\pi[(\xi_1 - \xi_2)^2 + (\eta_1 - \eta_2)^2]\right] \mathrm{d}\xi_1\,\mathrm{d}\eta_1\,, \tag{1.2-7}$$

where $\mathscr{M}_1$ represents the domain of $\xi_1\eta_1$-space which corresponds to the domain M_1 of x_1y_1-space. It is seen by inspection that for a family of geometrically similar mirrors, eq. (1.2-7) depends only on the parameter N (through $\mathscr{M}_1$).

In the case of rectangular mirrors of dimensions $2a$ and $2b$ (Fig. 2), one can separate the variables by putting $u(\xi, \eta) = u_\xi(\xi)\, u_\eta(\eta)$ and $\sigma = \sigma_\xi \sigma_\eta$. The equation for u_ξ is

$$\sigma_\xi u_\xi(\xi_2) = \exp\left[-i\frac{\pi}{4}\right] \int_{-\sqrt{N}}^{+\sqrt{N}} u_\xi(\xi_1) \exp\left[i\pi(\xi_1 - \xi_2)^2\right] \mathrm{d}\xi_1\,. \tag{1.2-8}$$

A similar equation is obtained for u_η, however with $N = b^2/d\lambda$. It is obvious that u_ξ and u_η represent solutions for infinite-strip mirrors, parallel to y and x, respectively. Thus, the eigenfunctions and the eigenvalues for the rectangular mirror are products of the infinite-strip eigenfunctions and eigenvalues, respectively. Specifying the different eigenfunctions by subscripts we shall put $u_{mn}(\xi, \eta) = u_{\xi,m}(\xi)\, u_{\eta,n}(\eta)$ and $\sigma_{mn} = \sigma_m \sigma_n$. This will be designated as the TEM_{mn} travelling-wave mode for the rectangular plane mirror interferometer; σ_{mn} specifies both the phase shift and the attenuation.

In the case of circular mirrors of radius a, by introducing polar co-ordinates $\xi = \varrho\cos\theta$, $\eta = \varrho\sin\theta$ and putting

$$u = R_n(\varrho) \exp[in\theta]\,, \tag{1.2-9}$$

the integral equation (1.2-7) yields

$$\sigma_n R_n(\varrho_2) = 2\pi \exp\left[i\pi\left(\varrho_2^2 - \frac{n+1}{2}\right)\right] \cdot \int_0^{\sqrt{N}} R_n(\varrho_1) J_n(2\pi\varrho_1\varrho_2) \exp[i\pi\varrho_1^2]\varrho_1\,\mathrm{d}\varrho_1\,. \tag{1.2-10}$$

The m-th eigenfunction R_{nm} of the integral equation gives us the distribution $u_{nm} = R_{nm}(\varrho)\exp[in\theta]$ of the TEM_{nm} mode, while the eigenvalue σ_{nm} represents phase shift and attenuation.

Equations (1.2-8) and (1.2-10) are homogeneous Fredholm equations of the second kind with regular kernels. The kernel of eq. (1.2-8) is symmetric, while eq. (1.2-10) has a polar kernel, which can be easily transformed into a symmetric one. The eigenmodes are therefore orthogonal over the surface of the mirrors.

An alternative but equivalent integral equation for the infinite-strip mirror, has been given by KOTIK and NEWSTEIN [9], by transformation to momentum space. These authors applied a variational principle for the solution. Variational techniques, however in co-ordinate space, have been applied by CULSHAW [10] and by BARONE [11].

FOX and LI [7] solved the integral equations for infinite-strip and circular mirrors numerically, by an iteration method, and using an IBM 704 computer. Physically, their procedure can be described as follows.

Consider a propagating wave which is reflected back and forth by the two parallel plane mirrors. Starting with an arbitrary initial field at the first mirror, one computes the field produced at the second mirror as a result of the first transit. The newly calculated field distribution is then used to compute the field produced at the first mirror as a result of the second transit. By repeating this calculation over and over again, FOX and LI were able to show that, after many transits, the relative field distribution approaches a steady state.

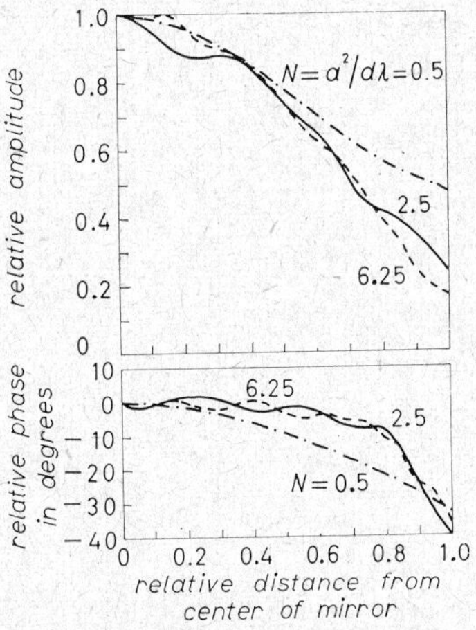

Fig. 3. – Amplitude and phase distributions across an infinite-strip end mirror for the lowest-order even-symmetric mode (from FOX and LI).

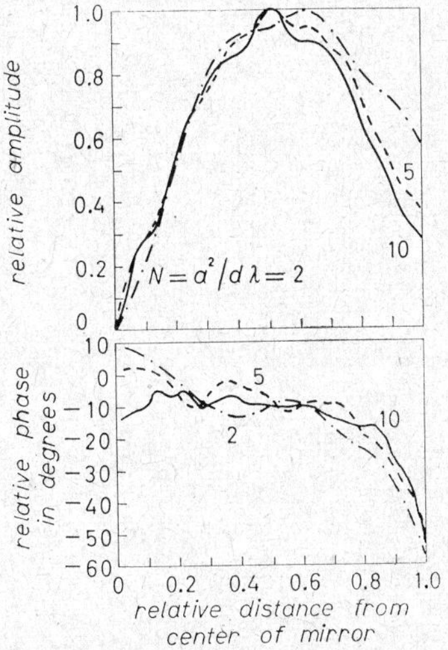

Fig. 4. – Amplitude and phase distributions across an infinite-strip end mirror for the lowest-order odd-symmetric mode (from FOX and LI).

According whether the starting field is symmetric or antisymmetric one ends up with the lowest symmetric or antisymmetric mode.

Figure 3 and Figure 4 show the results obtained by FOX and LI in the case of infinite-strip mirrors for the lowest-order even-symmetric and odd-symmetric modes respectively, and for different values of N. The amplitude distribution is far from being uniform and diminishes towards the edge of the mirror. This effect, which is the more pronounced the larger the N, reduces the power loss due to spill-over. The phase distribution is also nonuniform, which means that the field is not a plane wave.

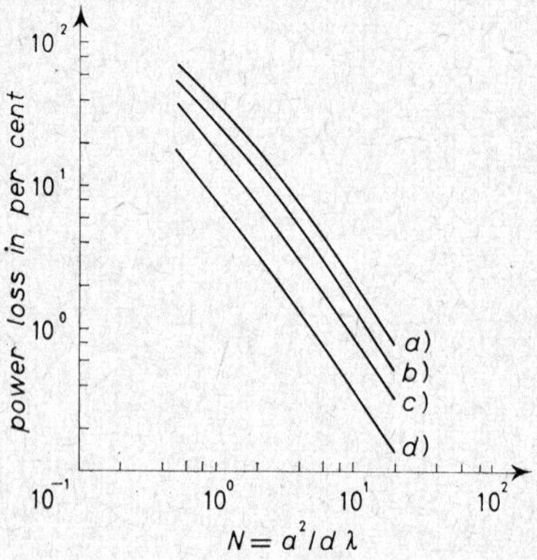

Fig. 5. – Power loss per transit *vs.* Fresnel number N: circular disc: *a*) TEM_{10} mode, *c*) dominant (TEM_{00}) mode; infinite strip, lowest order: *b*) odd-symmetric mode, *d*) even-symmetric mode (from FOX and LI).

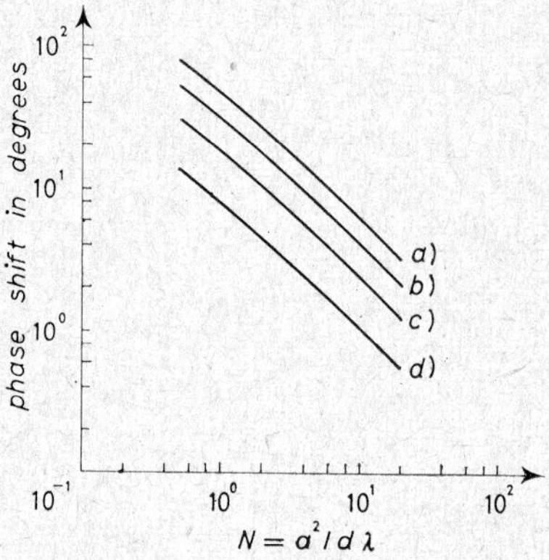

Fig. 6. – Phase shift per transit *vs.* Fresnel number N: circular disc: *a*) TEM_{10} mode, *c*) dominant (TEM_{00}) mode; infinite strip, lowest order: *b*) odd-symmetric mode, *d*) even-symmetric mode (from FOX and LI).

Figure 5 shows the power loss per transit plotted against N, for the aforementioned modes. Power loss falls off very rapidly with increasing N. Figure 6 shows the phase shift per transit, which also turns out a rapidly decreasing function of N.

The phase shift per transit is the essential parameter which determines the resonance frequency. At resonance, the separation d of the mirrors is an integral number of half-wavelengths plus an additional amount for the phase shift of the mode.

It is interesting to note that FOX and LI's analysis confirms that simple waveguide theory can be used to predict certain characteristics of the interferometer modes, as was done by SCHAWLOW and TOWNES [1]. For instance, the field distributions of the normal modes for infinite strip mirrors are very similar to those of the TE modes of a parallel-plane waveguide; also, by adding two orthogonally polarized TEM_{10} modes for circular plane mirrors, one obtains a field configuration which is very similar to that of the circular electric (TE_{01}) mode of a circular waveguide. Thus the amount of phase shift per transit computed for these modes of the interferometer agrees well with the phase shifts obtained for TE modes of parallel-plane waveguide and TE_{01} mode of circular waveguide. This is illustrated in Fig. 7. We see that agreement becomes better for larger values of N.

A uniform plane wave cannot resonate. It appears to do so in a passive Fabry-Perot interferometer simply because it can be resolved into a set of normal modes, which resonate at approximately the same frequency. Indeed, in an ordinary interferometer, N has a very large value and the phase shifts per transit are very small. At the same time, the Q is so low that the resonance line width contains a great number of normal mode frequencies. Thus the uniform plane wave undergoes very little decomposition when resonates. Nevertheless, in the case of an active interferometer, the decomposition may be complete.

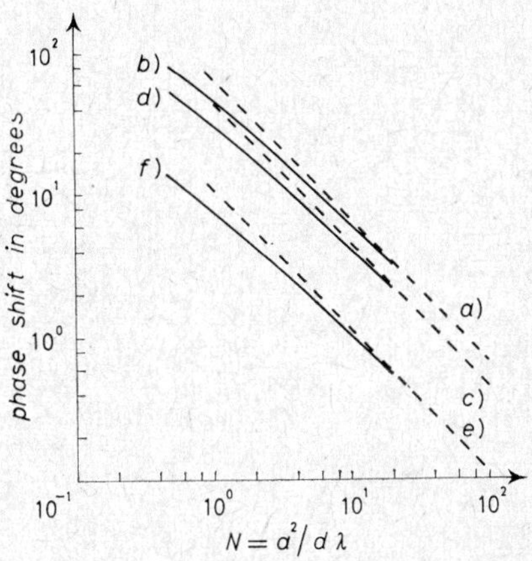

Fig. 7. – Comparison between phase shifts predicted by waveguide theory and by interferometer theory: – – – waveguide theory; —— interferometer theory. *a*) Circular waveguide, TE_{01} mode; *b*) circular disc, TEM_{10} mode; parallel plane, lowest order: *c*) odd-symmetric TE mode, *e*) even-symmetric TE mode; infinite strip, lowest order: *d*) odd-symmetric mode, *f*) even-symmetric mode (from FOX and LI).

If we denote by $\delta_r = 1 - \alpha$ the power loss in reflection and by δ_d the power loss due to spill-over (diffraction loss), the Q of the passive resonator is given by

$$\frac{1}{Q} = \frac{1}{Q_r} + \frac{1}{Q_d}, \tag{1.2-11}$$

where

$$Q_r = \frac{2\pi d}{\lambda \delta_r}, \quad Q_d = \frac{2\pi d}{\lambda \delta_d}. \tag{1.2-12}$$

Reflection losses are normally much higher than diffraction losses. However, when the interferometer is filled with an active medium, the medium can compensate for reflection losses. The Q's will be determined by diffraction losses and the modes may be resolved. If the medium compensates for reflection plus diffraction losses of some lower-order modes, those modes will become unstable and oscillate.

It is to be noted that the pumped laser medium can exert some (very small) pulling [9] of the resonant frequency with respect to that derived for a passive medium.

Fox and Li [12] and Kotik and Newstein [9] have made computations for the case when the plane end mirrors are not perfectly parallel, but are slightly tilted, as may happen in practice. It turns out that the power losses of the modes increase very rapidly with the tilt angle, especially for large values of N. Even a very small tilt, corresponding to a departure from parallelism of a fraction of a wavelength at the edge, can give rise to substantial loss.

This means that the alignment of a plane-parallel resonator is very critical. Moreover the lowest-order modes tend to become degenerate in loss. They will be present at the same time in the maser and give rise to beats at the detector.

The same authors have also computed the phase shifts as a function of the tilt angle and of N. It turns out that if the two lowest-order modes are made to beat together, the beat frequency increases as the tilt angle is increased. This phenomenon has been observed experimentally [13, 14].

Finally, we want to mention a very recent paper by Weinstein [15] who by developing an elegant idea due to Suckin, has succeeded to work out the theory of the plane-parallel resonator considered as a section of waveguide open at both ends and working slightly above cut-off frequency.

2. – The confocal resonator.

2·1. *General properties of confocal resonators.* – A type of resonator which has several good features is formed by two spherical mirrors with common focus. There is a very large family of systems which have the same optical behavior as the confocal resonator [16, 17]. We will first outline the general properties of this family.

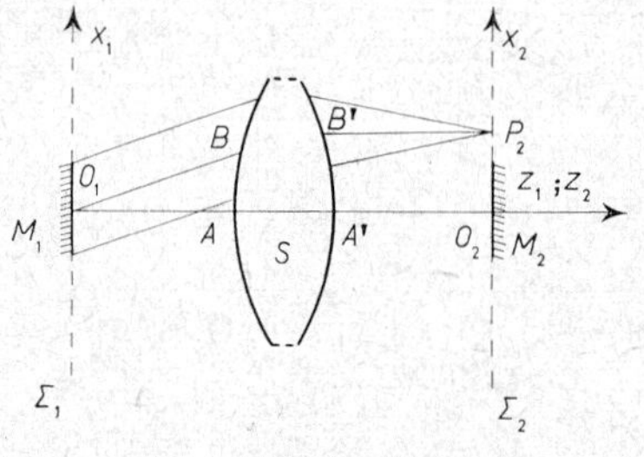

Fig. 8. – Generalized confocal resonator.

A typical resonator of this type is shown in Fig. 8. The two plane mirrors M_1, M_2 are placed at the two focal planes Σ_1, Σ_2 of an optical system S. System S will be assumed to be perfectly stigmatic for both planes Σ_1, Σ_2 and their images at infinity. The transmission coefficient of S will be put equal to unity all over its aperture. The light beams in both directions will be assumed to be limited only by the finite sizes of the mirrors. Thus M_1

nad M_2 represent the pupils for left-to-right and for right-to-left propagation, respectively.

We will refer to rectangular co-ordinates x_1, y_1 on Σ_1 and x_2, y_2 on Σ_2, while the optical axis will coincide with both the z_1 and z_2 axes.

A given field distribution $u_1(x_1, y_1)$ across Σ_1 will give rise by inverse interference to a set of plane waves. Each plane wave of the set will be specified by the two first direction cosines α, β of its propagation vector. The amplitude of the wave at the origin O_1 will be denoted by $A(\alpha, \beta)\,d\alpha\,d\beta$ and can be evaluated by [18]

$$A(\alpha, \beta) = \frac{1}{\lambda^2}\int_{M_1} u_1(x_1, y_1)\exp[-ik(\alpha x_1 + \beta y_1)]\,dx_1\,dy_1\,. \tag{2.1-1}$$

Thus, $A(\alpha, \beta)$ represents the Fourier transform of $u_1(x_1, y_1)$, a well-known result.

Now, system S will focus each plane wave $A(\alpha, \beta)$ onto a point P_2 of Σ_2. Since S has been assumed to be perfect, *i.e.*, free from aberrations, for plane Σ_1, it will fulfil the sine condition [19], which in turn is easily shown to yield for the co-ordinates x_2, y_2 of P_2

$$x_2 = f\alpha\,, \qquad y_2 = f\beta\,, \tag{2.1-2}$$

where f represents the focal length of S.

It can be shown that the energy carried by the wave $A(\alpha, \beta)$ is proportional to (*) $\lambda^2|A|^2\,d\alpha\,d\beta$. By (2.1-2), this energy illuminates the area $dx_2\,dy_2 = f^2\,d\alpha\,d\beta$ of Σ_2 and is proportional with the same factor of proportionality to $|u_2|^2 dx_2\,dy_2$, if $u_2(x_2, y_2)$ denotes the amplitude of the field across Σ_2. Hence $|u_2| = \lambda|A|/f$. To find the phase, note first that the optical path $O_1BB'P_2$ of any wave $A(\alpha, \beta)$ is identical to the optical path $O_1AA'O_2$ of the axial wave; this optical path will be denoted by d. Moreover, one must take into account the property of the anomalous propagation (**) by which a spherical wave arrives at its focus with a phase shift of $-\pi/2$. Hence we can write

$$u_2(x_2, y_2) = -i\lambda\frac{\exp[ikd]}{f}A(\alpha, \beta)\,. \tag{2.1-3}$$

If the mirrors M_1, M_2 are equal, and we require that $u_2(x_2, y_2)$ be proportional to $u_1(x_1, y_1)$, by combining (2.1-1) and (2.1-3), we find for the field u on any

---

(*) Ref. [18], p. 201.
(**) Ref. [18], p. 411-419.

one of the mirrors the integral equation

$$\sigma u(x_2, y_2) = \frac{\exp[i(kd - \pi/2)]}{\lambda f} \int_{M_1} u(x_1, y_1) \exp\left[-\frac{ik}{f}(x_1 x_2 + y_1 y_2)\right] dx_1 \, dy_1 \,. \tag{2.1-4}$$

Several authors have derived this integral equation as a first approximation for the case of spherical confocal mirrors. However, we have shown that as long as the optical system is free from aberrations, (2.1-4) is rigorous.

Henceforward we will assume that the mirrors M_1, M_2 are symmetric to both the x and y axes. Rectangular and circular mirrors are particular cases of this condition. Let us start with a real u (*) and split it into its symmetric and antisymmetric parts with respect to the origin, namely,

$$\begin{cases} u_+(-x, -y) = u_+(x, y) \,, \\ u_-(-x, -y) = - u_-(x, y) \,, \end{cases} \tag{2.1-5}$$

with $u_+(x, y) + u_-(x, y) = u(x, y)$. If we substitute u_+ or u_- for u in the integral (2.1-4), the result is again symmetric or antisymmetric, respectively. Hence the modes of the system can be split into a set of symmetric modes and a set of antisymmetric modes.

Next we note that the integral of (2.1-4) turns out real for u_+ and pure imaginary for u_-. Hence we find from (2.1-4) that the total phase shift for a round trip in the interferometer is $2kd - \pi$ for a symmetric mode and $2kd - \pi \pm \pi$ for an antisymmetric mode. Consequently, symmetric modes will resonate for

$$d = q\frac{\lambda}{2} + \frac{\lambda}{4} \tag{2.1-6}$$

and antisymmetric modes for

$$d = q\frac{\lambda}{2} \,, \tag{2.1-7}$$

where q is integer.

Hence the conclusion that the modes are highly degenerate. All symmetric (antisymmetric) modes can resonate at the same frequency. Discrimination can only be operated by the different diffraction losses of different modes.

To derive the losses, one must specify the shape of the mirrors and solve the integral equation (2.1-4).

(*) If u is complex, its real and imaginary parts can be dealt with separately.

2·2. *Eigenmodes and power losses.* – The solutions of eq. (2.1-4) have been analysed in particular cases of interest by GOUBAU and SCHWERING [20], by FOX and LI [7], by BOYD and GORDON [21].

It will be convenient to include the factor $\exp[-i(kd-\pi/2)]$ in σ and introduce the positions analogous to (1.2-4), (1.2-6),

$$N=\frac{a^2}{f\lambda}\,, \tag{2.2-1}$$

$$\xi_{1,2}=\sqrt{N}\,\frac{x_{1,2}}{a}\,,\qquad \eta_{1,2}=\sqrt{N}\,\frac{y_{1,2}}{a}\,. \tag{2.2-2}$$

Thus eq. (2.1-4) takes the standard form

$$\sigma u(\xi_2,\eta_2)=\int_{\mathscr{M}_1} u(\xi_1,\eta_1)\exp[-2\pi i(\xi_1\xi_2+\eta_1\eta_2)]\mathrm{d}\xi_1\mathrm{d}\eta_1\,. \tag{2.2-3}$$

Let us start with the case of rectangular mirrors of sizes $2a$, $2b$. The variables can be separated and eq. (2.2-3) splits into two Fredholm equations of the second kind with symmetric kernel. Each one of these integral equations holds for an infinite-strip mirror. Note that this separation of variables is now rigorously valid and not subject to condition (1.2-5).

The equation for the ξ co-ordinate is

$$\sigma_m u_m(\xi_2)=\int_{-\sqrt{N}}^{+\sqrt{N}} u_m(\xi_1)\exp[-2\pi i\xi_1\xi_2]\,\mathrm{d}\xi_1\,. \tag{2.2-4}$$

Now, the following integral relation is known in the literature [22]:

$$2i^m R^{(1)}_{0m}(c,1)\,S_{0m}(c,t)=\int_{-1}^{+1}\exp[icts]\,S_{0m}(c,s)\,\mathrm{d}s\,, \tag{2.2-5}$$

where, in the notation of FLAMMER [23], $S_{0m}(c,t)$ and $R^{(1)}_{0m}(c,t)$ are respectively the angular and radial prolate spheroidal functions. These functions are real for real t. Upon comparison, we find that the eigenfunctions of (2.2-4) are

$$u_m=S_{0m}(2\pi N,X)\,, \tag{2.2-6}$$

with $X=x_1/a$, and the eigenvalues are

$$\sigma_m=2(-i)^m\sqrt{N}\,R^{(1)}_{0m}(2\pi N,1)\,. \tag{2.2-7}$$

Hence, the eigenfunctions for the rectangular mirrors are

$$u_{mn} = S_{0m}(2\pi N_a, X)\, S_{0n}(2\pi N_b, Y) \tag{2.2-8}$$

with

$$N_a = \frac{a^2}{f\lambda}, \qquad N_b = \frac{b^2}{f\lambda}, \qquad X = \frac{x_1}{a}, \qquad Y = \frac{y_1}{b}, \tag{2.2-9}$$

and the eigenvalues are

$$\sigma_{mn} = 4(-i)^{m+n}\sqrt{N_a N_b}\, R^{(1)}_{0m}(2\pi N_a, 1)\, R^{(1)}_{0n}(2\pi N_b, 1)\,. \tag{2.2-10}$$

The function $S_{0m}(c, t)$ is even or odd according as m is even or odd. Thus we get the symmetric and antisymmetric modes. As is seen from (2.2-10), the eigenvalue of a symmetric mode is real, while the eigenvalue of an antisymmetric mode is pure imaginary. This is in agreement with the general rules (2.1-6), (2.1-7) for the resonance frequencies.

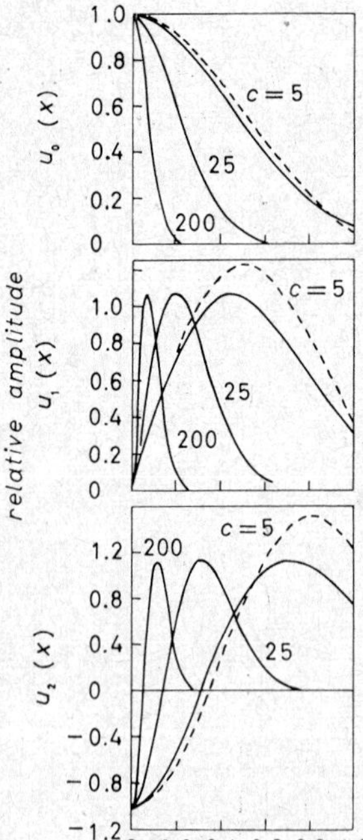

Fig. 9. – Amplitude distributions of the first three modes of the confocal resonator for different values of $c = 2\pi N_a$. Solid lines represent Hermite polynomial approximations, dashed lines exact solutions for $c=5$ (from BOYD and GORDON).

The functions $S_{0m}(c, t)$ are continuous functions for $c \geqslant 0$, are orthogonal and complete in $(-1, 1)$; $S_{0m}(c, t)$ has exactly m zeros in $(-1, 1)$.

FLAMMER [23] shows that for $t \ll 1$ (near the center of the reflector) $S_{0m}(c, t)$ becomes proportional to $H_m(\sqrt{c}\,t)\exp[-\frac{1}{2}ct^2]$, where H_m denotes the Hermite polynomial of order m. The approximation fails away from the center of the reflector. For reasonably large values of c, however, the field is weak there, and of little interest. The curves of Fig. 9, reproduced from BOYD and GORDON [21], show the relative field distribution of the first three modes as a function of X, for different values of $c = 2\pi N_a$. Solid lines represent the results obtained with the Hermite polynomial approximation. For $c = 5$ also the exact functions $S_{0m}(c, X)$ are plotted with dashed lines.

The exponential decay of the field with $cX^2 = 2\pi x_1^2/f\lambda$, which is independent of the reflector half-width a, leads one to define a

« spot size » at the reflector given by

$$w_s = \sqrt{\frac{f\lambda}{\pi}}\,. \tag{2.2-11}$$

The spot size is usually very small with respect to the mirror size. For instance, for $f=10$ cm, $\lambda=5\cdot10^{-5}$ cm, we have $w_s=1.3\cdot10^{-2}$ cm. In this situation it is evident that diffraction loss should be extremely small, one of the good points of the confocal resonator.

This conclusion is born out by computation of the eigenvalues (2.2-10). Power loss due to spill-over is given by

$$\delta_d = 1 - |\sigma_{mn}|^2 \tag{2.2-12}$$

and has been evaluated for a few modes by Boyd and Gordon [21], in the case of square reflectors. In Fig. 10 diffraction losses are plotted against $N=a^2/f\lambda$. For comparison, the results of Fox and Li [7] for the plane-parallel resonator with circular reflectors are also shown. The diffraction losses for the confocal resonator are seen to be orders of magnitude smaller than for the plane-parallel resonator.

Another advantage which is apparent upon comparison with Fig. 5 is that the ratio of the losses of the lowest two modes of the confocal resonator exceeds considerably the ratio of the losses of the lowest two modes of the plane-parallel resonator. The confocal resonator has thus greater loss discrimination between modes than the plane-parallel resonator.

We have considered here identical reflectors of rectangular cross-section. Boyd and Kogelnik [24] have considered rectangular reflectors of unequal sizes, say $2a_1$, $2b_1$ and $2a_2$, $2b_2$, respectively. They found that the resonance condition is not changed and that the diffraction losses are equal to the diffraction losses of a resonator with equal reflector dimensions $a^2=a_1a_2$, $b^2=b_1b_2$.

Resonators with circular reflectors have also been considered [7, 20]. The results are very similar to those found for square resonators. The Hermite-Gaussian functions are replaced in this case by associated Laguerre-Gaussian functions. Since ordinarily the spot size of the lower modes is much smaller than the reflector size, it is quite understandable that the mirror shape should have almost no influence on the field distribution.

2·3. *Optical systems for confocal resonators.* – A resonator having the general properties discussed in the previous Sections can be built in many different ways. We note however that unlike the ideal system of Fig. 8, real optical systems always present more or less pronounced aberrations. Moreover, many real systems present transmission coefficients appreciably different from unity, possibly variable with the inclination or with the distance of the ray from the axis. Finally the aperture stops may not be located at the mirrors M_1, M_2, but somewhere else in the system and additional stops may be effective for inclined beams (vignetting).

As a consequence of these individual features, the optical behavior is not identical for all real resonators, and as a matter of fact may depart substantially from that of the ideal system of Fig. 8. As a general requirement, system S should be corrected for monochromatic aberrations (*), should have very little absorption and its surfaces should be provided with antireflecting coatings.

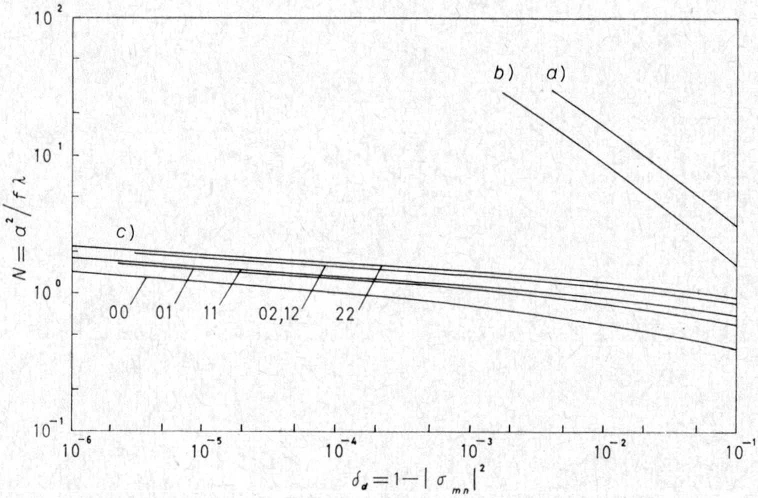

Fig. 10. – Diffraction losses per transit *vs.* Fresnel number for confocal and for plane-parallel geometry: circular plane reflectors: *a*) circular polarization, symmetric mode, *b*) linear polarization, symmetric mode; *c*) confocal reflectors, linear polarization, square aperture (from BOYD and GORDON).

We shall briefly mention some of the equivalent forms which may be given the system.

First of all the resonator may be « unfolded » by substituting real spaces for the virtual spaces created by the mirrors M_1, M_2. One thus arrives at the travelling-wave system represented in Fig. 11, where the mirrors are re-

(*) In the optical jargon a system is corrected for aberrations when third and fifth (and possibly higher) order aberrations are properly balanced. There always remain some small residual aberrations.

placed by periodical aperture stops M_n. A similar system, however with the lenses S_n located at the planes of the stops, was investigated theoretically by GOUBAU and SCHWERING [20] and experimentally (with microwaves) by CHRISTIAN and GOUBAU [25]. To bring this last system to our general form, it is

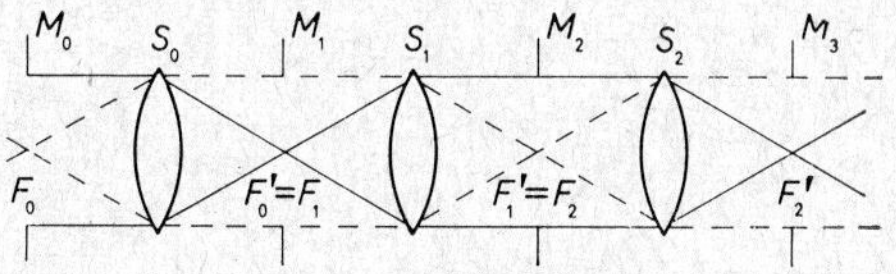

Fig. 11. – Travelling-wave system equivalent to confocal resonator.

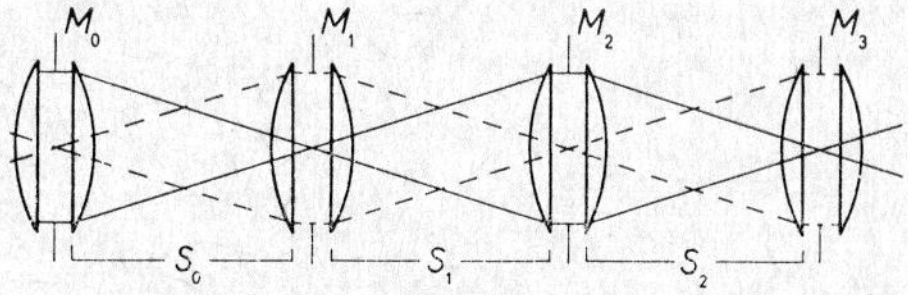

Fig. 12. – Another version of travelling-wave system equivalent to confocal resonator.

only necessary to think of the lenses as split each into two identical halves, one before and one after the stop and to unite the halves comprised between two consecutive stops into a single system S_n (Fig. 12).

The travelling-wave resonator can have the more practical ring form shown in Fig. 13.

The typical system of Fig. 8 has practical application in Burch's « cat's-eye ».

To build a well-corrected resonator, one should probably make use of a

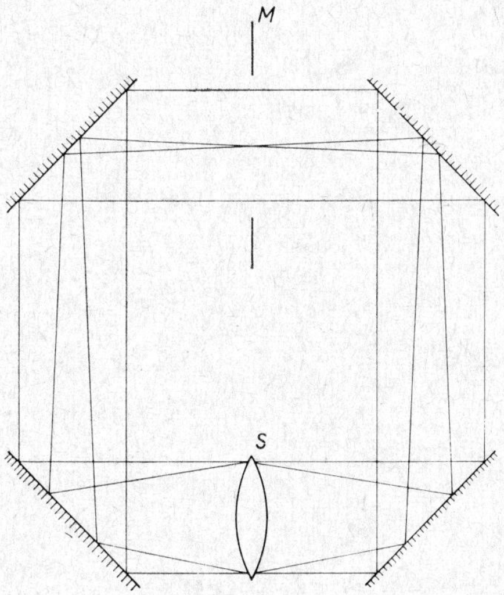

Fig. 13. – Cyclic travelling-wave system.

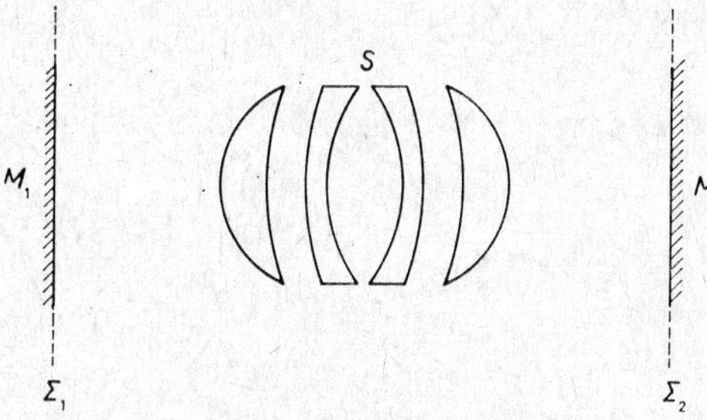

Fig. 14. – Generalized confocal system corrected for aberrations.

symmetric photographic lens of the Gaussian type (Fig. 14). Alternatively, two anastigmatic triplets (Fig. 15) can very well do the job.

Consider now the system of Fig. 15 in the first-order (Gaussian) approximation. It is evident that one can dispense with the lenses S_1, S_2, provided that twice their optical power be supplied by the mirrors M_1, M_2, which become concave (Fig. 16). We thus arrive at the simple confocal resonator described by many authors [7, 21, 25, 26]. Two identical spherical mirrors M_1 M_2, have common focus, or what amounts to the same, are separated by a distance d equal to their radius of curvature R. The extraordinary simplicity of construction and the comparative insensitivity to misalignment (*) would by themselves justify the popularity of this interferometer.

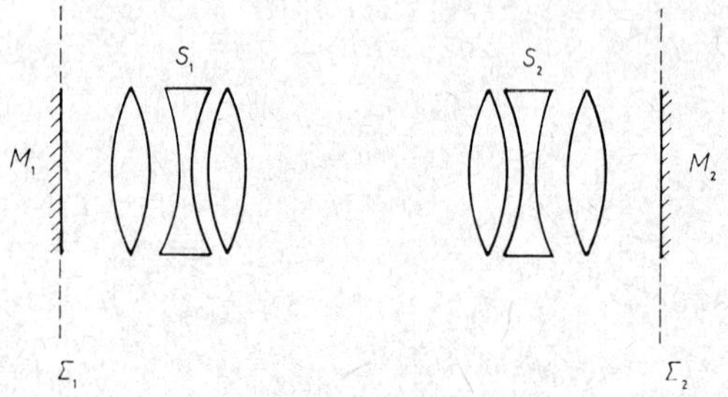

Fig. 15. – Another version of system corrected for aberrations.

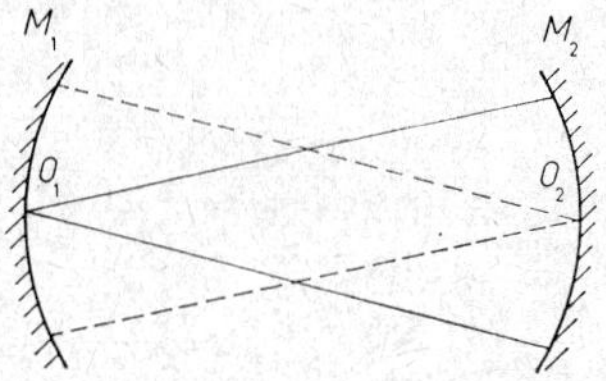

Fig. 16. – Conventional confocal resonator.

However, there is a fortunate circumstance, noted only recently [17], which may explain why this resonator works so well. In a round trip of the resonator, mirror M_1 is imaged onto itself. It is obvious that the image is free from spherical aberration and distortion. Coma is also absent, since the sine condition is fulfilled. Further investigation with the methods of optical design shows that the mean field curvature with respect to the surface M_1 vanishes. There only remains some astigmatism.

Notwithstanding the simplicity of its construction, the confocal resonator with spherical mirrors is almost corrected for aberrations and works almost as well as the system of Fig. 15.

Boyd and Gordon [21] have evaluated by means of Huygen's principle the expression of the field inside and outside of the resonator, starting from a mode distribution at one of the end mirrors. They found that the distribution is similar in all cross-sections of the interferometer (Hermite polynomial times exponential). The scale factor may be specified by the spot size, which turns out to be

$$w_s = \sqrt{\frac{d\lambda}{2\pi}\left[1 + \left(\frac{2z_0}{d}\right)^2\right]}\,, \tag{2.3-1}$$

where z_0 represents the distance from the center of the interferometer (focal plane of the mirrors). As is seen, the spot size is minimum at the focal plane

(*) This property depends on the fact that a spherical surface has no definite axis of symmetry.

and has the expression (2.2-11) at the reflectors (*). Figure 17 from BOYD and GORDON [21] represents schematically the field distribution for the fundamental mode within the confocal resonator.

Outside the resonator at large distance from the center, the spot size becomes proportional to z_0. Dividing by z_0, one finds the angular width of the spot size at infinity:

$$\theta = \sqrt{\frac{2\lambda}{\pi d}}. \tag{2.3-2}$$

In practical cases θ has the order of magnitude of a few milliradians.

The surfaces of constant phase are curved. Their radius of curvature at the axial point turns out to be

$$R' = \frac{R^2 + 4z_0^2}{4z_0}. \tag{2.3-3}$$

Of course, $R' = R$ at the reflectors. Note that the focal plane ($z_0 = 0$) is a surface of constant phase.

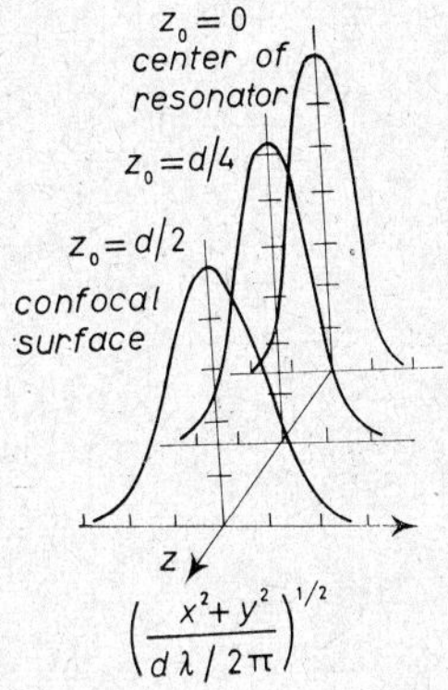

Fig. 17. – Field distribution inside confocal resonator, for fundamental mode (from BOYD and GORDON).

The comparative reduction (by a factor $1/\sqrt{2}$) of the spot size at the focal plane is an additional good point of the confocal resonator. It is seen from (1.1-4), which is valid also for a confocal resonator, that if diffraction losses are small compared to reflection losses, then the resonator Q is proportional to the spacing between the reflecting surfaces. Consider a confocal resonator and a plane-parallel resonator each of spacing d and of equal Q. The energy distribution in the former is more concentrated on the axis and thus the confocal resonator has a smaller effective mode volume. The volume of maser material will thus be less for the confocal than for the plane-parallel resonator. For maser oscillation the required excess density of excited states depends only on the cavity Q and in no other way upon the resonator shape [1]. The pump power is proportional to the volume of maser material times the density of excited states divided by the natural lifetime of the excited state. Thus, assuming equal Q, the confocal

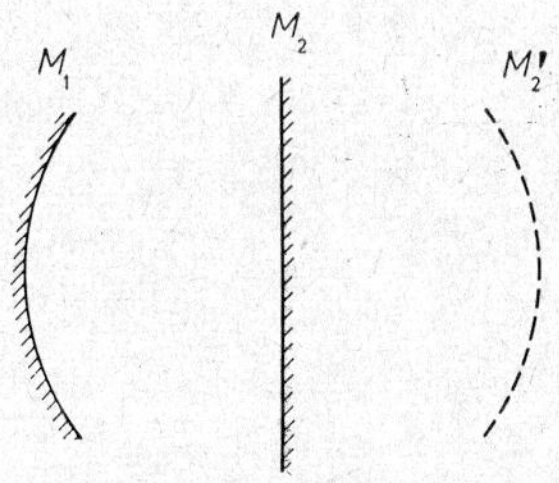

Fig. 18. – Virtual confocal system.

(*) Note that the focal length f used in the previous Sections is twice the focal length of the spherical mirrors.

resonator with its smaller volume of material requires less pump power than the plane-parallel resonator.

Finally, we note that one half of the confocal system can be made virtual (M_2'), by means of a plane mirror M_2 (Fig. 18).

3. – Nonconfocal resonators.

3·1. *Multi-transit afocal systems.* – The resonator shown in Fig. 18 represents the simplest example of a nonconfocal resonator which acquires the properties of the confocal resonator of Fig. 16 if considered for more than one round trip of light. To the approximation of Gaussian optics such systems can be built in a great variety of ways. Two simple examples [14] are shown in Fig. 19. Two identical spherical mirrors of radius R are spaced by a distance $d=(1\mp 1/\sqrt{2})R$. Point O of M_1 is imaged by M_2 at O', which is the center of M_1. It is evident that such systems are equivalent to the resonator of Fig. 16.

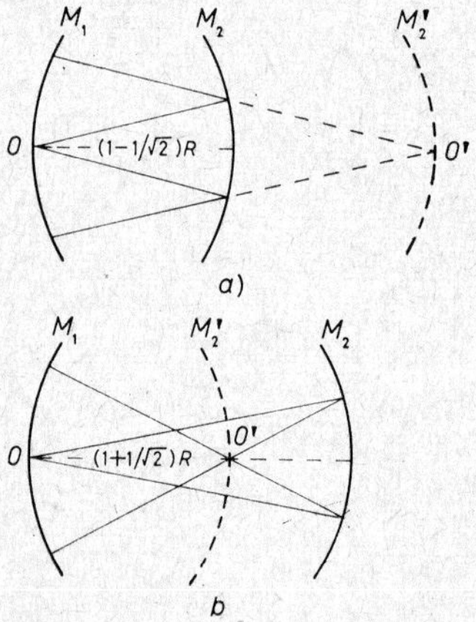

Fig. 19. – Two other versions of virtual confocal systems.

A very convenient and general approach to these problems has been given by BURCH [16]. It is expedient to refer to the travelling-wave systems of Fig. 11 or Fig. 12. Each pair of consecutive lenses, like S_0, S_1 represents an afocal system of unit magnification. The posterior focal point F_0' of S_0 coincides with the anterior focal point F_1 of S_1. The separation d between the posterior principal plane of S_0 and the anterior principal plane of S_1 equals twice the focal length. In a chain of such systems each (paraxial) ray repeats periodically its path with respect to the lenses.

If now the spacing d is made different from twice the focal length, the pair S_0, S_1 is no more afocal. However, one can hope that n successive subsystems $S_0, S_1, S_2, \ldots, S_{n-1}$ form an afocal system of unit magnification. The following analysis shows that this is possible.

Let the spacing of the identical systems S_n, whose focal length will be taken as unity, be such that F_{n-1}' precedes F_n by a distance α. We take an object point located on the axis at a distance x_0 to the left of the anterior focus F_0 of S_0. By Newton's relation, the image point will be located at a distance $x_0'=1/x_0$ to the right of F_0' and therefore at a distance $x_1=\alpha-1/x_0$ to the left of F_1. We thus obtain a recurrence relation

(3.1-1) $$x_1 = \alpha - \frac{1}{x_0}, \quad x_2 = \alpha - \frac{1}{x_1}, \text{ etc.}.$$

After traversal of n subsystems, there results the continued fraction

(3.1-2) $$\frac{1}{x_n} = \cfrac{1}{\alpha - \cfrac{1}{\alpha - \cfrac{1}{\alpha \cdots \cfrac{}{\alpha - \cfrac{1}{x_0}}}}}$$

where α appears n times.

For the system to be afocal we require $x_0 = x_n = \infty$, and obtain the $(n-1)$-th degree equation

(3.1-3) $$0 = \cfrac{1}{\alpha - \cfrac{1}{\alpha \cdots \cfrac{}{\alpha - \cfrac{1}{\alpha}}}}$$

whose solutions are represented by

(3.1-4) $$\alpha = 2 \cos \left(\frac{r}{n}\pi\right), \qquad r = 1, 2, \ldots, n-1.$$

The lateral magnification, which equals $(-1)^n/(x_0 x_1 \ldots x_{n-1})$ turns out to be $(-1)^r$. There are therefore $n-1$ distinct solutions. However it will be noted that among the solutions for n there are also the solutions for the submultiples of n.

If now one selects a value of α arbitrarily, two cases must be distinguished. If $|\alpha| > 2$ there are no values of r and n which satisfy (3.1-4). Indeed, as is well known in periscope design, in electron optics, in particle accelerator theory, if the spacing between the foci exceeds twice the focal length, the system is unstable [27, 28] in that any ray gradually turns away from the axis and walks off. If $|\alpha| < 2$, there may exist a pair of integers r, n which satisfy (3.1-4), and in that case we have an n-fold afocal system. However, even if such a pair of numbers does not exist, since the fraction r/n can approximate any irrational number as close as desired, we may conclude that any physical system with $|\alpha|<2$ is practically n-fold afocal, provided that n be made sufficiently large.

3·2. *Nonconfocal pairs of reflectors.* – Several authors [12, 28] have investigated the behavior of a pair of spherical mirrors with different radii and nonconfocal spacing. We will apply the theory of the previous Section.

Let us denote by R_1, R_2 the radii of curvature of the two reflectors (positive for concave mirrors, negative for convex mirrors) and by d their spacing. This system is equivalent to a succession of thin lenses having alternatively the focal length $f_1=R_1/2$ and $f_2=R_2/2$. A subsystem S_n will be formed by a pair of consecutive lenses. Since its focal length will be taken as unity, we shall write

(3.2-1) $$\frac{1}{f_1}+\frac{1}{f_2}-\frac{d}{f_1 f_2}=1\,.$$

Taking into account this equation, the distances l, l' from the anterior focus to the first lens and from the second lens to the posterior focus are expressed by

(3.2-2) $$l=1-\frac{d}{f_2}\,,\qquad l'=1-\frac{d}{f_1}\,.$$

We will now make use of two convenient parameters introduced by Fox and Li [12]

(3.2-3) $$g_1=1-\frac{d}{R_1}\,,\qquad g_2=1-\frac{d}{R_2}$$

or $g_1=1-d/2f_1$, $g_2=1-d/2f_2$. From these positions and from (3.2-1) one can derive

(3.2-4) $$d=2g_1+2g_2-4g_1g_2\,.$$

The distance $\alpha=d-l-l'$ from the posterior focus of one subsystem to the anterior focus of the following subsystem becomes

(3.2-5) $$\alpha=2-4g_1g_2\,.$$

For an n-fold system we have therefore by (3.1-4)

(3.2-6) $$g_1g_2=\sin^2\left(\frac{r}{n}\frac{\pi}{2}\right).$$

For stability, the product g_1g_2 must be positive and less than 1. We can plot a stability diagram (Fig. 20), as was done by BOYD and KOGELNIK [28] and by FOX and LI [12]. The co-ordinate axes represent g_1 and g_2. The shaded regions correspond to high-loss or unstable systems, while the unshaded regions, limited by the axes and by the hyperbola $g_1g_2 = 1$, represent low-loss or stable systems. Points corresponding to mirrors with equal radii of curvature lie on the 45° line defined by $g_1 = g_2$. The origin corresponds to identical mirrors spaced confocally, the point (1, 1) corresponds to plane parallel mirrors and the point (—1, —1) corresponds to concentric mirrors. Confocal systems lie on the dashed hyperbola $2g_1g_2 - g_1 - g_2 = 0$ and are seen to be all unstable, except the one with identical mirrors. However, it must be emphasized that the confocal resonator with identical mirrors lies on the frontier between stable and unstable regions. As a consequence, even a small departure from its ideal construction may cause substantial loss.

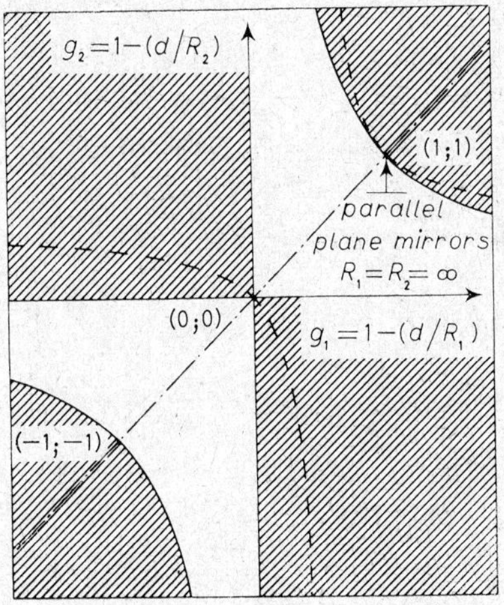

Fig. 20. – Stability diagram for curved mirror interferometers. Shaded areas: high-loss regions; white areas: low-loss regions. Solid lines: concentric system, $g_1g_2 = 1$, $R_1 + R_2 = 0$; dashed lines: confocal sistem, $g_1 = g_2/(2g_2 - 1)$, $R_1 + R_2 = 2d$; dash-dotted line: equal radii of curvature, $R_1 = R_2$ (from FOX and LI).

The low-loss regions of Fig. 20 represent the following three sets of possible mirror geometries:

1) Both mirrors are concave, and the center of curvature of each mirror lies beyond the other mirror.

2) Both mirrors are concave, and the center of curvature of each mirror lies between the other mirror and the center of curvature of the other mirror.

3) One mirror is convex and one is concave, and the center of curvature of the concave mirror lies between the convex mirror and the center of curvature of the convex mirror.

Of course, the transition between low-loss and high-loss regions is not so sharp as suggested by geometrical optics. It is rather a gradual passage, which has been described by FOX and LI [12]. However the transition becomes more and more abrupt as the Fresnel number N is increased. In any case, it turns out that equal radii with confocal spacing give rise to the lowest loss. The loss decreases with increase in the Fresnel number in the low-loss region, but fluctuates without eventual decrease in the high-loss region.

Equation (3.2-6) shows that all systems having the same product g_1g_2 are equivalent from the geometrical point of view and become afocal after the same number of transits.

For instance three such systems are those presented in Figs. 18 and 19, which belong to the family $r=1$, $n=2$.

Fox and Li [12] show that two systems with reversed signs of both g_1 and g_2 are equivalent also in the wave-optics approximation. They have equal mode functions and diffraction losses. Two such systems are the plane parallel ($g_1=g_2=1$) and the concentric ($g_1=g_2=-1$) systems.

As regards the resonance frequencies, it will be noted that in an n-fold system the total optical path is nd, and therefore the conditions (2.1-6), (2.1-7) become

$$nd = q\frac{\lambda}{2} + \varepsilon\frac{\lambda}{4}, \tag{3.2-7}$$

where $\varepsilon=1$ for symmetric modes and $\varepsilon=0$ for antisymmetric modes. The density of axial modes becomes n times greater than for the confocal resonator of spacing d.

However, it will be noted that not all the resonances (3.2-7) may be present in an actual system. This is a consequence of the system being folded upon itself. Some eigenfunctions may be identically zero, since they may give rise to destructive interference in successive round trips.

For instance, Boyd and Kogelnik [28] give for the case of rectangular mirrors the following formula

$$\frac{2d}{\lambda} = q + \frac{1}{\pi}(2s+\varepsilon)\,\mathrm{arc\,cos}\sqrt{g_1 g_2}, \tag{3.2-8}$$

where q and s are positive integers and ε has the same meaning as before. Upon elimination of $g_1 g_2$ by means of (3.2-6), it is easy to show that all the resonances (3.2-8) are included in the general expression (3.2-7), while the reverse is not true.

Further, it will be noted that a nonconfocal multi-transit resonator is equivalent to a confocal single-transit resonator with a set of intermediate apertures. The presence of these apertures may slightly modify the eigenfunctions of the former resonator with respect to the eigenfunctions of the latter, as was shown by Fox and Li [12] in two particular cases. The effect is not very pronounced, due to the contraction of the field of the confocal resonator toward the center of the system.

The field distribution in the modes of the nonconfocal resonator, has been shown by Boyd and Gordon [21] to be substantially the same as for the confocal resonator, however with a different spot size at each mirror. Precisely, the values of these spot sizes w_1, w_2, inside the low-loss region of Fig. 20 turn out to be

(3.2-9)
$$\begin{cases} w_1 = \sqrt{\dfrac{\lambda d}{\pi}}\left[\dfrac{g_2}{g_1(1-g_1g_2)}\right]^{\frac{1}{4}}, \\ \\ w_2 = \sqrt{\dfrac{\lambda d}{\pi}}\left[\dfrac{g_1}{g_2(1-g_1g_2)}\right]^{\frac{1}{4}}. \end{cases}$$

When one approaches the boundary of the low-loss region, one or both spot sizes tend to become infinitely large. This means that approaching the boundary, spill-over increases till instability is reached.

REFERENCES

[1] A. L. SCHAWLOW and C. H. TOWNES: *Phys. Rev.*, **112**, 1940 (1958).
[2] A. M. PROKHOROV: *Žurn. Ėksp. Teor. Fiz.*, **34**, 1658 (1958).
[3] R. H. DICKE: U. S. Patent 2851 652 (1958).
[4] G. TORALDO DI FRANCIA: *Electromagnetic Waves* (New York, 1955), p. 295.
[5] D. A. KLEINMAN and P. P. KISLIUK: *Bell. Sys. Techn. Journ.*, **41**, 453 (1962).
[6] R. J. COLLINS and J. R. GIORDMAINE: *New Modes of Optical Oscillation in Closed Resonators*, in *Third Quantum Electronics Conference* (Paris, 1963) (to be published).
[7] A. G. FOX and T. LI: *Bell Sys. Tech. Journ.*, **40**, 453 (1961).
[8] G. TORALDO DI FRANCIA: *Introduction to the Modern Theory of Electromagnetic Diffraction* (Ist. Naz. Ott., 1950), p. 12.
[9] J. KOTIK and M. C. NEWSTEIN: *Journ. Appl. Phys.*, **32**, 178 (1961).
[10] W. CULSHAW: *I.R.E. Trans., M.T.T.*, **10**, 331 (1962).
[11] S. R. BARONE: *Journ. Appl. Phys.*, **34**, 831 (1963).
[12] A. G. FOX and T. LI: *Proc. I.E.E.E.*, **51**, 80 (1963).
[13] D. R. HERRIOT: *Journ. Opt. Soc. Am.*, **52**, 31 (1962).
[14] W. R. BENNET, jr.: *Phys. Rev.*, **126**, 580 (1962).
[15] L. A. WEINSTEIN: *Žurn. Ėksp. Teor. Fiz.*, **44**, 1050 (1963).
[16] J. M. BURCH: *Design of Resonators*, in *Third Quantum Electronics Conference* (Paris, 1963) (to be published).
[17] G. TORALDO DI FRANCIA: *On the Theory of Optical Resonators*, *Symposium on Optical Masers of the Polytechnic Institute of Brooklyn* (New York, 1963) (to be published).
[18] G. TORALDO DI FRANCIA: *La diffrazione della luce* (Torino, 1958), p. 198.
[19] See for instance: M. BORN and E. WOLF: *Principles of Optics* (London, 1959), p. 167.
[20] G. GOUBAU and F. SCHWERING: *I.R.E. Trans., A. P.*, **9**, 248 (1961).
[21] G. D. BOYD and J. P. GORDON: *Bell Sys. Techn. Journ.*, **40**, 489 (1961).
[22] D. SLEPIAN and H. O. POLLAK: *Bell Sys. Techn. Journ.*, **40**, 43 (1961).
[23] C. FLAMMER: *Spheroidal Wave Functions* (Stanford, 1957).
[24] G. D. BOYD and H. KOGELNIK: *Bell Sys. Techn. Journ.*, **41**, 1347 (1962).
[25] J. R. CHRISTIAN and G. GOUBAU: *I.R.E. Trans., A.P.*, **9**, 256 (1961).
[26] P. CONNES: *Rev. d'Optique*, **35**, 37 (1956); *Journ. Phys. Radium.*, **19**, 262 (1958).
[27] J. R. PIERCE: *Theory and Design of Electron Beams* (New York, 1954).
[28] G. D. BOYD and H. KOGELNIK: *Bell Sys. Techn. Journ.*, **41**, 1347 (1962).

Theory of Optical Maser Oscillators.

W. E. LAMB jr.

Yale University - New Haven, Conn.

1. – Introduction.

We consider the optical maser oscillator to be a high Q cavity ($Q \simeq 10^7$) containing an active medium. The active medium consists of non-interacting atoms, or molecules whose energy levels are maintained in a state of negative temperature by means which need not be specified for the present. The electric field within the cavity $E(r, t)$ is described classically by Maxwell's equations, neglecting quantum and thermal fluctuations.

We understand the mechanism of maser oscillation as follows: an assumed electromagnetic field $E(r, t)$ polarizes the atoms of the medium creating electric dipole moments $p_i(r, t)$ which add up to produce a macroscopic polarization density $P(r, t)$. This polarization acts further as the source of a reaction field $E'(r, t)$ according to Maxwell's equations. The condition for maser oscillation is than that the assumed field be just equal to the reaction field. This is repre-

$$\boldsymbol{E}(\boldsymbol{r}, t) \xrightarrow[\text{mechanics}]{\text{quantum}} \langle P_i \rangle \xrightarrow[\text{summation}]{\text{statistical}} P(\boldsymbol{r}, t) \xrightarrow[\text{equations}]{\text{Maxwell's}} E'(\boldsymbol{r}, t)$$

Fig. 1. – Schematic basis for calculation of the properties of a maser oscillator.

sented schematically in Fig. 1. According to this scheme, our calculation proceeds in three separate steps *a*) E.M. field equations, *b*) quantum mechanical equation, *c*) statistical summation.

2. – E. M. field equations.

Let us write Maxwell's equations and the relations between the field vectors in m.k.s. units:

$$\text{(1)} \qquad \begin{cases} \operatorname{div} D = 0\,, & \operatorname{curl} E = -\dfrac{\partial B}{\partial t}\,, \\[2ex] \operatorname{div} B = 0\,, & \operatorname{curl} H = J + \dfrac{\partial D}{\partial t}\,, \end{cases}$$

and

$$D = \varepsilon_0 E + P\,, \qquad B = \mu_0 H\,, \qquad J = \sigma E\,.$$

Interferometer cavities used with optical masers pose difficult boundary-value problems which we prefer to side-step now. We may not ignore energy losses in the cavity altogether since these play an essential role in the description of a maser oscillator. To account in a simple way for reflection and diffraction losses without solving the boundary-value problem we introduce dissipation into our equations by attributing a volume conductivity σ to the medium. Combining (1) and (2) we obtain the wave equation

$$\text{(3)} \qquad \operatorname{curl}\operatorname{curl} E + \mu_0 \sigma \frac{\partial E}{\partial t} + \mu_0 \varepsilon_0 \frac{\partial^2 E}{\partial t^2} = -\mu_0 \frac{\partial^2 P}{\partial t^2}\,.$$

From (1) and (2) we see that if P is a small perturbation compared to $\varepsilon_0 E$, then $\operatorname{div} E \approx 0$ and $\operatorname{curl}\operatorname{curl} E \approx -\nabla^2 E$. Therefore (3) is a wave equation in which the r.h.s. acts as a source term.

An optical maser might typically emit radiation having a number of highly monochromatic frequency components all lying in a relatively narrow range, say between $\nu - \Delta\nu$ and $\nu + \Delta\nu$, where $\nu \sim 10^{15}$ rad/s and $\Delta\nu \sim 10^{9}$ rad/s. Hence in the r.h.s. of (3) we can use

$$-\frac{\partial^2}{\partial t^2} \approx +\nu^2$$

where ν(rad/s) is an angular frequency of the e.m. field. We now expand the $\boldsymbol{r}$ dependence of $E(\boldsymbol{r}, t)$ in orthonormal eigenfunctions of an ideal lossless cavity, that is,

$$\text{(4)} \qquad E(\boldsymbol{r}, t) = \sum_n A_n(t)\, U_n(\boldsymbol{r})\,,$$

where, from (3) the U_n's are given by

$$\text{(5)} \qquad \operatorname{curl}\operatorname{curl} \boldsymbol{U} - \mu_0 \varepsilon_0 \Omega_n^2 \boldsymbol{U}_n = 0 \quad (\Omega_n = \text{eigenfrequencies of the cavity})\,.$$

Introducing (4) into (3) and using orthogonality, we obtain

$$\frac{\mathrm{d}^2 A_n}{\mathrm{d}t^2} + \frac{\sigma}{\varepsilon_0}\frac{\mathrm{d}A_n}{\mathrm{d}t} + \Omega_n^2 A_n = \frac{\nu^2}{\varepsilon_0} P_n(t)\,, \tag{6}$$

where

$$P_n(t) = \frac{\int \mathrm{d}\boldsymbol{r}\,\boldsymbol{P}(\boldsymbol{r},t)\cdot \boldsymbol{U}_n(\boldsymbol{r})}{\int [U_n(\boldsymbol{r})]^2\,\mathrm{d}\boldsymbol{r}}\,, \tag{7}$$

that is, $P_n(t)$ is the n-th space Fourier component of $\boldsymbol{P}(\boldsymbol{r}, t)$. We also introduce a cavity Q through the relation

$$\sigma \to \frac{\varepsilon_0 \nu}{Q} \tag{8}$$

and to have more generality allow $Q \to Q_n$ to vary from mode to mode. It follows then that

$$\ddot{A}_n + \frac{\nu}{Q_n}\dot{A}_n + \Omega_n^2 A_n = \frac{\nu^2}{\varepsilon_0} P_n(t)\,. \tag{9}$$

We look now for a solution of the type

$$A_n(t) = E_n(t)\cos\big(\nu_n t + \varphi_n(t)\big)\,, \tag{10}$$

where amplitude $E_n(t)$ and phase $\varphi_n(t)$ are slowly varying functions and ν_n is not yet determined, but is a frequency around ν.

Assume that the mode separation Δ is much less than the frequency ν, but large than the bandwidth of a mode

$$\nu/Q \ll \Delta \ll \nu\,.$$

There is an ambiguity in (10) because the same slow variation in $A_n(t)$ can be due either to a change in E_n or in φ_n, but this does not cause trouble in our approximations.

Now, looking at (9), we can neglect Fourier components of $P_n(t)$ far from the central frequency ν, because of the stated assumptions. Let us write P_n as an « in phase » and an « in quadrature » parts with respect to A_n:

$$P_n(t) = C_n(t)\cos\big(\nu_n t + \varphi_n(t)\big) + S_n(t)\sin\big(\nu_n t + \varphi_n(t)\big) \tag{11}$$

with slowly varying coefficients $C_n(t)$ and $S_n(t)$. In order to handle the tentative solution (10) in eq. (9), we differentiate twice A_n neglecting $\ddot{E}_n$ and $\dot{E}_n\dot{\varphi}_n$:

$$\dot{A}_n = -(\nu_n + \dot{\varphi}_n)E_n \sin(\nu_n t + \varphi_n) + \dot{E}_n \cos(\nu_n t + \varphi_n) ,$$

$$\ddot{A}_n = -(\nu_n + \dot{\varphi}_n)^2 E_n \cos(\nu_n t + \varphi_n) - 2\nu_n \dot{E}_n \sin(\nu_n t + \varphi_n) ,$$

and then introduce the further approximation

$$(\nu_n + \dot{\varphi}_n)^2 - \Omega_n^2 \simeq 2\nu(\nu_n + \dot{\varphi}_n - \Omega_n) ,$$

since ν_n and Ω_n are near to ν, and much larger than $\dot{\varphi}_n$.

Introduce now A_n and its derivatives in the l.h.s. of (9) and (11) in the r.h.s., then equate coefficients in cos and sin $(\nu_n t + \varphi_n)$. We obtain two equations:

(12a) $$(\nu_n + \dot{\varphi}_n - \Omega_n)E_n = -\frac{1}{2}\frac{\nu}{\varepsilon_0} C_n ,$$

(12b) $$\left(\dot{E}_n + \frac{1}{2}\frac{\nu}{Q_n}\right) E_n = -\frac{1}{2}\frac{\nu}{\varepsilon_0} S_n .$$

The eqs. (12) gives the frequencies ν_n and the time-dependence of the amplitudes E_n and phases $\varphi_n(t)$ of the field for any given source terms C_n, S_n: The first will be called « frequency » or « phase » equations, the second « amplitude » equations.

Let us consider now two very simple particular cases.

1) *Absence of polarization*

(13) $$C_n = S_n = 0$$

and eqs. (12) become

(14) $$\begin{cases} \nu_n + \dot{\varphi}_n = \Omega_n , \\ \dot{E}_n = -\dfrac{1}{2}\dfrac{\nu}{Q_n} E_n . \end{cases}$$

The first gives, neglecting $\dot{\varphi}$: $\nu \simeq \Omega_n$, and the second $E_n \propto \exp[-\frac{1}{2}(\nu/Q_n)t]$; that is, we have free damped oscillation of the cavity at a frequency ν_n approximately equal to any eigenfrequency of the cavity.

2) *Linear medium*

(15) $$P = \varepsilon_0 E_n[\chi' \cos(\nu_n t + \varphi_n) + \chi'' \sin(\nu_n t + \varphi_n)] ,$$

that is,

(16) $$C_n = \varepsilon_0 E_n \chi' , \qquad S_n = \varepsilon_0 E_n \chi'' ,$$

and eqs. (12) become

$$(17)\qquad \begin{cases} \nu_n + \dot{\varphi}_n - \Omega_n = -\dfrac{1}{2}\nu\chi_n' , \\[2ex] \dot{E}_n + \dfrac{1}{2}\dfrac{\nu}{Q_n} E_n = -\dfrac{1}{2}\nu\chi_n'' E_n . \end{cases}$$

Neglecting again $\ddot{\varphi}_n$, the first eq. (17) says that the oscillation frequency differs from the eigenvalue Ω_n by a « pulling term » $-\frac{1}{2}\nu\chi_n'$, that is, the presence of the dielectric changes the cavity resonances.

The second eq. (17) indicates that there is an extra contribution to the coefficient of the exponential fall-off ($\chi_n''>0$). If $\chi_n''<-1/Q_n$, the exponent becomes positive and the oscillations build up until the linear approximation breaks down.

3. – Induced polarization.

We have now to find the atomic polarization which results from the assumed field $E(r, t)$. Suppose the medium consists of « atoms » with but two relevant *excited* energy levels $\hbar W_a$ and $\hbar W_b$. Let $W_a - W_b = \omega > 0$. Atoms are excited to a and b by some means, *e.g.*, electron collision and they decay to lower-lying states by spontaneous emission. Let the wave equation define stationary states:

$$(18)\qquad H_{\text{atom}}\psi_a = \hbar W_a \psi_a ,$$

so that

$$(19)\qquad \psi(r, t) = \exp[-iW_a t]\,\psi_a(r)$$

in the abscence of radiation damping. We should expect

$$(20)\qquad \psi(r, t) = \exp[-\tfrac{1}{2}\gamma_a t]\exp[-iW_a t]\,\psi_a(r) = a(t)\,\psi_a(r)$$

with damping included. Such a wave function implies exponential decay of the state a with a mean life γ_a^{-1}

$$(21)\qquad |a(t)|^2 = \exp[-\gamma_a t]\,|a(0)|^2$$

as suggested by the theory of Wigner and Weisskopf.

Proceeding in the usual manner of time-dependent perturbation theory we write

$$(22)\qquad H = H_{\text{atom}} + V$$

and expand using normalized eigenfunctions $\psi_a(r)$ and $\psi_b(r)$

$$\psi(r, t) = a(t)\,\psi_a(r) + b(t)\,\psi_b(r)\,. \tag{23}$$

Introducing (22) and (23) into Schrödinger equation $H\psi = i\hbar(\partial\psi/\partial t)$, this converts into the system

$$i\dot{a} = W_a a + V(t)b - \tfrac{1}{2} i\gamma_a a\,, \qquad i\dot{b} = W_b b + V(t)b - \tfrac{1}{2} i\gamma_b b\,. \tag{24}$$

We have supressed $\hbar$ by taking all energies in angular frequency units. The last terms on the right (damping terms) are inserted to yield the correct radiative decay when $V = 0$.

Since we are concerned here with electric dipole interactions

$$\hbar V = -\Big(e\sum_j x_j\Big)E(\boldsymbol{r}, t)\,, \tag{25}$$

if we suppose the field to point along x. Here the summation is over atomic electrons, and $\boldsymbol{r}$ is the position vector of the atomic nucleus. Then

$$(V(t) = -(\mathscr{P}/\hbar)E(\boldsymbol{r}, t)\,, \tag{26}$$

where the dipole matrix element $\mathscr{P}$ is given by

$$\mathscr{P} = +e\int_{\text{atom}} \psi_b^* \sum_j x_j \psi_a \,\mathrm{d}x\,.$$

Note that the matrix element $V(t)$ depends upon time because the assumed field depends upon time and also perhaps because the atom moves through the field.

The assumed field distorts the atomic wave function to a linear combination of ψ_a and ψ_b and brings into being an induced dipole

$$+e\langle x\rangle = +e\int_{\text{atom}} (a\psi_a + b\psi_b)^* x (a\psi_a + b\psi_b)\,\mathrm{d}x = +\mathscr{P}(a^* b + b^* a)\,. \tag{28}$$

Of course $\langle x\rangle = 0$ for the pure atomic states a or b.

It is possible to work directly with the Schrödinger amplitudes a and b, *i.e.*, to solve equations (24) in some approximation directly. We find it more convenient however to use the four bi-linear quantities $|a|^2$, $|b|^2$; ab^* and a^*b as variables. The quantities $|a|^2$ and $|b|^2$ are of course the probabilities of finding the system in states a or b. Note, however, that because of the damping terms $|a|^2 + |b|^2$ is not constant since the excited state decays. The other term quantities appear in equation (28).

We proceed to find equations of motion for the four bilinear quantities. Using equation (17) one finds, for example,

$$(29)\qquad i\frac{\mathrm{d}}{\mathrm{d}t}\,a^* b = i(\dot{a}^* b + a^* \dot{b}) = a^*\left(W_b b + Va - \frac{1}{2}\,i\gamma_b b\right) - \\ - \left(W_a a^* + Vb^* + \frac{1}{2}\,i\gamma_a a\right) b = \\ = (W_b - W_a)a^* b + V(|a|^2 + |b|^2) - \frac{1}{2}\,(\gamma_a + \gamma_b)a^* b$$

and similarly

$$(30)\qquad i\frac{\mathrm{d}}{\mathrm{d}t}\,a^* a = V(a^* b - b^* a) - i\gamma_a a^* a$$

and so on for ab^* and $|b|^2$.

Upon introducing the 2×2 matrices

$$(31)\qquad \varrho = \begin{pmatrix} a^* a & b^* a \\ a^* b & b^* b \end{pmatrix} = \begin{pmatrix} \varrho_{aa} & \varrho_{ab} \\ \varrho_{ba} & \varrho_{bb} \end{pmatrix},$$

$$(32)\qquad H = \begin{pmatrix} W_a & V \\ V & W_b \end{pmatrix}$$

and

$$(33)\qquad \Gamma = \begin{pmatrix} \gamma_a & 0 \\ 0 & \gamma_b \end{pmatrix},$$

equations (29) and (30) will be found to be components of the matrix equation

$$(34)\qquad i\frac{\mathrm{d}}{\mathrm{d}t}\,\varrho = H\varrho - \varrho H - \frac{1}{2}\,(\Gamma\varrho + \varrho\Gamma)\,.$$

The induced dipole is determined when the off-diagonal components of ϱ are known according to equation (28)

$$(35)\qquad p = \mathscr{P}(\varrho_{ab} + \varrho_{ba})\,,$$

or more generally the expectation value of any observable F is given by

$$(36)\qquad \langle F\rangle = \mathrm{Tr}(F\varrho) = \mathrm{Spur}(F\varrho)\,.$$

Note that a system definitely known to be in an eigenstate, say ψ_a, is represented by

$$\varrho(a) = \begin{pmatrix} 1 & 0 \\ 0 & 0 \end{pmatrix}. \tag{37}$$

Under the influence of the perturbation V a state represented by $\varrho(a)$ at some time $t = t_0$ evolves into a general $\varrho(a, t_0, t)$ for $t > t_0$ in accordance with eq. (34). Let $\varrho(a, t_0, t)$ be a solution of (34) which reduces to $\varrho(a)$ when $t = t_0$

$$\varrho(a, t_0, t_0) = \varrho(a) . \tag{38}$$

We are concerned here not with the state of a single atom but with all the atoms of the active medium. Suppose atoms are excited to state a at various times t_{0i}. In order to compute a macroscopic average we have to compute

$$\langle\!\langle F \rangle\!\rangle = \sum_i \operatorname{Spur} F\varrho(a, t_{0i}, t) = \operatorname{Spur} F \sum_i \varrho(a, t_{0i}, t) . \tag{39}$$

It is therefore expedient to introduce an averaged $\varrho(a, t)$

$$\varrho(a, t) = \sum_i \varrho(a, t_{0i}, t) , \tag{40}$$

summed over all $t_{0i} < t$. Let $\lambda_a(t_0)\mathrm{d}t_0$ = average number of atoms excited to state a from t_0 to $t_0 + \mathrm{d}t_0$. Then

$$\varrho(a, t) = \int_{-\infty}^{t} \lambda_a(t_0)\, \varrho(a, t_0, t)\, \mathrm{d}t_0 . \tag{41}$$

Here $\lambda_a(t_0)$ is the rate of excitation to state a at t_0. We need not here specify the nature of the excitation process except for a qualification to be mentioned presently. An equation analogous to (34) for $\varrho(a, t_0, t)$ may be derived for $\varrho(a, t)$ as follows:

$$i \frac{\partial}{\partial t} \varrho(a, t) = i\lambda_a \varrho(a) + \int_{-\infty}^{t} \lambda_a i \frac{\partial}{\partial t} \varrho(a, t_0, t)\, \mathrm{d}t_0 , \tag{42}$$

and using eq. (34)

$$i \frac{\partial}{\partial t} \varrho(a, t) = i\lambda_a \varrho(a) + H\varrho(a, t) - \varrho(a, t)H - \frac{1}{2}\left(\Gamma\varrho(a, t) + \varrho(a, t)\Gamma\right) . \tag{43}$$

The integration over t_0 has been carried out using the definition of $\varrho(a, t)$ and *assuming H is independent of t_0*.

In general one must suppose both a and b are excited and introduce the new matrix

$$\varrho(t) = \sum_{\alpha=a,\,b} \varrho(\alpha, t)\,, \tag{44}$$

which satisfies

$$i\frac{\mathrm{d}}{\mathrm{d}t}\varrho = H\varrho - \varrho H - \frac{1}{2}(\Gamma\varrho + \varrho\Gamma) + i\lambda \tag{45}$$

with

$$\lambda = \begin{pmatrix} \lambda_a & 0 \\ 0 & \lambda_b \end{pmatrix}. \tag{46}$$

The «source» matrix λ is diagonal because we have assumed independent excitation to pure states a and b. There could be excitation processes which introduce off-diagonal terms. The matrix $\varrho(t)$ might be called the «density matrix» except for the fact that Tr ϱ is not unity or even constant. The inhomogeneous source term λ in eq. (45) leads to the possibility of a steady-state solution for ϱ in which the processes of excitation and decay compete.

4. – First-order theory.

Consider an off-diagonal component of the matrix eq. (45):

$$\dot{\varrho}_{ab} = -i\omega\varrho_{ab} + iV(t)(\varrho_{aa} - \varrho_{bb})\gamma_{ab}\varrho_{ab}\,, \tag{47}$$

with

$$\omega = W_a - W_b\,, \tag{48}$$

and

$$\gamma_{ab} = \tfrac{1}{2}(\gamma_a + \gamma_b)\,. \tag{49}$$

The term $iV(t)(\varrho_{aa} - \varrho_{bb})$ may be considered a source term for the off-diagonal element ϱ_{ab}. For the present we regard $(\varrho_{aa} - \varrho_{bb})$ to be known and set

$$(\varrho_{aa} - \varrho_{bb}) = N(r)\,, \qquad a \text{ constant}\,. \tag{50}$$

We take, from eq. (4), (10) and (26),

$$V(t) = -\frac{\mathscr{P}}{\hbar}E_n U_n(r)\cos(\nu_n t + \varphi_n) = -\frac{\mathscr{P}}{2\hbar}E_n U_n(r)\exp[-i(\nu_n t + \varphi_n)] + \text{c.c.}\,. \tag{51}$$

As usual, only the factor proportional to $\exp[-i\nu_n t]$ gives a large contribution in eq. (47). We make the rotating-wave approximation and drop the anti-resonant term in (27). Considering only the steady-state solution of eq. (47) we find

$$\varrho_{ab} = -\frac{i\mathscr{P}}{2\hbar}\frac{E_n U_n(\boldsymbol{r})}{\gamma_{ab}+i(\omega-\nu_n)} N(\boldsymbol{r}) \exp[-i(\nu_n t+\varphi_n)] \tag{52}$$

for the excitation of the medium by the n-th field mode.

To check the approximation used in deriving eq. (52) we differentiate the solution and find

$$\dot{\varrho}_{ab} = -i\nu_n\varrho_{ab} - i\dot{\varphi}_n\varrho_{ab}\,.$$

Inserting back into eq. (47) we see that the approximation was to neglect $\dot{\varphi}_n$ in comparison to γ_{ab} which is about $10^7\,\mathrm{s}^{-1}$ for a gas maser.

The macroscopic polarization density is

$$P = \mathscr{P}(\varrho_{ab}+\varrho_{ab}^*)\,. \tag{53}$$

Using eq. (52) we find for the n-th spatial Fourier component of P

$$P_n = \frac{E_n\mathscr{P}^2}{2\hbar}\left\{\frac{-i\int N(\boldsymbol{r})\,[U_n(\boldsymbol{r})]^2\,\mathrm{d}\boldsymbol{r}}{\int[U_n(\boldsymbol{r})]^2\,\mathrm{d}\boldsymbol{r}}\frac{\exp[-i(\nu_n t+\varphi_n)]}{\gamma_{ab}+i(\omega-\nu_n)}+\text{c.c.}\right\}. \tag{54}$$

P_n has the form

$$P_n \propto -\frac{i\exp[-i\theta]}{\gamma+i\delta}+\text{c.c.} = -\frac{2\gamma}{\gamma^2+\delta^2}\sin\theta-\frac{2\delta}{\gamma^2+\delta^2}\cos\theta\,. \tag{55}$$

Introduce the definition

$$\bar{N}_n(t) = \int N(\boldsymbol{r},t)\,[U_n(\boldsymbol{r})]^2\,\mathrm{d}\boldsymbol{r}\Big/\int[U_n(\boldsymbol{r})]^2\,\mathrm{d}\boldsymbol{r}\,, \tag{56}$$

where $\bar{N}_n$ may depend upon time if the excitation process varies slowly in time. Comparing (54) with (11) we obtain;

$$C_n = -\frac{\mathscr{P}^2}{\hbar}\bar{N}_n E_n\frac{(\omega-\nu_n)}{\gamma_{ab}^2+(\omega-\nu_n)^2}\,, \tag{57}$$

$$S_n = -\frac{\mathscr{P}^2}{\hbar}\bar{N}_n E_n\frac{\gamma_{ab}}{\gamma_{ab}^2+(\omega-\nu_n)^2}\,. \tag{58}$$

Substituting into the amplitude eq. (12*b*), we find

$$\dot{E}_n = -\frac{1}{2}\frac{\nu}{Q_n}E_n + \frac{\nu}{2}\frac{\mathscr{P}^2}{\varepsilon_0\hbar}\bar{N}\gamma_{ab}\mathscr{L}(\omega-\nu_n)E_n\,, \tag{59}$$

where

$$\mathscr{L}(f) = \frac{1}{\gamma_{ab}^2 + f^2} \tag{60}$$

is a Lorentzian resonance function. We note that E_n will build up when the source prevails over the damping, that is when

$$\frac{\mathscr{P}^2}{\varepsilon_0\hbar}\mathscr{P}\gamma_{ab}\mathscr{L}(\omega-\nu_n) > \frac{1}{Q_n}\,. \tag{61}$$

We shall call threshold value of $\bar{N}$ the value $\bar{N}_T$ for which the l.h.s. of (61) equals $1/Q$ at resonance $\omega=\nu_n$. We have

$$\frac{\mathscr{P}^2}{\varepsilon_0\hbar}\frac{\bar{N}_T}{\gamma_{ab}} = \frac{1}{Q_n} \tag{62}$$

or, writing $\mathscr{P} = e\langle x\rangle$ and introducing the fine structure constant (in m.k.s. units)

$$\alpha = \frac{e^2}{4\pi\varepsilon_0\hbar c} = 1/137\,, \tag{63}$$

$$4\pi\alpha\bar{N}_T\langle x\rangle^2\frac{cQ_n}{\gamma_{ab}} = 1\,. \tag{64}$$

The left side is equal to the effective number of active atoms in a cylinder of base area $4\pi\alpha\langle x\rangle^2$ and height cQ_n/γ_{ab}.

Using also (57) in eq. (12*a*), the frequency equation becomes

$$\nu_n - \Omega_n = \frac{\mathscr{P}^2\nu}{2\varepsilon_0\hbar}\bar{N}_n\mathscr{L}(\omega-\nu_n)\cdot(\omega-\nu_n) \tag{65}$$

and using threshold condition (61)

$$\nu_n - \Omega_n = \frac{\nu}{Q_n\gamma_{ab}}(\omega-\nu_n) = \sigma(\omega-\nu_n)\,. \tag{66}$$

The r.h.s. is the pulling term which says how far the oscillation frequency is from the cavity eigenfrequency. σ is the ratio between the cavity band-width

ν/Q_n and the atom natural line-width γ_{ab} and is of the order of 1/10 to 1/100 for a gas maser. It has been called the « stabilization factor ».

From (66) we find

$$\nu_n = \frac{\Omega_n + \sigma\omega}{1+\sigma}\,, \tag{67}$$

which has an interpretation as a « center of mass ». It is seen that in this approximation the oscillator frequency depends linearly on the detuning $\Omega_n - \omega$. When $\sigma \ll 1$, we have $\nu_n \approx \Omega_n$. If several modes are above threshold, they will oscillate independently in this linear approximation.

5. – Nonlinear theory in rate-equation approximation.

Here we treat $\varrho_{aa} - \varrho_{bb}$ as slowly varying, but not necessarily equal to $N(\boldsymbol{r})$. From the matrix eq. (45), the diagonal component has a time-dependence

$$\dot{\varrho}_{aa} = -\gamma_a \varrho_{aa} + \lambda_a + iV(\varrho_{ab} - \varrho_{ba})\,. \tag{68}$$

As in the preceding Section, we look for a steady-state solution for ϱ_{ab}, but generalize for multi-mode operation. Then the perturbation V is

$$V = -\mathscr{P}\sum_{\sigma=1}^{M} E_\sigma(t)\, U_\sigma(\boldsymbol{r}) \cos\big(\nu_\sigma t + \varphi_\sigma(t)\big)\,, \tag{69}$$

where M = total number of modes excited. Using again the rotating-wave approximation

$$\varrho_{ab} = -i\frac{\mathscr{P}}{2\hbar}\sum_{\mu=1}^{M}\frac{E_\mu U_\mu(\boldsymbol{r})}{\gamma_{ab} + i(\omega - \nu_\mu)} \exp[-i(\nu_\mu t + \varphi_\mu)]\,(\varrho_{aa} - \varrho_{bb})\,. \tag{70}$$

Then

$$iV(\varrho_{ab} - \varrho^*_{ab}) = \left[-\frac{\mathscr{P}^2}{4\hbar}\sum_{\mu,\sigma}^{M}\frac{U_\sigma(\boldsymbol{r})\,U_\mu(\boldsymbol{r})\,E_\sigma E_\mu}{\gamma_{ab} + i(\omega - \nu_\mu)} \exp[i(\nu_\sigma - \nu_\mu)t + i(\varphi_\sigma - \varphi_\mu)] + \text{c.c.}\right]\cdot (\varrho_{aa} - \varrho_{bb})\,.$$

Inserting this into (68) yields equations which involve only diagonal components of ϱ, *i.e.*, « populations »:

$$\dot{\varrho}_{aa} = -\gamma_a \varrho_{aa} + \lambda_a + R(\varrho_{bb} - \varrho_{aa})\,, \tag{71a}$$

$$\dot{\varrho}_{bb} = -\gamma_b \varrho_{bb} + \lambda_b + R(\varrho_{aa} - \varrho_{bb})\,, \tag{71b}$$

with

$$R = \frac{\mathscr{P}^2}{4\hbar^2} \sum_\mu \sum_\sigma \frac{E_\mu E_\sigma U_\mu U_\sigma}{\gamma_{ab} + i(\omega - \nu_\mu)} \exp[i(\nu_\sigma - \nu_\mu)t] + \text{c.c.}\,. \tag{72}$$

Equations (71) have an intuitive appeal. The first two terms show the competition between decay and excitation whereas the last term causes a net rate of transition away from the more populated state ($R \geqslant 0$). We refer to (71) as rate equations. Note that the rate « constant » R contains components which pulsate at frequencies $(\nu_\sigma - \nu_\mu)$ when more than one e.m. mode is excited. Pulsations in R cause pulsations in ϱ_{aa} and ϱ_{bb} which might be detected, for example, by observing decay radiation from the lower maser level. These pulsations are also found in a more realistic treatment for the gas maser in which atomic motion is not neglected.

Important features of higher-order theory will be illustrated if we proceed to solve (71) for the steady-state populations while neglecting pulsating components of R. This is justified if $(\nu_\sigma - \nu_\mu) \gg \gamma_a$ or γ_b and for a typical gas maser the mode separation is perhaps 150 MHz while the natural line-width may correspond to ≈ 10 MHz. Neglecting pulsations

$$R = \left(\frac{\gamma_a \gamma_b}{2\gamma_{ab}}\right) \sum_\mu \left(\frac{\mathscr{P}^2 E_\mu^2}{2\hbar^2 \gamma_a \gamma_b}\right) (\gamma_{ab}^2 \mathscr{L}(\omega - \nu_\mu))\, U_\mu^2(\boldsymbol{r}) = \tag{73}$$

$$= 2R_s \sum_\mu I_\mu [\gamma_{ab}^2 \mathscr{L}(\omega - \nu_\mu)]\, U_\mu^2(\boldsymbol{r})$$

and from (71) for a steady state

$$(\varrho_{aa} - \varrho_{bb}) = \frac{(\lambda_a/\gamma_a - \lambda_b/\gamma_b)}{1 + R/(\gamma_a \gamma_b/2\gamma_{ab})} = \frac{N(\boldsymbol{r})}{1 + (R/R_s)} \tag{74}$$

after some algebra.

We have introduced I_μ as a dimensionless measure of the intensity of mode μ, and a quantity R_s with dimensions of a rate characterizing saturation. When $R = R_s = (1/\gamma_a + 1/\gamma_b)^{-1}$, the population difference is reduced to one half the value it would have in the absence of electromagnetic fields.

Since R has a spatial dependence through the factor $(U_\mu^2(\boldsymbol{r})$ so does $(\varrho_{aa} - \varrho_{bb})$. In a gas maser such striations would be partly washed out since atoms move through several optical wavelengths in a decay time.

Let us now proceed to calculate the induced polarization P to higher accuracy (neglecting pulsations). Insert (74) into (70) to find

$$\varrho_{ab} = -i \left(\frac{N(\boldsymbol{r})}{1 + (R/R_s)}\right) \frac{\mathscr{P}}{2\hbar} \sum_\mu \frac{E_\mu U_\mu(\boldsymbol{r}) \exp[-i(\nu_\mu t + \varphi_\mu)]}{\gamma_{ab} + i(\omega - \nu_\mu)}\,. \tag{75}$$

Then repeating the steps leading to (54) we have only to insert

$$N(\boldsymbol{r})[1+(R/R_s)]^{-1} \qquad \text{in place of } N(\boldsymbol{r}).$$

Instead of $\bar{N}_n$ (eq. (56)) we will have the more complicated quantity

$$\bar{N}'_n = \int \frac{U_n^2 N(\boldsymbol{r})}{1+(R/R_s)}\, \mathrm{d}\boldsymbol{r} \Big/ \int U_n^2(\boldsymbol{r})\, \mathrm{d}\boldsymbol{r}\,. \tag{76}$$

Now $\bar{N}'_n$ depends upon the mode intensities and frequencies.

5·1 *Single mode excited.* – To make further progress let us first suppose only one mode (n-th) weakly excited, *i.e.*, $R/R_s \ll 1$. The integrand in $\bar{N}'_n$ is expanded to first order in I_n as

$$\bar{N}'_n = \int N(\boldsymbol{r})\, U_n^2(\boldsymbol{r})[1 - I_n \gamma_{ab}^2 \mathscr{L}(\omega - \nu_n)\, U_n^2(\boldsymbol{r})]\, \mathrm{d}\boldsymbol{r} \Big/ \int U_n^2(\boldsymbol{r})\, \mathrm{d}\boldsymbol{r}\,. \tag{77}$$

To simplify the problem even further take $U_n \propto \sin kz$ and suppose that $N(r)$ varies slowly on the scale of an optical wavelength. Then

$$\bar{N}'_n \simeq \bar{N}[1 - \tfrac{3}{4} I_n \gamma_{ab}^2 \mathscr{L}(\omega - \nu_n)] \simeq \bar{N} \mathscr{L}^{-1}(\omega - \nu_n)[(\omega-\nu_n)^2 + \gamma_{ab}^2(1+\tfrac{3}{4}I_n)]^{-1}\,. \tag{78}$$

Entering $\bar{N}'_n$ into (58) yields

$$S_n = -\mathscr{P} \frac{\mathscr{P} E_n}{\hbar \gamma_{ab}} \bar{N} \gamma_{ab}^2 \left[(\omega - \nu_n)^2 + \gamma_{ab}^2 \left(1 + \frac{3}{4} I_n\right)\right]^{-1}\,. \tag{79}$$

We see that S_n at resonance is decreased by the factor $(1+\frac{3}{4}I_n)^{-1}$ while the effective width parameter in the resonance denominator is increased to $(1+\frac{3}{4}I_n)^{\frac{1}{2}}\gamma_{ab}$.

The threshold condition is given, of course, by the first-order calculation but now we are in a position to obtain the steady-state running condition from the higher-order calculation. Power saturation limits the gain to prevent the exponential runaway predicted by the first-order calculation. Entering S_n from (79) into the amplitude eq. (12b), using the definition (62) we obtain the condition for steady state (with $\dot{E}_n = 0$):

$$I_n = \tfrac{4}{3}[(\bar{N}/\bar{N}_T) - 1 - \{(\omega-\nu_n)^2/\gamma_{ab}^2\}]\,, \tag{80}$$

so that at resonance the dimensionless intensity of oscillation parameter is given by

$$I_n = \frac{4}{3}\left(\frac{\bar{N}}{\bar{N}_T} - 1\right). \tag{81}$$

Since our approximations require $I_n \ll 1$, (81) holds if $\bar{N}$ does not too greatly exceed the threshold value $\bar{N}_T$.

It is possible to evaluate (77) with more precision, but we will not do it here.

5·2 *Multimode excitation.* – Additional interesting features of maser operation will be obtained when we consider what happens when the excitation exceeds threshold for several modes. Different modes compete. They may oscillate simultaneously or under other conditions the stronger oscillation may quench the weaker.

Proceeding as before we evaluate the integral for $\bar{N}'_n$ of equation (76) in a power series and insert into (58). Then

$$S_n = S_n^{(1)} + S_n^{(3)} + \dots . \tag{82}$$

Now in addition to terms occurring in the single mode third-order theory (terms $\propto E_n$ and E_n^3) there are cross-terms proportional to $E_n E_\mu^2$ in $S_n^{(3)}$

$$S_n^{(3)} = \mathscr{P}\left(\frac{\mathscr{P}E_n}{\hbar\gamma_{ab}}\right)(\gamma_{ab}^2\,\mathscr{L}(\omega-\nu_n))\sum_\mu \frac{\mathscr{P}^2E_\mu^2}{\hbar^2\gamma_a\gamma_b}\gamma_{ab}^2\,\mathscr{L}(\omega-\nu_\mu)\cdot \cdot\int N(\boldsymbol{r})\,U_n^2\,U_\mu^2\,\mathrm{d}\boldsymbol{r}\Big/\int U_n^2\,\mathrm{d}\boldsymbol{r}\,. \tag{83}$$

When $S_n = S_n^{(1)} + S_n^{(3)}$ is introduced into the amplitude equations we obtain a coupled set of the form

$$\dot{E}_n = \alpha_n E_n - \beta_n E_n^3 - \sum_{\mu\neq n}\theta_{\mu n} E_n E_\mu^2\,, \tag{84}$$

with

$$\alpha_n = -(\nu/2Q_n) + \frac{\nu\mathscr{P}^2}{2\varepsilon_0\hbar\gamma_{ab}}\bar{N}\gamma_{ab}^2\,\mathscr{L}(\omega-\nu_n) \tag{85}$$

from the linear approximation

$$\beta_n = \frac{\mathscr{P}^4\gamma_{ab}^3}{\hbar^3\gamma_a\gamma_b}\mathscr{L}^2(\omega-\nu_n)\frac{3}{4}\bar{N}\frac{\nu}{2\varepsilon_0} \tag{86}$$

from the single-mode third-order result and

$$\theta_{n\mu} = \frac{\nu}{2\varepsilon_0}\frac{\mathscr{P}^4\gamma_{ab}^3}{\hbar^3\gamma_a\gamma_b}\mathscr{L}(\omega-\nu_n)\,\mathscr{L}(\omega-\nu_\mu)\left(\frac{\bar{N}}{2}+\frac{N_{2(n-\mu)}}{4}\right) \tag{87}$$

including mode-coupling effects to lowest order, where we have made simplifying assumptions as before. The coupling coefficients $\theta_{n\mu}$, $n \neq \mu$ depend upon space integrals

$$N_{2(n-\mu)} = \int N(r)\, U_n^2\, U_\mu^2\, \mathrm{d}\mathbf{r} \Big/ \int U_n^2\, \mathrm{d}\mathbf{r}\,. \tag{88}$$

If $U_n = \sin k_n z$

$$N_{2(n-\mu)} \simeq \frac{1}{L}\int_0^L N(z)\cos 2(n-\mu)\frac{\pi z}{L}\,\mathrm{d}z\,, \tag{89}$$

where we again assume that $N(z)$ varies slowly over an optical wavelength. Note that $N_0 = \bar{N}$. As we shall see $\theta_{\mu\nu}$ are important parameters determining the behavior of the maser oscillator.

Now assume that only two adjacent modes are above threshold. Then the amplitude equations reduce to

$$\dot{E}_1 = \alpha_1 E_1 - \beta_1 E_1^3 - \theta E_1 E_2^2\,, \qquad \dot{E}_2 = \alpha_2 E_2 - \beta_2 E_2^3 - \theta E_2 E_1^2\,, \tag{90}$$

where

$$\theta = \theta_{12} = \theta_{21}\,. \tag{91}$$

Let $x = E_1^2$, $y = E_2^2$. Then (90) assume the form

$$\tfrac{1}{2}\dot{x} = (\alpha_1 - \beta_1 x - \theta y)x\,, \qquad \tfrac{1}{2}\dot{y} = (\alpha_2 - \theta x - \beta_2 y)y\,, \tag{92}$$

of a pair of coupled nonlinear differential equations.

A steady-state solution $\dot{x} = \dot{y} = 0$ is obtained at four points of the x-y phase-plane. These points are singular points for the characteristic curves $y(x)$ because the slope $\mathrm{d}y/\mathrm{d}x$ is indeterminant. The singular points are:

$$\left\{\begin{array}{lllll} 1) & y = 0\,, & x = \alpha_1/\beta_1\,, & & \text{if } \alpha_1 > 0\,, \\ 2) & x = 0\,, & y = \alpha_2/\beta_2\,, & & \text{if } \alpha_2 > 0\,, \\ 3) & \left\{\begin{array}{l} \alpha_1 = \beta_1 x + \theta y \\ \alpha_2 = \theta x + \beta_2 y \end{array}\right. & \begin{array}{l} L_1\,, \\ L_2\,, \end{array} & & \\ 4) & x = y = 0\,. & & & \end{array}\right. \tag{93}$$

The state 4) is certainly unstable for any set of parameters above the threshold for oscillation. State 3) is a real solution provided the straight lines L_1 and L_2 intersect in the first quadrant. States 1) and 2) correspond to single-mode oscillation on modes 1 and 2, respectively.

The stability of the steady-state solutions of the differential eq. (92) may be conveniently studied by considering diagrams drawn in the x-y plane. The method originated with Poincaré and is applicable to many non linear differential equations. Any state of oscillation is described by a point x, y in the phase-plane. For each initial condition $x(0)$, $y(0)$ the state of the system evolves along a phase-curve $y(x)$ passing through $x(0)$, $y(0)$. Consider first the case of « weak coupling » for which $\beta_1\beta_2 < \theta^2$. The straight lines L_1 and L_2 might then be as shown in Fig. 2. By combining eq. (92) we find that the slope of $y(x)$ is given by

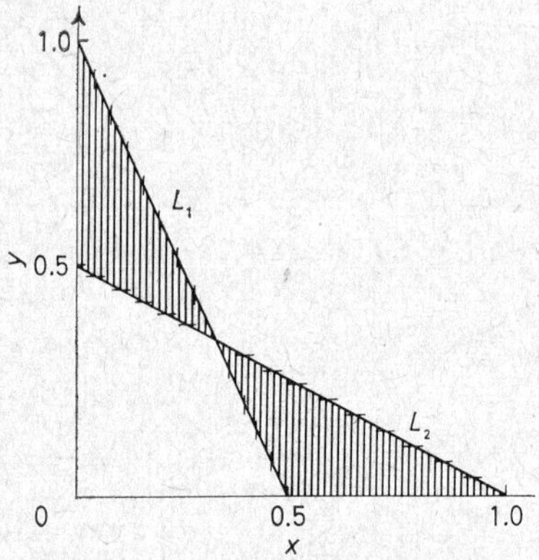

Fig. 2. – Diagram showing typical lines L_1 and L_2 of eq. (93) for the case of « weak » coupling. For illustrative purposes, the following values of parameters were assumed: $\alpha_1=\alpha_2=1$, $\beta_1=\beta_2=2$ and $\theta=1$. The slope of a phase-curve is negative in the shaded regions, zero when it crosses line L_2, infinite when it crosses line L_1 and positive in the unshaded regions.

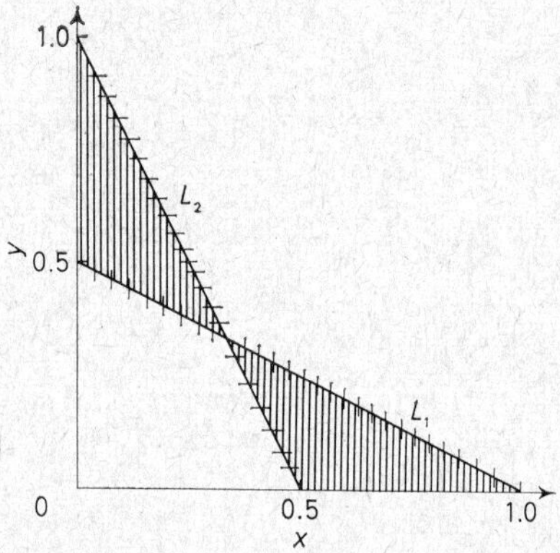

Fig. 3. – Diagram showing typical lines L_1 and L_2 similar to that of Fig. 2, but for the case of « strong » coupling. The following parameters were assumed: $\alpha_1=\alpha_2=1$ $\beta_1=\beta_2=1$, $\theta=2$.

$$\frac{\mathrm{d}y}{\mathrm{d}x}=\frac{\dot{y}}{\dot{x}}=\frac{y\,(\alpha_2-\theta x-\beta_2 y)}{x\,(\alpha_1-\beta_1 x-\theta y)}\,. \tag{94}$$

The slope is zero if a phase-curve ever crosses line L_2 and infinite if it crosses line L_1. These slopes are indicated in the diagram by short horizontal and vertical line segments. Furthermore in the shaded regions the slope of the phase-curve is negative, while it is positive in the unshaded region. Phase curves, of course, never cross each other away from singular points. The corresponding diagram for the case of « strong coupling » is given in Fig. 3. The above considerations serve to make possible a full qualitative understanding of the transient behavior of the oscillations.

The phase curves can, of course, be calculated by machine integration of the differential equations. Families of phase curves, so obtained are shown in

Fig. 4 and 5 for the weak-coupling case and in Fig. 6 for strong coupling. In Fig 4, all but an infinitesimal fraction of the phase curves lead to singular point 3). In Fig. 5, the two straight lines do not intersect in the first quadrant, and all phase curves lead to the singular point 1). No matter where one starts the system it will evolve toward the stable point at 3) in the course of time.

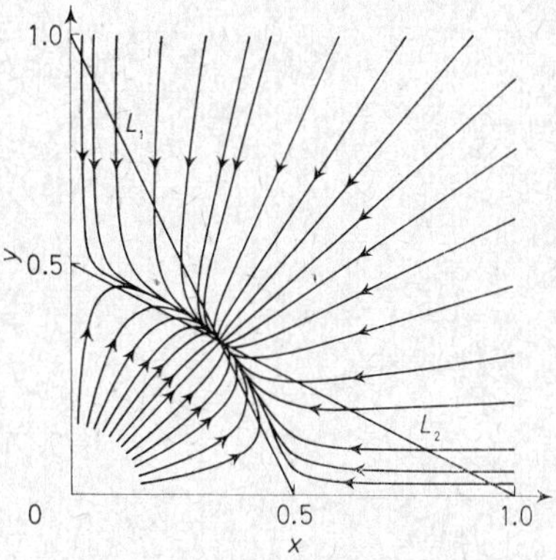

Fig. 4. – Phase curves for the case of Fig. 2 for a case where both modes are well above threshold.

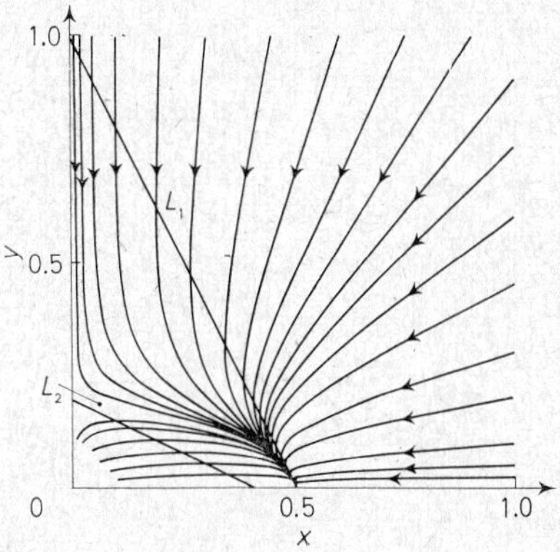

Fig. 5. – Phase curves for the case of Fig. 2 for a case where the gain parameter α_2 of the second modes has been reduced to $+0.4$. The lines L_1 and L_2 do not intersect in the first quadrant and the dominant mode inhibits oscillation in the second mode.

In the strong-coupling case (Fig. 6) the system behaves differently, and its state moves toward 1) and 2) depending upon the location of the initial point.

We remark in passing that VAN DER POL has considered a related problem. He treated a vacuum tube oscillator with two tank circuits, tuned to ν_1 and ν_2. For his feedback amplifier he assumed the i-v characteristic

$$i = -av + bv^3 .$$

Suppose

$$V = E_1 \cos \nu_1 t + E_2 \cos \nu_2 t ,$$

then, neglecting terms which oscillate at

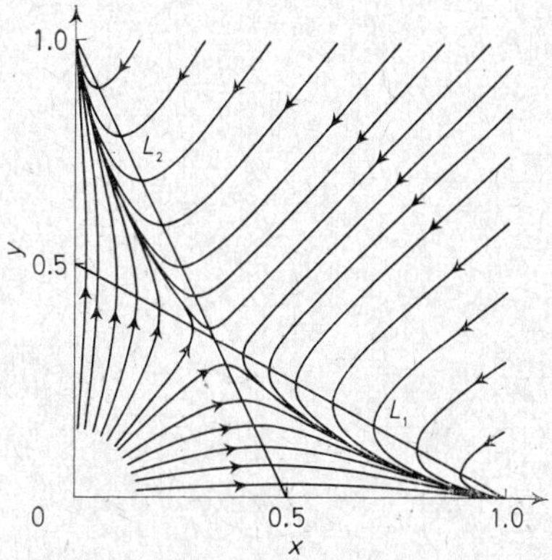

Fig. 6. – Phase curves for the case of Fig. 3, where all phase curves lead to one or the other of the single-mode operating points.

frequencies other than ν_1 or ν_2,

$$V^3 \simeq \tfrac{3}{4}(E_1^3 + 2E_1E_2^2)\cos\nu_1 t + \tfrac{3}{4}(E_2^3 + 2E_2E_1^2)\cos\nu_2 t \,.$$

Inserting V^3 into $i(v)$ we find and equation like (90) with $\theta = 2\beta_1 = 2\beta_2$. Since $\beta_1\beta_2 = \theta^2/4 < \theta^2$, VAN DER POL's case corresponds to strong coupling; the system oscillates in one or another mode but not in both at once. Such a bistable system can display hysteresis as its parameters are slowly varied back and forth.

Coming back to the maser one expects similar behavior. We find however that with parameters most usual in gas masers the coupling is « weak » implying multimode operation, a common occurrence, difficult to avoid in practice.

A degenerate case occurs when $\beta_1\beta_2 = \theta^2$. The loci L_1 and L_2 are either parallel or coincident. The mode of operation would of course be very sensitive to changes in external parameters but we shall not dwell upon this further.

5˙3. *Power Pushing and mode interaction.* – The set (90) determines the steady-state intensities E_1^2 and E_2^2 as functions of ω, Ω_1, Ω_2, $\bar{N}$, N_2, Q_1, Q_2, γ_a, γ_b, $\mathscr{P}$ and perhaps past history. Having otained E_1 and E_2 the result might be inserted in the « frequency equations » to yield formulae of form

$$\nu_1 = \Omega_1 + \sigma_1 + \varrho_1 E_1^2 + \tau_{12}E_2^2\,, \qquad \nu_2 = \Omega_2 + \sigma_2 + \varrho_2 E_2^2 + \tau_{21}E_1^2\,.$$

The second terms on the right imply pulling already deduced from the linear approximation. The third terms imply what might be called a power « pushing ». The maser frequency in the mode depends slightly upon its power level and may be raised or lowered depending on the numerical parameters. The last term implies a mode interaction which we find is usually attractive.

6. – Moving atoms.

We shall now attempt to outline changes in the foregoing approach which are necessary if (as in a gas maser) atoms move through many optical wavelengths in a decay time. Collisions will be neglected so that the atoms move uniformly with their initial velocity.

As a first attempt one might define a nonlinear susceptibility:

$$\chi(\omega - \nu_n, E_n) = P_n/\varepsilon_0 E_n \,. \tag{96}$$

A group of atoms moving with velocity v through an optical running wave sees a Doppler-shifted frequency $\nu_n \to \nu_n(1 - v/c)$ so one is tempted to define an effective susceptibility as an integral over the velocity distribution $W(v)$:

$$\chi_{\text{eff}} = \int \mathrm{d}v\, W(x)\, \chi\left(\omega - \omega\frac{v}{c} - \nu_n,\, E_n\right). \tag{97}$$

This is, in fact, correct only for a linear theory or more generally for running waves.

A better, though still approximate, approach is the following. Consider atoms excited in a or b in a small region at z_0, at time t_0 with velocity v_0. At later time t this group is located at $z = z_0 + v(t - t_0)$ if deflecting collisions are neglected.

The perturbation « seen » by this group of atoms is

$$V(z_0, t, t_0, v) = -\frac{\mathscr{P}}{\hbar}\sum_{\mu=1}^{M} E_\mu\, U_\mu(z_0 + v(t - t_0))\cos(\nu t + \varphi)\,. \tag{98}$$

If, as we will now assume, $U_\mu \propto \sin k_\mu z$, the atom sees fields oscillating at $\nu_\mu \pm k_\mu v$. Now, unfortunately, the important simplification which followed from the introduction of $\varrho(t)$ is denied us since we can no longer derive eq. (43). We must retreat to (34), solve for $\varrho(a, t_0, t, z_0, v)$ directly and then find $\varrho(a, t)$ from its definition with summation over (z_0, v) groups as well. We proceed first with an approximate calculation (case a) no dependence on z_0 and t_0). Then we consider the more general case (case b) introducing dependence on z_0 and t_0).

a) *No dependence on* z_0 *and* t_0. – We propose to try to get around the above-mentioned complications by making certain modifications in the perturbation acting on the atoms, and also by changing the nature of the atoms. This procedure has certain pedagogical advantages, but the approximations are difficult to control and there is no real substitute for the accurate calculation of case b).

The first step is to replace $U_\mu(z_0 + vt - t_0)$ in (98) by $U_\mu(z)\cos kvt$. In this modification of the interaction energy we have kept the right spectral distribution, but not the correct phase relationships. Having thereby freed ourselves of the t_0-dependence of the Hamiltonian we can use a density matrix for the ensemble of all atoms of velocity v which were excited at $t_0 \geqslant t$. By z, we presumably mean the location of the atoms at the time of interest.

We are then able to derive rate equations (71) with a rate constant like (72), but due to the doubling of the number of frequencies acting on the atoms, there will now be pulsations in R at frequency $2kv$ as well as at frequencies $\nu_0 - \nu_\mu$. The pulsations in R will lead to pulsations in populations $\varrho_{aa} - \varrho_{bb}$ of the moving atoms. Due to our careless bookkeeping, it is not clear whether the pulsations at $2kv$ will also occur for populations referred to a fixed point in the cavity. (In fact, a more careful calculation along the lines used in case b) shows that there are no such pulsations.) Neglecting both spurious and real pulsations, we obtain in generalization of (73)

$$R(z, v) = R_s \sum_\mu I_\mu \gamma_{ab}^2 \{\mathscr{L}(\omega - \nu_\mu - kv) + \mathscr{L}(\omega - \nu_\mu + kv)\} U_\mu^2(z) \,. \tag{99}$$

Proceeding exactly as before, we set

$$\lambda_\alpha(z, v, t) = \Lambda_\alpha(z, t)\, W(v) \,, \tag{100}$$

and find instead of (74)

$$\varrho_{aa}(z, v) - \varrho_{bb}(z, v) = \frac{W(v)\, N(z)}{1 + R(z, v)/R_s} \tag{101}$$

for the population inversion of the group of atoms at z which have velocity v.

Here we encounter an interesting effect, which has been the object of much qualitative discussion. The rate $R(z, v)$ has maxima for velocities v such that $(\omega - \nu_\mu \pm kv) = 0$, as we see from (99). According to (101) the active medium will be slightly deficient in inverted atoms moving with these velocities v. One might refer to « holes » burnt in the velocity distribution. It is particularly important to notice that the holes have a width $\Delta v \simeq \gamma_{ab}/k$, *i.e.*, determined by the *natural* width of the maser transition. When ν_μ coincides with the atomic resonance frequency ω, these holes coalesce at $v = 0$ making a deeper hole.

We now wish to calculate the polarization $P(z, t)$ due to the moving atoms. One might think that because the perturbation seen by them contains frequencies $\nu_\mu \pm kv$ the polarization would also contain these frequencies. It is clear, however, from very general considerations that this cannot be the case. In fact, since the atoms are moving, the coherent radiation emitted by them is Doppler-shifted so that the frequencies produced in the rest frame of the cavity are just the ν_μ (and combination tones of them). To avoid these complications, in our model we bring the atoms with velocity v to rest, and assume that as compensation for their lost motion half of them have their atomic resonance frequency ω shifted to $\omega + kv$, and half to $\omega - kv$ (because of the standing wave). The atoms then all see the unshifted frequencies ν_μ. Equation (75) for ϱ_{ab} is replaced by

$$\varrho_{ab}(z, v, t) = -\frac{i}{2} \frac{N(z)\, W(v)}{1 + R(z, v)/R_s} \frac{\mathscr{P}}{2\hbar} \cdot \sum_\mu E_\mu U_\mu(z) \exp[-i(\nu_\mu t + \varphi_\mu)][D(\omega - kv - \nu_\mu) + D(\omega - kv - \nu_\mu)] \,, \tag{102}$$

where

$$D(\omega) = 1/(\gamma_{ab} + i\omega) \,. \tag{103}$$

From (102) we may calculate $P(z, t)$ and $P_n(t)$ by integrations over v and z respectively.

We now limit ourselves to single-mode oscillation and assume that $W(v)$ is an even function of v. Instead of (58), we find

$$S_n = \int_0^L dz \int_{-\infty}^{\infty} dv [U_n(z)]^2 \frac{N(z)\, W(v)}{1 + R(z, v)/R_s} \frac{\mathscr{P}^2 E_n \mathscr{L}(\omega - kv - \nu_\mu)}{\hbar\gamma_{ab} \int_0^L [U_n(z)]^2 dz} . \tag{104}$$

We further suppose that $W(v)$ varies slowly compared to the Lorentzian factor, and take it outside the integral as $W((\omega - \nu_\mu)/k)$. We also expand the denominator of (104) to first order in saturation effects. The space integrals appearing are

$$\int_0^L dz\, U_n^2 = \frac{L}{2}$$

and

$$\int_0^L dz\, U_n^4 = \frac{3L}{8} . \tag{105}$$

The velocity integrals which appear are easily evaluated using Cauchy's theorem:

$$\int_{-\infty}^{\infty} dv\, \gamma_{ab}^2 \mathscr{L}(kv) = \pi\gamma_{ab}/k$$

and

$$\int_{-\infty}^{\infty} dv\, \gamma_{ab}^4 \mathscr{L}(kv - A) \mathscr{L}(kv - B) = \frac{\pi\gamma_{ab}}{2k} \mathscr{L}\left(\frac{A - B}{2}\right) . \tag{106}$$

We find

$$S_n = -\bar{N}\mathscr{P}\left(\frac{\mathscr{P}E_n}{\hbar\gamma_{ab}}\right)\frac{\pi\gamma_{ab}}{k} W\left(\frac{\omega - \nu_\mu}{k}\right) \cdot \left[1 - \frac{3}{16} I_n \cdot (1 + \gamma_{ab}^2 \mathscr{L}(\omega - \nu_n))\right] . \tag{107}$$

For a Maxwellian velocity distribution, we have

$$W(v) = \frac{1}{\sqrt{\pi}\,\mu} \exp[-v^2/u^2] , \qquad u^2 = 2\langle v^2 \rangle_{av} . \tag{108}$$

Let us introduce the threshold excitation density

$$\bar{N}_T = (\varepsilon_0 \hbar k u)/(Q_n \mathscr{P}^2 \sqrt{\pi}) . \tag{109}$$

(Note the change from eq. (62)). Then

$$(110)\quad S_n = -\frac{\varepsilon_0}{Q_n}\frac{\bar N}{\bar N_T}E_n \exp[-(\omega-\nu_n)^2/(ku)^2]\cdot \left[1-\frac{3}{16}I_n(1+\gamma_{ab}^2\mathscr{L}(\omega-\nu_n))\right].$$

From the amplitude eq. (12*b*) we find that the condition for a steady state ($\dot E_n = 0$) is that the dimensionless intensity or saturation parameter should be given by

$$(111)\quad I_n = \frac{16}{3}\left[1-\frac{\bar N_T}{\bar N}\cdot \exp[+(\omega-\nu_n)^2/(ku)^2]\right]\Big/[1+\gamma_{ab}^2\mathscr{L}(\omega-\nu_n)]$$

for $I_n > 0$. When $\omega=\nu_n$ and $\bar N = \bar N_T$, oscillations begin. A typical dependence of output on cavity tuning is shown in Fig. 7. Observe that the factor $(1+\gamma_{ab}^2\mathscr{L}(\omega-\nu_n))$ in the denominator produces flattening or even a dip in the power output curve. For values of $\bar N/\bar N_T > 1+2(\gamma_{ab}/ku)^2$ a double maximum should be observed. Such a dip has been recently observed by McFarlane *et al.*, and by Javan and Szöke.

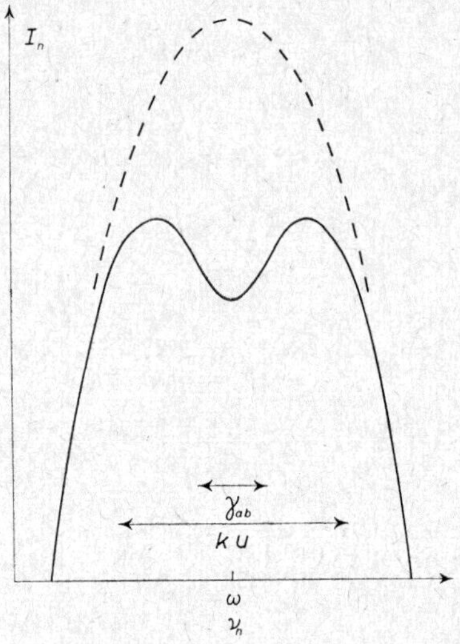

Fig. 7. – Relative intensity of oscillations as a function of detuning. The solid curve, drawn for parameters $\bar N = 2\bar N_T$ and $ku = 4\gamma_{ab}$ represents eq. (111). The dotted curve indicates the Doppler-gain profile of the numerator of (111).

b) Correct treatment with velocity. – In the treatment just presented we introduced random atomic velocities in an approximate way. The nature of the approximation was not even made clear. I shall now outline the more honest calculation which will appear in a forthcoming issue of the Physical Review and try to summarize the results where they differ from the simpler treatment.

We must revert to the elementary matrices $\varrho(a, z_0, t_0, v, t)$ which satisfy the initial condition $\varrho(a, z_0, t_0, v, t_0) = \varrho(a)$ and thereafter satisfy the equation of motion

$$(112)\qquad \dot\varrho = -i(H\varrho - \varrho H) - \tfrac{1}{2}(\Gamma\varrho + \varrho\Gamma),$$

$$(113)\qquad V = V(t, z_0, t_0) = \sum_n \mathscr{P}\, U_n(z_0 + v(t-t_0))E_n(t).$$

From $\varrho(a, z_0, t_0, v, t)$ we can calculate density matrices for any mixture. Thus if we are interested in those atoms near z with velocity v at time t, we sum over all times t_0 and all places z_0 of production such that

$$z = z_0 + v(t - t_0)\,,$$

$$(114)\qquad \varrho(a, z, v, t) = \int_{-\infty}^{t} \mathrm{d}t_0 \int \mathrm{d}z_0\, \lambda_a(z_0, v, t_0)\, \varrho(a, z_0, t_0, v, t)\, \delta\big(z - z_0 - v(t - t_0)\big)\,.$$

We now neglect the difference between $\lambda_a(z_0, v, t_0)$ and $\lambda_a(z, v, t)$ and perform the integration over $\mathrm{d}z_0$:

$$(115)\qquad \varrho(a, z, v, t) = \int_{-\infty}^{t} \mathrm{d}t_0\, \lambda_a(z, v, t_0)\, \varrho(a, z_0 \to z - vt + vt_0, t_0, v, t)\,.$$

An atom, initially at z_0 and with velocity v, sees a field at t'

$$E(z \to z_0 + vt' - vt_0, t')\,.$$

But, in the above mixture, we are considering the group of atoms for which $z_0 = z - vt + vt_0$, so that the electric field seen at t' is

$$E(z \to z + vt' - vt, t')\,,$$

independent of t_0. We proceed now to calculate $\varrho(a, z_0, t_0, v, t)$ using the equation of motion (49), which yields for off-diagonal and diagonal components equations of the type

$$(116)\qquad \begin{cases} \dot{\varrho}_{ab} = -i\omega\varrho_{ab} - \gamma_{ab}\varrho_{ab} + iV(t)\,(\varrho_{aa} - \varrho_{bb})\,, \\ \dot{\varrho}_{aa} = -\gamma_a\varrho_{aa} + iV(t)\,(\varrho_{ab} + \varrho_{ba})\,. \end{cases}$$

At $t = t_0$, $\varrho_{aa} = 1$ and the other components are zero.
For $t = t_0$, we shall solve in orders of V:

$$(117)\qquad \varrho_{aa} = \varrho_{aa}^{(0)} + \varrho_{aa}^{(2)} + \dots\,, \qquad \varrho_{ab} = \varrho_{ab}^{(1)} + \varrho_{ab}^{(3)} + \dots \text{ etc}\,.$$

One can easily calculate the various terms from eq. (115)

$$(118)\qquad \varrho_{aa}^{(0)} = \exp\left[-\gamma_a(t - t_0)\right],$$

$$(119)\qquad \varrho_{ab}^{(1)}(a, z_0, t_0, v, t) = i\int_{t_0}^{t} \mathrm{d}t'\, V(t') \exp\left[(\gamma_{ab} + i\omega)(t' - t)\right] \exp\left[\gamma(t_0 - t')\right],$$

$$(120)\qquad \varrho_{ab}^{(2)}(a, z_0, t_0, v, t) = -\int_{t_0}^{t} \mathrm{d}t' \int_{t_0}^{t'} \mathrm{d}t''\, V(t')\, V(t'')\cdot$$
$$\cdot \exp\left[\gamma_a(t' - t) + (\gamma_{ab} + i\omega)(t'' - t') + \gamma_a(t_0 - t'')\right] + \text{c.c.}\,,$$

with an analogous equation for $\varrho_{bb}^{(2)}$. We could iterate the process for higher orders.

7. – First-order approximation.

Let us first stop the calculation with $\varrho_{ab}^{(1)}(a, z_0, t_0, v, t)$. We introduce this into (115) and replace $\lambda_a(z, v, t_0)$ by $\lambda_a(z, v, t)$, to obtain integrals of the form

$$\int_{-\infty}^{t} \mathrm{d}t_0 \int_{t_0}^{t} \mathrm{d}t' \mathscr{F}(t, t') \exp[\gamma_a(t_0 - t')] .$$

The integration is over the region $A_\infty B C_\infty$ sketched in Fig. 8.

We can interchange the order of integration and obtain

$$(121) \qquad \int_{-\infty}^{t} \mathrm{d}t' \int_{-\infty}^{t'} \mathrm{d}t_0 \mathscr{F}(t, t') \exp[\gamma_a(t_0 - t')] = \frac{1}{\gamma_a} \int_{-\infty}^{t} \mathrm{d}t' \mathscr{F}(t, t') .$$

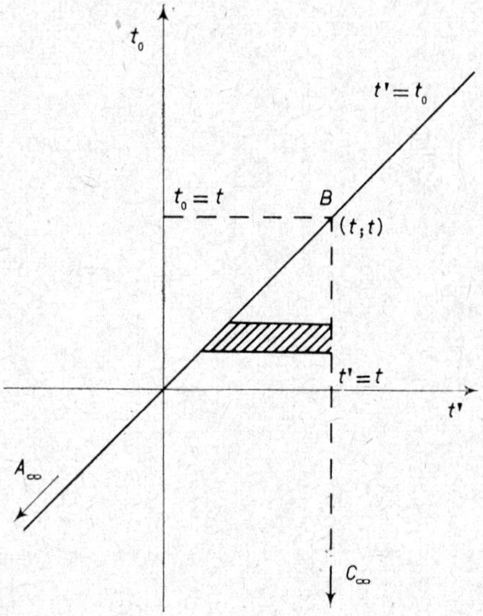

Fig. 8. – Diagram indicating the region of integration over the t_0, t' plane involved in the steps leading to eq. (121).

In this way one finds

$$(122) \qquad \varrho_{ab}^{(1)}(a, z, v, t) = -\frac{1}{2} i \left(\frac{\mathscr{P}}{\hbar}\right) \frac{\lambda_a(z, v, t)}{\gamma_a} \cdot$$

$$\cdot \sum_{\mu=1}^{M} \int_{-\infty}^{t} \mathrm{d}t' E_\mu(t') U_\mu(z - vt + vt') \exp[-i(\nu_\mu t + \varphi_\mu(t'))] \exp[-\gamma_{ab} + i(\nu_\mu - \omega)](t - t') .$$

Now, since E_μ and φ_μ are slowly varying, we may replace $E_\mu(t')$ by $E_\mu(t)$ and $\varphi_\mu(t')$ by $\varphi_\mu(t)$.

The excitation of state b has also to be considered in a similar manner. Then the first-order polarization will be, using (122) and (35),

$$(123) \qquad P^{(1)}(z, v, t) = -\frac{i}{2} \left(\frac{\mathscr{P}}{\hbar}\right)^2 \left[\frac{\lambda_a(z, v, t)}{\gamma_a} - \frac{\lambda_b(z, v, t)}{\gamma_b}\right] \cdot$$

$$\cdot \sum_{\mu} E_\mu(t) \left[\exp[-i(\nu_\mu t + \varphi_\mu)] \int_0^\infty \mathrm{d}\tau' U_\mu(z - v\tau') \exp[-[\gamma_{ab} + i(\omega - \nu_\mu)]\tau'] + \text{c.c.}\right] ,$$

where $\tau' = t - t'$.

Then the n-th spatial Fourier component of the polarization is

$$P_n^{(1)}(v, t) = \frac{2}{L}\int_0^L \mathrm{d}z\, P^{(1)}(z, v, t) \sin k_n z \,. \tag{124}$$

We now average $P_n^{(1)}(v, t)$ over the velocity distribution.

Take $\lambda_\alpha(z, v, t) = W(v)\Lambda_\alpha(z, t)$, and then introduce the « excitation density »

$$N(z, t) = \frac{\Lambda_a}{\gamma_a} - \frac{\Lambda_b}{\gamma_b} \,. \tag{125}$$

In the integral we have

$$\sin k_n z \sin k_\mu (z - v\tau') = \tfrac{1}{2} \cos\{(k_n - k_\mu)z + k_\mu v\tau'\} - \tfrac{1}{2}\cos\{(k_n + k_\mu)z - k_\mu v\tau'\} \,.$$

The last term will not contribute to the z-integration because the excitation density $N(z, t)$ changes little in an optical frequency wavelength. Since the velocity distribution is an even function of v only that part of the first term which is even in v will contribute to the polarization, *i.e.*,

$$\tfrac{1}{2}\cos(k_n - k_\mu)z \cdot \cos kv\tau' \,,$$

where the subscript μ has been dropped in the last factor since all of the modes considered have very nearly the same wave number $k = \nu/c$.

We find, for a Boltzmann distribution $W(v) = (1/\sqrt{\pi}\, u) \exp[-v^2/u^2]$,

$$P_n^{(1)}(t) = \frac{i}{2}\frac{\mathscr{P}^2}{\hbar}\sum_\mu E_\mu \exp[-i(\nu_\mu t + \varphi_\mu)]\, N_{n-\mu}(t)) \cdot \tag{126}$$

$$\cdot \int_{-\infty}^{+\infty} \mathrm{d}v\, W(v) \frac{1}{\gamma_{ab} + i(\omega - \nu_\mu + kv)} + \text{c.c.} =$$

$$= -\frac{\mathscr{P}^2}{2\hbar k u}\left[\sum_\mu E_\mu \exp[-i(\nu_\mu t + \varphi_\mu)]\, N_{n-\mu}(t)\, Z(\nu_\mu - \omega) + \text{c.c.}\right],$$

where

$$N_{n-\mu}(t) = \frac{1}{L}\int_0^L \mathrm{d}z\, N(z, t) \cos(n - \mu)\frac{\pi z}{L} \tag{127}$$

is a spatial Fourier component of the excitation density $N(z, t)$ and

$$Z(\nu - \omega) = iku \int_0^\infty \mathrm{d}\tau \exp\left[[i(\nu - \omega) - \gamma_{ab}]\tau - \frac{k^2 u^2 \tau^2}{4}\right]. \tag{128}$$

This function Z, well-known in the theory of Doppler broadening, depends on γ_{ab}/ku as well as $(\nu-\omega)/ku$. It can be written as a function of a complex variable $\zeta=\xi+i\eta$

(129) $$Z(\zeta)=Z_r+iZ_i=2i\int_{-\infty}^{i\zeta}\mathrm{d}t\,\exp[-(t^2+\zeta^2)]\,,$$

where

(130) $$\xi=\frac{\nu-\omega}{ku}\,,\qquad \eta=\frac{\gamma_{ab}}{ku}\,.$$

This function is discussed in MITCHELL and ZEMANSKY, in Born's « Optik » and is extensively tabulated in FREED and CONTE. We now write the contributions of $P_n^{(1)}$ to $C_n^{(1)}$ and $S_n^{(1)}$ in terms of Z

(131) $$\begin{cases} S_n^{(1)}=\dfrac{-\mathscr{P}^2}{\hbar ku}\bar{N}Z_i(\nu_n-\omega)E_n\,,\\[2ex] C_n^{(1)}=\dfrac{-\mathscr{P}^2}{\hbar ku}\bar{N}Z_r(\nu_n-\omega)E_n\,.\end{cases}$$

Now substitute into the amplitude and frequency equations. The amplitude equations will not show more features than the ones already shown in the previous approximation. The frequency equation yields a nonlinear pulling term, which has a simple form, for $\gamma_{ab}\ll ku$. In this case we can write

(132) $$Z(\xi,\eta)\approx(1-2i\eta\,\xi)\left[-2\int_0^{\xi}\exp[x^2]\,\mathrm{d}x+i\sqrt{\pi}\right]\exp[-\xi^2]-2i\eta$$

and it follows

(133) $$\nu_n\approx\Omega_n-\frac{1}{\sqrt{\pi}}\frac{\nu}{Q_n}\int_0^{\xi}\exp[x^2]\,\mathrm{d}x\,.$$

8. – Third-order polarization.

A similar calculation can be carried out for the third-order quantity $P_n^{(3)}(t)$. The integration of $\lambda_a(z,v,t_0)\varrho_{ab}^{(3)}(a,z,t_0,v,t)$ over times t_0 of excitation involves integrals like

$$\int_{-\infty}^{t}\mathrm{d}t_0\int_{t_0}^{t}\mathrm{d}t'\int_{t_0}^{t'}\mathrm{d}t''\int_{t_0}^{t''}\mathrm{d}t'''\,F(t,t',t'',t''')\exp[-\gamma_a(t'''-t_0)]\,.$$

By a repeated interchange of the orders of integration these integrals can be reduced to

$$\frac{1}{\gamma_a}\int_{-\infty}^{t} dt' \int_{-\infty}^{t'} dt'' \int_{-\infty}^{t''} dt''' \, F(t, t', t'', t''') \, .$$

Again, we keep only exponential factors in the time integration which are able to have resonance, and find after changes of variables

$$(134) \qquad \tau' = t - t' \, , \qquad \tau'' = t' - t'' , \qquad \tau''' = t'' - t'''$$

and algebraic manipulations a complicated relation for $P_n^{(3)}(t)$, that can be simplified in two limiting cases:

a) no atomic motion $(u = 0)$,

b) Doppler limit $\quad ku \gg \gamma_{ab}$.

In this second case, $P_n^{(3)}(t)$ takes the form

$$(135) \quad P_n^{(3)}(t) = \frac{i\sqrt{\pi}}{32}\frac{\mathscr{P}^4}{\hbar^3 ku}\sum_\mu\sum_\varrho\sum_\sigma E_\mu E_\varrho E_\sigma\big[\exp\left[-i(\nu_\mu - \nu_\varrho + \nu_\sigma)t - i(\varphi_\mu - \varphi_\varrho + \varphi_\sigma)\right]\big] \cdot$$
$$\cdot \big[N_{(\varrho-\sigma+\mu-n)} D(\omega - \tfrac{1}{2}\nu_\mu + \tfrac{1}{2}\nu_\varrho - \nu_\sigma) + N_{(\sigma-\varrho+\mu-\nu)} D\big(\nu_\varrho - \tfrac{1}{2}(\nu_\mu + \nu_\sigma)\big)\big] \cdot$$
$$\cdot \big[D_a(\nu_\varrho - \nu_\sigma) + D_b(\nu_\varrho - \nu_\sigma)\big] + \text{c.c.} \, ,$$

where

$$(136) \qquad D(f) = \frac{1}{\gamma_{ab} + if} , \qquad D_\alpha(f) = \frac{1}{\gamma_\alpha + if} \qquad (\alpha = a, b) \, .$$

Probably most of the interesting phenomena for optical gaseous masers can be understood without dealing explicitly with more than three frequencies.

We consider the expression (135) for the third-order polarization, in which the indices μ, ϱ and σ can each take on values 1, 2 and 3. It will be noted that besides the three frequencies ν_1, ν_2 and ν_3 assumed in the cavity excitation, there are nine additional frequencies present in the polarization of the medium. Hence there must be fields in the cavity at these new frequencies and the desired self-consistency for three-frequency operation is in jeopardy. However, under certain conditions, the fields at the new frequencies do not produce appreciable effects, even though the frequencies lie close to cavity resonances, so that the calculation can be made as planned.

As is already plausible from the single-frequency case, the oscillation frequencies ν_n are very close to the cavity frequencies Ω_n which are equally spaced, separated by $\Delta \sim 150$ MHz. Hence three of the new frequencies: $2\nu_2 - \nu_3$,

$\nu_1+\nu_3-\nu_2$ and $2\nu_2-\nu_1$ are very close to the three main frequencies ν_1, ν_2 and ν_3, respectively, and the corresponding terms are carried along in the calculations. The remaining frequencies can be ignored as long as the oscillator is appreciably below threshold for four-frequency operation.

The three amplitude equations will be of the type

$$\dot{E}_3=\alpha_3E_3-\beta_3E_3^3-\theta_{31}E_3E_1^2-\theta_{32}E_3E_2^2-(\eta_{1}\cos\psi+\xi_{21}\sin\psi)E_2^2E_1 .$$

The coefficients α_n and β_n were already calculated in the single-frequency case, and the angle

$$\psi=(2\nu_2-\nu_1-\nu_3)t+(2\varphi_2-\varphi_1-\varphi_3) \tag{138}$$

which appears might be called the «relative phase shift». Similarly the frequency equations will be like

$$\nu_3+\dot{\varphi}_3=\Omega_3+\sigma_3+\varrho_3E_3^2+\tau_{31}E_1^2+\tau_{32}E_2^2+\frac{E_2^2E_1}{E_3}(\eta_{21}\sin\psi-\xi_{21}\cos\psi) . \tag{139}$$

9. – Normal three-frequency operation.

Equation (137) and (139) are fairly complicated, but can be readily used to discuss a number of special cases. In general, unless care is taken to adjust the cavity tuning very accurately, the three frequencies ν_1, ν_2 and ν_3 will be such that the relative phase-angle ψ of equation (138) is a linear function of the time. Then the last terms in equations (137) and (139) are periodic functions of time, and in some approximation their effects average out. If we neglect these terms, we can get a steady-state solution for E_1, E_2, E_3 from

$$\left\{\begin{aligned}\alpha_1&=\beta_1E_1^2-\theta_{12}E_2^2-\theta_{13}E_3^2 ,\\ \alpha_2&=\beta_2E_2^2-\theta_{21}E_1^2-\theta_{23}E_3^2 ,\\ \alpha_3&=\beta_3E_3^2-\theta_{31}E_1^2-\theta_{32}E_2^2 ,\end{aligned}\right. \tag{140}$$

and for ν_1, ν_2, ν_3 from

$$\left\{\begin{aligned}\nu_1&=\Omega_1+\sigma_1+\varrho_1E_1^2+\tau_{12}E_2^2+\tau_{13}E_3^2 ,\\ \nu_2&=\Omega_2+\sigma_2+\varrho_2E_2^2+\tau_{21}E_1^2+\tau_{23}E_3^2 ,\\ \nu_3&=\Omega_3+\sigma_3+\varrho_3E_3^2+\tau_{31}E_1^2+\tau_{32}E_2^2 ,\end{aligned}\right. \tag{141}$$

again taking $\dot{\varphi}_1 = \dot{\varphi}_2 = \dot{\varphi}_3 = 0$. Since the coefficients in equations (140) and (141) are slowly varying functions of frequency, it will suffice first to determine the E_n^2 from (140) and then to calculate the ν_n's from (141). The equations are a fairly obvious generalization of those of the two-frequency case. It will be noted that operation with $E_1 \neq 0, E_2 \neq 0$ can inhibit oscillation at ν_3 until, with increasing excitation,

$$\alpha_3' = \alpha_3 - \theta_{31} E_1^2 - \theta_{32} E_2^2 ,$$

become positive.

10. – Combination tones.

As mentioned earlier, the third-order polarization $P_n^{(3)}(t)$ of the active medium has constituents which oscillate at all possible frequencies of the form $\nu_\mu - \nu_\varrho + \nu_\sigma$. Even for « two »-frequency oscillation, there are additional frequencies $2\nu_2 - \nu_1 \equiv \nu_3'$ and $2\nu_1 - \nu_2 = \nu_0'$ in the polarization which are very close to resonance with the principal cavity modes just above and below the two Ω_1 and Ω_2 of main interest. As a consequence of Maxwell's equations, fields at frequencies ν_3' and ν_0' necessarily exist in the cavity and can appear in the output. Well below the threshold for normal three-frequency oscillation, E_3 (and also E_0), will be much smaller than E_1 and E_2. We also assume $\gamma_{ab} \ll \Delta \ll ku$ so that

$$(142) \qquad \begin{cases} \eta_{21} \simeq -\dfrac{1}{16} \sqrt{\pi}\, \nu \mathscr{P}^4 (\varepsilon_0 \hbar^3 ku \Delta^2)^{-1} [\bar{N} + 2N_2] , \\ \xi_{21} \simeq 0 . \end{cases}$$

For a steady state, the equation (137) then gives

$$(143) \qquad E_3 \sim \eta_{21} E_2^2 E_1 [\alpha_3 - \theta_{31} E_1^2 - \theta_{32} E_2^2]^{-1} \cos \psi .$$

In order to obtain the combination tone $(2\nu_2 - \nu_1)$ experimentally, one should adjust the cavity tuning to Ω_2 slightly above the atomic transition frequency ω, thereby making Ω_1 a little nearer resonance than Ω_3. The excitation should be increased until « two »-frequency operation is obtained, but not yet genuine three-frequency operation.

Under these conditions, the θ's in equation (143) contain a factor Δ^{-2} and to simplify the discussion they will now be neglected. The equation for α_3 then has the form

$$(144) \qquad \alpha_3 \simeq -\tfrac{1}{2} (\nu / Q_3) / G_3 ,$$

where the gain factor G_3 is given approximately by

(145) $$G_3 \simeq \left[1-(\bar{N}/\bar{N}_T)\, Z_i(\Delta)/Z_i(0)\right]^{-1},$$

if one is not too near to threshold for normal three-frequency operation. Equations (142), (143) and (145), within their domain of validity, indicate that E_3 is smaller than E_1 by a factor

(146) $$E_3/E_1 \simeq \tfrac{1}{8}Q_3 \mathscr{P}^4 E_2^2 G_3 |\bar{N} + 2N_2| (\varepsilon_0\, ku\hbar^3\Delta^2)^{-1}.$$

It should be noted that eq. (146) could vanish if the spatial distribution of the excitation density is such that $2N_2 + \bar{N} = 0$. (If the excitation is confined to the central region of the Fabry-Perot tube, N_2 and $\bar{N} = N_0$ by their definition (127) have opposite signs.) An experimental study of the above phenomena might facilitate determination of some of the quantites which enter into our equations but for which direct experimental values are not yet available.

11. – Frequency locking phenomena.

It has been observed by JAVAN that when the cavity tuning is gradually changed in normal three-frequency operation, so that the separation of the beat notes $\nu_2 - \nu_1$ and $\nu_3 - \nu_2$ approaches a small value (typically of order 1 kHz), a frequency jump occurs such that only one beat note $\nu - \nu_1 = \nu_3 - \nu_2$ near Δ is found. This phenomenon can be easily understood by reference to eq (139). For simplicity, we neglect the small frequency pushing associated with the terms involving ϱ_{nm} and τ_{nm}, since the nonlinear pulling terms σ_n already give sufficient generality to the frequency relationship. By using eq. (139) for ν_3 and similar ones for ν_1 and ν_2, we find a differential equation for the relative phase-angle ψ of eq. (138) in the form

(147) $$\dot{\psi} = \sigma + A \sin\psi + B\cos\psi\,,$$

where

(148) $$\sigma = 2\sigma_2 - \sigma_1 - \sigma_3\,.$$

Let us now suppose that the maser is in normal three-frequency operation with two distinct beat notes $\nu_3 - \nu_2$ and $\nu_2 - \nu_1$ near to $\Delta = 150$ MHz, *i.e.*, $\sigma = (\nu_3 - \nu_2) - (\nu_2 - \nu_1)$ is somewhat greater than $(A^2 + B^2)^{\frac{1}{2}}$. As the middle-cavity frequency Ω_2 is tuned closer to the atomic-resonance frequency ω, the separation of beat-note frequencies $|\sigma|$ decreases. There should be some pulsations in phase which would increase in amplitude as symmetrical tuning is approached. As $|\sigma|$ reaches $(A^2 + B^2)^{\frac{1}{2}}$, a quick transition to the locked state should be made, and only one beat note should be observed. Under the additional simplifyng assumption $E_2 \gg E_1 = E_3$, and with use of the starting condition for single-frequency oscillation the separation of the two notes which could be attained just before locking occurs should be given by

$$|\sigma| = \tfrac{1}{8}\left[(\bar{N} + 2N_2)/\bar{N}_T\right](\mathscr{P}E_2/\hbar\Delta)^2\nu/Q\,, \tag{149}$$

which is conveniently expressed as a small fraction of the cavity bandwidth.

It might be pointed out that the phenomenon is very closely related to one discussed by VAN DER POL in 1924. He considered a self-sustained triode oscillator, capable of oscillation of frequency ν_1. If an external signal at ν is injected into the tank circuit, it may be possible to detect a beat note at $|\nu - \nu_1|$ using a square law detector.

If, however, ν is tuned gradually towards ν_1, a very sudden jump occurs, after which oscillations occur only ν and the beat note disappears. The width of the « quiet » frequency range depends approximately linearly on the amplitude of the injected signal, when this is small. In the case of the optical maser, we can think that an oscillator at ν_1 is being perturbated by an « external » signal at the combination tone frequency $\nu = 2\nu_2 - \nu_3$ which arises from the third-order polarization $P_1^{(3)}(t)$.

* * *

This work was supported in part by the Air Force Office of Scientific Research. A fuller account of the material has been published in the Physical Review, (**134**, A 1429 (1964)).

REFERENCES

[1] A. L. SCHAWLOW and C. H. TOWNES: *Phys. Rev.*, **112**, 1940 (1958).
[2] A. JAVAN, W. R. BENNETT, jr. and D. R. HERRIOTT: *Phys. Rev. Lett.*, **6**, 106 (1961).
[3] T. S. JASEJA, A. JAVAN and C. H. TOWNES: *Phys. Rev. Lett.*, **10**, 165 (1963).
[4] A. G. FOX and T. LI: *Bell Syst. Tech. Journ.*, **40**, 61 (1961).
[5] W. E. LAMB jr. and T. M. SANDERS jr.: *Phys. Rev.*, **119**, 1901 (1960), especially p. 1902-1903; L. R. WILCOX and W. E. LAMB jr.: *Phys. Rev.*, **119**, 1915 (1960), especially p. 1928.
[6] W. E. LAMB jr.: *Quantum Mechanical Amplifiers*, in *Lectures in Theoretical Physics*, vol. **2**, edited by W. E. BRITTIN and B. W. DOWNS (New York, 1960), especially, p. 472.
[7] M. BORN: *Optik* (Berlin, 1933), p. 482.
[8] B. D. FRIED and S. D. CONTE: *The plasma dispersion function* (Hilbert transform of the Gaussian) (New York, 1961).

[9] R. A. McFarlane, W. R. Bennett jr. and W. E. Lamb jr.: *Phys. Lett.*, **2**, 189 (1963); A. Szöke and A. Javan: *Phys. Rev. Lett.*, **10**, 521 (1963).
[10] B. van der Pol: *Phil. Mag.*, **43**, 700 (1922) and a review article *Proc. Inst. Radio Engineers*, **22**, 1051 (1934).
[11] B. van der Pol: *Phil. Mag.*, **3**, 65 (1927) and the review article cited in ref. [10].
[12] C. H. Townes: *Advances in Quantum Electronics*, edited by J. Singer (New York, 1961), p. 3.
[13] A. Javan, E. A. Ballik and W. L. Bond: *Journ. Opt. Soc. Am.*, **52**, 96 (1962).
[14] C. L. Tang and H. Statz: *Phys. Rev.*, **128**, 1013 (1962).
[15] W. G. Wagner and G. Birnbaum: *Journ. Appl. Phys.*, **32**, 1185 (1961).
[16] D. E. McCumber: *Phys. Rev.*, **130**, 675 (1963).
[17] H. Haken and H. Sauermann: *Zeits. f. Phys.*, **173**, 261 (1963) and further papers to be published.
[18] W. E. Bennett jr.: *Applied Optics Supplement on Optical Masers* (1962), p. 24, especially p. 58. It should be noted that the holes are in first instance burned in the curve of population difference *vs.* velocity, and only indirectly in a curve of gain *vs.* frequency.

Theory of Laser Action in Solid-State, Gaseous and Semiconductor Systems (*).

H. HAKEN and H. SAUERMANN

Institut für theoretische und angewandte Physik der Technischen Hochschule - Stuttgart

1. – Introduction.

The present paper represents a detailed and extended report on the work of the authors previously published [1] in several articles.

In the traditional laser theory the creation of light by the process of stimulated emission is treated neglecting the response of the atomic system. The topic of this study is to go one step further and to take into account the influence of the light on the atomic system and to study the alterations of the laser light by the atomic response. For this end we consider N atoms each with three or four levels. These atoms may either be situated at random lattice sites or may move with a given velocity distribution. Furthermore we consider the case in which the energy levels of the electrons belong to the valence and conduction band of a semiconductor.

The light field is assumed to consist of a set of cavity modes which decay exponentially with time. The atomic emission line may either be homogeneously broadened or in addition inhomogeneously broadened. The homogeneously broadened line is treated as a Lorentzian whereas for the inhomogeneous line a Gaussian or Lorentzian shape is assumed. The mathematical procedure consists of a certain iteration of the equations of motion of the light field and the matter system and applies for the solid-state case, for the gaseous case as well as for the semiconductor laser.

The atomic response consists of a time-independent and a time-dependent part. The time-independent part stems either from a spatially inhomogeneous depletion of atoms or from an inhomogeneously broadened line. Both effects

(*) Seminar held by H. SAUERMANN.

may lead to a simultaneous occurrence of laser modes as is shown in detail.

Furthermore the time-independent response leads to frequency-pushing effects for an inhomogeneously broadened line as has been treated for the gaseous laser by BENNETT [2] in a macroscopic description. Also the time-dependent response leads to a pushing of frequencies which can have the same size as that of the time-independent one.

The results for the solid-state laser are in qualitative agreement with line pushing as observed by SNITZER [3]. In the case of the He-Ne laser our results are in favorable agreement with various experimental findings by BENNETT [2].

Since the prediction of the optical maser in the fundamental paper of SCHAWLOW and TOWNES [4] in 1958 and the first detection of laser action by MAIMAN [5] just three years ago a huge amount of information on various laser systems has been obtained. In this period the detection of new effects and systems showing laser action predominated over those experimental and theoretical investigations in which the detailed aspects of laser action are studied. In order to reach technical applications as well as to obtain a deeper understanding of the laser process a detailed study of these phenomena seems to be highly desirable. We hope to contribute to this question from the theoretical point of view.

Some of the main questions are:

1) the possible coexistence or suppression of laser modes,

2) the actual frequencies of the lasing modes,

3) the line width of the lasing modes.

The first two questions will be the main topic of the present paper whereas the third one is almost completely left out (*). Especially we do not consider the effect of spontaneous emission. In contrast to the paper of WAGNER and BIRNBAUM [6] who consider the laser action as oscillations of a multimode cavity driven by the noise of the spontaneous emission of the atomic system we consider the free oscillations of a set of cavity modes where the oscillations are coupled to a set of atoms. These atoms may either be fixed at random lattice sites or many move with a given velocity distribution. The formalism is also applicable to the case of the semiconductor laser in which we have instead of distinct atomic levels the conduction and valence band. The only assumption necessary is the applicability of the k-selection rule.

(*) *Note added in proof.* - In the meantime we took into account noise effects within a nonlinear theory (H. HAKEN: to be published in *Zeits. f. Phys.*). Below the threshold as determined in this report the results of (linear) noise theories (for instance [6]) are recovered. Above this threshold the line width is essentially due to phase-fluctuations of the laser light.

In order to facilitate the reading of the present report we start with the derivation of the equations for the light-field and the atomic system from well-known expressions of textbooks (for instance HEITLER). The treatment is greatly simplified by the assumption of a one-to-one correspondence of the two optically active levels between which the optical transition occurs. This allows to introduce instead of pairs of electronic creation and annihilation operators single operators which behave formally like spin-$\frac{1}{2}$ operators. In order to allow for the pumping process three- or four-level systems must be considered. The present method is capable of treating both systems.

2. – Derivation of the equations of motion.

We start from the Hamiltonian [7] describing the interaction between a set of N atoms located at lattice sites $\boldsymbol{r}_\mu$ and the radiation field

$$H = H_{\text{el}} + H_{\text{rad}} + H_{\text{int}}\,, \tag{1}$$

where

$$H_{el} = \sum_\mu \frac{p_\mu^2}{2m} + V_\mu(\boldsymbol{r}'_\mu)\,, \tag{1a}$$

$$H_{\text{rad}} = \sum_\lambda \hbar\omega_\lambda b_\lambda^\dagger b_\lambda\,, \tag{1b}$$

$$H_{\text{int}} = -\sum_\mu \left\{\frac{e}{mc}\boldsymbol{p}_\mu \boldsymbol{A}_\mu - \frac{e^2}{2mc^2}\boldsymbol{A}_\mu^2\right\} + \frac{1}{2}\sum_{\mu\neq\nu}\frac{e^2}{r'_{\mu\nu}}\,. \tag{1c}$$

$V_\mu(\boldsymbol{r}'_\mu)$ gives the atomic potential of the μ-th electron, the co-ordinates of which are $\boldsymbol{r}'_\mu$. $\boldsymbol{A}_\mu$ is the transverse vector potential at the position $\boldsymbol{r}'_\mu$ of the μ-th electron. In (1b) one uses the fact that $\boldsymbol{A}(\boldsymbol{r})$ can be expanded into an arbitrary but complete and orthogonal set of functions $\boldsymbol{A}_\lambda$:

$$\boldsymbol{A}(\boldsymbol{r}) = \sum_\lambda q_\lambda \boldsymbol{A}_\lambda(\boldsymbol{r})\,. \tag{2}$$

Using creation and destruction operators $b_\lambda^\dagger$ and b_λ one has

$$q_\lambda = \sqrt{\frac{\hbar}{2\omega_\lambda}}\,(b_\lambda^\dagger + b_\lambda) \qquad \text{with} \qquad [b_\lambda, b_{\lambda'}^\dagger] = \delta_{\lambda\lambda'}\,.$$

The index λ enumerates the frequencies as well as the polarizations of the functions $\boldsymbol{A}_\lambda(\boldsymbol{r})$. As we are interested in the steady state operation of a laser, we use the standing-wave solutions of a Fabry-Perot resonator [8]. As one is merely interested in the behavior of axial and near axial modes, it is permissible to apply the following approximate standing-wave functions [9]:

$$A_\lambda(\boldsymbol{r}) = \sqrt{\frac{32\pi c^2}{V}}\, \boldsymbol{e}_\lambda \sin k_x \cdot x \sin k_y \cdot y \sin k_z \cdot z \tag{3}$$

where $k_x = n_x \pi / L_x$ etc. n_x is a positive integer, L_x the length of the Fabry-Perot, V its volume and $\boldsymbol{e}_\lambda$ the polarization vector. The normalization is chosen to be

$$\int \boldsymbol{A}_\lambda(\boldsymbol{r}) \boldsymbol{A}_\varrho(\boldsymbol{r})\, \mathrm{d}\tau = 4\pi c^2 \delta_{\lambda\varrho} \quad \text{(confr. [7])} . \tag{4}$$

In the following we shall often treat the axial modes as plane waves with a constant amplitude in the y- and z-direction. Returning to the Hamiltonian (1), we drop the Coulomb interaction of the electrons, as well as the term quadratic in the vector potential. The latter may be shown to be a rigorous concept by means of a canonical transformation, if one confines oneself to the dipole approximation [10]. Describing the electron field with the help of second quantization, the Hamiltonian (1) transforms into

$$H = \sum_{\mu k} a^\dagger_{\mu k} a_{\mu k} E_{\mu k} + \sum_\lambda \hbar\omega_\lambda b^\dagger_\lambda b_\lambda - \frac{e}{mc} \int \Psi^\dagger(\boldsymbol{r}) \boldsymbol{p}\, \boldsymbol{A}(\boldsymbol{r}) \Psi(\boldsymbol{r})\, \mathrm{d}\tau . \tag{5}$$

The field operator Ψ is assumed to consist of a sum of field operators ψ_μ, each referring to one electron being bound to a single nucleus. In doing this, we presume that the electrons are localized at individual atomic nuclei. This is justified physically in both, solid-state and gaseous lasers, because in both the active atoms are separated so far from one another, that the electrons move in the potential of a single atom. The operators ψ_μ may be represented as

$$\psi_\mu = \sum_k a_{\mu k} \varphi_{\mu k} ,$$

where $\varphi_{\mu k}$ denotes the eigenstates of the electrons in the μ-th atom.

For the semiconductor the Hamiltonian (5) can be interpreted in the following way: The index μ has now the meaning of the k-vector of an electron described by a Bloch wave function whereas the index k indicates the valence and conduction band. Correspondingly the $\varphi_{\mu k}$ are now the Bloch wave functions of the periodic lattice. For the formal treatment we can proceed like in the case of single atoms. The destruction and creation operators $a_{\mu k}$ and $a^\dagger_{\mu k}$ obey the usual anticommutation rules

$$a_{\mu k} a^\dagger_{\mu' k'} + a^\dagger_{\mu' k'} a_{\mu k} = \delta_{\mu\mu'} \delta_{kk'} . \tag{6}$$

Thus the interaction Hamiltonian becomes

$$H_{\text{int}} = \sum_{\mu,k,m,\lambda} a^{\dagger}_{\mu k} a_{\mu m} (b_{\lambda} + b^{\dagger}_{\lambda}) h_{\mu k m \lambda} , \tag{7}$$

where

$$h_{\mu k m \lambda} = -\frac{e}{mc}\sqrt{\frac{\hbar}{2\omega_{\lambda}}}\langle \varphi_{\mu k} | \boldsymbol{p} \boldsymbol{A}_{\lambda} | \varphi_{\mu m} \rangle .$$

We now restrict ourselves to an atom with only two levels, so that the index k can only have the values 1 (lower level) or 2 (upper level). Assuming that $h_{\mu k k \lambda}$ vanishes, we get

$$H_{\text{int}} = \sum_{\mu,\lambda} (a^{\dagger}_{\mu 2} a_{\mu 1} h_{\mu 21\lambda} + a^{\dagger}_{\mu 1} a_{\mu 2} h_{\mu 12\lambda})(b_{\lambda} + b^{\dagger}_{\lambda}) . \tag{8}$$

If we demand, that there is always one electron in the two levels of an atom, it is advantageous to introduce the new operators $a^{\dagger}_{\mu} = a^{\dagger}_{\mu 2} a_{\mu 1}$ and $a_{\mu} = a^{\dagger}_{\mu 1} a_{\mu 2}$. $a^{\dagger}_{\mu}$ lifts an electron from the lower to the upper level, while for a_{μ} the reverse is true. It is easily seen from (6) that they obey

$$a_{\mu} a^{\dagger}_{\mu} + a^{\dagger}_{\mu} a_{\mu} = 1 \tag{9}$$

and that they commute for different μ.

Since we have to consider a three- or four-level system this assumption requires that the electrons stay only for rather short times in the two other optically not active states.

Besides the products $a^{\dagger}_{\mu} b_{\lambda}$ and $b^{\dagger}_{\lambda} a_{\mu}$, also the two terms $a^{\dagger}_{\mu} b^{\dagger}_{\lambda}$ and $a_{\mu} b_{\lambda}$ occur in (8). We neglect them, as they can produce no first order transitions because of energy conservation. That means, that we allow only for elementary processes in the interaction Hamiltonian, which consist in the emission of a photon and the transition of an electron from the upper to the lower level or the absorption of a photon and the reverse electron transition. Speaking classically, we neglect antiresonant terms.

On account of these remarks, one finds

$$H = \tfrac{1}{2} \sum_{\mu} \hbar \varepsilon_{\mu} (a^{\dagger}_{\mu} a_{\mu} - a_{\mu} a^{\dagger}_{\mu}) + \sum_{\lambda} \hbar \omega_{\lambda} b^{\dagger}_{\lambda} b_{\lambda} + \hbar \sum_{\mu,\lambda} a_{\mu} b^{\dagger}_{\lambda} h_{\mu\lambda} + \sum_{\mu,\lambda} \hbar a^{\dagger}_{\mu} b_{\lambda} h^{*}_{\mu\lambda} , \tag{10}$$

where we introduced the notations

$$h_{\mu\lambda} = \frac{1}{\hbar} h_{\mu 12\lambda} , \qquad h^{*}_{\mu\lambda} = \frac{1}{\hbar} h_{\mu 21\lambda} , \qquad \hbar\varepsilon_{\mu} = E_{\mu,2} - E_{\mu,1} .$$

In the semiconductor laser $\hbar\varepsilon_\mu$ represents the difference of the valence and conduction band energy for a given K-vector. Let us briefly discuss the matrix element $h_{\mu\lambda}$

a) *For separated atoms.* It reads

$$h_{\mu\lambda} = -\frac{e}{m}\sqrt{\frac{16\pi}{\hbar\omega_\lambda V}}\,\langle\varphi_{\mu 1}|\boldsymbol{p}\boldsymbol{e}_\lambda \sin k_x\cdot x \sin k_y\cdot y \sin k_z\cdot z|\varphi_{\mu 2}\rangle\,.$$

If one notices that $\varphi_\mu(\boldsymbol{r}) = \varphi(\boldsymbol{r}-\boldsymbol{r}_\mu)$, where $\varphi(\boldsymbol{r}')$ is the wave function of an electron in the field of a nucleus, which is located at $\boldsymbol{r}'=0$, one finds that the above matrix element becomes in the dipole approximation

$$h_{\mu\lambda} = -\frac{e}{m}\sqrt{\frac{16\pi}{\hbar\omega_\lambda V}}\,\sin k_x x_\mu \sin k_y y_\mu \sin k_z z_\mu\,\langle\varphi_1|\boldsymbol{p}\boldsymbol{e}_\lambda|\varphi_2\rangle\,.$$

Finally, by introducing the atomic dipole moment $\boldsymbol{\mu} = e\boldsymbol{r}$,

$$h_{\mu\lambda} = i\sqrt{\frac{16\pi\varepsilon^2}{\hbar\omega_\lambda V}}\,\boldsymbol{e}_\lambda\boldsymbol{\mu}_{12}\sin k_x x_\mu \sin k_y y_\mu \sin k_z z_\mu\,. \tag{11}$$

It should be noted, that $\boldsymbol{\mu}_{12}$ depends on the orientation of the μ-th atom. In the following we always replace $\sum\limits_{\boldsymbol{\mu}}$ by $\varrho\int\ldots\mathrm{d}\tau$, where ϱ is the number of active atoms per unit volume. If the atoms are oriented statistically this integration also involves an averaging over the directions of the atomic dipoles. While this is true for a solid-state laser, in the case of a gaseous laser we are concerned with moving atoms. One then has to replace $\boldsymbol{r}_\mu$ by $\boldsymbol{r}_\mu + \boldsymbol{v}_\mu t$ in (11), where $\boldsymbol{v}_\mu$ is the velocity of the μ-th atom.

Assuming that we have a homogeneous velocity distribution over the volume of the Fabry-Perot interferometer, the summation over μ contains in addition an integration over $\boldsymbol{v}_\mu$. The integrations over $\boldsymbol{r}_\mu$ and $\boldsymbol{v}_\mu$ are then to be carried out independently from one another.

b) *For the semiconductor.* The matrix element has the same form as above where φ is, however, a Bloch wave function. Assuming the validity of the k-selection rule and working in a frame in which the light waves can be treated as running waves we end up immediately with

$$h = -\frac{e}{m}\sqrt{\frac{4\pi}{\hbar\omega V}}\int\varphi^*_{v,\boldsymbol{k}}(\boldsymbol{r})\boldsymbol{e}\boldsymbol{p}\,\varphi_{L,\boldsymbol{k}}(\boldsymbol{r})\,\mathrm{d}\tau\,. \tag{11a}$$

Let us return to the Hamiltonian (10). If we adopt the Heisenberg picture for the operators, we are led to the following equations of motion:

$$\dot{b}_\lambda^\dagger = \frac{i}{\hbar}[H, b_\lambda^\dagger] = i\omega_\lambda b_\lambda^\dagger + i \sum_\mu h_{\mu\lambda}^* a_\mu^\dagger \, , \tag{12}$$

$$\dot{a}_\mu^\dagger = \frac{i}{\hbar}[H, a_\mu^\dagger] = i\varepsilon_\mu a_\mu^\dagger - i \sum_\lambda h_{\mu\lambda} b_\lambda^\dagger \underbrace{(a_\mu^\dagger a_\mu - a_\mu a_\mu^\dagger)}_{\sigma_\mu} \, . \tag{13}$$

These equations still have to be modified in order to allow for a description of the actual physical phenomena occurring in a laser. Firstly, we replace ε_μ by $\varepsilon_\mu + i\gamma$ and ω_λ by $\omega_\lambda + i\varkappa_\lambda$, where γ accounts for the decay of atoms from the upper to the lower level through various kinds of processes and $\varkappa_\lambda$ for the radiation losses. The latter ones are mainly determined by the reflection coefficient of the silvered mirrors of the resonator.

Secondly we have to take care of the pumping process for a three- respectively four-level system.

a) Four-level system. We describe the pumping process by an additional equation for the occupation numbers of the upper and lower optical level. For the upper level the pumping process secures a finite occupation number. Taking into account both the pumping process as well as the interaction with the light field according to the Hamiltonian (10) the equation for the upper level reads

$$\dot{n}_{u,\mu} = \frac{1}{T_1}(d_{0,\mu} - n_{u,\mu}) + i \sum_\lambda a_\mu b_\lambda^\dagger h_{\mu\lambda} - i \sum_\lambda a_\mu^\dagger b_\lambda h_{\mu\lambda}^* \, . \tag{14}$$

For the lower level we take into account that this level may decay by various processes to the ground level. This can be described by the equation

$$\dot{n}_{l,\mu} = -\frac{1}{T_2} n_{l,\mu} + i \sum_\lambda a_\mu^\dagger b_\lambda h_{\mu\lambda}^* - i \sum_\lambda a_\mu b_\lambda^\dagger h_{\mu\lambda} \, . \tag{15}$$

b) Three-level system. Assuming that the recombination of the third level to the optically active second level occurs very rapidly it is sufficient to consider only one additional equation, describing the time variation of the inversion of the optically active levels. In this case we obtain

$$\dot{\sigma}_\mu = \frac{1}{T}(d_{0,\mu} - \sigma_\mu) + 2ia_\mu \sum_\lambda h_{\mu\lambda} b_\lambda^\dagger - 2ia_\mu^\dagger \sum_\lambda h_{\mu\lambda}^* b_\lambda \, , \tag{16}$$

where

$$\sigma_\mu = n_{u,\mu} - n_{l,\mu} \, .$$

As a consequence of eqs. (14), (15) and (16) $n_{u,\mu}$, $n_{l,\mu}$ and σ_μ become new variables which are no longer determined by a_μ and $a_\mu^\dagger$.

The physical justification for this results from the fact, that σ_μ contains an additional part being brought about by the completely random excitations. The corresponding fluctuating inhomogeneous part in eq. (13) plays no role, since it does not interfere with the coherent motion of the system.

Our procedure is completely analogous to that in the similar problem of electron spin resonance: If one introduces the matrix representation for the operators $a_\mu^\dagger$, a_μ and σ_μ, which is diagonal with respect to the energy, one realizes that a_μ and $a_\mu^\dagger$ correspond to the nondiagonal elements of the density matrix of the system, while σ_μ is in accordance with the difference of the diagonal elements. Then γ is to be identified with the reciprocal of Bloch's transverse relaxation time T_2, and T with the longitudinal one T_1.

Finally it should be noted, that (14) accounts quite generally for the conservation of particle number, since each lifting of an electron is accompanied by the emission of a photon and vice versa. This means that the absorbed pumping power $\big(N(d_0-d)\Delta E\big)/2T$, where $d=(1/N)\sum_\mu \sigma_\mu$ and ΔE is the excitation energy of the external light source, reappears in the radiation going through the silvered end-plates of the interferometer. We shall recover this fact later on and make an important use of it in the discussion of stability of various modes.

3. – Method of solution.

We describe in this Section the method of solution for the case of fixed atoms either at random lattice sites or for electrons belonging to k-states in the semiconductor. The gas laser can be treated quite similarly.

For sake of simplicity we treat the three-level case. The four-level case is treated in the Appendix (Section A). The iteration procedure works as follows. We first assume, that a certain inversion $\sigma_\mu(0)=d_{\mu,0}$ is already present. This inversion may depend on the index μ as will be explained below.

We make for $b_\lambda^\dagger$ the ansatz $b_\lambda^\dagger=B_\lambda^\dagger\exp[i\Omega_\lambda t]$ and obtain by integration of eq. (13)

$$a_\mu^\dagger(t)=-d_{\mu,0}\sum_\lambda B_\lambda^\dagger h_{\mu\lambda}\frac{\exp[i\Omega_\lambda t]}{(\Omega_\lambda-\varepsilon_\mu-i\gamma)}\,. \tag{17}$$

Inserting this result into eq. (16) and integrating we obtain an improved expression for the inversion σ_μ:

$$\sigma_\mu=d_{\mu,0}+\left\{2id_{0,\mu}^{*}\sum_{\lambda,\lambda'}B_\lambda B_{\lambda'}^\dagger h_{\mu\lambda}^{*}h_{\mu\lambda'}\frac{\exp[i(\Omega_{\lambda'}-\Omega_\lambda)t]}{(\Omega_{\lambda'}-\varepsilon_\mu-i\gamma)(1/T+i[\Omega_{\lambda'}-\Omega_\lambda])}+\text{c.c.}\right\}. \tag{18}$$

We insert now σ_μ into eq. (13) and obtain the following improved expression for the atomic response:

$$(19)\qquad a_\mu^\dagger(t) = -\,d_{0\mu}\sum_{\lambda'} B_{\lambda'}^\dagger h_{\mu\lambda'}\frac{\exp[i\Omega_{\lambda'}t]}{(\Omega_{\lambda'}-\varepsilon_\mu-i\gamma)} + 2d_{0,\mu}\sum_{\lambda,\lambda',\lambda'''} B_\lambda B_{\lambda'}^\dagger B_{\lambda''} h_{\mu\lambda}^* h_{\mu\lambda'} h_{\mu\lambda''}\cdot$$

$$\cdot\frac{\exp[i(\Omega_{\lambda'}+\Omega_{\lambda''}-\Omega_\lambda)t]}{i(1/T+i[\Omega_{\lambda'}-\Omega_\lambda]((\Omega_{\lambda'}-\Omega_\lambda+\Omega_{\lambda''}-\varepsilon_\mu-i\gamma)}\left(\frac{1}{\Omega_{\mu'}-\varepsilon_\mu-i\gamma}-\frac{1}{\Omega_\lambda-\varepsilon_\mu+i\gamma}\right).$$

Since we are finally interested in the equation of motion for the laser modes we eliminate the atomic co-ordinates by inserting the result for the atomic amplitude into eq. (12).

This yields

$$(20)\qquad \dot b_\lambda^\dagger = (i\omega_\lambda-\varkappa)b_\lambda^\dagger - id_{0;\mu}\sum_\mu |h_{\mu\lambda}|^2\frac{B_\lambda^\dagger\exp[i\Omega_\lambda t]}{(\Omega_\lambda-\varepsilon_\mu-i\gamma)}+$$

$$+\,2d_{0,\mu}\sum_{\mu,\lambda_1,\lambda_2,\lambda_3} B_{\lambda_1}B_{\lambda_2}^\dagger B_{\lambda_3}^\dagger h_{\mu\lambda}^* h_{\mu\lambda_1}^* h_{\mu\lambda_2} h_{\mu\lambda_3}\cdot$$

$$\cdot\frac{\exp[i(\Omega_{\lambda_2}+\Omega_{\lambda_3}-\Omega_{\lambda_1})t]}{[1/T+i(\Omega_{\lambda_2}-\Omega_{\lambda_1})][\Omega_{\lambda_2}+\Omega_{\lambda_3}-\Omega_{\lambda_1}-\varepsilon_\mu-i\gamma]}\left(\frac{1}{\Omega_{\lambda_2}-\varepsilon_\mu-i\gamma}-\frac{1}{\Omega_{\lambda_1}-\varepsilon_\mu+i\gamma}\right).$$

The set of eqs. (20) are the fundamental equations for the following analysis. In fact the whole further analysis consists simply in performing the summations, respectively, integrations over energies and atomic indices and by solving the set of eqs. (20). These equations describe the oscillation of the modes taking into account their interaction, which is brought about by the response of the atomic system. It should be noted, that in general new combination frequencies occur on the right-hand side. These combination frequencies give rise to corresponding frequencies of the modes. This kind of frequency mixing is treated in detail by BLOEMBERGEN *et al.* [11] (*).

In his paper the atoms serve as *inactive medium* and the frequency of the fundamental wave is prescribed by an external source. In our present analysis, however, we are mainly interested in *frequency shifts*, which are brought about by *active material*. This requires a self-consistent solution of (5). For this purpose we neglect combination frequencies.

In the following we will mostly solve the above equations in detail for one and two modes. For this end we write down explicitly the equations for these

(*) Due to the lack of inversion symmetry terms quadratic in the B's occur in Bloembergen's treatment instead of the cubic terms in our analysis.

two cases:

$$(21)\quad \varkappa + i(\Omega - \omega) = -i \sum_{\mu} \frac{|h_\mu|^2 d_{0,\mu}}{(\Omega - \varepsilon_\mu - i\gamma)} + \sum_{\mu} \frac{\langle B^\dagger B \rangle |h_\mu|^4 d_{0\mu} \cdot 4i\gamma T}{[\Omega - \varepsilon_\mu - i\gamma][(\Omega - \varepsilon_\mu)^2 + \gamma^2]}$$

and

$$(22)\quad \varkappa + i(\Omega_\lambda - \omega_\lambda) = \sum_{\mu} \frac{d_{0,\mu} |h_{\mu\lambda}|^2}{\gamma + i(\Omega_\lambda - \varepsilon_\mu)} -$$

$$- 4\gamma T \sum_{\mu\lambda'} \frac{d_{0,\mu} \langle B^\dagger_{\lambda'} B_{\lambda'} \rangle |h_{\mu\lambda}|^2 |h_{\mu\lambda'}|^2}{[\gamma + i(\Omega_\lambda - \varepsilon_\mu)][\gamma^2 + (\Omega_{\lambda'} - \varepsilon_\mu)^2]} +$$

$$+ 2 \sum_{\substack{\mu \\ (\lambda' \neq \lambda)}} \frac{d_{0,\mu} \langle B^\dagger_{\lambda'} B_{\lambda'} \rangle |h_{\mu\lambda}|^2 |h_{\mu\lambda'}|^2}{[1/T + i(\Omega_\lambda - \Omega_{\lambda'})][\Omega_\lambda - \varepsilon_\mu - i\gamma]} \left(\frac{1}{\Omega_\lambda - \varepsilon_\mu - i\gamma} - \frac{1}{\Omega_{\lambda'} - \varepsilon_\mu + i\gamma} \right).$$

We discuss eq. (21) briefly in order to give a physically deeper insight into our treatment. Let us consider the first sum on the right-hand side of eq. (21) which can be split up into real and imaginary part. If γ is rather small the real part contains a δ-function with the argument $\Omega - \varepsilon_\mu$. This represents the emission of photons by those transitions in which the energy is conserved. Such an expression can be also obtained by usual first-order perturbation theory with a given inversion of the atomic states $d_{0,\mu}$ present. The imaginary part of this sum has the same form as the dispersion formula with a given occupation, respectively, inversion of the atomic system.

This expression could have also been obtained by second-order perturbation theory. The only essential difference is that we have already used a renormalized frequency Ω instead of ω as occurring in the usual perturbation procedure. This treatment corresponds to summing up an infinite set of graphs. What is essentially new in our present treatment is, however, represented by the occurrence of the second sum. In it the square of the light amplitude or correspondingly the number of photons occurs. This term therefore describes the change of the gain as well as that of the dispersion due to the adjustment of the atomic occupation to the intensity of the light field. It may be noted, that this response of the atomic system is time-independent. In the steady-state case the photon number adjusts in such a way that gain and loss compensate each other, which is reached by equating the real part of the right-hand side of eq. (21) to the left-hand side. With the photon number such fixed we can calculate the dispersive part of the right-hand side of eq. (21), which leads immediately to an expression for the frequency shift in the inverted system as compared to the unloaded cavity. Let us consider now the additional features which occur in two-mode operation as described by eq. (22). The essentially new term is given by the third sum on the right-hand side. This term stems from a time-dependent oscillation of the atomic system under the influence of the light field as can be seen for instance by following up the different iteration steps.

4. – Application to solid-state lasers.

Shifts of frequency and preliminary discussion of stability of laser modes.

4·1. *Homogeneously broadened line.*

4·1.1. One mode. – For the treatment of this case we can either use the eq. (21) which we found by an iteration procedure, or an exact treatment of the total set of equations of motion. In order to elucidate the general procedure we start with treating the approximate eq. (21).

The sums in eq. (21) over the atomic indices μ can be evaluated by replacing them by integrals over the atomic positions $\boldsymbol{r}_\mu$. In the following we assume always that $d_{0,\mu} \equiv d_0$ does not depend on μ. Because we have a homogeneously broadened line no integration over energies is required.

Splitting into real and imaginary parts we find the following expressions:

$$\gamma\varkappa - (\Omega - \omega)(\Omega - \varepsilon) = \frac{2\pi\varepsilon^2 |\mu_{12}|^2 \varrho d_0}{\hbar\omega}\left\{1 - \frac{12\pi\varepsilon^2 |\mu_{12}|^2 \gamma T n}{\hbar\omega[\gamma^2 + (\Omega - \varepsilon)^2]}\right\}, \tag{23}$$

$$\Omega = \frac{\gamma\omega + \varkappa\varepsilon}{\gamma + \varkappa}. \tag{24}$$

Solving eq. (23) for n we arrive at

$$n = \frac{2n_0(\varkappa) d_k(\Delta)}{3d_0}\left(1 - \frac{d_k(\Delta)}{d_0}\right), \tag{25}$$

where we use the abbreviations

$$n = \frac{\langle B^\dagger B \rangle}{V}, \qquad \Delta = \omega - \varepsilon, \qquad n_0 = \frac{\varrho d_0}{4T\varkappa}$$

and

$$d_k(\Delta) = \frac{2\hbar\gamma\varkappa\omega}{4\pi\varrho\varepsilon^2 |\mu_{12}|^2}\left(1 + \frac{\Delta^2}{(\gamma + \varkappa)^2}\right). \tag{26}$$

As can be seen from the following remark, d_k represents just the value of d_0, which is necessary to obtain laser action.

From eq. (25) follows immediately a laser condition for zero gain which reads $d_0 = d_k(\Delta)$.

For the special case that the laser frequency coincides with the center of the emission line the laser condition is identical with that given by SCHAWLOW and TOWNES [4] or by FAIN and KHANIN [12].

As can be seen immediately the only displacement of frequency of the laser mode as compared to the frequency in the unloaded cavity is given by the well-known expression (24) [13] which is pump-independent.

As the case of a single mode in a homogeneously broadened line is the only one which can also be solved exactly, we briefly report this solution. Again putting $b^\dagger(t) = B^\dagger \exp[i\Omega t]$, one evaluates from eqs. (12), (13) and (16)

$$\varkappa + i(\Omega - \omega) = \sum_\mu \frac{|h_\mu|^2 \sigma_\mu}{\gamma + i(\Omega - \varepsilon)}, \tag{27}$$

$$\sigma_\mu = d_0 - \frac{4\gamma T |h_\mu|^2}{\gamma^2 + (\Omega - \varepsilon)^2} \langle B^\dagger B \rangle \sigma_\mu . \tag{28}$$

The imaginary part of (27) again yields (24), whereas combining the real part of (27) with (28) leads to

$$\frac{d_k}{2d_0} = \frac{1}{V} \int \frac{\sin^2 \boldsymbol{kr}\, \mathrm{d}\tau}{1 + (2nd_0/n_0 d_k) \sin^2 \boldsymbol{kr}} . \tag{29}$$

Instead of determining n directly as a function of d_0 it is more convenient and elucidates the physical situation better to correlate the photon density n with the absorbed pump power. For this end we introduce the average inversion $d = (1/N)\sum_\mu \sigma_\mu$, which by means of (28) reads

$$Nd = \varrho d_0 \int \frac{\mathrm{d}\tau}{1 + (2nd_0/n_0 d_k) \sin^2 \boldsymbol{kr}} . \tag{30}$$

From (29) and (30) we find immediately

$$n = n_0(\varkappa) \left(1 - \frac{d}{d_0}\right) \tag{31}$$

which can also be written in the form $4\varkappa n = \varrho(d_0 - d)/T$. In it $2\varkappa n V$ is the photon flux, whereas $N(d_0 - d)/2T$ is the number of atomic excitations per second. We thus recover the conservation law of particle number as announced in Sect. **2**. We obtain by integration from (30)

$$\frac{d}{d_0} = \sqrt{\frac{1}{1 + 2nd_0/n_0 d_k}} \tag{32}$$

and after some algebra with additional help of (31)

$$d = \frac{d_k}{4}\left(1 + \sqrt{1 + 8\frac{d_0}{d_k}}\right) . \tag{33}$$

Thus we know n as a function of pumping power d_0, if we insert (33) into (31). The condition $n > 0$ again yields $d_0 > d_k(\Delta)$.

4.1.2. Two modes. – For the case of two modes two new effects show up:

a) due to the time-dependent nonlinearities a frequency pushing occurs,

b) although the line is homogeneously broadened a simultaneous co-existence of laser modes becomes possible.

This latter result is derived quite generally below for several modes.

We evaluate the sums in eq. (22) by integrating over the atomic positions as in the case of one mode and put $d_0 = d_k(0)(1+\eta)$:

$$(34)\quad \left(1 + i\,\frac{\Omega_1 - \omega_1}{\varkappa}\right)\left(1 + i\,\frac{\Omega_1 - \varepsilon}{\gamma}\right) = 1 + \eta - \frac{3n_1}{2n_0}\cdot\frac{(1+\eta)^2}{1 + (\Omega_1 - \varepsilon)^2/\gamma^2} -$$

$$- \frac{n_2(1+\eta)^2}{2n_0(1 + iT[\Omega_1 - \Omega_2]}\left\{\frac{1}{1 - i(\Omega_2 - \varepsilon)/\gamma} + \frac{1}{1 + i(\Omega_1 - \varepsilon)/\gamma}\right\} - \frac{n_2}{n_0}\cdot\frac{(1+\eta)^2}{1 + (\Omega_2 - \varepsilon)^2/\gamma^2}\,.$$

Assuming a moderate pumping power we suppose $\eta \ll 1$. As n_λ/n_0 is of order of magnitude η, we may neglect the factors $(1+\eta)^2$ of n_λ/n_0 thus retaining only terms linear in η. Furthermore we may expand the interaction term with respect to $1/\gamma$. We make no approximation concerning T. We are led to

$$(35)\quad \left(1 + i\,\frac{\Omega_1 - \omega_1}{\varkappa}\right)\left(1 + i\,\frac{\Omega_1 - \varepsilon}{\gamma}\right) = 1 + \eta - \frac{3n_1}{2n_0} - \frac{n_2}{n_0} -$$

$$\frac{n_2(1 - iT[\Omega_1 - \Omega_2])(2 - (i/\gamma)[\Omega_1 - \Omega_2])}{2n_0(1 + T^2[\Omega_1 - \Omega_2]^2)}$$

and by comparing real and imaginary part

$$(36)\quad -\frac{(\Omega_1 - \varepsilon)(\Omega_1 - \omega_1)}{\varkappa\gamma} = \eta - \frac{3n_1}{2n_0} - \frac{n_2}{n_0} - \frac{n_2(2 - (T/\gamma)[\Omega_1 - \Omega_2]^2)}{2n_0(1 + T^2[\Omega_1 - \Omega_2]^2)}\,,$$

$$(37)\quad \Omega_1 - \varepsilon = \frac{\Delta_1}{1 + \varkappa/\gamma} + \frac{(2T + 1/\gamma)\varkappa}{1 + \varkappa/\gamma}\cdot\frac{n_2}{2n_0}\cdot\frac{\Omega_1 - \Omega_2}{1 + T^2(\Omega_1 - \Omega_2)^2}\,.$$

We shall solve eqs. (35)–(37) in some special cases approximately in order to get a survey of the dependence of the solution on parameters such as the pumping power.

Numerical calculations may be done more exactly by assuming fixed values for at least some of the parameters. If $T^2(\Omega_1 - \Omega_2)^2 \gg 1$, (37) and the corresponding equation for $\Omega_2-\varepsilon$ yield

$$(38)\qquad \Omega_1-\Omega_2=\frac{\Delta_1-\Delta_2}{1+\varkappa/\gamma}+\frac{\varkappa(2T+1/\gamma)}{1+\varkappa/\gamma}\cdot\frac{n_1+n_2}{2n_0}\cdot\frac{1}{T^2(\Omega_1-\Omega_2)}.$$

Solving for $\Omega_1-\Omega_2$ one finds from (37)

$$(39)\qquad \Omega_1-\omega_1=\frac{\Delta_1}{1+\varkappa/\gamma}+$$
$$+\frac{2\varkappa n_2}{Tn_0(\Delta_1-\Delta_2)\{1+\sqrt{1+4\varkappa(1+\varkappa/\gamma)^2(n_1+n_2)/Tn_0(\Delta_1-\Delta_2)^2}\}}.$$

On the other hand one gets from (36) and the corresponding equation with reversed indices:

$$(40)\qquad \frac{n_1}{n_0}\left\{5-\frac{2(2-(T/\gamma)(\Omega_1-\Omega_2)^2)}{1+T^2(\Omega_1-\Omega_2)^2}\left[2+\frac{2-(T/\gamma)(\Omega_1-\Omega_2)^2}{2(1+T^2(\Omega_1-\Omega_2)^2)}\right]\right\}=$$
$$=2\eta+\frac{6(\Omega_1-\varepsilon)(\Omega_1-\omega_1)}{\varkappa\gamma}-\frac{4(\Omega_2-\varepsilon)(\Omega_2-\omega_2)}{\varkappa\gamma}-$$
$$-4\left(\eta+\frac{(\Omega_2-\varepsilon)(\Omega_2-\omega_2)}{\varkappa\gamma}\right)\frac{2-(T/\gamma)(\Omega_1-\Omega_2)^2}{2(1+T^2(\Omega_1-\Omega_2)^2)}.$$

As $(2-(T/\gamma)(\Omega_1-\Omega_2)^2)/(1+T^2(\Omega_1-\Omega_2)^2)$ is always a small quantity in the case treated here, one can expand the right-hand side of (40) after division with the curly bracket on the left-hand side:

$$(41)\qquad \frac{n_1}{n_0}=\frac{2}{5}\eta+\frac{6}{5}\cdot\frac{(\Omega_1-\varepsilon)(\Omega_1-\omega_1)}{\varkappa\gamma}-\frac{4}{5}\cdot\frac{(\Omega_2-\varepsilon)(\Omega_2-\omega_2)}{\varkappa\gamma}-$$
$$-\left(\frac{2\eta}{25}-\frac{24}{25}\cdot\frac{(\Omega_1-\varepsilon)(\Omega_1-\omega_1)}{\varkappa\gamma}+\frac{26}{25}\cdot\frac{(\Omega_2-\varepsilon)(\Omega_2-\omega_2)}{\varkappa\gamma}\right)\frac{2-(T/\gamma)(\Omega_1-\Omega_2)^2}{T^2(\Omega_1-\Omega_2)^2}.$$

Evaluating $(\Omega_1-\varepsilon)(\Omega_1-\omega_1)$ from (39) it is seen, that terms n_λ/n_0 on the right-hand side of (41) occur only if multiplied by factors $\ll 1$. Thus it is permissible to replace them by $n_\lambda^{(0)}/n_0$, which are the photon numbers in the case of no interaction, given by

$$\left\{\begin{aligned}\frac{n_1^{(0)}}{n_0}&=\frac{2}{5}\left(\eta-3\frac{\Delta_1^2}{(\gamma+\varkappa)^2}+2\frac{\Delta_2^2}{(\gamma+\varkappa)^2}\right),\\ \frac{n_2^{(2)}}{n_0}&=\frac{2}{5}\left(\eta-3\frac{\Delta_2^2}{(\gamma+\varkappa)^2}+2\frac{\Delta_1^2}{(\gamma+\varkappa)^2}\right).\end{aligned}\right.$$

An elementary but tedious calculation yields, using (39),

$$(42)\quad \frac{n_1}{n_0}=\frac{n_1^{(0)}}{n_0}+\frac{8\varkappa(3n_2^{(0)2}-2n_1^{(0)2})}{5\gamma T^2 n_0^2(\Delta_1-\Delta_2)^2(1+\sqrt{\ })^2}+\frac{4(1-\varkappa/\gamma)(3n_2^{(0)}\Delta_1-2n_1^{(0)}\Delta_2)}{5T(\gamma+\varkappa)n_0(\Delta_1-\Delta_2)(1+\sqrt{\ })}-$$
$$-\frac{2}{25}\left\{\eta+12\frac{\Delta_1^2}{(\gamma+\varkappa)^2}-13\frac{\Delta_2^2}{(\gamma+\varkappa)^2}+\frac{4\varkappa(13n_1^{(0)2}-12n_2^{(0)2})}{\gamma T^2 n_0^2(\Delta_1-\Delta_2)^2(1+\sqrt{\ })^2}-\right.$$
$$\left.-\frac{2(1-\varkappa/\gamma)(12n_2^{(0)}\Delta_1+13n_1^{(0)}\Delta_2)}{T(\gamma+\varkappa)n_0(\Delta_1-\Delta_2)(1+\sqrt{\ })}\right\}\frac{2-(T/\gamma)(\Omega_1-\Omega_2)^2}{T^2(\Omega_1-\Omega_2)^2},$$

where the argument of the square root is the same as in (39). Specliaizing to $\Delta_1^2 \gg \gamma/T$ and $\Delta_2=0$ we derive

$$(43)\quad \begin{cases} \dfrac{n_1}{n_0}=\dfrac{n_1^{(0)}}{n_0}+\dfrac{2}{25\gamma T}\left(7\eta+24\dfrac{\Delta_1^2}{(\gamma+\varkappa)^2}\right)-\dfrac{4}{25T^2\Delta_1^2}\left(\eta+12\dfrac{\Delta_1^2}{(\gamma+\varkappa)^2}\right),\\[2ex] \dfrac{n_2}{n_0}=\dfrac{n_2^{(0)}}{n_0}-\dfrac{6}{25\gamma T}\left(\eta+7\dfrac{\Delta_1^2}{(\gamma+\varkappa)^2}\right)-\dfrac{4}{25T^2\Delta_1^2}\left(\eta-13\dfrac{\Delta_1^2}{(\gamma+\varkappa)^2}\right). \end{cases}$$

Calculations may be extended so as to hold still for $\Delta_1^2\approx 1/T^2$. As no essential modification arises, we will drop them. Because the photon numbers are altered only little, we may replace them in the formula for $\Omega_1-\Omega_2$ by $n_\lambda^{(0)}$. Again putting $\Delta_2=0$ it is found

$$(44)\quad \frac{\Omega_1-\Omega_2}{\Delta_1}=\frac{1+\sqrt{1+16\varkappa\eta(1+\varkappa/\gamma)/5T\Delta_1^2}}{2(1+\varkappa/\gamma)},$$

which is valid even for $\Delta_1^2\approx 1/T^2$ (we presumed above, that $T^2(\Omega_1-\Omega_2)^2\gg 1$; but as $\Omega_1-\Omega_2$ might become considerably larger than $\Delta_1-\Delta_2$, if $\Delta_1-\Delta_2\approx \approx 1/T$, this is true). If $\Delta_1^2\gg\gamma/T$, we may expand the square root obtaining

$$(45)\quad \frac{\Omega_1-\Omega_2}{\Delta_1}=1-\frac{\varkappa}{\gamma}\left(1-\frac{2\gamma}{5T\Delta_1^2}\left[2\eta-\frac{\Delta_1^2}{\gamma^2}\right]\right),$$

For the comparison with experimental data we refer to Sect. 5·2.

4·1.3. Several modes. – The full solution of eqs. (20) is very elaborate and therefore we discuss only the most important features of this case. As can be demonstrated by inserting experimental values for the parameters involved in a first approximation the time-dependent response can be neglected as compared to the time-independent one, or with other words that terms containing $1/((1/T)+i(\Omega_{\lambda_2}-\Omega_{\lambda_1}))$ with $\lambda_2\neq\lambda_1$ in eq. (20) can be disregarded.

Further we have to neglect now explicitly the possibility of frequency mixing, an effect which is very small anyhow under the present assumptions.

With these simplifications the eqs. (20) lead to the following set for the real part:

$$\frac{d_k(\Delta_1)}{d_0} = 1 - \frac{3n_1 d_0}{2n_0(\varkappa_1)\, d_k(\Delta_1)} - \frac{n_2 d_0}{n_0(\varkappa_2)\, d_k(\Delta_2)} - \ldots - \frac{n_M d_0}{n_0(\varkappa_M)\, d_k(\Delta_M)} \tag{46}$$

and similar equations for all modes $1 \ldots M$. Note that (46) allows for different losses of the modes.

The imaginary part determines the frequencies as in the case of a single mode to

$$\Omega_\lambda = \omega_\lambda + \frac{\varepsilon - \omega_\lambda}{1 + \gamma/\varkappa_\lambda}.$$

Introducing the abbreviations:

$$\frac{n_M d_0}{2n_0(\varkappa_M)\, d_k(\Delta_M)} = \tilde{n}_M, \qquad 1 - \frac{d_k(\Delta_M)}{d_0} = l_M$$

where $n_0(\varkappa)$ and $d_k(\Delta)$ have been introduced in Sect. **4**.1.1. we get the following set of equations

$$\left\{\begin{array}{l} 3\tilde{n}_1 + 2\tilde{n}_2 + \ldots + 2\tilde{n}_M = l_1, \\ 2\tilde{n}_2 + 3\tilde{n}_2 + \ldots + 2\tilde{n}_M = l_2, \\ \cdot \quad \cdot \quad \cdot \quad \cdot \quad \cdot \\ 2\tilde{n}_1 + 2\tilde{n}_2 + \ldots + 3\tilde{n}_M = l_M. \end{array}\right. \tag{47}$$

This set of equations allows now the discussion of the co-existence of modes. If a mode lases, the photon number of it must be necessarily positive. If any of the photon numbers becomes negative the corresponding equation within the system (47) has to be dropped. This is self-consistent because in writing down eqs. (46) we divided both sides by $b_\lambda^\dagger$. The solution of this set of equations is straightforward and gives for the i-th mode

$$n_i = \frac{2n_0(\varkappa_i)\, d_k(\Delta_i)}{d_0} \left\{ \frac{1}{2M+1} - \frac{d_k(\Delta_i)}{d_0} + \frac{2\,[d_k(\Delta_1) + \ldots + d_k(\Delta_M)]}{(2M+1)d_0} \right\}. \tag{48}$$

Let us discuss first the special case that we have only two modes. Equation (48) then reads for mode 1

$$n_1 = \frac{2n_0(\varkappa_1)\, d_k(\Delta_1)}{5d_0} \left(1 - 3\,\frac{d_k(\Delta_1)}{d_0} + 2\,\frac{d_k(\Delta_2)}{d_0} \right)$$

and similarly for mode 2.

We see immediately that with increasing pumping power both n's can become positive. A closer inspection shows that this stems from the fact that the spatial averages over the atomic depletion as described by

$$\sum_{\mu} |h_{\mu\lambda}|^2 |h_{\mu\lambda'}|^2 \sim \int \sin^2 k_{\lambda'} x \cdot \sin^2 k_{\lambda} x \, dx$$

differ by a factor $\frac{3}{2}$ for a single mode $\lambda' = \lambda$ and two modes $\lambda'' \neq \lambda$. This effect can be tracked down to the following physical situation:

If we have two modes then the nodes, respectively, antinodes of both modes are situated at different lattice sites so that both modes affect the atoms differently. This physical reasoning leads to the question if it is possible to suppress the additional lasing mode by an inhomogeneous pumping which compensates just for the spatial inhomogeneous depletion of atoms. A detailed calculation by one of us has shown that this is in fact possible within a certain pumping range by a modulation of the pumping power with a wave length corresponding to the double difference of the k-numbers of the two modes.

Now let us return to the general case of M modes and assume that the mode with lowest $\varkappa$ is exactly at resonance and the next ones are off-axial modes. We assume for simplicity that these modes lie all in the same plane of k-space. Since the modulation is now different perpendicular to the crystalline axis, again a difference occurs in the atomic depletion which brings about exactly the same factor $\frac{3}{2}$ as treated above. In this case of equal modes we can neglect the change with frequency but we have to take into account the increasing losses with increasing angles relative to the cavity axis. Therefore, if we put $d_k(\Delta_i) = d_0(1-\eta_i)$, eq. (48) becomes

$$n_i = \frac{2n_0(\varkappa_i)\, d_k(\Delta_i)}{(2M+1)\, d_0} \left((2M+1)\eta_i - 2 \sum_{l=1}^{M} \eta_l \right). \tag{49}$$

Note, that the factor in front of the bracket does not depend on $\varkappa_i$.

Putting for the losses in the usual way

$$\eta_1 = \eta_0\,, \quad \eta_2 = \eta_0(1-q)\,, \ldots, \eta_M = \eta_0(1-q)^{M-1} \qquad \text{with } q \ll 1,$$

we obtain for the condition of oscillation of the M-th mode

$$(2M+1)\,\eta_0(1-q)^{M-1} > 2 \sum_{l=1}^{M} \eta_0(1-q)^{l-1}\,. \tag{50}$$

Keeping only terms of first order in q one readily evaluates

$$M \approx \frac{1}{2}\sqrt{\frac{2}{q}}\,.$$

Thus, if $q=10^{-2}$ for instance, 7 modes may oscillate even slightly above threshold. This consideration can be simply generalized to the true three-dimensional case in which the off-axial modes fill a cone of the spatial angle. It may be noted that in cases in which two modes differ not only in the axial k-number but also in the additional one a factor $\frac{4}{9}$ instead of $\frac{2}{3}$ occurs and if they differ in all three k-numbers a factor of $\frac{8}{27}$ appears.

The solution of the corresponding equations is rather simple but shall be dropped here.

The above analysis shows that in principle several modes can coexist. However, the question if this configuration is stable against changes in the occupation numbers was left open so far. However, one may demonstrate that this stability is in fact present (compare Sect. **6**).

Finally we draw the attention to the following important point. If one does not take into account a spatial-dependent inversion as has been done for instance in the paper by WAGNER and BIRNBAUM [6] one would obtain only one stable mode. This can be seen in the following way:

We assume that all atoms have the same degree of inversion, σ_μ thus being independent of μ.

Making the ansatz

$$b_\lambda^\dagger(t) = B_\lambda^\dagger \exp[i\Omega_\lambda t], \qquad a_\mu^\dagger(t) = \sum_\lambda A_\lambda^\mu \exp[i\Omega_\lambda t],$$

where Ω_λ may be complex, $\Omega_\lambda = \Omega_\lambda^0 + i\Gamma_\lambda$, we obtain from (12) and (16)

$$(51)\qquad \begin{cases} A_\lambda^\mu(\gamma + i[\Omega_\lambda - \varepsilon]) = -ih_{\mu\lambda} B_\lambda^\dagger \bar{\sigma}, \\ B_\lambda^\dagger(\varkappa_\lambda + i[\Omega_\lambda - \omega_\lambda]) = i\sum_\mu h_{\mu\lambda}^* \sum_{\lambda'} A_{\lambda'}^\mu. \end{cases}$$

Combining the equations leads to

$$(\varkappa_\lambda + i[\Omega_\lambda - \omega_\lambda])(\gamma + i[\Omega_\lambda - \varepsilon]) = \bar{\sigma}\sum_\mu |h_{\mu\lambda}|^2.$$

or by separating real and imaginary parts,

$$(52)\qquad \begin{cases} \Omega_\lambda^0 - \varepsilon = \dfrac{\Delta_\lambda}{1 + (\varkappa_\lambda - \Gamma_\lambda)/(\gamma - \Gamma_\lambda)}, \\ \{-(\Omega_\lambda^0 - \omega_\lambda)(\Omega_\lambda^0 - \varepsilon) + (\gamma - \Gamma_\lambda)(\varkappa_\lambda - \Gamma_\lambda)\} = \bar{\sigma}\sum_\mu |h_{\mu\lambda}|^2. \end{cases}$$

From (52) we may determine $\Gamma_\lambda = \Gamma_\lambda(\Delta_\lambda, \varkappa_\lambda, \bar{\sigma})$. Now, in a stationary state, clearly all Γ_λ must be zero. That means, that we would have to fix $\bar{\sigma}$ from (16) such that these relations are fulfilled. Inserting (51) into (16) and averaging over μ in order to obtain $\bar{\sigma}$, thereby accounting for the orthogonality of the $h_{\mu\lambda}$ yields

$$\bar{\sigma} = d_0 - 2T \left\{ \sum_\lambda \frac{\overline{|h_\lambda|^2} \langle n_\lambda \rangle \bar{\sigma}}{\gamma - i(\Omega_\lambda^* - \varepsilon)} + \text{c.c.} \right\}, \tag{53}$$

where

$$\overline{|h_\lambda|^2} = \frac{1}{N} \sum_\mu |h_{\mu\lambda}|^2 .$$

Now it is evident, that we can adjust the photon numbers $\langle n_\lambda \rangle$ in several ways in order to determine $\bar{\sigma}$ for example such that $\Gamma_1 = \Gamma_1(\varkappa_1, \Delta_1, \bar{\sigma}) = 0$.

Let us assume, that this mode is just the one, which is closest to resonance and which has the highest lifetime in the unloaded cavity. It is then immediately clear, that all other modes are damped out exponentially, so that only mode 1 should occur in the steady state. This result is a consequence of the fact, that we replaced σ_μ by $\bar{\sigma}$.

On the other hand such a space-independent inversion can in fact be obtained by using a laser cavity which allows for running modes instead of standing waves as has been demonstrated for instance in the case of the gyroscope. In the case of the gyroscope we have two oppositely running waves having the same frequency. If we neglect the difference of polarization it can rather easily be seen that the configuration of two simultaneous lasing modes is unstable for the solid state laser as will be discussed below. However, we will get a stable configuration if we take into account different polarizations of the two lasing modes.

As we will demonstrate below, however, in the gas laser the running waves will eat from different portions of the Doppler broadened line so that both modes can coexist due to the inhomogeneous broadening.

4.1.4. Extension to higher pump power. – The applicability of our method of solution depends on two points.

Firstly it presumes, that all effects being brought about by the time-dependent response of the atomic system, such as frequency mixing and frequency pushing, can be considered as corrections to the ones being produced by the time-independent response. That this is indeed the case, has been shown in detail in the previous Sections.

Secondly it assumes, because of the iteration of eq. (16) that the actual inversion σ_μ does not depart essentially from the pumping level d_0, or with other words, that the pumping level d_0 does not exceed too much the critical inversion of the lasing modes.

In the present Section we shall inspect this questions more closely, disregarding all terms which stem from the time-dependent response. Making the ansatz $b_\lambda^\dagger(t) B_\lambda^\dagger \exp[i\Omega_\lambda t]$ and $\sigma_\mu(t) = S_\mu$, where S_μ does not depend on t, one evaluates from (12), (13) and (16)

$$\frac{d_k(\lambda)}{2d_0} = \frac{1}{L}\int_0^L \frac{\sin^2 k_\lambda x \, dx}{1 + \sum_\lambda (2n_\lambda d_0/n_0 d_k(\lambda)) \sin^2 k_\lambda x} \tag{54}$$

where L is the length of the cavity. The frequencies of the modes are again given by (24). In verifying this formula one realizes that it holds only if the « orthogonality » integral

$$\int_0^L \frac{\sin k_1 x \sin k_2 x \, dx}{1 + \sin^2 k_1 x \cdot a + b \sin^2 k_2 x},$$

where

$$a = \frac{2n_1 d_0}{n_0 d_k(1)}, \qquad b = \frac{2n_0 d_0}{n_0 d_k(2)},$$

vanishes. Otherwise the above ansatz would not suffice. We have proved that it is at least by a factor $1/k^2 (k^2 \approx k_\lambda^2)$ smaller than the integral of eq. (54), so that it is completely negligible. As a general evaluation of (54) leads to an elliptic integral of the third kind whose parameters are essentially the photon numbers, we have restricted to the case, that $b < 1$, *i.e.*, mode 1 may oscillate with an arbitrary high amplitude, whereas mode 2 is just above threshold. Expanding the integral to first order in b, it becomes for $\lambda = 1$

$$\mathscr{F}_1 = \frac{L}{a}\left\{1 - \frac{1}{\sqrt{1+a}}\left(1 + \frac{a}{4(1+a)}\, b\right)\right\} \tag{55a}$$

and for $\lambda = 2$

$$\mathscr{F}_2 = \frac{L}{4\sqrt{1+a}}\left(2 - \frac{3}{4}\frac{2+a}{1+a}\, b\right). \tag{55b}$$

Introducing $\xi_\lambda = n_\lambda / n_0$ and $\varphi_\lambda = 2d_0/d_k(\lambda)$ we deduce from (54) for the unknown quantities ξ_1 and ξ_2 using (55a) and (55b):

$$\xi_1 = 1 - \frac{1}{\sqrt{1+\xi_1\varphi_1}}\left(1 + \frac{\varphi_1\varphi_2}{4(1+\xi_1\varphi_1)}\, \xi_1\xi_2\right), \tag{56a}$$

$$1 = \frac{\varphi_2}{4(1+\xi_1\varphi_1)}\left(2 - \frac{3}{4}\varphi_2\xi_2 \frac{2+\xi_1\varphi_1}{1+\xi_1\varphi_1}\right), \tag{56b}$$

In accordance with the above assumption we linearize these two equations by putting $\xi_1 = \xi_1^{(0)} - \delta\xi$ and neglect all products of the form $\xi_2 \cdot \delta\xi$. $\xi_1^{(0)}$ satisfies the unperturbed equation

$$\xi_1^{(0)} = 1 - \frac{1}{\sqrt{1 + \xi_1^{(0)} \varphi_1}}$$

which is nothing but eq. (31) for single-mode operation. Solving for $\xi_2 = n_2/n_0$ leads to

$$\xi_2 = \frac{n_2}{n_0} = \frac{4(d_k(2)/d_0)(d/d_0 + 2)(1 - d_k(2)/d)}{(d/d_0)^3 + 2(d/d_0)^2 + d/d_0 + 6}, \tag{57}$$

where d is given by eq. (33). Now the function

$$f\left(\frac{d}{d_0}\right) = \frac{(d/d_0 + 2)}{(d/d_0)^3 + 2(d/d_0)^2 + (d/d_0) + 6}$$

which depends in a complicated manner on the pumping level d_0, ranges between 0.33 ± 0.02 if d/d_0 covers its allowed values $0 < d/d_0 < 1$. Thus $f(d/d_0)$ may be looked upon as a constant, which depends not on d_0. Comparing (57) with (48) one states that our iteration procedure provides a very good approximation even in the case of higher pumping levels. Specializing (57) to the case where the amplitude of mode 1 is still small, too, one controls that the numerical factors of (57) and (48) become identical.

Finally one recognizes from (57) that the oscillation condition of mode 2 is $d > d_k(2)$ or, using (33),

$$d_0 > d_k(2)\left(2\frac{d_k(2)}{d_k(1)} - 1\right). \tag{58}$$

That is, if one mode is present a second mode goes into oscillation, if the *actual average* inversion exceeds the *critical* inversion of mode 2. This is completely analogous to the laser condition for a single mode, $d_0 > d_k(\Delta)$, which was derived in Sect. **4**.1.1, because in this former case the actual average inversion is d_0 when this mode is at threshold.

4.2. *Inhomogeneously broadened Gaussian line.* – The essential difference between the preceding Section and the present one is that we must not only sum up over the atomic positions but also over the transition energy.

4.2.1. One mode (*). – As an example we choose a Gaussian distribution for ε. It should be noted, that other distributions can be treated similarly

(*) We assume in Sect. **4**.2.1 and **4**.2.2, that due to a crystal symmetry the atomic dipole moments point in only one direction. If the atomic dipole moments are at random the formulas are slightly changed. The corresponding results are given in the Appendix (Section B).

or in the case of a Lorentzian line shape even more simply (compare Sect. 4·3).

The sums over the atomic indices μ then lead to the following expression

$$(59)\qquad \varkappa + i(\Omega - \omega) = \frac{\varrho A d_0}{2}\int\left\{\frac{\gamma - i(\Omega-\varepsilon)}{\gamma^2 + (\Omega-\varepsilon)^2} - \right.$$

$$\left. - 3\gamma T A n \frac{\gamma - i(\Omega-\varepsilon)}{[\gamma^2+(\Omega-\varepsilon)^2]^2}\right\}\frac{\exp\left[-\left((\varepsilon-\varepsilon_0)/\alpha\right)^2\right]\mathrm{d}\varepsilon}{\alpha\sqrt{\pi}},$$

where

$$A = \frac{4\pi\varepsilon_0^2\,|\mu_{12}|^2}{\hbar\omega}.$$

In eq. (59) we have already performed the integrals over $\boldsymbol{r}$. Further it was assumed, that the polarization vector $\boldsymbol{e}$ is parallel to the atomic-dipole moment $\boldsymbol{\mu}$. The integrals over ε are evaluated under the assumption, that the inhomogeneous line-width is large as compared to the homogeneous Lorentzian line-width, which is described by the imaginary part γ of ε. For the evaluation of the integrals compare Appendix (Section C).

Using the result of the evaluation of the integrals and splitting eq. (59) into real and imaginary part, we find the following equations:

$$(60)\qquad \Omega - \omega = -\frac{\varrho A d_0}{2}\int_0^\delta \exp[u^2 - \delta^2]\,\mathrm{d}u + \frac{3A^2\varrho d_0 T\sqrt{\pi}\,n\delta\exp[-\delta^2]}{2\alpha^2},$$

$$(61)\qquad \varkappa = \frac{\varrho A d_0}{2}\left\{\frac{\sqrt{\pi}}{\alpha}\exp[-\delta^2] - 3ATn\frac{\sqrt{\pi}\exp[-\delta^2]}{2\gamma\alpha}\right\},$$

where

$$\delta = \frac{\Omega - \varepsilon_0}{\alpha}.$$

The equation for the real part determines the number of photons n of the equilibrium inversion, which is a function of pumping power. Solving this equation for n we arrive at

$$(62)\qquad n = \frac{2\gamma}{3AT}\left(1 - \frac{d_k(\delta)}{d_0}\right) = \frac{\gamma}{\alpha}\frac{\sqrt{\pi}\,\varrho d_k(0)}{3\varkappa T}\left(1 - \frac{d_k(\delta)}{d_0}\right),$$

where we use the abbreviation $d_k(\delta)$ for the critical inversion

$$d_k(\delta) = \frac{\hbar\alpha\varkappa\omega\exp[\delta^2]}{2\sqrt{\pi^3}\,\varrho\,|\varepsilon_0|^2|\mu_{12}|^2}.$$

If we introduce the expression for n into eq. (60) we obtain the following expression for the frequency shift under the assumption that Ω on the right-hand side of (61) may be replaced by the frequency ω of the unloaded cavity

$$\Omega = \omega - \varkappa \frac{2d_0}{d_k(\delta)}\left\{\int_0^\delta \exp[u^2]\,du - \delta\frac{\gamma}{\alpha}\sqrt{\pi}\left(1-\frac{d_k(\delta)}{d_0}\right)\right\}. \tag{63}$$

We discuss the different terms giving rise to the frequency shift $\Omega-\omega$. The first term is peculiar for the Doppler broadening, as is well known from the analysis of other papers [2]. Note that this shift is pump-dependent on account of its factor d_0. It gives rise to a pulling of the frequency of the line in the unloaded cavity to the center of the emission line. The next term, which is small as compared to the first one on account of its factor γ/α, describes a repulsion from the center of the line. It has been predicted by BENNETT by qualitative arguments «hole-burning of one line on itself», which, however, have left especially the sign of this term open.

4·2.2. Two modes. – Again we consider the case of fixed atoms at random lattice sites. Replacing the sums over the atomic indices by integrals, which are again evaluated up to order γ/α and splitting the equations for the two amplitudes $B_1^\dagger$ and $B_2^\dagger$ into real and imaginary part, we obtain the following two equations

$$\begin{aligned}\frac{d_k(1)}{d_0} = 1 &- \frac{3n_1AT}{2\gamma} - \frac{2n_2AT\gamma}{4\gamma^2+\Delta\Omega^2}\left\{1+\exp[\delta_1^2-\delta_2^2]+\right.\\ &\left.+\frac{4\gamma}{\sqrt{\pi}\Delta\Omega}\left[\int_0^{\delta_1}\exp[u^2]\,du-\exp[\delta_1^2-\delta_2^2]\int_0^{\delta_2}\exp[u^2]\,du\right]\right\}-\\ &-\frac{ATn_2}{(4\gamma^2+\Delta\Omega^2)(1+T^2\Delta\Omega^2)}\left\{2\gamma(1+\exp[\delta_1^2-\delta_2^2])+\right.\\ &\left.+\frac{2\Delta\Omega}{\sqrt{\pi}}\left(\exp[\delta_1^2-\delta_2^2]\int_0^{\delta_2}\exp[u^2]\,du-\int_0^{\delta_1}\exp[u^2]\,du\right)\right\}-\\ &-\frac{ATn_2}{1+T^2\Delta\Omega^2}\left\{\frac{2}{\alpha\sqrt{\pi}}-\frac{4}{\alpha\sqrt{\pi}}\int_0^{\delta_1}(\delta_1-u)\exp[u^2]\,du\right\}+\frac{ATn_2T\Delta\Omega}{1+T^2\Delta\Omega^2}\frac{2\delta_1}{\alpha}-\\ &-\frac{ATn_2\cdot T\Delta\Omega}{(4\gamma^2+\Delta\Omega^2)(1+T^2\Delta\Omega^2)}\left\{-\Delta\Omega(\exp[\delta_1^2-\delta_2^2]+1)+\right.\\ &\left.+\frac{4\gamma}{\sqrt{\pi}}\left(\exp[\delta_1^2-\delta_2^2]\int_0^{\delta_2}\exp[u^2]\,du-\int_0^{\delta_1}\exp[u^2]\,du\right)\right\}\end{aligned} \tag{64}$$

and

$$(65)\qquad \Omega_1 = \omega_1 + \frac{\sqrt{\pi}\varrho A d_0 \exp[-\delta_1^2]}{2\alpha}\Bigg\{-\frac{2}{\sqrt{\pi}}\int_0^{\delta_1}\exp[u^2]\,\mathrm{d}n +$$

$$+\frac{3ATn_1\delta_1}{\alpha} + \frac{2An_2T}{\Delta\Omega(4\gamma^2+\Delta\Omega^2)}\Bigg[(\Delta\Omega^2+2\gamma^2)\exp[\delta_1^2-\delta_2^2] - 2\gamma^2 +$$

$$+\frac{2\gamma\Delta\Omega}{\sqrt{\pi}}\left(\int_0^{\delta_1}\exp[u^2]\,\mathrm{d}u - \exp[\delta_1^2-\delta_2^2]\int_0^{\delta_2}\exp[u^2]\,\mathrm{d}u\right)\Bigg] -$$

$$-\frac{ATn_2}{(4\gamma^2+\Delta\Omega^2)(1+T^2\Delta\Omega^2)}\Bigg[-\Delta\Omega(1+\exp[\delta_1^2-\delta_2^2]) +$$

$$+\frac{4\gamma}{\sqrt{\pi}}\left(\exp[\delta_1^2-\delta_2^2]\int_0^{\delta_2}\exp[u^2]\,\mathrm{d}u - \int_0^{\delta_1}\exp[u^2]\,\mathrm{d}u\right)\Bigg] +$$

$$+\frac{ATn_2T\Delta\Omega}{(4\gamma^2+\Delta\Omega^2)(1+T^2\Delta\Omega^2)}\Bigg[\frac{2\Delta\Omega}{\sqrt{\pi}}\left(\exp[\delta_1^2-\delta_2^2]\int_0^{\delta_2}\exp[u^2]\,\mathrm{d}u - \int_0^{\delta_1}\exp[u^2]\,\mathrm{d}u\right) +$$

$$+2\gamma(1+\exp[\delta_1^2-\delta_2^2])\Bigg] + \frac{ATn_2}{1+T^2\Delta\Omega^2}\frac{2\delta_1}{\alpha} +$$

$$+\frac{ATn_2T\Delta\Omega}{1+T^2\Delta\Omega^2}\left(\frac{2}{\alpha\sqrt{\pi}} - \frac{4}{\alpha\sqrt{\pi}}\int_0^{\delta_1}(\delta_1-u)\exp[u^2)]\,\mathrm{d}u\right)\Bigg\}$$

and two corresponding equations with interchanged indices. Thus far no assumption concerning $\Delta\Omega = \Omega_1 - \Omega_2$ has been made. We have solved these equations for the *photon numbers* n_1 and n_2 neglecting all terms, which originate in the time-dependent response of the atoms. This is justified, because the effects of this response on the field strengths of the two modes are small.

The main purpose of the following equation is therefore to describe how the photon number n_1 of mode one is affected by the presence of a second mode as a function of their frequency separation $\Delta\Omega$ in the lowest order (time-independent) approximation.

$$(66)\qquad n_1 = \frac{2\gamma}{3AT}\Bigg[\left(1-\frac{d_k(1)}{d_0}\right) + \frac{4}{3(4+(\Delta\Omega/\gamma)^2)}\Bigg\{1+\exp[\delta_1^2-\delta_2^2] +$$

$$+\frac{4\gamma}{\sqrt{\pi}\Delta\Omega}\left(\int_0^{\delta_1}\exp[u^2]\,\mathrm{d}u - \exp[\delta_1^2-\delta_2^2]\int_0^{\delta_2}\exp[u^2]\,\mathrm{d}u\right)\Bigg\}\left(\frac{d_k(2)}{d_0}-1\right)\Bigg]\cdot$$

$$\cdot\Bigg[1-\frac{16}{9(4+(\Delta\Omega/\gamma)^2)^2}\cdot\Bigg\{1+\exp[\delta_1^2-\delta_2^2] + \frac{4\gamma}{\sqrt{\pi}\Delta\Omega}\Bigg(\int_0^{\delta_1}\exp[u\;]\,\mathrm{d}u -$$

$$-\exp[\delta_1^2-\delta_2^2]\int_0^{\delta_2}\exp[u^2]\mathrm{d}u\Big)\Big\}\Big\{1+\exp[\delta_2^2-\delta_1^2]+$$

$$+\frac{4\gamma}{\sqrt{\pi}\Delta\Omega}\Big(\exp[\delta_2^2-\delta_1^2]\int_0^{\delta_1}\exp[u^2]\mathrm{d}u-\int_0^{\delta_2}\exp[u^2]\mathrm{d}u\Big)\Big\}\Big]\,.$$

Equation (66) shows, that the photon numbers of the two modes influence one another notably only if the frequency separation is of the order of the natural line width γ. The coupling between the two photon numbers decreases roughly as $(\gamma/\Delta\Omega)^2$. As we will show immediately the mutual influence of the frequencies is larger and decreases only as $\gamma/\Delta\Omega$ if $\Delta\Omega>\gamma$ in the same order of approximation.

Let us discuss the frequency shift for instance of mode number one. The corresponding expression (67) contains three parts ((67) is derived from (65) by assuming $\Delta\Omega/\gamma>1$, that means, that the photon numbers in (67) may be considered as independent from one another):

$$\Omega_1=\omega_1+\frac{\varkappa d_0}{d_k(1)}\Big((\Gamma_1+\Gamma_2+\Gamma_3)\Big)\,, \tag{67}$$

where

$$\Gamma_1=-\frac{2}{\sqrt{\pi}}\int_0^{\delta_1}\exp[u^2]\,\mathrm{d}u+\frac{3ATn_1\delta_1}{\alpha}\,, \tag{67a}$$

$$\Gamma_2=\frac{2An_2T}{\Delta\Omega}\exp[\delta_1^2-\delta_2^2]\,, \tag{67b}$$

$$\Gamma_3=\frac{ATn_2}{1+T^2\Delta\Omega^2}\Big\{\frac{1}{\Delta\Omega}(1+\exp[\delta_1^2-\delta_2^2])+ \tag{67c}$$

$$+\frac{2\delta_1}{\alpha}+\frac{2T}{\sqrt{\pi}}\Big(\exp[\delta_1^2-\delta_2^2]\int_0^{\delta_2}\exp[u^2]\,\mathrm{d}u-\int_0^{\delta_1}\exp[u^2]\,\mathrm{d}u\Big)+$$

$$+\frac{2T\Delta\Omega}{\alpha\sqrt{\pi}}\Big(1-2\int_0^{\delta_1}(\delta_1-u)\exp[u^2]\,\mathrm{d}u\Big)\Big\}\,.$$

The first two terms (67*a*) are exactly the same as those of one mode, which, as we have discussed above, give rise to a pulling of the line toward the center of the emission line. The following term (67*b*) is brought about by a time-independent depletion of the excited atomic states due to their interaction with the other mode. It is thus a hole-burning effect as has been described in a macroscopic language by BENNETT [2].

The group (67*c*) consists of terms, which stem from the time-dependent response of the atomic system. Whereas for a homogeneously broadened line the latter group is most important for the explanation of the repulsion of the frequencies of modes in the case of an inhomogeneously broadened line the first groups will be more important in general. The size of the terms (67*c*) depends in a crucial manner on the relaxation time T under which the inversion of the atomic system is achieved. The other groups of terms (67*a*) and (67*b*) do not depend on this relaxation time, since the n's are inversely proportional to T. One might therefore hope to find systems in which the measurement of line shifts leads to a direct determination of the relaxation time.

4·3. *Lorentzian line-shape.* – If one chooses a Lorentzian distribution

$$w(\varepsilon)=\frac{\alpha}{\pi}\frac{1}{\alpha^2+(\varepsilon-\varepsilon_0)^2} \tag{68}$$

for the center frequencies of the active atoms, all integrals over the transition energy can be evaluated exactly with the help of the calculus of residues. In the limit $\alpha\to 0$, $w(\varepsilon)$ tends to $\delta(\varepsilon-\varepsilon_0)$, so that we reobtain the results of the homogeneously broadened line in this case. On the other hand, if $\alpha\gg\gamma$, the following formulas correspond to the situation, which was treated in Sect. **4**·2 for a Gaussian.

As calculations are straightforward, we merely quote the results.

For a single mode we get

$$n=\frac{\big((\alpha+\gamma)/3AT\big)\big(1-d_k(\delta)/d_0\big)}{\alpha/2\gamma+1/(1+\delta_1^2)}\,, \tag{69}$$

$$\Omega=\omega-\varkappa\delta\left\{1+\frac{(d_0/d_k-1)}{1+2\gamma/\alpha(1+\delta^2)}\right\}, \tag{70}$$

where

$$\delta=\frac{\omega-\varepsilon_0}{\alpha+\gamma}\qquad\text{and}\qquad d_k(\delta)=\frac{2\varkappa(\alpha+\gamma)(1+\delta^2)}{\varrho A}$$

is the critical inversion. A is defined as in Sect. **4**·2.1.

In-two mode operation we find for the frequency shifts:

$$\begin{aligned}\Omega_1=\omega_1-\varkappa\delta_1+\varkappa\frac{d_0}{d_k(0)}\Bigg\{&-\frac{\tilde{n}_1\delta_1\alpha}{2\gamma(1+\delta_1^2)}+\frac{\alpha\tilde{n}_2[\Delta(1+2/(1+\alpha/\gamma))-\delta_1]}{3\gamma(1+\delta_2^2)(1+\Delta^2)}+\\&+\frac{\tilde{n}_2}{3(1+T^2\Delta\Omega^2)}\left[\frac{T\Delta\Omega-\delta_2}{1+\delta_2^2}+\frac{T\Delta\Omega+\delta_1}{1+\delta_1^2}+\frac{\alpha}{\gamma}\frac{T\Delta\Omega(1+\Delta\delta_2)+\Delta-\delta_2}{(1+\delta_2^2)(1+\Delta^2)}\right]\Bigg\},\end{aligned} \tag{71}$$

where

$$\tilde{n} = \frac{3nAT}{\gamma + \alpha} \qquad \text{and} \qquad \Delta = \frac{\Omega_1 - \Omega_2}{2\gamma} = \frac{\Delta\Omega}{2\gamma}.$$

Inspection of (71) shows, that in the range $\alpha \approx \gamma$, which was not covered by the results of A and B no new physical effects occur.

5. – Application to gas lasers (*).

5·1. *Inhomogeneously broadened Gaussian line.* – For gas lasers a series of high-precision measurements have been performed by JAVAN *et al.* [14] and BENNETT *et al.* [2]. For our present paper the experimental findings of Bennett about frequency shifts are of fundamental importance. In order to apply our results derived below we have to discuss first some general features of gas lasers.

First of all we have to take into account the motion of atoms which leads to a Doppler broadened line. It is not clear, however, from the very beginning if this line is to be treated as a homogeneously or an inhomogeneously broadened one. The crucial parameter is the collision time for wide-angle scattering. If this time is short, scattering occurs so quickly that the line is almost homogeneous.

On the other hand, for rather slow scattering times no homogeneization occurs at all. According to a tentative estimate by BENNETT [2] the wide-angle collision time should be rather slow. To cover this case we perform a calculation with an inhomogeneously broadened Gaussian line. It should be noted, however, that at present there are no direct measurements of the wide-angle collision time available.

In the following we take into account explicitly that the atoms may move according to a Gaussian velocity distribution.

5·1.1. One mode. – We take into consideration explicitly the motion of the atoms and assume a given velocity distribution. Our former index of atomic number μ is therefore to be replaced by the velocity and the position of these atoms. The new equation of motion can be obtained from those of fixed atoms (12)–(16) simply by substituting in the matrix element $h_{\mu\lambda}$, $\boldsymbol{r}_\mu$ by $\boldsymbol{r}_\mu + v_x t$, *i.e.*,

$$h_\mu = \frac{-ih}{2}\left(\exp[ikx + ikvt] - \exp[-(ikx + ikvt)]\right)\cos\theta\,,$$

(*) This case was also treated by W. E. LAMB (*Talk Given at the Third Internat. Symposium on Quantum Electronics* Febr. 1963, Paris), by a different method. A detailed account of Lamb's work is given in this volume, p. 78.

where θ is the angle between the polarization vector of the light wave and the dipole moment of the μ-th atom. We specialize our treatment to one- and two-mode operation and start with one mode, making for the time dependence of the amplitude again an exponential ansatz: $b^\dagger(t) = B^\dagger \exp[i\Omega t]$. All the steps which have been done in Sect. **3** can be immediately repeated, and we obtain with the same degree of approximation for the amplitude the following equation

$$[\varkappa + i(\Omega - \omega)] B^\dagger \exp[i\Omega t] = i \sum_\mu \cos\theta\, h_\mu^*(t)\, a_\mu^\dagger(t)\,, \tag{72}$$

where

$$\begin{aligned}
a_\mu^\dagger(t) = {} & \frac{id_0 h\cos\theta}{2}\left(\frac{\exp[i(kx+\varepsilon t)]}{\Omega-\varepsilon_0-i\gamma+\varepsilon} - \frac{\exp[-i(kx+\varepsilon t)]}{\Omega-\varepsilon_0-i\gamma-\varepsilon}\right) B^+ \exp[i\Omega t] - \\
& -\gamma T\langle n\rangle d_0 |h|^2 \cos^3\theta\left[\frac{1}{(\Omega-\varepsilon_0+\varepsilon)^2+\gamma^2}+\frac{1}{(\Omega-\varepsilon_0-\varepsilon)^2+\gamma^2}\right]\cdot \\
& \cdot\left[\frac{\exp[-i(kx+\varepsilon t)]}{i(\Omega-\varepsilon_0-i\gamma-\varepsilon)} - \frac{\exp[i(kx+\varepsilon t)]}{i(\Omega-\varepsilon_0+\varepsilon-i\gamma)}\right]\frac{h}{2} B^+ \exp[i\Omega t] + \\
& + \frac{B^+\langle n\rangle d_0(\gamma+i\varepsilon)\cos^3\theta h|h|^2 \exp[ikx]\exp[i(\Omega+\varepsilon)t]}{2i(1/T+2i\varepsilon)[(\Omega-\varepsilon_0)^2-(\varepsilon-i\gamma)^2][\Omega-\varepsilon_0+\varepsilon-i\gamma]} - \\
& - \frac{B^+\langle n\rangle d_0(\gamma-i\varepsilon)\cos^3\theta h|h|^2 \exp[-ikx]\exp[i(\Omega-\varepsilon)t]}{2i(1/T-2i\varepsilon)[(\Omega-\varepsilon_0)^2-(\varepsilon+i\gamma)^2][\Omega-\varepsilon_0-\varepsilon-i\gamma]} - \\
& - \frac{B^+\langle n\rangle d_0 h|h|^2\cos^3\theta(\gamma+i\varepsilon)\exp[3ikx]\exp[i(\Omega+3\varepsilon)t]}{2i(1/T+2i\varepsilon)[(\Omega-\varepsilon_0)^2-(\varepsilon-i\gamma)^2][\Omega-\varepsilon_0+3\varepsilon-i\gamma]} + \\
& + \frac{B^+\langle n\rangle d_0(\gamma-i\varepsilon)\cos^3\theta h|h|^2\exp[-3ikx]\exp[i(\Omega-3\varepsilon)t]}{2i(1/T-2i\varepsilon)[(\Omega-\varepsilon_0)^2-(\varepsilon+i\gamma)^2][\Omega-\varepsilon_0-3\varepsilon-i\gamma]}\,,
\end{aligned} \tag{72a}$$

where $\varepsilon = kv$.

Now it can be seen, that we are left on the right-hand side of (72) with terms, which have the same time-dependence as the left-hand side of this equation. This results from the properties of the functions $\exp[ikx]$ etc. Performing the integrals over $\boldsymbol{r}$ and the average over θ and assuming a symmetric velocity distribution $w(\varepsilon)$ as well as a homogeneous spatial distribution of the active atoms, we get

$$\begin{aligned}
\varkappa + i(\Omega-\omega) = {} & \frac{\varrho A d_0}{6}\int\frac{\gamma+i(\varepsilon+\varepsilon_0-\Omega)}{(\Omega-\varepsilon-\varepsilon_0)^2+\gamma^2}\cdot \\
& \cdot\left\{1-\frac{3\gamma TnA}{5[(\Omega-\varepsilon_0-\varepsilon)^2+\gamma^2)]}-\frac{3\gamma TnA}{5[(\Omega-\varepsilon_0+\varepsilon)^2+\gamma^2]}\right\} w(\varepsilon)\,d\varepsilon + \\
& + \frac{\varrho A^2 d_0 n}{10}\int\frac{\varepsilon+i\gamma}{(1/T-2i\varepsilon)(\Omega-\varepsilon_0-\varepsilon-i\gamma)^2(\Omega-\varepsilon_0+\varepsilon+i\gamma)} w(\varepsilon)\,d\varepsilon\,.
\end{aligned} \tag{73}$$

The terms containing A under the first integral arise from a static depletion of excited atomic states, while the second integral arises from the time-dependent response of the atomic system. This can be seen most easily by following the single steps of our iteration procedure.

Assuming a Gaussian velocity distribution it can be shown using constants typical for a He-Ne laser [2] that the last integral is one order of magnitude smaller than the first one and therefore may be neglected. Up to order γ/α we are then left with the following two equations, if we split them into real and imaginary part:

$$\varkappa = \frac{\sqrt{\pi}\,\varrho A d_0 \exp[-\delta^2]}{6\alpha}\left\{1 - \frac{3}{5}\,AnT\left[\frac{1}{2\gamma} + \frac{\gamma}{2(\gamma^2 + (\Omega - \varepsilon_0)^2)}\right]\right\}, \tag{74}$$

$$\Omega - \omega = \frac{\sqrt{\pi}\,\varrho A d_0 \exp[-\delta^2]}{6\alpha}\left\{-\frac{2}{\sqrt{\pi}}\int_0^\delta \exp[u^2]\,du + \frac{3AnT(\Omega - \varepsilon_0)}{10(\gamma^2 + (\Omega - \varepsilon_0)^2)} + \frac{3AnT\delta}{5\alpha}\right\}. \tag{75}$$

The small last term of (75) which is already familiar from eq. (63) may be dropped. Then we determine the photon number n equal to

$$n = \frac{(10\gamma/3AT)(1 - 3d_k(\delta)/d_0)}{1 + \gamma^2/(\gamma^2 + (\Omega - \varepsilon_0)^2)}. \tag{76}$$

Further we obtain

$$\Omega = \omega - \varkappa\frac{2}{\sqrt{\pi}}\int_0^\delta \exp[u^2]\,du + \varkappa\left(\frac{d_0}{3d_k(\delta)} - 1\right)\cdot \left(-\frac{2}{\sqrt{\pi}}\int_0^\delta \exp[u^2]\,du + \frac{\gamma(\Omega - \varepsilon_0)}{2\gamma^2 + (\Omega - \varepsilon_0)^2}\right) \tag{77}$$

for the frequency shift. If we plot for the given pumping power the photon number as a function of frequency, we find a dip, which has also been predicted by LAMB. It is interesting to note, that this dip is brought about by the fact, that the atoms move in both directions, so giving rise to two holes being burned into the inhomogeneously broadened line at two symmetric points of the line shape. If we have fixed atoms instead no such dip occurs, as had been stated already in our previous paper [1].

The shift of frequency is determined by eq. (77) and arises from the Doppler shape of the line and the time-independent atomic inversion. The first term gives the well-known power-dependent mode pulling [2], while the second one describes the mode pushing, which becomes dominant if the mode is tuned to the center of the line within about a natural line-width. This effect is due to the existence of two holes in the inversion.

5·1.2. Two modes. – The procedure as described in the foregoing leads to the following two equations for the two laser modes

$$(\varkappa + i[\Omega_1 - \omega_1]) B_1^+ \exp[i\Omega_1 t] = i \sum_\mu h_{\mu 1}^* a_\mu^+(t) \cos\theta_1 ,$$

where

$$(78)\quad a_\mu^+(t) = \left\{ -i \cos\theta_1 B_1^+ \left[\frac{(h/2)\exp[-ik_1 x]\exp[i\Omega_1 t - ik_1 vt]}{\Omega_1 - \varepsilon_0 - k_1 v - i\gamma} - \right.\right.$$
$$\left. - \frac{(h/2)\exp[ik_1 x]\exp[i\Omega_1 t + ik_1 vt]}{\Omega_1 - \varepsilon_0 + k_1 v - i\gamma} \right] - i\cos\theta_2 B_2^+ \cdot$$
$$\left.\cdot \left[\frac{(h/2)\exp[-ik_2 x]\exp[i(\Omega_2 - k_2 v)t]}{\Omega_2 - \varepsilon_0 - k_2 v - i\gamma} - \frac{(h/2)\exp[ik_2 x]\exp[i(\Omega_2 + k_2 v)t]}{\Omega_2 - \varepsilon_0 + k_2 v - i\gamma} \right] \right\} \cdot$$
$$\cdot \left\{ d_0 - \frac{\gamma T d_0 |h|^2 \cos^2\theta_1 \langle n_1 \rangle}{(\varepsilon_0 - \Omega_1 + k_1 v)^2 + \gamma^2} - \frac{\gamma T d_0 |h|^2 \cos^2\theta_1 \langle n_1 \rangle}{(\varepsilon_0 - \Omega_1 - k_1 v)^2 + \gamma^2} - \right.$$
$$\left. - \frac{\gamma T d_0 |h|^2 \cos^2\theta_2 \langle n_2 \rangle}{(\varepsilon_0 - \Omega_2 - k_2 v)^2 + \gamma^2} - \frac{\gamma T d_0 |h|^2 \cos^2\theta_2 \langle n_2 \rangle}{(\varepsilon_0 - \Omega_2 + k_2 v)^2 + \gamma^2} \right\} .$$

Equation (78) contains only the time-independent part of the inversion. In evaluating the sum over μ, *i.e.*, integrating over $\boldsymbol{r}$ as well as averaging over the orientations of the atomic dipoles all terms cancel which have a time-dependence other than $\exp[i\Omega_1 t]$. We are then led to noting that

$$\overline{\cos^2\theta} = \frac{1}{3} , \qquad \overline{\cos^4\theta} = \frac{1}{5} , \qquad \overline{\cos^2\theta_1 \cos^2\theta_2} = \frac{1}{15}(1 + 2\cos^2\alpha) ,$$

(here α is the angle between the polarization vectors of the two modes),

$$(79)\quad \varkappa + i(\Omega_1 - \omega_1) = \frac{\varrho A d_0}{6} \int \frac{i}{\varepsilon_0 + k_1 v - \Omega_1 + i\gamma} \cdot$$
$$\cdot \left\{ 1 - \frac{3\gamma T A n_1}{5[(\varepsilon_0 - \Omega_1 + k_1 v)^2 + \gamma^2]} - \frac{3\gamma T A n_1}{5[(\varepsilon_0 - \Omega_1 - k_1 v)^2 + \gamma^2]} - \right.$$
$$\left. - \frac{(1 + 2\cos^2\alpha)\gamma T A n_2}{5[(\varepsilon_0 - \Omega_2 - k_2 v)^2 + \gamma^2]} - \frac{(1 + 2\cos^2\alpha)\gamma T A n_2}{5[(\varepsilon_0 - \Omega_2 + k_2 v)^2 + \gamma^2]} \right\} w(v)\, dv$$

and a corresponding equation with reversed indices. As the fact, that $k_1 \neq k_2$ in expression (79) is entirely negligible (which may be shown by decomposition into partial fractions) these integrals have been evaluated up to order γ/α, which leads to the following set of equations, when split into real and imaginary part:

$$(80)\quad \frac{3d_k(1)}{d_0} = 1 - \frac{3ATn_1}{10\gamma}\left(1 + \frac{\gamma^2}{\gamma^2 + (\Omega_1 - \varepsilon_0)^2}\right) - \\ - \frac{ATn_2}{10\gamma}(1 + 2\cos^2\alpha)\left(\frac{4\gamma^2}{4\gamma^2 + \Delta\Omega^2} + \frac{4\gamma^2}{4\gamma^2 + (\Omega_1 + \Omega_2 - 2\varepsilon_0)^2}\right)$$

and

$$(81)\quad \Omega_1 = \omega_1 + \varkappa\frac{d_0}{3d_k(1)}\left\{-\frac{2}{\sqrt{\pi}}\int_0^{\delta_1}\exp[u^2]\,du + \frac{3ATn_1}{10}\,\frac{\Omega_1 - \varepsilon_0}{\gamma^2 + (\Omega_1 - \varepsilon_0)^2} + \right. \\ \left. + \frac{ATn_2}{10}\exp[\delta_1^2 - \delta_2^2](1 + 2\cos^2\alpha)\left(\frac{2\Delta\Omega}{4\gamma^2 + \Delta\Omega^2} + \frac{2(\Omega_1 + \Omega_2 - 2\varepsilon_0)}{4\gamma^2 + (\Omega_1 + \Omega_2 - 2\varepsilon_0)^2}\right)\right\}$$

and two corresponding equations with exchanged indices. Note that in the case of a symmetric configuration ($\Omega_1 + \Omega_2 - 2\varepsilon_0 = 0$), the factors of n_1 and n_2 in (80) and (81) become identical if $\alpha = 0$. This is to be expected, since we are treating *moving* atoms and the different spatial distribution of the modes plays no role in the lowest order of approximation.

The solution of these equations for $n_{1,2}$ is given by

$$(82)\quad n_1 = \frac{10\gamma}{3AT}\left[\left(1 - \frac{3d_k(1)}{d_0}\right)\left(1 + \frac{\gamma^2}{\gamma^2 + (\Omega_2 - \varepsilon_0)^2}\right) - \left(1 - \frac{3d_k(2)}{d0_0}\right)(1 + 2\cos^2\alpha)\cdot\right. \\ \left.\cdot\frac{4\gamma^2}{3}\left(\frac{1}{4\gamma^2 + \Delta\Omega^2} + \frac{1}{4\gamma^2 + (\Omega_1 + \Omega_2 - 2\varepsilon_0)^2}\right)\right]\left[\left(1 + \frac{\gamma^2}{\gamma^2 + (\Omega_1 - \varepsilon_0)^2}\right)\cdot\right. \\ \left.\cdot\left(1 + \frac{\gamma^2}{\gamma^2 + (\Omega_2 - \varepsilon_0)^2}\right) - \frac{1}{9}(1 + 2\cos^2\alpha)^2\, 4\gamma^2\left(\frac{1}{4\gamma^2 + \Delta\Omega^2} + \frac{1}{4\gamma^2 + (\Omega_1 + \Omega_2 - 2\varepsilon_0)^2}\right)^2\right]^{-1}.$$

$$(83)\quad \Omega_1 = \omega_1 + \frac{\varkappa d_0}{3d_k(1)}\left\{-\frac{2}{\sqrt{\pi}}\int_0^{\delta_1}\exp[u^2]\,du + \frac{3ATn_1}{10}\,\frac{\Omega_1 - \varepsilon_0}{\gamma^2 + (\Omega_1 - \varepsilon_0)^2} + \right. \\ \left. + \frac{ATn_2}{10}(1 + 2\cos^2\alpha)\exp[\delta_1^2 - \delta_2^2]\left[\frac{2\Delta\Omega}{4\gamma^2 + \Delta\Omega^2} + \frac{2(\Omega_1 + \Omega_2 - 2\varepsilon_0)}{4\gamma^2 + (\Omega_1 + \Omega_2 - 2\varepsilon_0)^2}\right]\right\}.$$

Let us discuss the following two cases:

If $\alpha = 0$, *i.e.*, the two modes are polarized parallel, formula (82) holds as long as the two modes are placed unsymmetrically with respect to the center of the line. If they are in a symmetric position within the accuracy of a natural line-width, then both modes are fed by identical atoms, since each mode lives on both sides of the Doppler line. As long as one neglects the different spatial distribution, as is done in our present approximation, one obtains thus an instable situation in which either one or the other mode can exist. This is reflected mathematically by (82), by the fact that the photon numbers become infinite. As we show below for the example of a Lorentzian line shape higher terms lead again to a stabilization. This means that the velocity of the atoms is still so slow, that different modes can interact again with atoms at different lattice sites in a different way which leads to the same effect as in the solid-state laser.

If $\alpha = \pi/2$, *i.e.*, the polarization vectors are orthogonal, then (82) gives a stable configuration in each case, even in the symmetric one, as will be proved in the next Section. The latter result agrees with experimental observations, which are reported by TANG and STATZ [15]. It is also compatible with BENNETT's experiments [2] on frequency shifts, because there was always used a polaroid, when observing beat notes between different modes. It should be noted, that the size of the frequency-pushing effect depends on the size of the angle between the polarization vectors of the two modes.

Similarly to the case of fixed atoms with an inhomogeneous line, we find the occurrence of mode pushing given by the last three terms of formula (83), which are due to the photon number or, with other words, to the depletion of atomic states of the two modes. This effect has been predicted by BENNETT [2], who called it « hole-burning ».

5·2. *Comparison with experimental results* (*). – A detailed experimental investigation of frequency shifts as dependent on pumping power has been performed by BENNETT [2]. For this end we compare our results with his experimental findings. Let us start with the more likely assumption that the line is inhomogeneously broadened.

As a typical example for the occurrence of mode pushing we choose the following two cases, being suggested by BENNETT's experimental results, using the following parameters [2, 15]

$$T = 10^{-7}\,\text{s}\,, \quad \alpha = \frac{2\pi}{\sqrt{\ln 2}}\, 4\cdot 10^{8}\,\text{s}^{-1}\,, \quad \gamma = 7\pi\cdot 10^{7}\,\text{s}^{-1}$$

and

$$\nu_1 - \nu_2 = \Delta\nu \quad = 1.6\cdot 10^{8}\,\text{Hz}\,, \quad 1 - R = 2\cdot 10^{-2}\,, \quad L = 10^{2}\,\text{cm}\,,$$

where R is the reflection coefficient of the mirrors and L the length of the cavity.

(*) A decision between the occurrence of an inhomogeneously or a homogeneously broadened line can be made by taking into account the dipping effect as predicted by LAMB and also derived in our above theory. According to R. A. MCFARLANE, W. R. BENNETT and W. E. LAMB: *Appl. Phys. Lett.*, **2**, 189 (1963), it has been found that in single mode operation the light intensity shows a dip if the atomic resonance is reached.

In both cases we choose $\alpha = \pi/2$. The only free parameter, still occurring in (83), is the pumping level d_0. In order to give quantitative values for frequency shifts, we fix d_0 according to various experimental situations.

Let at first the two modes be placed symmetrically with respect to the line center. We determine the pumping power in such a way that modes 3 and 4 (which are of course also symmetric to the line center) are just at threshold (clearly n_3, n_4 are actually zero in this case, but they would grow up by a slight increase of d_0). Of course the latter modes have no effects on the frequency shifts of modes 1 and 2, because their field strengths are just vanishing. In this case the power-dependent frequency repulsion of modes 1 and 2 is 30 kHz.

Secondly we take an unsymmetric placement of the two modes. Their frequencies in the unloaded cavity are supposed to be $\omega_1 = \varepsilon_0 + (\Delta\omega/4)$, $\omega_2 = \varepsilon_0 - \frac{3}{4}\Delta\omega$, where $\Delta\omega = 2\pi\,\Delta\nu$ is given above. Evidently their beat note becomes just observable, when mode 2 goes into oscillation. If one determines d_0 from this condition, the beat note is shifted by 13 kHz with respect to that value, which accounts only for the *power-independent pulling* to the center of the Doppler line.

This result is produced by the *power-dependent pulling* of the first line and the hole burning effect of this line on the second one. Finally let us assume that mode 1 and 2 are actually lasing. If we choose the power level such that a third mode is at threshold (the frequency of which in the unloaded cavity is given by $\omega_3 = \varepsilon_0 + \frac{5}{4}\Delta\omega$) then the power-dependent splitting of the beat note of the first two modes amounts to 30 kHz. These values are in good accordance with BENNETT's measurements, who found a typical splitting of beat notes of about 20 kHz. This splitting increased with increasing pumping power to 30 kHz. As the positions of the frequencies of the lasing modes relative to the line center are not given exactly by BENNETT a still closer comparison is not possible. It is clear from these remarks, that one has a convenient experimental tool in order to measure d_0 by observing modes which go into oscillation successively. A direct measurement of d_0 should be much more complicated. On the other hand it seems amusing to look what results are predicted if one assumes a completely homogeneously broadened line. In our above calculation we have been able to do this only for a Lorentzian line. As a consequence the power-dependent pulling effects do not show up. On the other hand one gets again a power-dependent frequency pushing. If we take the whole line width as a homogeneous one and use the parameters cited above, formula (45) gives a power-dependent repulsion of frequencies of 8 kHz for the case that mode 2 lies at the center of the emission line, whereas mode 1 is just at threshold. Thus one finds again a rather good agreement with the experimental results ($\approx 5\cdot10^3$ Hz at low pumping) which may be, however, fortuitous.

6. – Stability of laser modes.

We check now the stability of laser modes. We first investigate the homogeneously broadened line taking into account the mode-dependent inversion. In order to simplify calculations we restrict our discussion to two modes. Our procedure will be as follows: We allow the photon numbers $\langle n_{1,2}\rangle = \langle B^{\dagger}B\rangle_{1,2}$ for small deviations $\delta\langle n_1\rangle$, $\delta\langle n_2\rangle$ from their stationary state values. Consequently, the frequencies Ω_λ must also be allowed to change into $\Omega_\lambda + i\mathscr{F}_\lambda$. The $\mathscr{F}_\lambda$ are complex quantities the real parts of which determine the behavior of the modes against changes in the photon numbers. Accounting for the conservation law of occupation numbers, the variations must satisfy

$$\delta\langle n_1\rangle + \delta\langle n_2\rangle = 0\,.$$

This means, that we alter the distribution of energy between various modes without changing the atomic configuration. In other words we investigate, if for a certain atomic state the light field is determined uniquely.

It will be shown, that $\mathscr{F}_1 > 0$ and $\mathscr{F}_2 < 0$ for $\delta\langle n_1\rangle > 0$ which means, that the excess population of mode 1 decreases while that of mode 2 increases, *i.e.*, stationary state is approached, our solution thus being stable.

Proceeding as in Sect. **2**, one derives

$$(84)\quad (\varkappa + i[\Omega_\lambda + i\mathscr{F}_\lambda - \omega_\lambda])(\gamma + i[\Omega_\lambda + i\mathscr{F}_\lambda - \varepsilon]) = \\ = \sum_\mu |h_{\mu\lambda}|^2 d_0 - 4T\sum_{\mu\lambda'} \frac{|h_{\mu\lambda}|^2|h_{\mu\lambda'}|^2(\langle n_{\lambda'}\rangle + \delta\langle n_{\lambda'}\rangle)(\gamma - \mathscr{F}_{\lambda'})}{(\gamma - \mathscr{F}_{\lambda'})^2 + (\Omega_\lambda - \varepsilon)^2}\,.$$

Assuming small deviations from stationary state values, we keep only terms linear in $\delta\langle n_\lambda\rangle$ and $\mathscr{F}_\lambda$:

$$(85)\quad -\mathscr{F}_\lambda(\gamma + \varkappa) = -4\gamma T\sum_{\mu\lambda'} \frac{|h_{\mu\lambda}|^2|h_{\mu\lambda'}|^2\,\delta\langle n_{\lambda'}\rangle}{\gamma^2 + (\Omega_\lambda - \varepsilon)^2} + 4T\sum_{\mu\lambda'} \frac{|h_{\mu\lambda}|^2|h_{\mu\lambda'}|^2\langle n_{\lambda'}\rangle\mathscr{F}_{\lambda'}}{\gamma^2 + (\Omega_\lambda - \varepsilon)^2}\,.$$

It will be seen below, that it is justified to omit $\mathscr{F}_{\lambda'}$ in the denominator of the right-hand side of (84).

One derives

$$(86)\quad -\mathscr{F}_1(\gamma + \varkappa) = -\gamma\varkappa\left\{\frac{3\delta n_1}{2n_0}\left(\frac{(1+\eta)^2}{1 + ((\Omega_1 - \varepsilon)/\gamma)^2} + \frac{\delta n_2}{n_0}\,\frac{(1+\eta)^2}{1 + ((\Omega_2 - \varepsilon)/\gamma)^2}\right\} + \\ + \varkappa\left\{\frac{3n_1}{2n_0}\,\frac{(1+\eta)^2}{1 + ((\Omega_1 - \varepsilon)/\gamma)^2}\,\mathscr{F}_1 + \frac{n_2}{n_0}\,\frac{(1+\eta)^2}{1 + ((\Omega_2 - \varepsilon)/\gamma)^2}\,\mathscr{F}_2\right\};$$

where we have put $d_0 = 2\,d_k(0)(1+\eta)$ and $\varkappa_1 = \varkappa_2$. As $((\Omega_\lambda - \varepsilon)/\gamma)^2$, and η are small quantities and remembering that $\delta n_1 = -\delta n_2$, one may write

$$\text{(87)}\qquad \left\{\begin{aligned} \frac{1}{2}\frac{\delta n_1}{n_0}\gamma\varkappa &= \mathscr{F}_1\left(\varkappa+\gamma+\varkappa\frac{3n_1}{2n_0}\right)+\mathscr{F}_2\varkappa\frac{n_2}{n_0}\,,\\ -\frac{1}{2}\frac{\delta n_1}{n_0}\gamma\varkappa &= \mathscr{F}_2\left(\gamma+\varkappa+\varkappa\frac{3n_2}{2n_0}\right)+\mathscr{F}_1\varkappa\frac{n_1}{n_0}\,. \end{aligned}\right.$$

As $\varkappa \ll \gamma$ and n_λ/n_0 is of order of magnitude η, we have

$$\text{(88)}\qquad \mathscr{F}_1 = \frac{\varkappa}{2}\frac{\delta n_1}{n_0} \qquad \mathscr{F}_2 = -\frac{\varkappa}{2}\frac{\delta n_1}{n_0}\,.$$

Thus $\mathscr{F}_1 > 0$, $\mathscr{F}_2 < 0$ if $\delta n_1 > 0$, as stated above. Expansion of the denominator of (84) would give rise to a term $1+(2\mathscr{F}_\lambda/\gamma) = 1+(\varkappa/\gamma)\,\delta n_1/n_0$. Clearly $(\varkappa/\gamma)\,\delta n_1/n_0 \ll 1$, which corroborates the above treatment.

Let us turn in a next step to the case of an inhomogeneously broadened Gaussian in a gaseous system. The corresponding case for a solid-state laser is contained, too, in the following discussion. In order to work out clearly the physical reasons for stability, we proceed in two steps. First we consider parallel polarized modes ($\alpha = 0$).

We assume, that by an arbitrary perturbation the number of photons is changed into $n_\lambda + \delta n_\lambda$.

If all holes in the atomic inversion, produced by the two modes are separated from each other by more than a full natural line width, the variations δn_1 and δn_2 are arbitrary. In this case the two modes are supported by quite different atoms, that is, the discussion of stability of the two modes reduces to the question whether already one mode is stable. That this is indeed the case one may see easily from the expressions we derived for one mode.

If this is not so (for example if two modes in a gas laser are placed symmetrically with respect to the line center), we must restrict the variation to $\delta n_1 + \delta n_2 = 0$ accounting for the conservation law of particle number.

We start from eq. (79) and expand up to orders linear in δn and $\mathscr{F}$, where $\Omega_\lambda \to \Omega_\lambda + i\mathscr{F}_\lambda$. We obtain the following equations

$$\text{(89)}\qquad -\frac{\mathscr{F}_1}{\varkappa} = \frac{d_0}{5d_k(1)}\left\{\frac{10\mathscr{F}_1}{3\alpha\sqrt{\pi}}\exp[\delta_1^2] - \frac{AT\delta n_1}{2\gamma}\left(1+\frac{\gamma}{\gamma+i(\Omega_1-\varepsilon_0)}\right) - \right.$$
$$- AT\delta n_2\left(\frac{2\gamma - i\,\Delta\Omega\exp[\delta_1^2-\delta_2^2]}{4\gamma^2+\Delta\Omega^2} + \frac{2\gamma - i(\Omega_1+\Omega_2-2\varepsilon_0)\exp[\delta_1^2-\delta_2^2]}{4\gamma^2+(\Omega_1+\Omega_2-2\varepsilon_0)^2} + \right.$$
$$+ \frac{(\mathscr{F}_2-\mathscr{F}_1)ATn_2\exp[\delta_1^2-\delta_2^2]}{4\gamma^2+\Delta\Omega^2} + 2i\,\Delta\Omega(\mathscr{F}_1-\mathscr{F}_2)\cdot$$

$$\cdot\frac{ATn_2(2\gamma-i\Delta\Omega\exp[\delta_1^2-\delta_2^2])}{(4\gamma^2+\Delta\Omega^2)^2}-(\mathscr{F}_1+\mathscr{F}_2)\frac{ATn_2\exp[\delta_1^2-\delta_2^2]}{4\gamma^2+(\Omega_1+\Omega_2-2\varepsilon_0)^2}-$$

$$-\frac{2ATn_2}{\alpha^2}\exp[\delta_1^2-\delta_2^2][\mathscr{F}_1(\Omega_1-\varepsilon_0)-\mathscr{F}_2(\Omega_2-\varepsilon_0)]\cdot$$

$$\cdot\left[\frac{\Delta\Omega}{4\gamma^2+\Delta\Omega^2}+\frac{\Omega_1+\Omega_2-2\varepsilon_0}{4\gamma^2+(\Omega_1+\Omega_2-2\varepsilon_0)^2}\right]+\frac{2iATn_2(\mathscr{F}_1+\mathscr{F}_2)}{[4\gamma^2+(\Omega_1+\Omega_2-2\varepsilon_0)^2]^2}\cdot$$

$$\cdot[2\gamma-i(\Omega_1+\Omega_2-2\varepsilon_0)\exp[\delta_1^2-\delta_2^2]](\Omega_1+\Omega_2-2\varepsilon_0)+$$

$$\left.+\frac{ATn_1}{2}\frac{\mathscr{F}_1}{[\gamma+i(\Omega_1-\varepsilon_0)]^2}\right\}-\frac{2i\mathscr{F}_1(\Omega_1-\varepsilon_0)}{3\alpha^2}\left(1+\frac{i}{\varkappa}(\Omega_1-\omega_1)\right)$$

and a corresponding equation for $\mathscr{F}_2$ (89*a*). $\mathscr{F}_{1,2}$ are complex quantities, so that for given deviations $\delta n_{1,2}$ from equilibrium, their real and imaginary parts are determined by (89) and (89*a*).

As the coefficients of $\mathscr{F}_1$ and $\mathscr{F}_2$ on the right-hand side of (89) are small in the range of parameters which are characteristic, *e.g.*, for the He-Ne laser as compared to $1/\varkappa$ on the left-hand side, they may be neglected, *i.e.*, we retain only the inhomogeneous terms on the right. Then it is easily verified, that one obtains a stable configuration if the two modes are placed unsymmetrically with respect to the center of the Doppler-broadened line. In the case of a symmetric placement, the inhomogeneous terms vanish. As the determinant of (89) and (89*a*) is not zero, $\mathscr{F}_1=\mathscr{F}_2=0$, which means, that we get an unstable situation. In the case of a symmetric line position again a stable configuration is obtained, if the equations of motion are treated more exactly including terms of order $1/(1+\alpha T)$. These then secure, that one has again a spatial inhomogeneous depletion of the atoms, which leads to a stabilization of the modes, as will be shown below for the case of an inhomogeneously broadened Lorentzian line.

In the solid-state laser no instability occurs at all, because the inhomogeneous terms on the right of (89) never vanish. Let us turn finally to the discussion of stability including the effects of the polarization of the modes. If we alter the angle α between the polarization vectors by a small amount, we derive as above

$$(90)\qquad \mathscr{F}_1=\varkappa\frac{d_0}{d_k(1)}\frac{ATn_2}{2\gamma}\left[\frac{4\gamma^2}{4\gamma^2+\Delta\Omega^2}+\frac{4\gamma^2}{4\gamma^2+(\Omega_1+\Omega_2-2\varepsilon_0)^2}\right]\frac{2}{15}\delta(\cos^2\alpha)$$

or

$$(91)\qquad \mathscr{F}_1=-\text{const}\cdot\sin 2\alpha\cdot\delta\alpha\,,$$

where const >0.

As $\sin 2\alpha > 0$ for $0 < \alpha < \pi/2$, we get $\mathcal{F}_1 \lessgtr 0$ for $\delta\alpha \gtrless 0$. The reverse is true for $\pi/2 < \alpha < \pi$. Therefore, there are two equilibrium angles, namely $\alpha = 0$ and $\alpha = \pi/2$. While $\alpha = 0$ gives a labile equilibrium, $\alpha = \pi/2$ describes a stable equilibrium configuration.

Finally we examine the case of moving atoms more rigorously. For this end we assume an inhomogeneously broadened Lorentzian line instead of the actually appearing Gaussian. We have choosen the Lorentzian for our present purpose because all integrals appearing may be evaluated exactly for this case. In our previous discussion of gaseous systems we restricted ourselves to highest-order terms, *i.e.*, we neglected all terms stemming from the time-dependent response of the atoms. By following the single steps of our iteration procedure one realizes, that there also appears a term in the atomic inversion oscillating with $2\,kv$. As this term would contribute in the case of fixed atoms to the time-independent response its influence for moving atoms is surely more important than that of those terms oscillating with $\Omega_1 - \Omega_2$.

It gives rise to an additional contribution to eq. (79) which reads

$$\frac{1}{2} A^2 \varrho d_0 n_1 \overline{\cos^4 \theta} \, \frac{-1 + i\delta_1}{(\alpha+\gamma)^2(1+\delta_1^2)^2(1/T + 2\alpha)},$$

where

$$\delta_1 = \frac{\Omega_1 - \varepsilon_0}{\alpha + \gamma}.$$

Now in the case of a symmetric line position and parallel polarizations this term gives rise to a contribution to eq. (89),

$$\mathcal{F}_\lambda = \text{const} \cdot \delta n_\lambda\,, \qquad \text{where const} > 0,$$

which clearly means that it produces a stabilization. Note, that the above additional contribution is smaller by a factor $1/(1+2\alpha T)$ as compared to the terms containing n_1 in eq. (79). This means, that it is equal to these terms if $\alpha = 0$, *i.e.*, the atoms are fixed. In this case we reobtain a homogeneously broadened line, where the factors of n_1 and n_2 differ by $\frac{2}{3}$. If α is large, *i.e.*, the atoms are moving very quickly this difference in the factors becomes very small. The above treatment of the inhomogeneously broadened Gaussian corresponds to the situation where $\alpha = \infty$.

7. – Semiconductor lasers.

In the present Section we want to demonstrate how the method developed in the present report, can be applied to a special model of a semiconductor laser [16].

For this end we assume the valence and conduction band to be parabolic. Further we remind the reader that the atomic index μ occurring in the previous equations is to be replaced by the k-vector of the Bloch wave function. In the usual approximation one may neglect the wave-vector of the light field and one may also assume the matrix element to be independent of the k-vector. Since we deal with unperturbed Bloch wave functions the well-known k-selection rule holds. This represents some limitation to the application to real systems, because there is some evidence that in the laser transition also localized states are involved. The semiconductor laser can be treated as a four-level system. If we assume, however, that the pump times for the lower and upper optical levels belonging to the conduction, respectively valence band, are equal, the whole pumping process can be described by eq. (16).

In contrast to our preceding Sections in which the equilibrium inversion was assumed to be equal for all atoms we have now to take into account, that the equilibrium inversion is determined by quasi-Fermi-distribution functions with

$$(92)\quad d_k = f_{L,k} - f_{V,k} = \left\{1 + \exp\left[\frac{1}{kT}\left(E_L(k) - \varepsilon_L\right)\right]\right\}^{-1} - \\ - \left\{1 + \exp\left[\frac{1}{kT}\left(|\varepsilon_v| - |E_v(k)|\right)\right]\right\}^{-1}.$$

In it k is the Boltzmann constant, T the absolute temperature, $E_L(k)$ is the energy of the electron with the vector k in the conduction band and similarily E_v the value of the electron energy in the valence band. ε_L and ε_v are the quasi-Fermi-energies.

In order to determine the frequency shift we can immediately apply eq. (21), where we have to sum up over all k states of the electron.

For the evaluation we assume that γ is very small. We then can apply the formulas

$$(93)\quad \frac{1}{\gamma + i\eta} = \pi\delta(\eta) - \frac{iP}{\eta} + \ldots \quad \text{and} \quad \frac{1}{\gamma + i\eta}\,\frac{1}{\gamma^2 + \eta^2} = \left(\frac{\pi}{2\gamma^2}\,\delta(\eta) + \ldots\right) + \frac{i\pi}{2\gamma}\,\delta'(\gamma)$$

so that most integrals disappear on account of the δ-function. The only remaining integral stems from the first sum in (21) and describes the dispersion of the whole crystal in the inverted state. For its calculation we represent it as a difference between the dispersion of the noninverted crystal and the relatively small deviation due to the inversion. The first part can be taken into account by using the empirical connection between the frequency ω and the wavelength (which anyhow appears nowhere explicitly in the formulas). The essential contributions to the integral for the physically interesting deviations come from a small k-range close to the band edges so that we can use for the energies the effective mass approximation. The integration can then be done elementarily. Using the above-mentioned conditions we obtain the following two equations after separation of real and imaginary part:

$$\varkappa = C(f_L - f_V)\sqrt{\Delta} - Dn(f_L - f_V)\sqrt{\Delta}\,, \tag{94}$$

$$\Omega = \omega + \frac{2}{\pi}C\left\{2\sqrt{\varepsilon} + \sqrt{\Delta}\ln\frac{|\sqrt{\varepsilon}-\sqrt{\Delta}|}{|\sqrt{\varepsilon}+\sqrt{\Delta}|}\right\} + \frac{\pi}{6}C(kT)^2\left[\left(\frac{m_L}{m'}\right)^2 + \left(\frac{m_V}{m'}\right)^2\right]\cdot$$
$$\cdot\left[-\frac{\sqrt{\varepsilon}}{(\varepsilon-\Delta)^2} + \frac{1}{2}\frac{1}{\sqrt{\varepsilon}\,(\varepsilon-\Delta)}\right] - \gamma Dn\frac{\mathrm{d}}{\mathrm{d}\Omega}\left((f_L - f_V)\sqrt{\Delta}\right). \tag{95}$$

We have used the following abbreviations:

$$C = \frac{\hbar g^2}{(2\pi)^2}\left(\frac{2m'}{\hbar^2}\right)^{\frac{3}{2}}$$

with

$$g = \frac{h}{\sqrt{V}}\,; \qquad \frac{1}{m'} = \frac{1}{m_L} + \frac{1}{m_v}\,;$$

m_L, m_v effective mass of conduction, respectively, valence band, n = density of photons, $\Delta = \hbar\Omega - E_G$, E_G = width of the band gap, $D = (2T_1/\gamma)\,g^2C$. In the Fermi functions $f_L = (1+e^x)^{-1}$ and $f_v = (1+e^y)^{-1}$ the following arguments are to be used

$$x = \frac{1}{kT}\left[\frac{m'}{m_L}(\hbar\Omega - E_G) - \varepsilon_L'\right], \qquad y = \frac{1}{kT}\left[\frac{-m'}{m_v}(\hbar\Omega - E_G) + |\varepsilon_v|\right].$$

ε_L' is the quasi-Fermi-energy as determined from the lower edge of the conduction band. We have further $\varepsilon = \varepsilon_L m_L/m'$.

Equation (94) allows the calculation of the density of photons of the laser mode as a function of the pump intensity which is determined by the inversion factor $(f_L - f_v)$.

If we begin with an inversion equal zero and let it increase the laser mode which occurs first is that one for which the losses described by $\varkappa$ are smallest and the effective inversion

$$(f_L - f_v)\sqrt{\Delta} \tag{96}$$

is largest. If the quasi-Fermi-levels are prescribed the expression (96) is still a function of the laser frequency Ω. In first approximation we expect that frequency Ω to occur first for which

$$\frac{\mathrm{d}}{\mathrm{d}\Omega}\left(\sqrt{\Delta}\,[f_L - f_v]\right) = 0\,. \tag{97}$$

From this condition we can deduce very simply the frequency shift of the laser line as compared to the maximum of the band of spontaneous emission. The maximum Ω_{spontan} of the spontaneous emission is determined by the requirement that the function

$$f_L(x)\big(1 - f_v(y)\big)\sqrt{\Delta} \tag{98}$$

has a maximum. As can be seen immediately from both expressions (97) and (98) Ω_{laser} and Ω_{spontan} coincide only at absolute temperature T equal 0, whereas with increasing temperature Ω_{laser} is shifted as compared to Ω_{spontan} to higher wavelengths.

With the requirement (97) and that, that $\varkappa$ is a minimum a certain laser mode (usually of axial type) is selected. At the threshold of inversion we have

$$C = \frac{\varkappa}{[(f_L - f_v)\sqrt{\Delta}]_{\text{crit}}}$$

If we increase the inversion by increasing the quasi-Fermi-levels this mode experiences an additional frequency shift as given by eq. (95). If we eliminate from eq. (94) the photon number n and insert the corresponding expression into eq. (95) we obtain

$$\begin{aligned}\Omega = \omega + \frac{2}{\pi}\varkappa[(f_L - f_v)\sqrt{\Delta}]_{\text{cr}}^{-1}\Bigg[2\sqrt{\varepsilon} + \sqrt{\Delta}\ln\frac{|\sqrt{\varepsilon}-\sqrt{\Delta}|}{|\sqrt{\varepsilon}+\sqrt{\Delta}|} + \\ + \frac{\pi}{12}\left[\left(\frac{m_L}{m'}\right)^2 + \left(\frac{m_v}{m'}\right)^2\right](kT)^2\left\{-\frac{\sqrt{\varepsilon}}{(\varepsilon-\Delta)^2} + \frac{1}{2}\frac{1}{\sqrt{\varepsilon}\,(\varepsilon-\Delta)}\right\}\Bigg] - \\ - \gamma\varkappa\{([f_L - f_v]\sqrt{\Delta})_{\text{cr}}^{-1} - ([f_L - f_v]\sqrt{\Delta})^{-1}\}\left(\frac{\mathrm{d}}{\mathrm{d}\Omega}[f_L - f_v]\sqrt{\Delta}\right).\end{aligned} \tag{99}$$

The right-hand side of eq. (99) is again a function of Ω. Since the corrections of ω are relatively small, however, we may replace everywhere on the right-hand side Ω by ω.

8. – Discussion of results.

Let us discuss first the case in which the temperature is so small that we can neglect the term proportional to $(kT)^2$.

The second term on the right-hand side describes the change of frequency due to the dispersion of the inverted electronic states, neglecting the reaction on the light field. The last term describes the hole-burning effect of one mode on itself. It is rather small for laser modes close to the maximum of the emission line but increases with increasing distance from this position. The temperature-dependence arises from different contributions. First of all the frequency ω depends itself on temperature, on account of the temperature-dependence of the refractive index of the noninverted crystal as well as on account of its temperature extension. Further the quasi-Fermi-distributions are shifted with temperature which favours for different temperatures different modes, and finally an explicit term depending on k. T also contributes to a tempera ture shift to longer wavelengths. A more detailed discussion as well as a treatment of several laser modes will be published elsewhere.

9. - Concluding remarks.

In the above treatment we have left completely out the question of line width. A full discussion requires, of course, the consideration of the contribution of spontaneous emission. On the other hand our above derivations show up an important contribution to frequency shifts and correspondingly to a finite line width. If we neglect the special case of one mode occurring in a homogeneously broadened line it turns out that all frequencies depend on pumping power. Consequently any temporal or also spatial fluctuations of pumping power lead to a finite line width. As can be seen immediately from our above formulas, this line width becomes larger, the larger the losses of the unloaded cavity.

Appendix A

Extension to a four-level system.

In order to show that our results derived for a two-level system hold for three- or four-level systems too, we have to modify our equations of motion as follows:

$$\dot{a}^\dagger_\mu = (i\varepsilon_\mu - \gamma)a^\dagger_\mu - i\sum_\lambda h_{\mu\lambda} b^\dagger_\lambda (n_{u,\mu} - n_{l,\mu}) , \tag{A.1}$$

$$\dot{n}_{u,\mu} = \frac{1}{T_1}(d_0 - n_{u,\mu}) + i\sum_\lambda a_\mu b^\dagger_\lambda h_{\mu\lambda} - i\sum_\lambda a^\dagger_\mu b_\lambda h^*_{\mu\lambda} , \tag{A.2}$$

$$\dot{n}_{l,\mu} = -\frac{1}{T_1} n_{l,\mu} + i\sum_\lambda a^\dagger_\mu b_\lambda h^*_{\mu\lambda} - i\sum_\lambda a_\mu b^\dagger_\lambda h_{\mu\lambda} , \tag{A.3}$$

$$\dot{b}^\dagger_\lambda = (i\omega_\lambda - \varkappa) b^\dagger_\lambda + i\sum_\mu h^*_{\mu\lambda} a^\dagger_\mu , \tag{A.5}$$

where $n_{u,\mu}$ or $n_{l,\mu}$ are the population numbers of the upper or lower level of the μ-th atom, respectively. Whereas for a two-level system we could treat

$\sigma_\mu = n_{u,\mu} - n_{l,\mu}$ as a single variable, we now have to consider $n_{u,\mu}$ and $n_{l,\mu}$ separately, because the decay time T_2 of the lower level will differ in general from the relaxation time T_1 under which the inversion d_0 is established.

In complete analogy to Sect. 3 we iterate the above equations starting with $n_{u,\mu}^{(0)} = d_0$ and $n_{l,\mu}^{(0)} = 0$. We find

$$\text{(A.5)} \quad \dot{b}_\lambda^\dagger = (i\omega_\lambda - \varkappa) b_\lambda^\dagger - i d_0 \sum_\mu B_\lambda^\dagger |h_{\mu\lambda}|^2 \frac{\exp[i\Omega_\lambda t]}{\Omega_\lambda - \varepsilon_\mu - i\gamma} +$$

$$+ d_0 \sum_{\mu\lambda_1\lambda_2\lambda_3} B_{\lambda_1} B_{\lambda_2}^\dagger B_{\lambda_3}^\dagger h_{\mu\lambda}^* h_{\mu\lambda_1}^* h_{\mu\lambda_2} h_{\mu\lambda_3} \frac{\exp[i(\Omega_{\lambda_2} + \Omega_{\lambda_3} - \Omega_{\lambda_1})t]}{(\Omega_{\lambda_2} + \Omega_{\lambda_3} - \Omega_{\lambda_1} - \varepsilon_\mu - i\gamma)} \cdot$$

$$\cdot \left(\frac{1}{\Omega_{\lambda_2} - \varepsilon_\mu - i\gamma} - \frac{1}{\Omega_{\lambda_1} - \varepsilon_\mu + i\gamma} \right) \left(\frac{1}{1/T_1 + i(\Omega_{\lambda_2} - \Omega_{\lambda_1})} + \frac{1}{1/T_2 + i(\Omega_{\lambda_2} - \Omega_{\lambda_1})} \right).$$

The following statements are easily realized from (A.5): if $T_1 = T_2$ (A.5) agrees with (20). If $T_1 \neq T_2$ our former results are valid exactly, if we take into account the time-independent response only. One has merely to replace T by $\frac{1}{2}(T_1 + T_2)$, since, by following our iteration procedure, it can be seen that all terms with $\lambda_1 = \lambda_2$ in (A.5) stem from the time-independent parts of $n_{u,\mu}^{(1)}$ or $n_{l,\mu}^{(1)}$, respectively.

In physical systems $1/T_2$ will be, in general, much larger than $1/T_1$, so that the term containing $1/T_2$ may be dropped. Defining $B'_\lambda = (1/\sqrt{2}) B_\lambda$, our former results hold both for the time-independent as well as the time-dependent response, if we replace T by T_1 and the physical amplitudes B_λ by the corresponding dashed quantities. This does *not* affect the frequency shifts as a function of pumping power, the separation of the frequencies of the modes etc., whereas the photon numbers are enhanced by a factor 2.

APPENDIX B

Statistically oriented atomic dipole moments.

Finally we discuss the case, in which the atomic dipoles are oriented statistically in a solid-state laser. As the averaging over their directions is performed in completely the same manner as in the gaseous case, we merely quote the results:

In single mode operation we get instead of (62)

$$\text{(A.6)} \qquad n = \frac{10\gamma}{9AT}\left(1 - \frac{3d_k(\delta)}{d_0}\right) = \frac{\gamma}{\alpha} \frac{5\sqrt{\pi}\,\varrho d_k(0)}{9\varkappa T}\left(1 - \frac{3d_k(\delta)}{d_0}\right)$$

and instead of (63)

$$\text{(A.7)} \qquad \Omega = \omega - \varkappa \frac{2d_0}{3\sqrt{\pi} d_k(\delta)} \left\{ \int_0^\delta \exp[u^2]\, du - \delta \frac{\gamma}{\alpha} \sqrt{\pi} \left(1 - \frac{3d_k(\delta)}{d_0}\right) \right\}.$$

As in the gaseous case the critical inversion is now given by $3d_k(\delta)$. If two modes are oscillating simultaneously, we have to replace (66) by

$$n_1 = \frac{10\gamma}{9AT} \frac{\left(1 - \frac{3d_k(1)}{d_0}\right) + \frac{4(3d_k(2)/d_0 - 1)(1 + 2\cos^2\alpha)}{9(4 + (\Delta\Omega/\gamma)^2)} k_1}{1 - \frac{16(1 + 2\cos^2\alpha)^2}{81[4 + (\Delta\Omega/\gamma)^2]^2} k_1 k_2} \tag{A.8}$$

where

$$k_1 = 1 + \exp[\delta_1^2 - \delta_2^2] + \frac{4\gamma}{\sqrt{\pi}\Delta\Omega} \int_0^{\delta_1} \exp[u^2]\,\mathrm{d}u - \frac{4\gamma}{\sqrt{\pi}\Delta\Omega} \exp[\delta_1^2 - \delta_2^2] \int_0^{\delta_2} \exp[u^2]\,\mathrm{d}u$$

and k_2 is obtained from k_1 by interchanging the indices 1 and 2 (note that $\Delta\Omega \to -\Delta\Omega$).

(67) is to be replaced by

$$\Omega_1 = \omega_1 + \varkappa \frac{d_0}{3d_k(1)} (\Gamma_1' + \Gamma_2' + \Gamma_3'), \tag{A.9}$$

where

$$\Gamma_1' = -\frac{2}{\sqrt{\pi}} \int_0^{\delta_1} \exp[u^2]\,\mathrm{d}u + \frac{9ATn_1\delta_1}{5\alpha}, \tag{A.9a}$$

$$\Gamma_2' = \frac{2ATn_2(1 + 2\cos^2\alpha)}{5\Delta\Omega} \exp[\delta_1^2 - \delta_2^2], \tag{A.9b}$$

$$\Gamma_3' = \frac{1 + 2\cos^2\alpha}{3} \Gamma_3. \tag{A.9c}$$

Γ_3 is given by (67c), n_1 and n_2 by eq. (A.8), respectively. As we proved in Sect. **6** a stable configuration is reached for $\alpha = \pi/2$.

Appendix C

We indicate in this Appendix how the integrals over a Gaussian distribution of the energies, which occur in the text, have been evaluated.

The integral from which all others can be derived by means of decomposition into partial fractions reads

$$k_0 = \frac{1}{\alpha\sqrt{\pi}} \int \frac{1}{\gamma^2 + (\Omega - \varepsilon)^2} \exp\left[-\left(\frac{\varepsilon - \varepsilon_0}{\alpha}\right)^2\right] \mathrm{d}\varepsilon. \tag{A.10}$$

Using standard formulas [17] one derives

$$k_0 = \frac{\exp[-\delta^2]}{\alpha^2} \left\{ \frac{\sqrt{\pi}}{p} \exp[p^2] \cos 2\delta p - \frac{2}{p} \int_0^{\varrho} \exp[p^2 - x^2]\,\mathrm{d}x \cos 2\delta p + \right.$$
$$\left. + 4 \sum_{k=1}^{\infty} (2p)^{2(k-1)} (-1)^{k-1} \int_0^{\delta} \ldots \int_0^{\delta_3} \int_0^{\delta_2} \exp[\delta_1^2]\,\mathrm{d}\delta_1 \ldots \mathrm{d}\delta_{2k} \right\} \tag{A.11}$$

where $\delta = (\Omega - \varepsilon_0)/\alpha$ and $p = \gamma/\alpha$. As p is assumed to be sm ıll in our paper, for our purpose only highest order terms, such as p^{-1}, p^0, p^1 are essential.

The integral

$$(\text{A.12}) \qquad k_1 = \frac{\gamma}{\alpha\sqrt{\pi}} \int \frac{\exp[-((\varepsilon-\varepsilon_0)/\alpha)^2]\,\mathrm{d}\varepsilon}{[\gamma^2 + (\Omega_2 - \varepsilon)^2][\gamma + i(\Omega_1 - \varepsilon)]},$$

which occurs in Sect. 4.2.2, can be deduced from (A.11) noticing the above remarks, to yield

$$(\text{A.13}) \quad k_1 = \frac{\sqrt{\pi}}{\alpha}\exp[-\delta_2^2]\frac{\gamma\Delta\Omega - i(\Delta\Omega^2 + 2\gamma^2)}{\Delta\Omega(4\gamma^2 + \Delta\Omega^2)} - \\ - \frac{2\gamma(2\gamma - i\Delta\Omega)\exp[-\delta_2^2]}{\alpha\Delta\Omega(4\gamma^2+\Delta\Omega^2)}\int_0^{\delta_2}\exp[u^2]\,\mathrm{d}u + \frac{1}{\Delta\Omega(\Delta\Omega^2 + 4\gamma^2)}\frac{\gamma}{\alpha}\exp[-\delta_1^2]\cdot \\ \cdot\left\{\sqrt{\pi}\Delta\Omega + 4\gamma\int_0^{\delta_1}\exp[u^2]\,\mathrm{d}u + 2\gamma i\sqrt{\pi} - 2i\Delta\Omega\int_0^{\delta_1}\exp[u^2]\,\mathrm{d}u\right\}.$$

We have used in (A.13) for the real and imaginary part only highest-order contributions from (A.11) as regards to p.

It should be noted, however, that *no* approximation concerning

$$\Delta\Omega = \Omega_1 - \Omega_2,$$

the frequency difference of the modes, has been made.

Completely analogous to (A.13) one finds

$$(\text{A.14}) \quad k_2 = \frac{1}{\alpha\sqrt{\pi}}\int\frac{\exp[-((\varepsilon-\varepsilon_0)/\alpha)^2]\,\mathrm{d}\varepsilon}{[\gamma - i(\Omega_2-\varepsilon)][\gamma + i(\Omega_1 - \varepsilon)]} = \\ = \frac{2\gamma - i\Delta\Omega}{4\gamma^2 + \Delta\Omega^2}\left\{\frac{\sqrt{\pi}}{\alpha}\exp[-\delta_1^2] - \frac{2i}{\alpha}\exp[-\delta_1^2]\int_0^{\delta_1}\exp[u^2]\,\mathrm{d}u + \right. \\ \left. + \frac{\sqrt{\pi}}{\alpha}\exp[-\delta_2^2] + \frac{2i}{\alpha}\exp[-\delta_2^2]\int_0^{\delta_2}\exp[u^2]\,\mathrm{d}u\right\}$$

and

$$(\text{A.15}) \quad k_3 = \frac{1}{\alpha\sqrt{\pi}}\int\frac{\exp[-((\varepsilon-\varepsilon_0)/\alpha)]^2}{[\gamma + i(\Omega_1 - \varepsilon)]^2}\,\mathrm{d}\varepsilon = \\ = 2\,\frac{\exp[-\delta_1^2]}{\alpha^2} - 4\,\frac{\exp[-\delta_1^2]}{\alpha^2}\int_0^{\delta_1}\int_0^{u_2}\exp[u_1^2]\,\mathrm{d}u_1\,\mathrm{d}u_2 - \frac{2i\delta_1\sqrt{\pi}}{\alpha^2}\exp[-\delta_1^2].$$

The double integral in (A.15) can be transformed in a single integral, which has been used in the text.

As has been described in Sect. **5**.1.1 the time-dependent contribution of the atomic response, oscillating with $2\,kv$, has been neglected. This is justified because it leads to the integral

$$k_4 = \frac{1}{\alpha\sqrt{\pi}}\int\frac{(\varepsilon + i\gamma)\exp[-(\varepsilon^2/\alpha^2)]\,d\varepsilon}{(1/T - 2i\varepsilon)(\Omega - \varepsilon_0 - \varepsilon - i\gamma)^2(\Omega - \varepsilon_0 + \varepsilon + i\gamma)}, \tag{A.16}$$

which, by means of the above procedure, turns out to be one order of magnitude smaller than the contribution stemming from the time-independent response.

Compare, concerning this question, also Sect. **6**.

REFERENCES

[1] H. HAKEN: *Conference on Optical Pumping* (Heidelberg, 1962); H. HAKEN and H. SAUERMANN: *Zeits. f. Phys.*, **173**, 261 (1963); **176**, 58 (1963).

[2] W. R. BENNETT: *Phys. Rev.*, **126**, 580 (1962); *Journ. Appl. Opt.*, *Suppl. on Optical Masers* (Dec. 1962).

[3] E. SNITZER: *Third Internat. Symposium on Quantum Electronics* (Paris, Febr. 1963).

[4] A. W. SCHAWLOW and C. H. TOWNES: *Phys. Rev.*, **112**, 1940 (1958).

[5] T. H. MAIMAN: *Nature*, **187**, 493 (1960).

[6] W. G. WAGNER and G. BIRNBAUM: *Journ. Appl. Phys.*, **32**, 1185 (1961).

[7] W. HEITLER: *The Quantum Theory of Radiation*, 3rd ed. (Oxford, 1954).

[8] A. G. FOX and T. LI: *Bell Syst. Techn. Journ.*, **40**, 453 (1961).

[9] G. D. BOYD: *Adv. in Quantum Electronics*, Ed. J. R. SINGER (New York and London, 1961).

[10] M. GÖPPERT-MAYER: *Ann. d. Phys.*, **9**, 273 (1931).

[11] J. A. ARMSTRONG, N. BLOEMBERGER, J. DUCUING and P. S. PERSHAN: *Phys. Rev.*, **127**, 1919 (1962).

[12] V. M. FAIN and YA. J. KHANIN: *Soviet Physics J.E.T.P.* **14**, 1069 (1962).

[13] C. H. TOWNES: *Adv. in Quantum Electronics*, Ed. J. R. SINGER (New York and London, 1961), p. 3.

[14] A. JAVAN, T. S. JASEJA and C. H. TOWNES: *Bull. Am. Phys. Soc.*, **8**, 380 (1963); T. S. JASEJA, A. JAVAN, J. MURRAY and C. H. TOWNES: *Bull. Am. Phys. Soc.*, **8**, 396 (1963).

[15] C. L. TANG and H. STATZ: *Phys. Rev.*, **128**, 1013 (1962). In this paper also a theoretical account of some questions, concerning polarization effects, is given.

[16] E. HAKEN and H. HAKEN: *Zeits. f. Phys.* **176**, 421 Hilsch Festheft (1963).

[17] I. M. RYSHIK and I. S. GRADSTEIN: *Tables of Series, Products and Integrals* (Berlin, 1957).

Noise at Optical Frequencies; Information Theory.

J. P. GORDON

Bell Telephone Laboratories, Incorporated - Murray Hill, N. J.

Introduction.

The subject of random fluctuations in amplifiers and oscillators has received considerable attention in the past, mostly from electrical engineers, and mostly from a classical point of view. With the advent of masers, and more particularly with lasers for which $h\nu \gg kT$, it has become important to reconsider this whole subject to make it consistent with quantum mechanics. The same may also be said of communication theory. It is indeed rather interesting that the laser forms a meeting ground for three fields; communications, physical optics, and quantum mechanics.

In these lectures we shall endeavour to treat the subject of amplifier noise by several methods which are consistent with quantum-mechanical ideas. The first method follows from Einstein's famous A and B coefficients for spontaneous and induced emission. This method yields correct answers, but completely avoids questions of coherence. To get the answers one must make assumptions about the statistical relationships between the emitted electromagnetic fields and the incident fields. The second method, based on the use of statistical moment generating functions, gives a proof of the validity of these assumptions. After some brief comments on the behavior of laser oscillators perturbed by quantum or spontaneous emission noise, we present some speculations about the application of quantum mechanics to the theory of information. Some of the earlier results are used to illustrate these ideas.

1. – Elementary theory. The Einstein method.

We think of a rectangular region in space of dimensions (X, Y, Z). Let the radiation field in the region be described by the vector potential (in the

Coulomb gauge)

$$\boldsymbol{A}(\boldsymbol{r}, t)\,.$$

We can expand a typical cartesian component, say A_x, of $\boldsymbol{A}$, into a countable set of plane waves

$$A_x(\boldsymbol{r}, t) = \sum_{l=-\infty}^{\infty} \sum_{m=-\infty}^{\infty} \sum_{n=-\infty}^{+\infty} A^{(x)}_{l,m,n(t)} \exp[i\boldsymbol{k}_{l,m,n} \cdot \boldsymbol{r}]\,, \tag{1.1}$$

where the wave vectors k are required to satisfy periodic boundary conditions

$$\boldsymbol{k}_{l,m,n} = \left(\frac{2\pi l}{X}, \frac{2\pi m}{Y}, \frac{2\pi m}{Z}\right),$$

where l, m, and n are integers. The choice of boundary conditions insures orthogonality of the modes in the volume XYZ.

Note that in a three-dimensional k space, the density of representative points $\boldsymbol{k}_{l,m,n}$ is $XYZ/(2\pi)^3$. If we substitute (1) in the wave equation

$$\nabla^2 A_2(\boldsymbol{r}, t) = \frac{1}{c^2} \frac{\partial^2 A_x(\boldsymbol{r}, t)}{\partial t^2} \tag{1.2}$$

and make use of the spatial orthogonality of the plane waves, we get the set of equations

$$k^2_{l,m,n} A^{(x)}_{l,m,n}(t) = \frac{1}{c^2} \frac{\partial^2 A^{(x)}_{l,m,n}}{\partial t^2}\,, \tag{1.3}$$

where

$$k^2_{l,m,n} = (2\pi)^2 \left[\left(\frac{l}{X}\right)^2 + \left(\frac{m}{Y}\right)^2 + \left(\frac{m}{Z}\right)^2\right].$$

Equations (1.3) have the two solutions

$$A^{(x)}_{l,m,n}(t) = A^{(x)\pm}_{l,m,n} \exp[\pm i\omega_{l,m,n} t]$$

where

$$\omega_{l,m,n} = ck_{l,m,n} = 2\pi c \left[\left(\frac{l}{X}\right)^2 + \left(\frac{m}{Y}\right)^2 + \left(\frac{n}{Z}\right)^2\right].$$

The condition for the reality of $A_x(r, t)$ is

$$A^{(x)-}_{l,m,n} = (A^{(x)+}_{-l,-m,-n})^*$$

where ( )* means complex conjugate.

Putting together the various components of A, we get for the total expansion of the field in the volume XYZ, the result

$$(1.4)\qquad \boldsymbol{A}(\boldsymbol{r}, t) = \sum_{l,m,n=-\infty}^{\infty} \sum_{\lambda=1}^{2} \omega_{l,m,n}^{(\lambda)} A_{l,m,n}^{(\lambda)}(\boldsymbol{r}, t) = \sum_{l,m,n=-\infty}^{\infty} \sum_{\lambda=1}^{2} \hat{u}_{l,m,n}^{(\lambda)} \{A_{l,m,n}^{(\lambda)} \exp[i(\boldsymbol{k}_{l,m,n} \cdot \boldsymbol{r} - \omega_{l,m,n} t)] + \text{c. c.}\},$$

where $\hat{u}_{l,m,n}^{(\lambda)}$ are unit polarization vectors which can take on two orthogonal directions ($\lambda = 1, 2$) perpendicular to $\boldsymbol{k}_{l,m,n}$. Thus there are two modes for each representative point in k-space. The number of such modes with frequencies less than ν is the number of points in the spherical volume in k-space of radius $k_\nu = 2\pi\nu/c$; *i.e.*,

$$\frac{4}{3}\pi k_\nu^3 = \frac{4\pi}{3}\left(\frac{2\pi\nu}{c}\right)^3.$$

This number is

$$N_\nu = 2\left[\frac{XYZ}{(2\pi)^3}\right]\left[\frac{4\pi}{3}\left(\frac{2\pi\nu}{c}\right)^3\right] = \frac{8\pi\nu^3(XYZ)}{3c^3}.$$

Finally the mode density per unit volume per unit frequency interval, which we can label $p(\nu)$, is

$$(1.5)\qquad p(\nu) = \frac{1}{XYZ}\frac{\mathrm{d}N_\nu}{\mathrm{d}\nu} = \frac{8\pi\nu^2}{c^3}.$$

The result is of course familiar.

We can derive from $p(\nu)$ the Planck black-body energy density formula by using the equipartition energy,

$$\langle W_{\text{mode}}\rangle = \frac{h\nu}{\exp[h\nu/kT] - 1},$$

which yields for the energy density

$$(1.6)\qquad \varrho(\nu) = \frac{8\pi h\nu^3}{c^3}\frac{1}{\exp[h\nu/kT] - 1}.$$

From $\varrho(\nu)$ and from the Boltzmann law for the distribution of atoms in energy levels, we can also easily derive, according to the method of Einstein [1], the ratio of spontaneous to induced transition rates, and from this the noise factor of linear maser or laser amplifiers.

Consider, then, Einstein's equation

$$N_1 \varrho(\nu) B_\uparrow(\nu) = N_2[A(\nu) + \varrho(\nu) B_\downarrow(\nu)], \tag{1.7}$$

where N_1 and N_2 are the numbers of atoms in upper and lower states of transitions which interact with the radiation field, while $A(\nu)$ and the $B(\nu)$'s are respectively rate coefficients for spontaneous and induced transitions. Equation (1.7) is valid for thermal equilibrium, and states that the total rate of upward transitions (induced only) must be the same as the total rate of downward transitions. Rearranging terms we get

$$\varrho(\nu) = \frac{A(\nu)}{(N_1/N_2) B_\uparrow(\nu) - B_\downarrow(\nu)}. \tag{1.8}$$

Now with Boltzmann's law

$$\frac{N_1}{N_2} = \exp\left[\frac{h\nu}{kT}\right]$$

we see that (1.8) can match (1.6) for any temperature only if

$$B_\uparrow(\nu) = B_\downarrow(\nu) \equiv B(\nu)$$

and

$$\frac{A(\nu)}{B(\nu)} = \frac{8\pi h\nu^3}{c^3}.$$

Since $B_\uparrow = B_\downarrow$, we can omit the arrow henceforth. The necessary ratio A/B determines the noise properties of the maser. With (1.5), the ratio A/B can be written

$$\frac{A(\nu)}{B(\nu)} = h\nu\, p(\nu). \tag{1.9}$$

We note, from (1.7), that the spontaneous and induced downward transition rates are equal when

$$\varrho(\nu) = \frac{A(\nu)}{B(\nu)} = h\nu\, p(\nu), \tag{1.10}$$

hence when there is an average energy corresponding to one photon in each mode of the radiation field. This last result is of course quite general, and applies equally well to cavity resonators which support only a single mode in the frequency range of interest, and to transmission lines which support only a single transverse mode.

Now if we suppose that the electromagnetic field resulting from the induced absorption and emission represented by the B's is coherent with the exciting field, while the spontaneous emission, represented by A, is completely random (*i.e.*, incoherent), we can immediately translate (1.9) into a fundamental equation for the gain coefficient in terms of the spontaneous emission coefficient. Consider a particular resonance line, whose spontaneous emission line shape is described by the normalized function $g(\nu)$. The normalization is taken as

$$\int_{\text{line}} g(\nu)\,\mathrm{d}\nu = 1\,.$$

Then we can write

$$A(\nu) = \frac{g(\nu)}{\tau_{\text{rad}}}\,, \tag{1.11}$$

where τ_{rad} is the radiative lifetime for an atom in the upper level for the specific transition to the lower level. Then (1.9) yields

$$B(\nu) = \frac{g(\nu)}{h\nu\, p(\nu)\, \tau_{\text{rad}}}\,.$$

For an exciting field with energy density per unit frequency interval $\varrho(\nu)$, the induced transitions contribute additiinal energy at a rate

$$\left(\frac{\mathrm{d}\varrho(\nu)}{\mathrm{d}t}\right)_{\text{ind}} = h\nu(N_2 - N_1)\,B(\nu)\,\varrho(\nu)\,,$$

hence

$$\gamma(\nu) \equiv \frac{1}{\varrho(\nu)}\left(\frac{\mathrm{d}\varrho(\nu)}{\mathrm{d}t}\right)_{\text{ind}} = \frac{(N_2 - N_1)\,g(\nu)}{p(\nu)\,\tau_{\text{rad}}}\,; \tag{1.12}$$

$\gamma(\nu)$ is the logarithmic increment in $\varrho(\nu)$ per unit time. From this and the assumption of coherence, we can easily obtain the logarithmic gain coefficient; *i.e.*,

$$\alpha(\nu) = \frac{1}{\varrho(\nu)}\left(\frac{\mathrm{d}\varrho(\nu)}{\mathrm{d}x}\right)_{\text{ind}} = \frac{1}{\varrho(\nu)}\left(\frac{\mathrm{d}\varrho(\nu)}{v_g\,\mathrm{d}t}\right)_{\text{ind}} = \frac{(N_2 - N_1)\,g(\nu)}{p(\nu)\,\tau_{\text{rad}}\,v_g}\,, \tag{1.13}$$

where v_g is the group velocity of the wave. Note that this equation must be equally as valid in dielectric media as in free space. Of course, $p(\nu)$ must then be appropriately modified.

The rate of which energy (total energy, not energy density) is being emitted spontaneously into each mode is

$$(1.14)\qquad \left(\frac{\mathrm{d}W_{\text{mode}}}{\mathrm{d}t}\right)_{\text{spont}} = \frac{h\nu N_2 A(\nu)}{p(\nu)} = h\nu\,\frac{N_2}{N_2 - N_1}\,\gamma(\nu)\,;$$

that is, the rate of spontaneous emission per unit volume per unit frequency divided by the number of modes per unit volume per unit frequency, and in the last equality we have used (1.11) and (1.12). These equations determine the noise behavior of linear maser amplifiers. In eq. (1.12) the total energy W_{mode} of a single mode can equally well be used in place of $\varrho(\nu)$, hence we can write

$$(1.15)\qquad \frac{1}{W_{\text{mode}}}\left(\frac{\mathrm{d}W_{\text{mode}}}{\mathrm{d}t}\right)_{\text{ind}} = \gamma(\nu)\,.$$

The ratio of (1.14) to (1.15), *i.e.*,

$$(1.16)\qquad W_{\text{mode}}\,\frac{(\mathrm{d}W_{\text{mode}})_{\text{spont}}}{(\mathrm{d}W_{\text{mode}})_{\text{ind}}} = \frac{N_2}{N_2 - N_1}\,h\nu$$

is what may be called the equivalent input noise energy per mode, and again applies to each mode of a resonator or transmission line as well as to the traveling-wave mode we have been discussing. To see this equivalence, we note that the equation for the build-up of energy in the mode, including both spontaneous and induced emission, is

$$\frac{\mathrm{d}W}{\mathrm{d}t} = \gamma(\nu)\left[W + \frac{N_2}{N_2 - N_1}\,h\nu\right].$$

The solution to this equation is

$$(1.17)\qquad W = W_0 \exp[\gamma t] + \left(\frac{N_2}{N - N_1}\right) h\nu\,(\exp[\gamma t] - 1)\,,$$

where W_0 is the initial energy in the mode at $t = 0$.

The first term of (1.17) is then the amplified initial energy, while the second is the (also amplified) spontaneous emission noise. If the gain is large, so that $\exp[\gamma t] \gg 1$, (1.17) behaves as though there were an additional initial noise energy in the mode of amount given by (1.16), and the amplification proceeded noiselessly.

It is customary and useful in some situations to speak of the inverted population of maser media in terms of negative temperature, simply by retaining Boltzmann's law for transitions in the narrow frequency range of interest.

Hence

$$\frac{N_2}{N_1} = \exp\left[-\frac{h\nu}{kT_m}\right] \tag{1.18}$$

implies that T_m, the maser medium temperature, is negative when $N_2 > N_1$. It is also customary to define an equivalent black-body temperature T_{eq} for noise purposes as the black-body temperature which yields an energy per mode equal to the equivalent input noise of (1.15). This gives

$$\frac{h\nu}{\exp[h\nu/kT_{eq}] - 1} = \frac{h\nu}{1 - \exp[h\nu/k|T_m|]}.$$

Hence

$$\frac{h\nu}{\exp[h\nu/kT_{eq}]} = \frac{h\nu}{1 - \exp[-h\nu/k|T_m|]}.$$

Hence

$$\frac{h\nu}{kT_{eq}} = \ln\left\{2 - \exp\left[-\frac{h\nu}{k|T_m|}\right]\right\}.$$

However, we will not make further use of this result.

2. – A quantum treatment.

The considerations of the previous Section, while they yield the correct result for noise in linear maser amplifiers (or attenuators), provide no justification for the separation of the emitted field into an induced *coherent* part and a spontaneous *incoherent* part. Such justification cannot, in fact, come from any theory which deals only with transition probabilities, since such a theory provides no information on the statistical relationships between the emitted electromagnetic field and the exciting field. In this Section we shall endeavor to examine these statistical relationship using a relatively simple quantum-mechanical treatment of the electromagnetic field.

The amplitudes of the individual field modes (1.4) may be written

$$A^{(\lambda)}_{l,m,n}(\boldsymbol{r}, t) = A^{(\lambda)}_{l,m,n} \exp[i\boldsymbol{k}_{l,m,n}\cdot\boldsymbol{r}] \exp[i\omega_{l,m,n} t] + \text{c.c.}$$

The time dependence of an individual mode amplitude is that of a harmonic oscillator, and this makes it clear how to quantize the field. With the usual expression for the fields

$$\boldsymbol{E} = -\frac{1}{c}\frac{\partial \boldsymbol{A}(\boldsymbol{r}, t)}{\partial t}, \qquad \boldsymbol{H} = \operatorname{curl} \boldsymbol{A}(\boldsymbol{r}, t),$$

one finds that the energy of the mode (l, m, n, λ) is, classically,

$$W_{\text{mode}} = \frac{1}{8\pi} \int\limits_{XYZ} (\boldsymbol{E}^2 + \boldsymbol{H}^2)\, \mathrm{d}v = \frac{k^2 XYZ}{2\pi} A^* A \,,$$

where we have now dropped all subscripts because we are dealing with only one mode. Thus if we set

$$\left[\frac{k^2 XYZ}{2\pi v}\right]^{\frac{1}{2}} A \exp[-i\omega t] = a(t)\,, \tag{2.2}$$

the boson destruction operator in the Heisenberg picture, and replace the complex conjugate by the adjoint, we have done the job.

The Hamiltonian which replaces the energy is simply

$$H = \hbar\omega a^\dagger a \tag{2.3}$$

and the commutation relation between a and $a^\dagger$ is

$$a a^\dagger - a^\dagger a \equiv [a, a^\dagger] = 1\,,$$

which serves to establish the equation of motion

$$\frac{\mathrm{d}a}{\mathrm{d}t} = -\frac{i}{\hbar}[a, H] = -i\omega a; \qquad a = a_0 \exp[-i\omega t]\,. \tag{2.4}$$

The operators which correspond to the electric and magnetic field amplitudes are made from linear combinations of the Hermitian operators

$$p \equiv \frac{1}{\sqrt{2}}(a + a^\dagger) \qquad \text{and} \qquad q \equiv \frac{i}{\sqrt{2}}(a - a^\dagger)\,,$$

which vary sinusoidally with time.

In fact, since observables are supposed to correspond to Hermitian operators, we expect that these last operators and the photon number operator $a^\dagger a$ might be the most interesting observables.

Now there are certain wave functions and density operators (matrices) which are useful in discussing the maser process, and we shall talk about these for a moment. As we shall use the Heisenberg picture throughout, the state vectors (*i.e.*, wave functions) and density operators are constant in time, while the observable operators are time-dependent.

First, of course, there are the energy eigenstates

$$|n\rangle\,,$$

whose basic properties are

$$(2.5a)\qquad a_0|n\rangle = \sqrt{n}\,|n-1\rangle\,,\qquad a_0^\dagger|n\rangle = \sqrt{n+1}\,|n+1\rangle$$

and hence

$$(2.5b)\qquad a_0^\dagger a_0|n\rangle = n|n\rangle\,,\qquad |n\rangle = (n!)^{-\frac{1}{2}}(a_0^\dagger)n|0\rangle\,,$$

where (see eq. (2.4)) $a_0 \equiv a(t=0)$. These states form a complete and orthogonal set for the harmonic oscillator, so that any problem can in principle be solved using them as a basis. However, they are often not the most useful set for maser problems.

There are also an infinite variety of complete orthogonal sets of states which might be called displaced states; each such set is comprised of the eigenfunctions of the operator

$$(a_0^\dagger - \alpha^*)(a_0 - \alpha)\,,$$

where α can be any complex number. For each α there is a complete and orthogonal set of states which we can label

$$|n_\alpha\rangle\,.$$

They are derived in the same manner as the harmonic oscillator states and thus have equivalent properties. The states $|n_\alpha\rangle$ are in fact related to the states $|n\rangle$ through the unitary displacement operator [2]

$$D(\alpha) = \exp[\alpha a_0^\dagger - \alpha^* a_0)\,,$$

i.e.,

$$|n_\alpha\rangle = D(\alpha)|n\rangle\,.$$

The numbers n are the positive integers, and

$$(2.5c)\qquad \begin{cases} (a_0-\alpha)|n_\alpha\rangle & = \sqrt{n}\,|(n-1)_\alpha\rangle\,, \\ (a_0^\dagger-\alpha^*)|n_\alpha\rangle & = \sqrt{n+1}\,|(n+1)_\alpha\rangle\,, \\ (a_0^\dagger-\alpha^*)(a_0-\alpha)|n_\alpha\rangle & = n|n_\alpha\rangle\,. \end{cases}$$

Note that these states have also the properties,

$$(2.6)\qquad \langle n_\alpha|a|n_\alpha\rangle=\alpha\exp[-i\omega t]\,,\qquad \langle n_\alpha|aa^\dagger|n_\alpha\rangle=|\alpha|^2+n\,.$$

They can be thought of as representing a combination of n photons with a known (and therefore coherent in a sense) field. They can in principle be created from the ground state $|0\rangle$ by initial excitation to the state $|n\rangle$ followed by insertion, via very weak coupling, of an appropriate amount of energy from a highly energetic and monochromatic oscillator whose phase has just recently been measured. These displaced states form a useful expansion basis when the initial conditions of a problem assume that the expectation value of the field is known to be different from zero.

Finally, GLAUBER [2] has recently made extensive use of an expansion in a complete but not orthogonal set of states which in our present notation would be the states $|0_\alpha\rangle$, where α is allowed to vary over the complex plane. Since in general

$$\langle 0_\alpha|0_{\alpha'}\rangle\neq\delta(\alpha-\alpha')\,,$$

such expansions are not unique but can be none the less very useful. They have the completeness property

$$\frac{1}{2\pi}\iint d^{(2)}\alpha\,|0_\alpha\rangle\langle 0_\alpha|=1\,,$$

where the integration extends over the complex α-plane.

Where questions of noise are concerned, one is always dealing with situations where one has only partially complete knowledge about the state of the pertinent system. This is, of course, just the situation where density operators are necessary. One well-known density operator is

$$(2.7)\qquad \varrho_N=\left(1-\exp\left[-\frac{h\nu}{kT}\right]\right)\exp\left[-\frac{H}{kT}\right]=$$
$$=(1-\exp[-\mu])\exp[-\mu a^\dagger a]\,,\qquad \mu=\frac{h\nu}{kT}\,.$$

This is, of course, the density operator corresponding to thermal excitation of the mode, and yields the following probability distributions and averages:

$$(2.8)\qquad \begin{cases}\text{prob}\,(n)\equiv\langle n|\varrho_N|n\rangle=(1-\exp[-\mu])\exp[-\mu n]\,,\\ \langle a^\dagger a\rangle=\text{Tr}\,(\varrho_N a^\dagger a)=\sum_n(1-\exp[-\mu])\,n\exp[-\mu n]=\\ \qquad=\dfrac{1}{\exp[\mu]-1}\equiv N\qquad(\text{this defines } N)\,.\end{cases}$$

N of course need not be an integer.

Also if we are interested in the continuous probability distribution of an observable such as p, then we find

$$\text{prob}\,(p') = \langle p'|\varrho_N|p'\rangle = \frac{1}{\sqrt{2\pi\sigma^2}}\exp\,[p'^2/2\sigma^2]\,, \tag{2.9}$$

where $|p'\rangle$ is an eigenstate of the operator p, satisfying

$$p|p'\rangle = p'|p'\rangle\,, \qquad \int_{-\infty}^{\infty} \mathrm{d}p'|p'\rangle\langle p'| = 1\,,$$

and where

$$\sigma^2 = \left(N + \frac{1}{2}\right) = \frac{1}{\exp\,[h\nu/kT]-1} + \frac{1}{2}\,.$$

Thus for the thermal density operator the probability of occurrence of a certain number of photons decreases exponentially with the number, while the probability of occurrence of a certain value of an observable such as $p(t)$ (any linear Hermitian combination a and $a^\dagger$ will do [3]) is a stationary Gaussian distribution centered on zero. The density operator ϱ_N has the maximum entropy of all density operators exhibiting the same expectation value of the energy.

For deriving probabilities such as (2.9) a very useful quantity is the characteristic or moment generating function

$$C_p(\xi, t) = \langle\exp\,[i\xi p]\rangle = \mathrm{Tr}\,[\varrho\exp\,[i\xi p]], \tag{2.10}$$

where ξ is a real parameter.

If we expand the trace (2.10) in the representation $|p'\rangle$ (see eq. (2.9)) for which p is instantaneously diagonal, this yields immediately

$$C_p(\xi, t) = \int_{-\infty}^{\infty} \mathrm{d}p'\langle p'|\varrho|p'\rangle\exp\,[i\xi p']\,.$$

Clearly, then, by the Fourier transform

$$\langle p'|\varrho|p'\rangle = \frac{1}{2\pi}\int_{-\infty}^{\infty} C_p(\xi, t)\exp\,[-i\xi p']\,\mathrm{d}\xi\,. \tag{2.11}$$

For the case $\varrho = \varrho_N$ (eq. (27)) we have

$$C_p(\xi, t) = (1-\exp\,[-\mu])\,\mathrm{Tr}\left[\exp\,[-\mu a^\dagger a]\exp\left[\frac{i\xi}{\sqrt{2}}[a^\dagger + a]\right]\right].$$

With some algebra and the identity [4]

$$\exp\left[\frac{i\xi}{\sqrt{2}}(a^\dagger + a)\right] = \exp\left[-\frac{\xi^2}{4}\right]\exp\left[\frac{i\xi}{\sqrt{2}}a^\dagger\right]\exp\left[\frac{i\xi}{\sqrt{2}}a\right],$$

the characteristic function can be worked out to give

$$C_p(\xi, t) = \exp[-\tfrac{1}{2}\xi^2(N + \tfrac{1}{2})] \tag{2.12}$$

from which (2.9) follows by (2.11).

A density operator which is more useful for discussing problems in quantum electronics is the displaced thermal operator

$$\varrho_N(\alpha) = (1 - \exp[-\mu])\exp[-\mu(a_0^\dagger - \alpha^*)(a_0 - \alpha)]\,. \tag{2.13}$$

This density operator is diagonal in the representation $|n_\alpha\rangle$, just as the thermal density operator is diagonal in the representation $|n\rangle$, *i.e.*,

$$\langle n_\alpha|\varrho_N(\alpha)|n_\alpha\rangle = (1 - \exp[-\mu])\exp[-\mu n]\,. \tag{2.14}$$

For the density operator $\varrho_N(\alpha)$ we find

$$\begin{cases} \langle a\rangle = \alpha\exp[-i\omega t]\,, \\ \langle a^\dagger a\rangle = |\alpha|^2 + \dfrac{1}{\exp[\mu]-1} = |\alpha|^2 + N. \end{cases} \tag{2.15}$$

and

$$\langle p'|\varrho_N(\alpha)|p'\rangle = \frac{1}{\sqrt{2\pi\sigma^2}}\exp\left[-\frac{(p' - \langle p\rangle)^2}{2\sigma^2}\right], \tag{2.16}$$

where

$$\langle p\rangle = \frac{1}{\sqrt{2}}[\langle a^\dagger\rangle + \langle a\rangle] = \frac{1}{\sqrt{2}}[\alpha^*\exp[i\omega t] + \alpha\exp[-i\omega t]]$$

and σ^2 is as in (2.9). Hence the fields have Gaussian distributions about their expectation values, and the expectation value of the energy is a simple sum of a thermal part and a part coming from the expectation value of the field. Such a field may be thought of as a signal field (identified with the expectation value) plus an additive Gaussian noise field.

The characteristic function for the observable p is in this case

$$C_p(\xi, t) = \exp[i\xi\langle p\rangle - \tfrac{1}{2}\xi^2(N + \tfrac{1}{2})]\,. \tag{2.17}$$

This can be seen by noting that

$$\mathrm{Tr}\,\{\varrho_N(\alpha)\exp[i\xi(p-\langle p\rangle)]\}$$

expanded in the representation $|n_\alpha\rangle$,has no dependence on α and thus equals (2.12).

It is of interest to find out what happens during a process of linear amplification. In particular, suppose that at some initial time $t=0$, the state of of the field has the properties

$$\left\{\begin{aligned}&\langle a\rangle=\alpha\,,\\&\langle a^\dagger a\rangle=|\alpha|^2+N\,,\end{aligned}\right. \tag{2.18}$$

and is properly represented by $\varrho_N(\alpha)$, which incidentally has the highest entropy of any density operator satisfying the conditions (2.18). Suppose the field is now coupled weakly to a large number of atoms which have a spread of resonant frequencies and which are in a state of positive or negative temperature T_a for frequencies in the vicinity of the mode frequency. If the interaction is not allowed to saturate the atomic transitions the atoms act simply as a linear maser amplifier or as an attenuator.

It has been shown [5] that at times $t>0$, one gets

$$C_p(\xi,t)=\exp\left[i\xi\sqrt{G}\,\langle p\rangle_u-\frac{1}{2}\,\xi^2\left\{GN+\frac{G-1}{1-\exp[h\omega/kT_m]}+\frac{1}{2}\right\}\right], \tag{2.19}$$

where $G=e^{\gamma t}$ is the power gain and

$$\langle p\rangle_u=\frac{1}{\sqrt{2}}\,(\alpha\exp[-i\omega t]+\alpha^*\exp[i\omega t])\,;$$

that is, the value $\langle p\rangle$ would have had, had the interaction with the atoms never been turned on. In the calculation leading to (2.19) dispersion was neglected. When included, its effect is to give an additional phase shift to the exponential term linear in ξ; this represents a frequency shift of the mode.

In (2.19) we see that p may be considered to be comprised of a perfectly definite part, which is its expectation value, *i.e.*,

$$\langle p\rangle=G^{\frac{1}{2}}\langle p\rangle_u\,,$$

plus a random Gaussian part, which itself has three parts, the amplified initial noise energy, the amplified spontaneous emission noise, and the ever-present zero-point contribution.

This same type of calculation can be applied to a resonator mode. Losses can be introduced by coupling the field to positive temperature atoms, as well as to the amplifying ones, and a classical driving term can be added [6]. Here it is preferable to keep the gain less than unity to obtain steady-state solutions (provided the driving term is steady). Again, one finds nothing very surprising. The response of the field expectation value $\langle p \rangle$ as a function of frequency is just the classical response of the resonator, while the average noise energy is determined by matching the rate of generation (eq. (1.14), summed over all sources) against the rate of loss. The presence of the driving term does not affect the noise field in this linear approximation.

In sum, then, one finds that in linear process of amplification or attenuation 1) signal fields behave classically, 2) spontaneous emission noise fields are additive and Gaussian, and 3) the zero-point fields simply persists throughout.

There are in the literature a number of treatments of noise in maser type amplifiers. Some of these are listed in ref. [7].

3. – Oscillators.

We know that the gain coefficient $\alpha(\nu)$ eq. (1.13) expresses the shape of the resonance line. The total gain for a length L of amplifying substance is, however,

$$G(\nu) = \exp[\alpha(\nu)L],$$

which for high gain is a sharper curve than $\alpha(\nu)$. This sort of bandwidth reduction is typical of traveling-wave masers or lasers. In simple regenerative resonator devices, the bandwidth reduction with gain is much faster, the bandwidth times the voltage gain at the line center approaching a constant at high gain.

In the original paper on the ammonia maser [8] an approximation to the spectral width of its oscillation was obtained simply by treating the oscillator as a linear amplifier of its noise input and adjusting the gain so that the total power generated matched what was available from the molecules. Of course, an oscillator is distinct from a noise amplifier of similar bandwidth because of the amplitude-stability of the oscillator. However, it is tempting to assume that the effective noise source is not greatly affected by the necessary non-linearity, and thus can be identified with the effective Gaussian source for the high-gain amplifier. If this is so, then the noise behavior of a maser or laser oscillator operating in a single mode should not be strikingly different from that of the classical oscillators which have been treated in the literature [9]. These treatments give the following results. First, consider the noise resulting from amplitude fluctuations. If the amplitude is displaced slightly from its equilibrium value, it will return to equilibrium in a manner determined by the nonlinearity. The Fourier transform of this return to equilibrium determines the amplitude noise spectrum in much the same way as occurs for passive circuits, except that only half (the in-phase part) of the noise power is involved. Hence if the return to equilibrium is rapid the amplitude noise will be broad and weak; if it is slow this noise will be sharp and strong. Second, consider phase noise. If the phase of the oscillator is displaced there is no restoring force; hence successive phase shifts introduced by the noise add in a random-walk manner. Furthermore, the phase shifts have almost no relation to the behavior of the nonlinearity; hence the phase noise depends primarily on the noise source and on the amplitude of the oscillation. The r.m.s. accumulated phase shift $\Delta\theta$ in a period τ, according to such analyses, can be expressed as (*) [10]

$$(\Delta\theta)^2 = \frac{W_N \tau}{2p[1/\Delta\omega_r + 1/\Delta\omega_m]^2},$$

where W_N is the equivalent input noise energy [eq. (1.16) plus the contribution from the positive resistance of the resonator], $\Delta\omega_r$ is the full width at half power of the passive resonator, $\Delta\omega_m$ is the full width at half maximum of the amplifying resonance line, and P is the total oscillation power delivered by the amplifying resonance. From this result one may define a phase-coherence time τ_c as the time for which $\Delta\theta = 1$; the full spectral width of the phase noise spectrum is τ_c^{-1}. This result for the spectral width of the phase noise is just one half of the result obtained for the oscillator bandwidth in the linear approximation mentioned above. The difference may be explained qualitatively since for the actual situation, 1) only the noise components in quadrature with the oscillation produce phase shifts, and 2) since the amplitude is stabilized the phase shifts introduced by the quadrature noise are on the average smaller than they would be if the amplitude were to fluctuate greatly, as happens in the linear approximation.

4. – Communication theory.

The mathematical theory of communication was developed in the late 1940's by SHANNON [11], WIENER [12], and others. In addition, BRILLOUIN [13] has discussed the general relationship of entropy to the information obtained by measurements. We shall try to make plausible the rudiments of Shannon's theory, see how it might be taken into the quantum theory, and see what consequences ensue.

(*) This form of the expression was suggested by some recent theoretical work on maser oscillators by M. LAX. It is valid for an homogeneously broadened amplifying resonance.

One must envisage a sender of information and a receiver. We shall label them X and Y, respectively. X has at his command an « alphabet » and some method of sending the symbols of the alphabet (*i.e.*, letters) to Y in an orderly sequence. Disturbances in the transmission path modify the symbols so that Y can make mistakes in recognizing them. X and Y must of course have a common language so that the symbols are meaningful to Y when he receives them; we will presume that this is so.

To proceed to a mathematical definition of information we must define some terms.

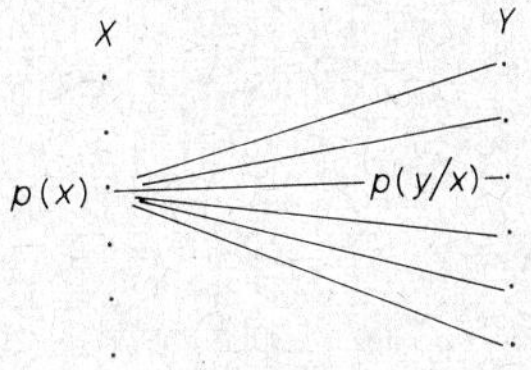

Fig. 1.

In Fig. 1, the column of points below X are supposed to represent the different possible symbols of his alphabet, and we presume that there is some (quite possibly unknown at the outset) probability $p(x)$ for the occurrence of the x-th symbol in a typical long message of many symbols. (It may be that some symbols take more energy and/or time to send than others, and so X will tend to use them less often.) For simplicity it is presumed here and throughout the discussion that the sequence of symbols in a typical long message represent a Markoff process; that is, the probability of the occurrence of a particular symbol somewhere in the sequence has no dependence on the prior symbols. The column of points before Y are supposed to represent the different possible interpretations Y might give to each received symbol. The probability that Y might interpret X's x-th symbol as his own y-th are the so-called conditional probabilities $p(y/x)$. Thus $p(y/x)$ is the probability that y is received when x was sent. From the probabilities $p(x)$ and $p(y/x)$ we can define a joint probability,

$$p(x, y) \equiv p(x)\, p(y/x) \tag{4.1}$$

for the combined occurrence (x sent, y received) in a typical long message.

Let us suppose that we know the statistical properties of the transmission channel, so that we know the $p(y/x)$, for all x and y. If for each x, the spread of the probability $p(y/x)$ over y is broad, then the channel is noisy. A noiseless channel on the other hand would have

$$\left\{\begin{array}{l} p(y/x) = \delta(x, y(x)) \\ \text{and} \\ y(x) \neq y(x') \qquad \text{if} \qquad x \neq x', \end{array}\right. \tag{4.2}$$

so that each sent symbol has a unique and definite interpretation by Y.

The average information per symbol for a typical long message sent over this channel is defined as

$$I \equiv \sum_{x,y} p(x, y) \log \left[\frac{p(y/x)}{p(y)}\right], \tag{4.3}$$

where

$$p(y) \equiv \sum_x p(x, y) = \sum_x p(x)\, p(y/x)$$

is the average receiver probability for the result y. Equation (4.3) can be written in several different forms, one of which is

$$I = -\sum_y p(y) \log p(y) + \sum_x p(x) \sum_y p(y/x) \log p(y/x) = \\ = H(Y) - \sum_x p(x)\, H(Y/x), \tag{4.4}$$

where H is the classical entropy function

$$H(Y) \equiv -\sum_y p(y) \log p(y), \tag{4.5a}$$

$$H(Y/x) \equiv -\sum_y p(y/x) \log p(y/x). \tag{4.5b}$$

We have used a capital letter Y in the argument of H to indicate the sum over y. The entropy $H(Y)$ may be called the overall average received entropy per symbol, while $H(Y/x)$ is the average received entropy per symbol when the sent symbol is known to be x. SHANNON defines the average of $H(Y/x)$ over the probabilities $p(x)$ as the conditional entropy, which we label $H(Y/X)$. Hence

$$H(Y/X) \equiv \sum_x p(x)\, H(Y/x) \tag{4.6}$$

and so (4.4) becomes

$$I = H(Y) - H(Y/X), \tag{4.7}$$

that is, the information is just the overall received entropy less the conditional entropy.

It is beyond the scope of this lecture to justify (4.3) or (4.4) completely. The interested student is referred to Shannon's book. However, we can make (4.3) plausible, perhaps, by examining some of its properties.

Property 1: $I \geqslant 0$.
This is easy to prove with the inequality

$$\log x \geqslant 1 - \frac{1}{x}. \tag{4.8}$$

If (4.8) is used in (4.3), one finds

$$I \geqslant \sum_{x,y} [p(x, y) - p(y)\, p(x)] ;$$

since each term sums to unity we have

$$I \geqslant 0 .$$

Property 2: If

$$p(y/x) = p(y) ,$$

then

$$I = 0 .$$

This is mathematically obvious from (4.3). What it means is that the channel is sufficiently noisy that the conditional probabilities $p(y/x)$ no longer depend on x. Clearly no information is transmitted in this case.

Property 3: If there are M different symbols in the sender's alphabet, then

$$I_{\text{max}} = \log M ;$$

that is, simply the logarithm of the number of possible symbols.

To see this we note that a sum like (4.5a) is maximum when all the $p(y)$'s are equal to $1/M$, for which case

$$H(Y) = -\sum_{y=1}^{M} \frac{1}{M} \log \frac{1}{M} = \log M ,$$

also if any $p(y)$ approaches zero, we have

$$\lim_{p(y)\to 0} p(y) \log p(y) = 0 ,$$

so such a term in the sum just drops out. If any $p(y)$ approaches unity it forces all the others to zero, and hence the whole sum goes to zero. Thus the most informative channel is one with no noise, so that (4.2) holds and the conditional entropy is zero; and where all symbols are used with equal probability. This set of conditions gives

$$I = \log M$$

as stated.

So much for the properties of (4.3) or (4.4). It is apparently the only suitable mathematical measure of information.

One problem in information theory is to find the probabilities $p(x)$ which maximize I, presuming that the $p(y/x)$ are known, and subject to whatever other constraints are put on the channel. We will give an example of this shortly. The problen is much simplified in the case of *additive noise.* In this case $H(Y/x)$ (see (4.5*b*)) is independent of x, and hence for any x,

$$H(Y/x) = H(Y/X) \equiv H(N) , \tag{4.9}$$

where N stands for noise. Thus for the case of additive noise (4.7) becomes

$$I = H(Y) - H(N) . \tag{4.10}$$

Since $H(N)$ is presumed known, the problem of maximizing I with respect to the probabilities $p(x)$ becomes the simpler task of maximizing $H(Y)$.

In cases where the possible symbols and measurements form continuous rather than discrete sets, the sums in the previous equations become integrals, while the probabilities become probability densities. In this case all entropies acquire an undefined additive constant which changes with a change of scale, but the information remains well-defined [11].

An example. Suppose that information is being transmitted via electrical signals in a transmission line, and that the receiver measures the voltage across the line. Suppose that the average transmitter power is fixed. Suppose that there is a stationary additive Gaussian noise of known average power accompanying the signal when it reaches the receiver. This means that for a given signal voltage $x(t)$, the actual total voltage (signal and noise) $y(t)$ will have an instantaneous Gaussian probability density

$$p[y(t)/x(t)] = \frac{1}{\sqrt{2\pi}\,\sigma_N} \exp\left[-\frac{[y(t)-x(t)]^2}{2\sigma_N^2}\right] , \tag{4.11}$$

where

$$\sigma_N^2 = ([y(t)-x(t)]^2)_{\text{ave}} \equiv \int_{-\infty}^{\infty} [y(t)-x(t)]^2\, p[y(t)/x(t)]\, dy(t)$$

is proportional to the noise power. The assumption that the noise is stationary means that σ_N^2 is time-independent.

Now let us suppose that we have available a measuring apparatus that can measure $y(t)$ with no appreciable increase in the uncertainty of the resulting estimation of $x(t)$. This means that the internally generated receiver noise, referred back to its input, must have an effective power much less than the incident noise. Then for a measurement at some particular time t, $x(t)$ may be identified with the sent symbol, $y(t)$ with the received symbol, and (4.11) may be identified with the conditional probability density.

The entropy of the conditional probability density (4.11) is easily evaluated to be

$$H[Y(t)/x(t)] = \tfrac{1}{2} \log [2\pi e \sigma_N^2] = H(N)\,,$$

which obviously satisfies the condition (4.9) for an additive noise.

Now to maximize the information per measurement we must find the appropriate probability density $p[x(t)]$. The answer here is well known. A Gaussian probability density

$$p[x(t)] = (2\pi\sigma_S^2)^{-\frac{1}{2}} \exp\left[-\frac{x^2(t)}{2\sigma_S^2}\right] \tag{4.12}$$

in combination with the statistically independent Gaussian noise yields the Gaussian form

$$p[y(t)] = \{2\pi(\sigma_S^2 + \sigma_N^2)\}^{-\frac{1}{2}} \exp\left[-\frac{y^2(t)}{2(\sigma_S^2 + \sigma_N^2)}\right] \tag{4.13}$$

for the receiver density, which in turn maximizes the received entropy $H[Y(t)]$ subject to the assumed constraint of a fixed average transmitter power. Finally evaluation of the entropy of the density (4.13) yields for the information per measurement the simple expression

$$I_{\max} = \frac{1}{2} \log \left[\frac{\sigma_S^2 + \sigma_N^2}{\sigma_n^2}\right]$$

or

$$I_{\max} = \frac{1}{2} \log \left(1 + \frac{P_S}{P_N}\right),$$

where P_S is the average signal power and P_N the average noise power, both of course taken at the receiver input.

So far we have said nothing about bandwidth. However, sampling theory indicates that if signal and noise occupy a small bandwidth B with uniform spectral density (here we assume that noise components in frequency ranges outside B have been rendered ineffectual by appropriate filtering), then independent measurements can and must be taken at a rate $2B$ to determine $y(t)$ exactly. Hence the maximum information rate or information capacity C

for this system is just as obtained by SHANNON

$$C = 2BI_{\max} = B \log\left(1 + \frac{P_S}{P_N}\right). \tag{4.14}$$

The above example is obviously a classical one, since the quantum nature of the pertinent electromagnetic field was not invoked, nor were any limitations imposed on the receiver's ability to sample and measure the field at the rate $2B$. The classical theory must become invalid in the limit of zero noise; conversely, we should expect any proper quantum theory to yield (4.14) in the limit of large noise.

Quantum theory. – Let us see now what modifications of information theory are necessary to make it compatible with quantum mechanics. The set of symbols which comprise the sender's alphabet must be identified with some sort of physical systems which obey the laws of quantum mechanics. For example the field in the transmission line can be resolved into a set of independent harmonic oscillators. In a given frequency-time interval $BT \gg 1$ such a resolution gives BT independent harmonic oscillators; hence a receiver of bandwidth B which measures the incoming field in a transmission line can be likened to a receiver which measures harmonic oscillators at a rate B per second. The different symbols might then be identified with different possible conditions of excitation of each oscillator. The two measurements which are necessary to establish both amplitude and phase of each oscillator in the classical theory yield the $2B$ measurements per second which were invoked in our previous classical example.

In the quantum theory the appropriate statistical description of each symbol (oscillator) after transmission and just prior to its measurement is through a density operator. These operators (one for each symbol) must reflect the effect of attenuation and the addition of noise which occur in trasmission. A simple and yet not unreasonable example might be the set of density operators $\varrho_N(\alpha)$ (eq. (2.13)), where it is presumed that the sender determines the expectation value of the amplitude and phase of each oscillator and hence determines α, while the thermal noise introduced by the transmission line determines N. Such a presumption is consistent with the discussion of the attenuation process of Sect. **2**, if the transmitter is essentially classical.

Now we can observe a difference between the classical and quantum theories. The two classically independent measurements which are necessary to determine the amplitude and phase of an harmonic oscillator must, in the quantum theory, be thought of as two related parts of what is essentially one measurement, a measurement of the state of the oscillator. In our classical example the information per oscillator (per two measurements) is simply

$$2I_{\max} = \log\left(1 + \frac{P_S}{P_N}\right) \tag{4.15}$$

and so we must demand a quantum theory which yields this result for the information per oscillator in the limit of large noise.

At this point we would like to introduce a hypothesis concerning an upper limit to information, which, while it yet lacks proof, hasintuitive appeal, and so far seems to lack counter-examples. We will attempt to justify it in part here through some examples. This hypothesis, which is based on the classical eq. (4.4), can be stated as follows: If we define an average density operator

$$\varrho(X) \equiv \sum_x p(x)\, \varrho(x)\,,$$

then

$$I \leqslant S[\varrho(X)] - \sum_x p(x)\, S[\varrho(x)]\,, \tag{4.16}$$

where S is the quantum entropy function

$$S(\varrho) \equiv -\operatorname{Tr}\,[\varrho \log \varrho]\,. \tag{4.17}$$

Here x is again the sender variable which identifies the different symbols, the $p(x)$ are again the probabilities for the occurrence of the different symbols in a typical long message, and I may be thought of as the available information at the receiver input. In essence, (4.16) hypothesizes an upper bound to the information that *any* receiver can extract from the channel. The right side of (4.16) does not depend on the receiver; hence if (4.16) is in fact valid, a good communications system can be evolved by first establishing a maximum value for the right side of (4.16) through optimization of the behavior of the transmitter; then one can look for a measuring apparatus which yields a value of I not greatly smaller. In order to compute I, some particular receiver *must* be specified; the various possible results of its measurements can then be identified with the y's of (4.3).

Let us now consider some of the properties of (4.16). There is one (and I believe only one) situation where the equality holds and where in fact (4.16) reduces to (4.4). This happens when all the $\varrho(x)$ are diagonal matrices in the same representation, and the receiver makes exact measurements of the observables (more precisely, the complete set of commuting observables) which create that representation. Let us call the representation the Y representation, with orthonormal eigenvectors $|y\rangle$. Then the probability that the measurement of the symbol whose density operator is $\varrho(x)$ will yield the value y is just the diagonal element $\langle y|\varrho(x)|y\rangle$. This is the conditional probability which was earlier called $p(y/x)$. Hence for this case

$$p(y/x) = \langle y|\varrho(x)|y\rangle$$

and so (see (4.5b))

$$H(Y/x) = -\sum_y \langle y|\varrho(x)|y\rangle \log(\langle y|\varrho(x)|y\rangle) = S[\varrho(x)],$$

where the last equality holds because $\varrho(x)$ is diagonal in the representation Y. Likewise, we see that (see (4.3))

$$p(y) = \sum_x p(x)\langle y|\varrho(x)|y\rangle = \langle y|\sum_x p(x)\,\varrho(x)|y\rangle = \langle y|\varrho(X)|y\rangle,$$

whence (see (4.5a))

$$H(Y) = S[\varrho(X)].$$

With these results, (4.16) with the equality sign is seen to be identical to (4.4).

Now let us look at the transmission-line case, with the presumption that the density operator representing each harmonic oscillator at the receiver just before measurement has the form $\varrho_N(\alpha)$, with α identified as the sender variable x. Hence

$$\varrho(x) = (1-\exp[-\mu])\exp[-\mu(a^\dagger - x^*)(a-x)]. \tag{4.18}$$

Note that x is now continuous complex variable, so $p(x)$ becomes a two-dimensional probability density. However, for convenience and continuity we will continue to use the symbol $\sum_x$ to represent the two-dimensional integral

$$\int_{-\infty}^{\infty}\int_{-\infty}^{\infty} \mathrm{d}^{(2)}(x).$$

From Sect. 2 it is clear that the diagonal representation for $\varrho(x)$ has the eigenvectors $|n_x\rangle$ which do indeed depend on x; hence the considerations of the last example do not apply. However, the entropy $S[\varrho(x)]$ can be easily evaluated, since the matrix elements of $\varrho(x)$ in its diagonal representation are (see (2.14) and (2.8))

$$\langle n_x|\varrho(x)|n_x\rangle = (1-\exp[-\mu])\exp[-\mu n] = \left(\frac{1}{N+1}\right)\left(\frac{N}{N+1}\right)^n,$$

whence

$$S[\varrho(x)] = -\sum_n \left(\frac{1}{N+1}\right)\left(\frac{N}{N+1}\right)^n \log\left\{\left(\frac{1}{N+1}\right)\left(\frac{N}{N+1}\right)^n\right\} = \tag{4.19}$$

$$= \log(N+1) + N\log\left(1+\frac{1}{N}\right).$$

The quantum equivalent of an additive noise may be defined as the case where $S[\varrho(x)]$ is independent of x, as it is here. Because of this independence we can define

$$S[\varrho(x)] \equiv S(N) = \log(N+1) + N\log\left(1+\frac{1}{N}\right) \tag{4.20}$$

for all x, and (4.16) becomes

$$I \leqslant S[\varrho(X)] - S(N)\,. \tag{4.21}$$

Now as in the classical case of additive noise, the task of maximizing the right side of (4.21) with respect to the $p(x)$ reduces the task of maximizing $S[\varrho(X)]$, subject again to whatever constraints we impose on the system. Let us take the same simple constraint as before; *i.e.*, we presume that the average transmitter power is fixed so that the average signal power incident on the receiver is P_S. The overall average energy per oscillator is given by

$$W_{\text{av}} = h\nu\,\text{Tr}\,[\varrho(X)\,a^\dagger a] = h\nu \sum_x p(x)\;\text{Tr}\,[\varrho(x)\,a^\dagger a]\,,$$

which evaluates to (see (2.15))

$$W_{\text{av}} = h\nu \sum_x p(x)[\,|x|^2 + N] = h\nu[\,|x|^2_{\text{av}} + N]\,, \tag{4.22}$$

where

$$|x|^2_{\text{av}} \equiv \sum_x p(x)\,|x|^2$$

can clearly be identified as the average received signal energy per oscillator, in units of $h\nu$. As we have B oscillators per second, this average signal energy per oscillator can be expressed in terms of the average signal power P_S as

$$|x^2|_{\text{av}} = P_S/h\nu B \tag{4.23}$$

and the average noise energy per oscillator in terms of the average noise power

P_N (note that P_N excludes the zero-point noise) as

$$N = P_N/h\nu B\,. \tag{4.24}$$

Hence $\varrho(X)$ must be chosen to maximize its entropy subject to the single constraint (4.22). The result clearly must have the thermal form

$$\varrho(X) = (1-\exp[-\beta])\exp[-\beta a^\dagger a]\,, \tag{4.25}$$

where the constant β is evaluated from the constraint (4.22), (4.23) and (4.24),

$$\frac{P_S+P_N}{h\nu B} = \mathrm{Tr}[\varrho(X)a^\dagger a] = (\exp[\beta]-1)^{-1}\,. \tag{4.26}$$

In fact $\varrho(X)$ is obtained by choosing $p(x)$ as a two-dimensional Gaussian function with radial symmetry around the origin, but the derivation of $\varrho(X)$ does not actually require knowledge of $p(x)$.

The evaluation of $S[\varrho(X)]$ is now straightforward and yields, similar to (4.19),

$$S[\varrho(X)] = \log\left(1+\frac{P_S+P_N}{h\nu B}\right) + \left(\frac{P_S+P_N}{h\nu B}\right)\log\left(1+\frac{h\nu B}{P_S+P_N}\right), \tag{4.27}$$

whence, finally, using $N = P_N/h\nu B$ in (4.20), (4.21) can be written

$$I \leqslant \log\left(1+\frac{P_S}{P_N+h\nu B}\right) + \left(\frac{P_S+P_N}{h\nu B}\right)\log\left(1+\frac{h\nu B}{P_S+P_N}\right) - \frac{P_N}{h\nu B}\log\left(1+\frac{h\nu B}{P_N}\right). \tag{4.28}$$

It may be observed that the classical limit (4.15) is correctly established in the high noise limit

$$P_N \gg h\nu B$$

and in fact the equality sign appears to be correct for this case. We might have expected this result as a symptom of the correspondence principle. In the limit $P_N \to 0$, however, the right side of (4.28) remains finite, and does in fact appear to provide an upper imit to I. For example, if a maser-type amplifier is used to amplify the field to the point where « classical » measurements are sufficiently precise to determine the *output* field, then the minimum effective input noise introduced by the amplifier is $h\nu B$, and thus the maximum information per oscillator is (an extension of (4.15))

$$I_{\text{max, amp}} = \log\left(1+\frac{P_S}{P_N+h\nu B}\right),$$

which satisfies (4.28) for all P_S and P_N. We note that if $P_S \gg h\nu B$ then $I_{\max,\text{amp}}$ approaches our hypothesized upper limit and we would not expect any other receiving device to be much better. On the other hand if $P_N \ll P_S \ll h\nu B$ then $I_{\max,\text{amp}}$ is much smaller than the upper limit and so we might expect some other type receiver would be better. In fact, in this region an energy detection device is indeed better; we refer the reader to the literature [14] for a fuller discussion of this point.

To proceed to a rigorous proof of (4.16) or to determine information capacities for the various possible ways of measuring the received symbols requires a detailed investigation of the quantum mechanics of measuring processes. The theory of measurement has been the subject of considerable work [15], but it would appear that the possibilities for further development have not been exhausted. Preliminary attemtps to prove (4.16) even for finite discrete density matrices and for mathematically simplified approximations to measurement theory have not been completely successful. Its main justification at present is that it seems to work.

REFERENCES

[1] A. Einstein: *Phys. Zeits.*, **18**, 121 (1917).
[2] R.J. Glauber: *Phys. Rev.*, **131**, 2766 (1963).
[3] A. Messiah, *Quantum Mechanics*, vol. **1** (Amsterdam, 1961), p. 449.
[4] A. Messiah: *Quantum Mechanics*, vol. **1** (Amsterdam, 1961), p. 442.
[5] J. P. Gordon, W. H. Louisell and L. R. Walker: *Phys. Rev.*, **129**, 481 (1963).
[6] W. H. Louisell: *Proceedings of the Third International Symposium on Quantum Electronics*, to be published.
[7] R. V. Pound: *Ann. Phys.* (*N. Y.*), **1**, 24 (1957); M. W. Muller: *Phys. Rev.*, **106**, 8 (1957); W. M. P. Strandberg: *Phys. Rev.*, **106**, 617 (1957); J. Weber: *Rev. Mod. Phys.*, **31**, 681 (1959); W. H. Wells: *Ann. Phys.* (*N. Y.*), **12**, 1 (1961); I. R. Senitsky: *Phys. Rev.*, **123**, 1525 (1961); K. Shimoda, H. Takahasi and C. H. Townes: *Journ. Phys. Soc. Japan*, **12**, 686 (1961); D. E. McCumber: *Phys. Rev.*, **130**, 675 (1962).
[8] J. P. Gordon, H. J. Zeiger and C. H. Townes: *Phys. Rev.*, **99**, 1264 (1955).
[9] See for example, W. A. Edson: *Proc. IRE*, **48**, 1454 (1960).
[10] M. Lax: *Phys. Rev.*, to be published.
[11] C. E. Shannon and W. Weaver: *The Mathematical Theory of Communication* (Urbana, 1949).
[12] N. Wiener: *Extrapolation, Interpolation and Smoothing of Stationary Time Series* (New York, 1949).
[13] L. Brillouin: *Science and Information Theory*, 2nd ed. (New York, 1962).
[14] J. P. Gordon: *Proc. IRE*, **50**, 1898 (1962).
[15] See, for example, D. Bohm: *Quantum Theory*, part IV (New York, 1951).

Thermal Effects in a He-Ne Optical Maser.

F. T. ARECCHI

Laboratori CISE - Segrate, Milano

1. – Introduction.

The power output from a He-Ne optical maser has a strong dependence on the temperature of the discharge and the power of excitation.

The experimental features of this dependence and its theoretical explanation have been given elsewhere [1, 2]. I would like to give here a brief report and make some comments.

The effects we shall talk about are connected to a thermal enhancement of the mechanism of population inverson an can be explained by the equations describing the He-Ne transfer the photon-electron interaction, and the quenching mechanism of the Ne metastable $1s$ level.

The used Ne laser is a usual 1 m long laser with external confocal mirrors. The container is sealed off and eventual degassed impurities are adsorbed by a getter. The discharge is excited by a d.c. supply.

The laser frequency for the I.R. operation is $2.6 \cdot 10^{14}$ Hz and the Doppler width of the transition $\Delta\nu_D \simeq 800$ MHz.

The main lines of the laser operation are now briefly summarized.

In the He-Ne discharge a resonant transfer of excitation occurs from the He ($2\,^3S$) to the Ne ($2s$) levels, with a cross-section [3]

$$\sigma = 3.7 \cdot 10^{-17}\,\text{cm}^2 . \tag{1}$$

The four $2s$ levels are connected by radiative transitions to the ten $2p$ levels. The strongest laser action has been observed on the $2s_2 \to 2p_4$ transition. We are interested in analysing this one. Now the $2s_2$ level is also optically connected to the ground state. However at the operating pressure ultra-violet photons arising from this transition are completely trapped and the radiative lifetime of $2s_2$ is essentially determined by the rate of decay to the $2p$ levels [3]

We shall denote by τ the whole spontaneous decay time from the $2s_2$ state, and by $\tau_{23} = 1/\gamma_{23}$ the lifetime pertaining to the particular $2s_2 \to 2p_4$ transition. This value is not known and only a guess can be made [4].

The $2p$ terminal level of the laser transition is connected to the $1s$ metastable level by a very fast decay time of the order of 10^{-8} s. A discussion on the lifetime of the $1s$ level will be given in the next Section.

For a fixed d.c. discharge current, a thermal transient with a 200 s time constant has been observed, during which the output power goes up starting from zero. For each value of the discharge power, we can define a «short time» and a «long time» output. The first one is obtained starting from some initial condition and sweeping the power in a time short compared to 200 s. The second output corresponds to the asymptotic value at the temperature of equilibrium between heat generation

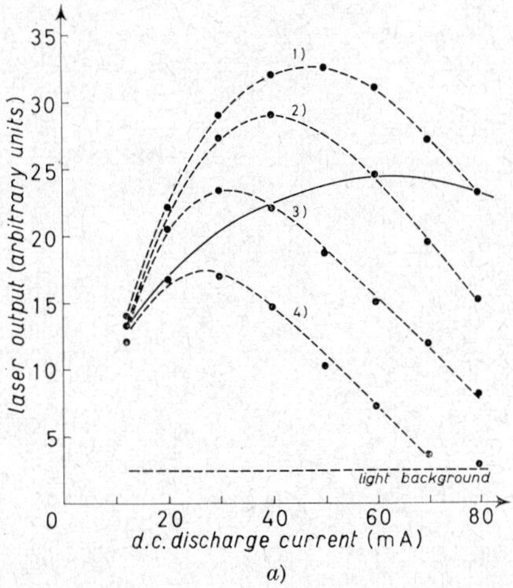

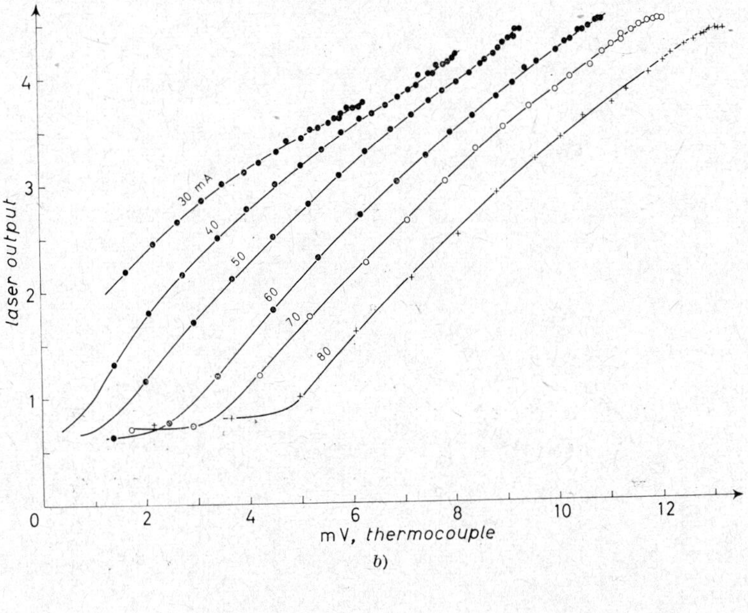

Fig. 1. – «Short time» and «long time» behaviour of the laser output power: – – – short-time curves at the equilibrium temperature corresponding to: 1) $i=80$ mA, 2) $i=60$ mA, 3) $i=40$ mA, 4) $i=20$ mA; —— long-time curve.

and dissipation. The two outputs are plotted *vs.* the discharge current in Fig. 1*a*. The « long time » output is also plotted *vs.* temperature in Fig. 1*b*.

2. – Parameters for the He-Ne laser equations.

2·1. *Pumping and depletion of the metastable level.* – For the sake of simplicity, the level diagram of the laser system is simplified as in Fig. 2.

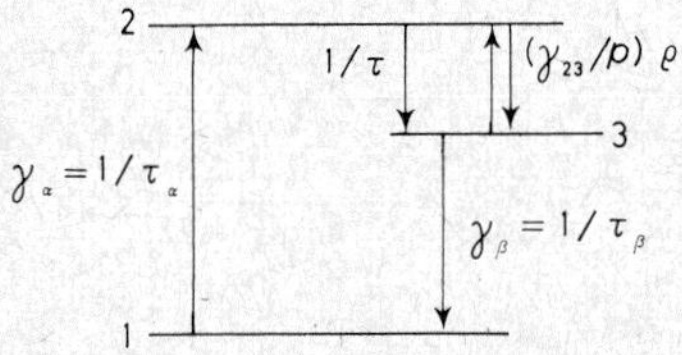

Fig. 2. – Simplified three-level diagram of the laser action.

The transition $1 \to 2$ stays for the excitation of the He ($2\,{}^3S$) state and transfer to Ne ($2s$). The density of $2\,{}^3S$ states is a fraction η of the total density N_{He} of He atoms.

Since we work with a sealed-off container, the density will be kept constant.

Using the transfer cross-section (1) the mean free path for a Ne atom before being excited is

$$l = \frac{1}{\sigma\eta N_{\text{He}}} \simeq \frac{1}{\eta}\ (\text{cm})$$

for the filling pressure of 1 Torr.

The most probable velocity of Ne atoms at 300 °K has the value

$$v \simeq \sqrt{\frac{kT}{M}} \sim 5\cdot 10^4\ \text{cm/s}$$

and changes as $\sqrt{T}$.

Therefore the transition rate $1/\tau_{\alpha 0} = \gamma_{\alpha 0}$ at room temperature will be

$$\gamma_{\alpha 0} = \frac{1}{\tau_{\alpha 0}} = 5\cdot 10^4\,\eta\ (\text{s}^{-1}) \tag{2}$$

and will depend on the temperature with the following law:

$$\gamma_\alpha = \gamma_{\alpha 0}\sqrt{\frac{T}{300}}\,. \tag{3}$$

The transition $2 \to 3$ stays for the $2s \to 2p$ laser transition The transition $3 \to 1$ stays for the $2p \to 1s$ transition and for the quenching of the Ne ($1s$) metastable state. As well known [3] this latter occurs pratically only by ionizing collision to the walls, and the long lifetime of the $1s$ level is the bottleneck where the whole process slows down.

Since the research for an added impurity which acts as a quencher without increasing the electron population has not yet given any result, the only ways of reducing this lifetime are: *a*) the reduction of the mean distance from the wall or *b*) the increasing of the diffusion velocity of Ne atoms. The first way would reduce the number of active atoms and therefore the photon yield. The second way seems quite promising because it does not introduce limitations (see the experiments of Ref. [1]) and will be analysed here.

The expression for $\gamma_\beta = 1/\tau_\beta$ is

$$\gamma_\beta = \gamma_{34}\frac{\sqrt{T/300}}{a+\sqrt{T/300}}, \qquad a = \frac{\gamma_{43}}{\overset{0}{\gamma}_{41}}, \tag{4}$$

where γ_{34}, γ_{43}, $\overset{0}{\gamma}_{41}$ are convenient rates defined in the Appendix.

2·2. *The laser transition.* – The interaction constant $1/\tau^*$ for the single photon-electron transition is connected to the radiative lifetime $\tau_{23} = 1/\gamma_{23}$ through the density $p = 8\pi\nu^2\Delta\nu_i/c_3$ of e.m. modes within some « linewidth » $\Delta\nu_i$:

$$\frac{1}{\tau^*} = \frac{1}{p\tau_{23}}\ (\text{cm}^3\ \text{s}^{-1})\ . \tag{5}$$

$\Delta\nu_i$ can be defined only by making some assumptions on the physical system. Two limit cases will be considered.

First the upper-state atoms may migrate over the Doppler distribution during their lifetimes, by a large-angle elastic scattering [4] which drastically changes the location of the atoms' center frequencies within the Doppler line.

If the cross-section for this process is high enough compared to $1/\tau_{23}$, an excited atom can supply a photon to whatever e.m. mode in the Dopper width, and therefore

$$\Delta\nu_i = \Delta\nu_\text{D} \simeq 800\ \text{MHz}\ . \tag{6}$$

In the second case, we assume a wery small cross-section for the elastic scattering process (*). Each atom will be clamped to a definite frequency for a time much longer than a radiative lifetime.

We will assume, following the reasoning of BENNETT [4] supported by experimental evidence, an approximate value of

$$\Delta\nu_i \simeq 50\ \text{MHz}\ , \tag{7}$$

which gives a density of modes $p = 3.6\cdot 10^6\ \text{cm}^{-3}$.

(*) This approximation is closer to the real cases than the first one.

In writing the rate equations for the radiative transition $2 \to 3$, we should take into account the effective population n_2 of the $2s_2$ state, which is less than the total excited Ne population. However the value of the reduction factor is immaterial for the dependence we are exploring, and therefore we do not need any assumption on it.

3. – Laser equations for a homogeneous line.

In the first case of the Sect. **2**'2. where the whole Doppler line can contribute to the same e.m. mode, it is easily realized that only one mode can be over laser threshold, that is the nearest to the center frequency of the Doppler line.

With reference to Fig. 2, let us call n_1, n_2, n_3 the populations per unit volume in the levels 1,2,3; N the total Ne atoms density; ϱ the average density of photons at the laser frequency inside the e.m. cavity.

The coupled equations for the three levels of Fig. 2 and for the photon population will be:

$$\frac{\mathrm{d}n_2}{\mathrm{d}t} = \frac{n_1}{\tau_\alpha} - \frac{\varrho}{p\tau_{23}}(n_2 - n_3) - \frac{n_2}{\tau}, \tag{8}$$

$$\frac{\mathrm{d}n_3}{\mathrm{d}t} = \frac{\varrho}{p\tau_{23}}(n_2 - n_3) + \frac{n_2}{\tau_{23}} - \frac{n_3}{\tau_\beta}, \tag{9}$$

$$n_1 + n_2 + n_3 = N, \tag{10}$$

$$\frac{\mathrm{d}\varrho}{\mathrm{d}t} = -\frac{\varrho}{T_d} + \frac{\varrho}{p\tau_{23}}(n_2 - n_3) + \frac{n_2}{p\tau_{23}}. \tag{11}$$

In the right-hand side of the first equation, the first term is the pumping rate, the second the stimulated decay, the third the spontaneous decay.

In the second equation, the first term is the stimulated contribution, the second is the fraction of the total spontaneuos decay of the 2 S_2 level reaching the $2p_4$ level, the third is the depletion term discussed in the Appendix.

In the fourth equation, the first term is the e.m. decay due to the finite Q of the cavity. The decay time T_d is given by the transit time between the mirrors times the reciprocal of the losses per pass. The second term is the stimulated contribution, the third is the fraction of the spontaneous photons falling into the mode.

The stationary value of ϱ is easily found by taking into account that $N/\tau_\alpha \gg p/T_d$ (the two orders of magnitude are 10^{20} and 10^{14} ($\text{cm}^{-3}\,\text{s}^{-1}$), respectively):

$$\varrho = \frac{T_d N}{\tau_\alpha} \cdot \frac{1/\tau_\beta - 1/f\tau}{2/\tau_\alpha + 1/\tau_\beta + ((f-1)/f)(1/\tau)} - p, \tag{12}$$

where

$$f = \frac{\tau_{23}}{\tau}. \tag{13}$$

4. – Laser equations for an inhomogeneous line.

Due to the resonant nature of the radiative decay an excited atom cannot interact with an e.m. mode outside its natural linewidth. Since the axial mode separation is much larger than the natural width [4], we can assume several independent modes oscillating simultaneously.

The rate equation for the photons of the i-th mode will be written

$$\frac{d\varrho_i}{dt} = -\frac{\varrho_i}{T_d} + \frac{\varrho_i \Delta n_i}{p_i \tau_{23}} + \frac{n_{2i}}{p_i \tau_{23}}, \tag{14}$$

where ϱ_i is the photon density of the i-th mode; Δn_i is the population difference $(n_2 - n_3)_i$ which falls within a natural linewidth $\Delta\nu_i$ centered around the center frequency ν_i of the mode; p_i the density of modes within $\Delta\nu_i$. We call θ the fractional width $\Delta\nu_i/\Delta\nu_D$ of the natural line; then p_i will be equal to $p\theta$.

Since the frequency distribution of the population difference $\Delta n = n_2 - n_3$ over the Doppler width is a Gaussian distribution [4] of halfwidth $\Delta\nu_D$, it is easy to obtain, for a mode close to the peak of the distribution

$$\Delta n_i \simeq \Delta n \frac{\theta}{\sqrt{2\pi}} \tag{15}$$

and

$$n_{2i} \simeq n_2 \frac{\theta}{\sqrt{2\pi}}. \tag{16}$$

Assuming now that we are not very far from threshold, and therefore only a small number K of modes around the center of the Doppler line will be above laser threshold, we can sum all the eq. (14), taking into account (15) and (16), $\sum_{i=1}^{k} \varrho_i = \varrho$ and obtain the rate equation for the whole photon population that will be essentially similar to eq. (11), except for a factor $1/\sqrt{2\pi}$ in the stimulated term and $K/\sqrt{2\pi}$ in the spontaneous one.

Similarly, in the eq. (8) and (9), only the stimulated contribution has to be modified by the factor $1/\sqrt{2\pi}$.

As final result, as long as only few modes are above threshold, the results of Sect. **3** are still valid.

5. – Comparison of theory with experiment.

Equation (12) can be re-written putting in evidence the dependence of the pumping and depletion rates on power and temperature.

In order to fit the experimental data, it is useful to introduce the nondimensional power and square-root of temperature:

$$y = P/P_0\,, \tag{17}$$

$$x = \sqrt{\frac{T}{T_0}}\,, \tag{18}$$

having assumed the discharge power $P_0 = 40$ and the room temperature $T_0 = 300\ ^\circ\mathrm{K}$ as reference. The range of reasonable values for x and y is

$$1 < x < 2\ \ (300\ ^\circ\mathrm{K} < T < 1200\ ^\circ\mathrm{K})\ \text{ and }\ 0 < y < \sigma\ \ (0 < P < 240\ \mathrm{W}).$$

The pumping rate γ_α will be proportional to y through the fraction η of He ($2\,^3S$) atoms, and to x through the thermal velocity of the atoms:

$$\gamma_\alpha \propto \eta_0\, xy\,, \tag{19}$$

(η_0 is the value of η at P_0).

From the considerations of the Appendix, γ_β can be written as

$$\gamma_\beta = \gamma_{34}\,\frac{x}{a_0 y + x}\,, \tag{20}$$

where $a_0 = \gamma^0_{43}/\gamma^0_{41}$ is the ratio of the two rates at $y = 1$, $x = 1$, respectively.

The density p of modes is proportional to x, because of the thermal dependence of the Doppler linewidth. Let p_0 be the value at $x = 1$, then

$$p = p_0\, x\,. \tag{21}$$

Equation (12) can be written now (C being a constant) beside some minor approximations [2]

$$\varrho = Cxy\,\frac{(\gamma_{34}/\gamma - 1/f)x - (a_0/f)y}{((\gamma_{34}/\gamma + (f-1)/f)x + ((f-1)/f)\,a_0 y}\,. \tag{22}$$

In eq. (22) three floating parameters have been left, because no definite values were available for them in the literature. They are:

a) the fraction η_0 of the He atoms in the $2\,^3S$ state, at the discharge power of 40 W;

b) the ratio $f=\gamma/\gamma_{23}$ between the total radiative decay rate of the $2s_2$ level and the rate of the $2s_2 \to 2p_4$ transition (here, the unknown is γ_{23});

c) the ratio $a_0=\gamma^0_{43}/\gamma^0_{41}$ between the $1s \to 2p$ transfer rate calculated at 40 mW and the $1s \to$ ground-state decay rate calculated at 300 °K (here the unknown is γ^0_{43}).

We fit now the floating parameters with the experiments.

5'1. *Photon density vs. discharge power at constant temperature.* – First, the theoretical dependence of ϱ on power at constant temperature is studied. In the plot of fig. 1*b*, the discharge-current axis can also be measured in power units (the discharge voltage is known from measurements to be around 1700 V), that is in y units.

The points of each « short-time » curve have been measured at a constant temperature. These temperatures are known from the thermal measurements which have led to the plot of fig. 1*a* and are reported in Table I below, for the curves 1) 3) and 4) of Fig. 1*b*). In the same Table we report the values y_0 of y at which the photon density goes to zero after having reached a maximum.

TABLE I.

Curve no.	x	y_0	a_0		
			($f=1$)	($f=10$)	($f=20$)
4)	1.01	3.1	2.3	26	52.1
3)	1.12	4.0	1.96	22.1	45.0
1)	1.2	5.0	1.68	19	38.5

From eq. (23) it follows that, in the y range given above, the theoretical curves look like parabolas with a zero at the origin and another at y_0.

Introducing the experimental values of y_0 and x from Table I into eq. (23), a_0 can be deduced once given f, and viceversa. Three tentative values $f=1, 10, 20$ have been assumed. For each of them the corresponding a_0 is calculated and reported in Table I, in connection with the experimental curve 3) of Fig. 1*b*.

The three theoretical curves for $f=1, 10, 20$ have been plotted in Fig. 3*a* together with some experimental points. The best fit should be obtained for f slightly less then 10. Anyhow, $f=10$ is a good approximation.

We have therefore the following results:

1) our theory fits the experiments;

2) approximate values of τ_{23} and γ^0_{43} are

$$\tau_{23} = 10\tau = 10^{-6}\ (\text{s})\ ,$$

$$\gamma^0_{43} = 22\gamma^0_{41} = 4.4\cdot 10^6\ (\text{s}^{-1})\ .$$

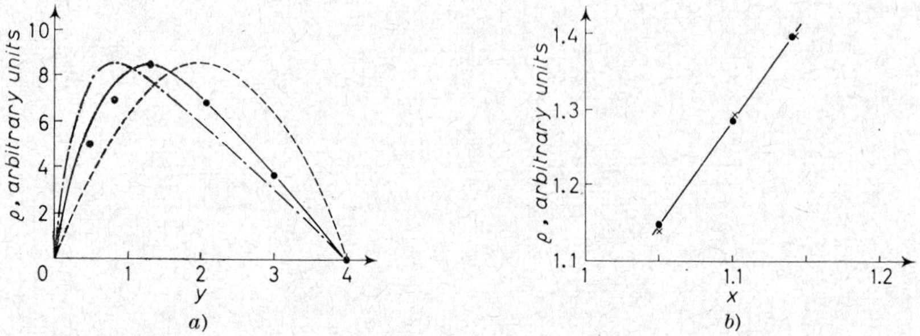

Fig. 3. – Fitting of the theoretical values to the experimental curves: *a*) photon density *vs*. discharge power at constant temperature: ● experimental points; – – – theoretical plot for $f=1$, $a=1.96$; —— theoretical plot for $f=10$, $a=22$; –·–·– theoretical plot for $f=20$, $a=45$. *b*) Photon density *vs*. square root of temperature at constant discharge power: × theoretical points; ● experimental points.

5·2. *Photon density vs. temperature at constant discharge power.* – The theoretical thermal behaviour is compared with the experimental one.

A plot of ϱ *vs*. temperature of the type of Fig. 1*a*, corresponding to a discharge current of 40 mA, has been fitted with the theoretical data given by eq. (26) for values:

$$y = 1.96\ (i = 40\ \text{mA})\ , \qquad f = 10\ , \qquad a_0 = 22\ .$$

Here again the theoretical results are in agreement with measurements, as shown in Fig. 3*b*.

Appendix

Derivation of the « effective » depletion rate of the lower laser level.

A detailed analysis is given here of the depletion mechanism of the lower laser level in order to characterize an « effective » depletion rate $1/\tau_\beta$ for the simplified level scheme of Fig. 3.

In Fig. 4 the last part of the whole laser process is shown.

Let us call F the source rate to the $2p$ level, from the upper states. (Its actual value is immaterial for the present discussion).

The spontaneous decay rate γ_{34} has the value of $8\cdot10^7\ \text{s}^{-1}$ [4]. γ_{43} is the rate of excitation of the $2p$ states by electrons' impact with the Ne atoms in the $1s$ level. If we call σ_{43} the cross-section for this process, N_e the density of free electrons in the discharge and V_e the electron velocity, it is easy to see that

$$\gamma_{43} = N_e V_e \sigma_{43}\,. \tag{A.1}$$

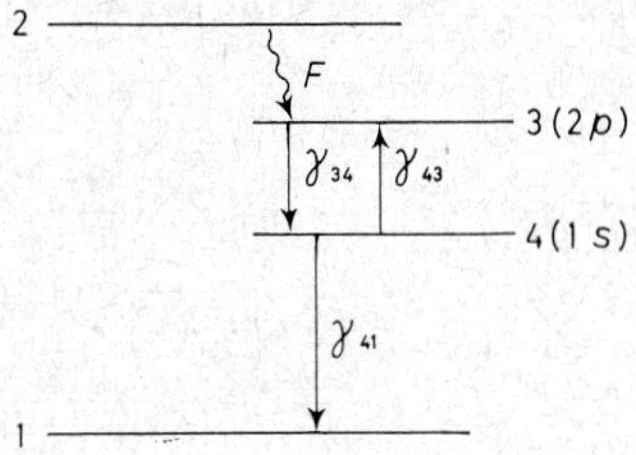

Fig. 4. – Four-level diagram of the laser action.

If we assume that N_e increases linearly with the discharge power, then γ_{43} will be proportional to the same power.

The quenching rate of metastable states γ_{41} will depend on the mean distance from the wall and on the thermal velocity of Ne atoms. By the same procedure used for calculating τ_α, it follows

$$\gamma_{41} = \overset{0}{\gamma}_{41}\sqrt{\frac{T}{300}}\,, \tag{A.2}$$

where

$$\overset{0}{\gamma}_{41} \simeq 2\cdot10^5\ \text{s}^{-1}\,.$$

The rate equations for the levels 3 and 4 will be for stationary conditions:

$$\frac{\mathrm{d}n_3}{\mathrm{d}t} = F - \gamma_{34}n_3 + \gamma_{43}n_4 = 0\,, \tag{A.3}$$

$$\frac{\mathrm{d}n_4}{\mathrm{d}t} = -\gamma_{41}n_4 - \gamma_{43}n_4 + \gamma_{34}n_3 = 0\,. \tag{A.4}$$

This system is easily reduced to the one-ratio equation

$$\frac{\mathrm{d}n_3}{\mathrm{d}t} = F - \gamma_\beta n_3 = 0\,, \tag{A.5}$$

where

$$\gamma_\beta = \gamma_{34}\left(\frac{\gamma_{41}}{\gamma_{41}+\gamma_{43}}\right). \tag{A.6}$$

REFERENCES

[1] F. T. Arecchi and A. Sona: *Alta Frequenza*, **31**, 722 (1962).
[2] F. T. Arecchi: *Proceedings of the Third Quantum Electronics Conference* (Paris, Feb. 11-15, 1963).
[3] A. Javan: *Advances in Quantum Electronics* (New York, 1961), p. 18.
[4] W. R. Bennett: *Phys. Rev.*, **126**, 580 (1961).

The Dynamics of Quantum Oscillators.

A. Z. GRASIUK and A. N. ORAEVSKIJ

Akademija Nauk S.S.S.R. - Moskva

1. – Equations and method of analysis.

According to the theory developed in previous papers [1, 2], the dynamical equations of quantum oscillators in terms of dipole interaction of the active medium with the field can be written as follows:

$$(1)\quad \begin{cases} \dfrac{\mathrm{d}^2\mathscr{E}_k}{\mathrm{d}t^2}+\dfrac{\omega_k}{Q_k}\dfrac{\mathrm{d}\mathscr{E}_k}{\mathrm{d}t}+\omega_k^2\mathscr{E}_k=-4\pi\dfrac{\mathrm{d}^2P_k}{\mathrm{d}t^2}\,,\\[2ex] \dfrac{\mathrm{d}^2P}{\mathrm{d}t^2}+\dfrac{2}{T_2}\dfrac{\mathrm{d}P}{\mathrm{d}t}+\omega_r^2P=-\dfrac{2\omega_{21}|\mu_{21}|^2}{\hbar}\mathscr{E}N\,,\\[2ex] \dfrac{\mathrm{d}N}{\mathrm{d}t}+\dfrac{1}{T_1}(N-N_0)=\dfrac{2}{\hbar\omega_{21}}\mathscr{E}\left(\dot{P}+\dfrac{1}{T_2}P\right). \end{cases}$$

$\mathscr{E}_k$ and P_k are the coefficients of components of the fields $\mathscr{E}(\boldsymbol{r}, t)$ and the polarization $P(\boldsymbol{r}, t)$ expanded in eigenfunctions of the resonator. Thus, $\mathscr{E}(r, t) = \sum_k \mathscr{E}_k(t)\,\boldsymbol{E}_k(r)$. ω_k is the eigenfrequency and Q_k the quality factor of the k-th mode of the resonator. μ_{21} is the dipole matrix element of the particles, ω_{21} the molecular radiation frequency; $\omega_r^2=\omega_{21}^2+(1/T_2)^2$ and N_0 is the active particle flux due to pumping.

We assume in these equations that the absorption-line shape is Lorentzian and is governed by the two relaxation times T_1 and T_2.

We consider the case of single-mode operation. In this case $P_k\equiv P(r, t)$. For convenience of the analysis we introduce dimensionless quantities as follows:

$$(2)\quad \begin{cases} t\to\omega_r t\,,\quad x=\dfrac{\mu_{21}\mathscr{E}}{\hbar}T_2\,,\quad v=\dfrac{P_k}{\mu_{21}N_0}\,,\quad W=\dfrac{N}{N_0}-1\,,\quad h_1=\dfrac{1}{\omega_r T_1}\,,\\[2ex] h_2=\dfrac{1}{\omega_r T_2}\,,\quad 2h=\dfrac{\omega_k}{\omega_r}\dfrac{1}{Q_k}\,,\quad 2k=4\pi N_0|\mu_{21}|^2\hbar^{-1}T_2\,,\quad 2\delta=\dfrac{\omega_r^2-\omega_k^2}{\omega_r^2}\,, \end{cases}$$

then the eqs. (1) reduce to the following:

$$(3)\quad \begin{cases} \ddot{x} + x = \varepsilon(-2\delta x - 2h\dot{x} - 2k\ddot{v}) , \\ \ddot{v} + v = \varepsilon(-2h_2\dot{v} - 2h_2(1+W)x) , \\ \dot{W} \quad = \varepsilon(-h_1 W + 2h_2 x\dot{v} + 2h_2^2 \varepsilon xv) . \end{cases}$$

In these equations we introduce the dimensionless parameter ε and assume $\varepsilon \ll 1$. This is reasonable because the original values h, h_1, h_2, k, δ are much smaller than unity. We can now consider the new values of h, h_1, h_2, k, δ to be of the order of unity and look for solutions of our equations in the form of power series in ε.

This gives us an orderly method for solution of the nonlinear equations. (One can consider in the solution that $\varepsilon = 1$.). We assume a solution of the equations in the form

$$(4)\quad \begin{cases} x = X(\theta)\cos[t+\varphi(\theta)] + \varepsilon \sum\limits_{k=1} P^{(k)} \cos k[t+\varphi(\theta)] + Q^{(k)} \sin k[t+\varphi(\theta)] , \\ v = V(\theta)\cos[t+\varphi(\theta)] + U\sin[t+\varphi(\theta)] + \varepsilon \sum\limits_{k>1} P^{(k)} \cos k[t+\varphi)\theta)] + \\ \qquad\qquad + \varepsilon \sum\limits_{k} q^{(k)} \sin k[t+\varphi(\theta)] , \\ W = W(\theta) + \varepsilon \sum\limits_{k>1} S^{(k)} \cos k[t+\varphi(\theta)] + T^{(k)} \sin k[t+\varphi(\theta)] , \end{cases}$$

where X, φ, V, U, W (and so on) are the functions of the « slow » time $\theta = \varepsilon t$ so that

$$\frac{\mathrm{d}X}{\mathrm{d}t} = \varepsilon \frac{\mathrm{d}X}{\mathrm{d}\theta} \equiv \varepsilon X'$$

etc. In our description, the functions must be sought in series form, namely,

$$5)\quad \begin{cases} X = X_0 + \varepsilon X_1 + \varepsilon^2 X_2 + \dots , \\ \varphi = \varphi_0 + \varepsilon\varphi_1 + \varepsilon^2\varphi_2 + \dots . \end{cases}$$

Substituting (4) in (3) and comparing the terms with equal powers of ε gives the equations for the first, second etc., approximations.

In the remainder of this paper only the equations for the first-order approximation are required, namely,

$$(6)\quad \begin{cases} X_0' = -h_0 X_0 - k U_0\,, \\ \varphi_0' = \quad \delta - k\dfrac{V_0}{X_0}\,, \\ U_0' = -h_2 U_0 - h_2(1 - W_0)X_0 + V_0\varphi_0'\,, \\ V_0' = -h_2 V_0 - U_0\varphi_0'\,, \\ W_0' = -h_1 W_0 + h_2 X_0 U_0\,. \end{cases}$$

2. – The steady state and its stability.

For the steady-state monochromatic oscillation $X_0' = U_0' = V_0' = W_0' = 0$, so that

$$(7)\quad \begin{cases} X_0^2 = \dfrac{h_1}{h_2}\left(\dfrac{k}{h} - 1 - \dfrac{\delta^2}{(h_1 + h_2)^2}\right), \\ \varphi_0' = 1 - \dfrac{\omega}{\omega_r} = \dfrac{1}{2}\,\delta\,\dfrac{h_2}{h_1 + h_2}\,. \end{cases}$$

These are the familiar equations for the amplitude and the phase of the oscillation in a single-mode laser and maser [3, 4]. A more complete analysis requires an investigation of the stability of this stationary steady-state solution. For this purpose, we assume that the functions are slightly perturbed from the equilibrium state. Thus

$$(8)\quad \begin{cases} X_0 = \overline{X}_0 + \xi\,, & V_0 = \overline{V}_0 + \nu = \nu\,, \\ U_0 = \overline{U}_0 + \eta\,, & \varphi_0 = \bar{\varphi}_0 + \psi = \psi\,, \\ W_0 = \overline{W}_0 + \zeta\,, \end{cases}$$

To simplify the investigation, we consider in (6) that $\delta = 0$, so that

$$(9)\quad V_0 = 0\,, \qquad \varphi_0' = 0\,.$$

Substituting (8) in (6) and keeping only the terms which are linear in ξ, η, ζ. etc., we obtain the system of linear equations for the perturbations

$$(10)\quad \begin{cases} \dot{\xi} = -h\xi - k\eta\,, \\ \dot{\eta} = -h_2\eta - h_2(1 + \overline{W}_0)\xi - h_2\overline{X}_0\zeta\,, \\ \dot{\zeta} = -h_2\zeta + h_2\overline{X}_0\eta + h_2\overline{U}_0\xi\,. \end{cases}$$

It should be remarked that at $\delta = 0$, the equations for ν, ψ have no influence on the stability of the system (6) as a whole.

We look for the solution of these equations in the exponential form to be proportional to $\exp[\lambda t]$. From (10) we have the equation for $\lambda = \lambda' + i\lambda''$, namely,

$$(11) \qquad \begin{vmatrix} \lambda + h & k & 0 \\ h_2(1 + \overline{W}_0) & \lambda + h_2 & h_0\overline{X}_0 \\ -h_2\overline{U}_0 & -h_2\overline{X}_0 & \lambda + h_2 \end{vmatrix} = 0 .$$

If $\lambda' < 0$, the steady state is stable; if $\lambda' > 0$, the steady state solution of (7) is unstable.

Using the Rauth-Hurwitz criterion for eq. (11), we find that $\lambda' < 0$ if

$$(12) \qquad h_1 + h_2 > h$$

or if

$$(13) \qquad h_1 + h_2 < h, \quad \text{with} \quad k < k_{cr} .$$

We have $\lambda' > 0$ if

$$(14) \qquad h_1 + h_2 < h \quad \text{with} \quad k > k_{cr},$$

where

$$(15) \qquad k_{cr} = \frac{h^2}{h_2} \cdot \frac{h + 3h_2 + h_1}{h - h_1 - h_2} .$$

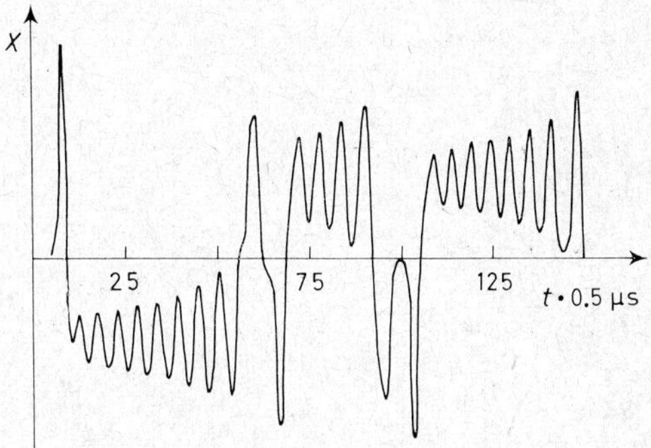

Fig. 1.

If $k > k_{cr}$, the steady-state maser operation becomes unstable.

The general solution of the nonlinear eq. (6) is very difficult. We have obtained the solution for $k > k_{cr}$ with the help of a computer. The amplitude of the oscillations as a function of time has the form shown in Fig. 1.

In this case, we have a periodic amplitude modulation which can be called « automodulation ».

We now estimate the values of k_{cr} and the relation between h, h_1, h_2 in specific cases.

a) *Ruby laser.* For the ruby laser we have $h_2 \gg h_1$ and $h_2 > h$. In this case the condition (12) holds and the steady-state oscillation is stable.

It is possible that a Lorentzian-line shape with two relaxation times and a single-mode model is not the correct basis for the description of pulsations in ruby lasers and that the stability conditions must be modified. In another paper [8] the authors attempt to connect instability of the steady state at

$k > k_{cr}$ with pulsations in the ruby laser modifying the line shape. We think that the consistent explanation of ruby-laser pulsation should be investigated in a multimode model taking cross-relaxation into consideration.

b) *Ammonia maser.* For the ammonia maser $h_1 = h_2 = h_0 \ll h$ because the linewidth of the ammonia maser is much narrower than bandwitdh of the cavity. Usually $h_0/h \simeq 10^{-3}$ and $k_{cr} \approx 0.1$ for $Q_c = 10^4$. At the same values the threshold value of k is about 10^{-3}. Therefore, in order to have the unstable automodulation state of operation at $Q_c \simeq 10^4$, it is necessary to surpass the threshold value of the active particles' flux by 100 times.

However, at $Q_c \simeq 10^5$ we already have $k_{cr} \simeq 10^{-3}$. In this case, one can realize the automodulation condition (14), (15). Such a value of $Q_c \simeq 10^5$ can be obtained in a superconducting cavity.

3. – Stabilization of the automodulation.

The automodulation of the maser (laser) can be stabilized by the signal of another maser (laser) operating in the stable state and having a smaller output power. The equation describing stabilization by the influence of the external force can be obtained in the first approximation from (3) by substitution of a small external force $\varepsilon F \cos \Omega t$ into the right-hand side of the first equation. This gives

$$(16) \qquad \begin{cases} X_0' = -hX_0 - kU_0 - F \sin\varphi_0\,, \\ \varphi_0' = -k\dfrac{V_0}{X_0} - \dfrac{F}{X_0}\cos\varphi\,, \\ U_0' = -h_0 U_0 - h_0(1+W_0)X_0 + V_0\varphi'\,, \\ V_0' = \quad h_0 V_0 - U_0\varphi_0'\,, \\ W_0' = -h_0 W_0 + h_0 X_0 U_0\,. \end{cases}$$

For simplicity we assume $\delta = 0$, with the external drive frequency equal to that of the spectral line and with $h_2 = h_1 = h_0$. The steady state obtained from the condition that

$$(17) \qquad X_0' = \varphi_0' = U_0' = V_0' = W_0' = 0$$

is stable in such a case if the value F satisfies the condition

$$(18) \qquad \frac{F}{\bar{X}_0} > \frac{\alpha S^2 - 2\alpha S - 4S - 1}{\frac{4}{3}S^2(\alpha S - 1)^{\frac{1}{2}} + (2\alpha S^3 - \alpha S^2 + 4S + 2)\,\frac{3}{2}\,(\alpha S)^{-\frac{1}{2}}}\,,$$

where $S = h_0/h$, $\alpha = k/h_0$, and $\bar{X}_0$ (defined by (7)) takes on the steady-state amplitude value in the absence of the external drive.

For usual values of the parameters of the quantum oscillator we have $F/\bar{X}_0 < 1$. Thus a relatively small external drive can suppress the automodulation in the more powerful quantum oscillator.

If the external force frequency differs slightly from that of the oscillator then even at $k < k_{cr}$ a value of the external drive needed for the synchronization of the quantum oscillator, is [1]

$$F/\bar{X}_0 > h_2 \cdot \Delta \,, \tag{19}$$

where $\Delta = |\Omega - 1|$ is the absolute value of the frequency difference.

If the condition (19) is fulfilled then the oscillations of the quantum oscillator are synchronous with the external driving frequency.

* * *

The authors are indebted to A. S. AGABEKIAN, I. G. ZUBAREV, and V. I. SVERGUN for assistance in the calculations.

REFERENCES

[1] A. N. ORAEVSKIJ: *Radiotehnika i Ėlektronika*, **4**, 718 (1959).
[2] W. E. LAMB: this volume, p. 78.
[3] N. G. BASOV and A. M. PROKHOROV: *Usp. Fiz. Nauk 63*, **57**, 485 (1955).
[4] K. SHIMODA, T. C. WANG and C. H. TOWNES: *Phys. Rev.*, **102**, 1508 (1956).
[5] A. Z. GRASIUK and A. N. ORAEVSKIJ: *4th International Congress on Microwave Tubes 446*, (Scheveningen, 1962).
[6] A. V. USPENSKIJ: *Radiotehnika i Ėlektronika*, **8**, 1165 (1963).
[7] A. S. GURTOVNIK: *Izv. Vysš. Ucebnyh Zavedeniĭ. Radiofizika*, **1**, 5-6, 83 (1958).
[8] V. V. KOROBKIN and A. V. USPENSKIJ: *Žurn. Ėksp. Teor. Fiz.*, **45**, 1003 (1963).

Fourier-Transform Spectroscopy.

P. Connes

C.N.R.S. - Bellevue

Here, we shall describe a comparatively new method of spectroscopy which should be considered as a very promising one, especially for the infra-red region of the spectrum.

Its principle and essential properties will be given first and the first experimental results afterwards.

1. – Principle and essential properties.

1·1. *Principle.* – The light coming from the source under study goes through a two-beam interferometer (for instance, a Michelson interferometer, as in Fig. 1, but this is by no means essential). After the two beams are re-united with a path difference Δ they fall on a receiver which gives an output proportional to the total light intensity. The variable part of the signal is recorded as a function of Δ. Presently, we shall show that this recording, termed an *interferogram*, is the *cosine Fourier transform* of the wanted spectrum. Therefore, it is possible to re-construct the spectrum by computing the *cosine Fourier transform* of the interferogram; this operation will generally be performed a posteriori by a digital computer.

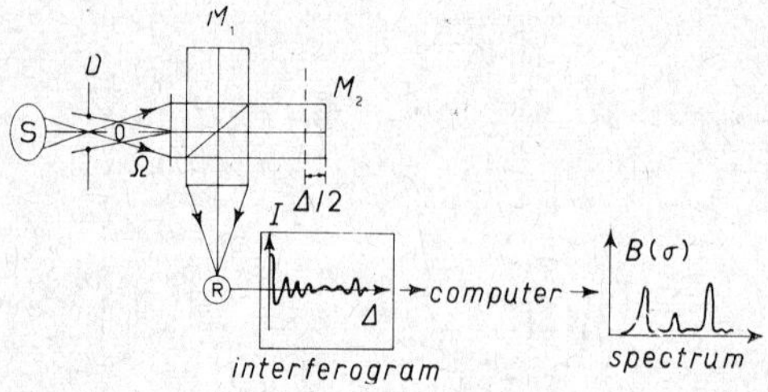

Fig. 1.

Let $B(\sigma)$ be the wanted spectrum as a function of the wavenumber σ; the intensity emitted by the source in the interval $d\sigma$ is $B(\sigma)d\sigma$. Since the intensity of the interference phenomenon with path difference Δ and wavelength λ

is proportional to $\cos^2 \pi\Delta/\lambda = \cos^2 \pi\sigma\Delta$, the intensity of radiation falling on the receiver is

$$\int_0^\infty B(\sigma) \cos^2 n\sigma \Delta \, d\sigma ,$$

the variable part of which is (whithin a factor of 2)

$$I(\Delta) = \int_0^\infty B(\sigma) \cos 2\pi\sigma\Delta \, d\sigma = TF_{\cos}[B(\sigma)] . \tag{1}$$

Fourier transforms being reciprocal, we may write that (to within a proportionality factor):

$$B(\sigma) = \int_0^\infty I(\Delta) \cos 2\pi\sigma\Delta \, d\Delta = TF_{\cos}[I(\Delta)] . \tag{2}$$

This result can also be reached directly by considering the light vibration. Let $S(t)$ be this vibration whose power spectrum is $B(\nu)$, $\nu = c\sigma$ being the optical frequency. If $T = \Delta/c$ is the time delay introduced by the interferometer between the two beams, the vibration falling on the receiver is $S(t) + S(t + T)$. The corresponding output wil be proportional to its intensity, *i.e.*

$$\overline{S(t) + S(t + T)} + \overline{2S(t) \cdot S(t + T)} .$$

The last term which varies with T (and so with Δ) is what we termed the interferogram. On the other hand, it is the autocorrelation function of $S(t)$. We know from the Wiener-Khintchine theorem that the power spectrum of a vibration is the Fourier transform of its autocorrelation function. Thus, we are led to the same result but we see the meaning of the interferogram better. It is a kind of statistical representation of the wave train itself. Figure 2 shows the spectrum and the corresponding interferogram in a few simple cases: *a*) one line; *b*) two lines (of negligible width); *c*) a broad line; *d*) a continuous spectrum.

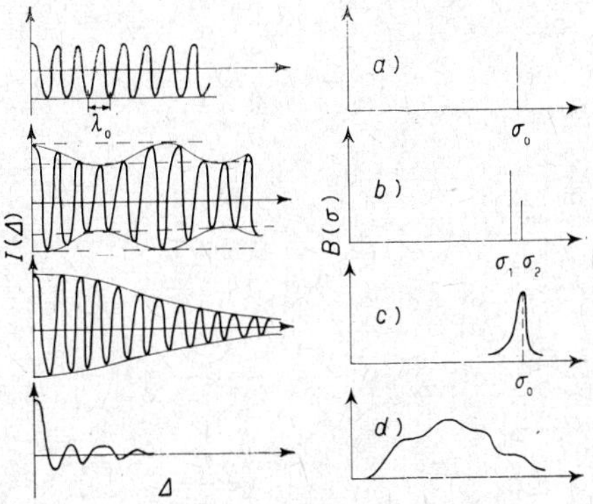

Fig. 2.

A third reasoning enables us to understand the nature of the method still better. Let us suppose that Δ is a linear function of time, $\Delta = vt$ (one of the two mirrors being moved at a constant speed $v/2$ and that the spectrum has but one line of frequency ν_0. The vibration falling on the receiver then comes from two lines, one of unperturbed frequency ν_0 the other of frequency $\nu_0(1 + v/c)$, displaced by Doppler effect. Hence the receiver output contains a term of frequency $N_0 = (v/c)\nu_0$ which may be considered as beats between those two coherent lines. Now, if the spectrum is a complex one, each spectral element of frequency ν will contribute a term of proportional frequency $N = (v/c)\nu$. Thus, thanks to the two-beam variable path difference interferometer, a lowering of optical frequencies has been realized. The light wave is represented by an electrical signal whose frequency range may be placed at will (by varying v) in the LF or VLF range. This signal can be studied by any of the classical methods of harmonic analysis. In practice, however, only a few are suitable. Of course, it is by no means essential that the variation of Δ with time be linear since formulas (1) and (2) do not contain t.

1·2. *Essential properties.* – Classical methods of spectroscopy come under two types: *spectrographic* methods in which the spectrum spreads out on a photographic plate and all the elements are simultaneously recorded, and spectrometric methods in which the spectrum is scanned with a single receiver (photoelectric, photoconductive of thermal). The latter have the following advantages: a much greater accuracy for intensity measurements, a capacity to detect much smaller photon numbers, and they can be used in all spectral regions, the infra-red in particular. But they suffer a considerable drawback; at a given time the energy of all spectral elements except one is wasted. A spectral element is usually defined as a portion of a spectrum whose width is equal to the wanted resolution σ_r. If $\Delta\sigma = \sigma_{max} - \sigma_{min}$ is the spectral range under study, the number of spectral elements is

$$M = \frac{\sigma_{max} - \sigma_{min}}{\sigma_r} = \frac{\Delta\sigma}{\sigma_r}.$$

M is the number of independent informations that can be extracted from the spectrum. It can be said that the photographic plate (or more generally speaking, an image detector) acts as an array of M receivers in parallel, and so is M times more efficient.

With Fourier-transform spectroscopy, no dispersion is needed. The interferometer acts as a mere *coder* which differentiates the spectral elements by modulating them at different frequencies. The wohle spectrum falls on the receiver during the whole time of measurement; the receiver is *multiplexed*. If the noise which puts a limit to the accuracy of the measurement is *not* increased, the Fourier-transform method, compared to a classical scanning method, has the fundamental advantage of enabling one to study a given spectral range M times faster, or with a $\sqrt{M}$ times greater accuracy. In practice, these results can indeed be obtained in the infra-red (more precisely with photoconductive or thermal receivers), but not in the visible or ultra-violet regions where photoelectric receivers can be used. Indeed, when a photoelectric cell is cooled at sufficiently low temperatures, the remaining dark current can be as small as a few electrons per second which corresponds to a light flux Φ_{obs} of the order of 10 to 10^3 photon/s if the quantum efficiency is somewhere between 10^{-1} and 10^{-3}. Except in the extreme and exceptional case where the total measured flux Φ would be lower than Φ_{obs}, the noise will be increased by the *simultaneous* appearance of the M spectral elements on the receiver. In the special case of a uniform continuous spectrum (and supposing $\Phi \gg \Phi_{obs}$), the noise will be increased by a factor precisely equal to $\sqrt{M}$, and *all* the gain due to the multiplexing will be lost. With a line or an absorption spectrum, the result is not so easy to state, in most cases, however, the gain will be small, even negligible. Nevertheless, the Fourier transform method has other interesting properties which will be discussed later on, and which remain in the visible and ultra-violet portions of the spectrum.

In the infra-red the situation is very different. The most sensitive receivers are PbS cells, usable between 1 and 3μm. They have a NEP of 10^{-12} to 10^{-13} watt when their area is of the order of one mm^2 (which is necessary in order to match them to most spectroscopes). We can easily compute the value of the light flux Φ that would produce a perceptible increase in the noise. We find about 10^{13} photons/s at $\lambda = 1$ μm, and proportionally greater values at longer wavelengths. Less sensitive receivers give still higher values. In all practical cases, the measured flux will be much smaller. Hence, the full multiplexing gain will be effective.

Fourier-transform spectroscopy, as we have just described it, was conceived independently by FELLGETT [1] and JACQUINOT [2]. However, it offers some analogies with Michelson's older method which we are going to discuss briefly. Michelson only measured the fringe visibility corresponding to the envelope of the curves in Fig. 2. It has been shown by Lord RAYLEIGH that this introduces an ambiguity: two spectral profiles symmetrical with respect to a certain wavenumber give identical visibility curves. Yet it is quite clear that MICHELSON understood that this ambiguity could be eliminated by measuring not only the amplitude but also the phase of the fringes.

However, the main difference between the fringe-visibility method and that which we use today is elsewhere. MICHELSON had thought out his method in order to get higher resolving powers than those of existing gratings. He only applied it to very narrow spectral regions (with small M factors) giving simple interferograms and Fourier transforms easily computable with the means at his disposal.

Today the situation greatly differs. Modern gratings and Fabry-Perot interferometers enable us to reach sufficient resolving power for all spectroscopic problems; also digital computers can work out Fourier transforms with thousands of output points. On top of that, the advantage of multiplexing has become obvious. This is why the Fourier transform method is chiefly of interest for very extended spectra with any kind of resolving powers.

1·3. *Resolving power, instrumental line shape.* – Theoretically the spectrum could be rigorously reconstructed without any kind of distortion were it possible to perform the operation (2). In practice, the interferogram is recorded only within finite limits $(0, \Delta_{max})$. Let us define a function $D(\Delta)$ which is equal to zero outside the interval $0, \Delta_{max})$; the reconstructed spectrum will of necessity be $B'(\sigma) \neq B(\sigma)$, and given by

$$B'(\sigma) = \int_0^\infty D(\Delta)\cdot I(\Delta) \cos 2\pi\sigma\Delta \, d\,\Delta = TF_{cos}[D(\Delta)\cdot I(\Delta)] .$$

From the convolution theorem,

$$TF_{cos}[D(\Delta)\cdot I(\Delta)] = TF_{cos}[D(\Delta)] * TF_{cos}[I(\Delta)] .$$

So

$$B'(\sigma) = B(\sigma) * A(\sigma) , \tag{4}$$

by putting

$$A(\sigma) = TF_{cos} D(\Delta)] . \tag{5}$$

$A(\sigma)$ will be the instrumental line shape, *i.e.*, the image of a monochromatic line given by the entire operation.

Figure 3 gives two types of instrumental line shapes obtained from two different functions, one triangular and the other rectangular. Function D is termed the apodization function because its shape governs the size of the secondary maxima. The product ID can be obtained either by physical means during recording or mathematically when computing the Fourier transform. In most cases, the triangular function (or slightly different ones) will be preferred

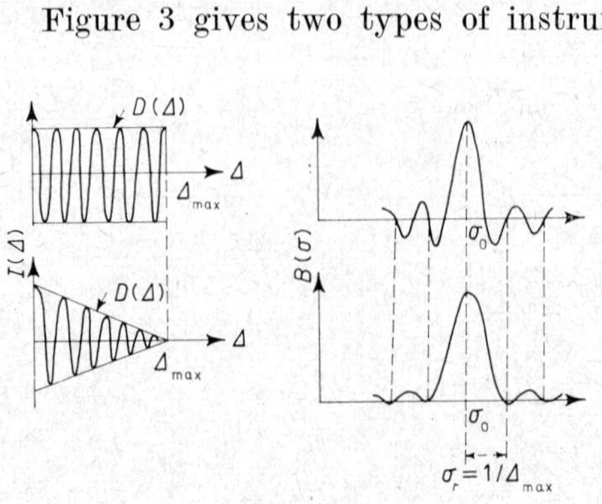

Fig. 3.

because of the acceptable secondary maxima. We will assume it is used from now on. We can then give the resolution (by making use of Lord Rayleigh's criterion) which is simply $\sigma_r = 1/\Delta_{max}$, a result common to all spectroscopic methods. The theoretical resolving power is then $R_0 = \sigma/\sigma_r = \Delta_{max}/\lambda$. It is simply equal to the number of recorded fringes for wavelength λ.

These results have been worked out in the theoretical case where the path difference has a perfectly definite value, which means that the spread of incidence angles on the mirrors is negligible. In practice, it is necessary to tolerate a beam with a finite solid angle Ω; so the path difference for a given mirror position varies between the extreme values Δ_0, for normal rays and $\Delta_0 \cos I = \Delta_0 \cos(1 - \Omega/2\pi)$ for the maximum incidence angle I. Thus, the situation is similar to the one with the Fabry-Perot interferometer. It is possible to show that the final result is the same, *i.e.*, the effective instrumental function is the convolution of the theoretical function by a rectangular one of width $\sigma(\Omega/2\pi)$. The best compromise between light gathering power and resolving power will be had when Ω satisfies the relationship

$$\Omega R_0 = 2\pi \, . \tag{6}$$

Thus, the use of Michelson's interferometer gives the same gain in light gathering power, when compared to a classical slit spectrometer, as does the Fabry-Perot interferometer. This is an important advantage which persists even when the multiplexing advantage is lost.

2. – Computation of Fourier transforms.

2·1. *Analog computation.* – The interferogram is recorded on a closed loop of magnetic tape; the loop is then read at a much increased speed. The signal is sent to a LF harmonic analyser, whose Q should be at least equal to the optical resolving power. After each turn of the loop, the analysed frequency is displaced by an interval equal to the wanted resolution and a new spectral element is measured. With this method, the spectrum is reconstructed without any ambiguity due to overlapping of orders just as the case would be with a prism spectrometer. This comes from the fact that in both cases a *continuous* set of values of path difference is utilized.

This simple and rapid method can be used for very low resolving powers only (less than 10^2) on account of unavoidable speed variations of the moving mirror and of the magnetic tape.

It should be noticed that the analysis ought to be performed a posteriori. If the receiver output were fed directly to the harmonic analyser, only one spectral element would be measured at a given moment and there would be no multiplexing.

2·2. *Digital computation.* – The use of digital computation is based on two successive applications of the sampling theorem. Since both $I(\Delta)$ and $B'(\sigma)$ have limited Fourier transforms, they can be sampled and fully represented by a finite set of discrete values. For $B'(\sigma)$ there will be M values $B'(p\sigma_r)$, p

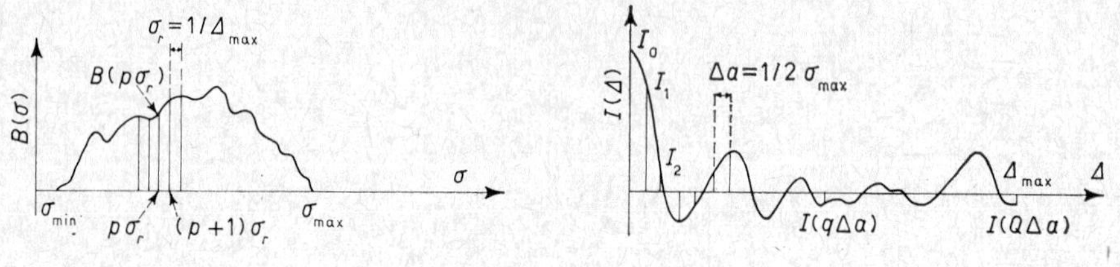

Fig. 4.

being an integer wich can take M values within the interval $p_{\min} = \sigma_{\min}/\sigma_r$ and $p_{\max} = \sigma_{\max}/\sigma_r$ In this way, we shall obtain *one* intensity value for each spectral element, and this is enough to describe $B'(\sigma)$ fully (Fig. 4). On the other hand, the computation of the integral

$$B'(p\sigma_r) = \int_0^\infty I(\Delta)\, D(\Delta) \cos 2\pi p\sigma_r \Delta \, \mathrm{d}\Delta \tag{6}$$

can be replaced by that of the sum:

$$B'(p\sigma_r) = \sum_{q=0}^{q=Q} I(q\Delta a)\, D(q\Delta a) \cos 2\pi pq\sigma_r \Delta a \,, \tag{7}$$

the interferogram being sampled at Q points with spacing Δa. The sampling theorem shows that it is *sufficient* to take $\Delta a = 1/2\sigma_{\max}$. Since $Q\Delta a = \Delta_{\max} = 1/\sigma_r$, we can infer that the number of ordinates to measure on the interferogram is $Q = 2(\sigma_{\max}/\sigma_r = 2R_{\max}$, $R_{\max}$ being the *maximum* wanted resolving power (corresponding to the highest frequency in the spectrum). But in the rather common case where the spectral range is narrow, *i.e*, if $\sigma_{\min} > \sigma_{\max} - \sigma_{\min}$, it can be shown that the factor Q can be greatly reduced. In the most favorable case it can be made equal to $2M$. Now we have seen that M spectral values have to be computed. Since the computation time for a Fourier transform is obviously proportional to the number of imput *and* output points, it can be written as $T = M^2\theta$, where θ is a time interval which depends both on the computer and on the program. For instance, with an IBM 704 we have obtained approximately $\theta = 10^{-3}$ s. If $M = 10^3$, we get $T = 2\,000$ s. Consequently, one sees that the method is no longer applicable if $M \gg 10^3$ because the duration (and the cost) of the computation becomes prohibitive.

Sampling of the interferogram with exactly constant spacing is achieved with the help of a reference line of known wavelength; the corresponding beam travels through the interferometer and falls on a separate receiver. The sinusoidal ouput, which is recorded together with the interferogram, is used as a plot of path difference, or better still, directly triggers an automatic sampling system. If the path difference varies continuously, it is obvious that an important fraction of the measurement time is used to record the interferogram *between* measured points, thus, it is wasted. It is then better to move the mirror discontinuously, stopping at points of interest; this can be done with servo-control.

2·3. *Special analog-digital computer.* – A specialized computer for Fourier transform spectroscopy is being built at Bellevue. Its principle is as follows: both the interferogram and the sine-wave signal, given by the reference line of wavenumber σ_0, are recorded on two parallel tracks of a closed loop of magnetic tape. During analysis, both signals are read simultaneously. The reference line gives a signal of frequency N_0; this frequency is first divided by an integer k, then multiplied by another integer p. The resulting signal, whose frequency is $(p/k)N_0$, and the interferogram are sent to the two inputs of an analog multiplier. The product is integrated during one full turn of the loop. In this way one gets the intensity of the spectral element of wavenumber $(p/k)\sigma_0$. After each turn, p is automatically increased by one unit. In the spectrum thus computed, the abscissae are measured by a purely digital process and the ordinates by an analog one. Since p can take any integral value up to 10^6, it will be possible to reach a resolving power of 10^6. On top of that, the computational speed should be about 100 times greater than the one given for the IBM 704, and so M could be as large as 10^5.

3. – First applications.

The first spectra achieved by FELLGETT [1] were star spectra between 1 and 3 μm. Resolving power was of the order of 50 only, and yet much superior to those achieved by classical methods.

GEBBIE and VANASSE [4] obtained spectra in the far-red (from 50 to 500 μm) by means of an interferometer, without a dividing plate, consisting of a lamellar grating with variable groove depth. CONNES and GUSH [5] obtained emission spectra of the night sky between 1 and 2 μm with a resolving power reaching up to 1500, *i.e.*, about 10 times greater than the best spectra given by grating spectrometers.

Finally GEBBIE, ROLAND and DELBOUILLE [4, 6] have studied molecular emission spectra of hot gases in the medium infra-red (from 2 to 12 μm).

Maximum path difference was 2 cm, which means the resolution is 0.5 cm^{-1} and that the resolving power varies from 10 000 to 1600.

In conclusion, we see that Fourier transform spectroscopy, despite its comparative complexity and the serious practical drawback arising from the long time delay which generally occurs before the spectrum is available, should open new vistas in the study of faint infra-red sources.

REFERENCES

[1] P. Fellgett: *Jour. Phys.*, **19**, 187 (1958).
[2] P. Jacquinot: *XVII Congres du GAMS* (1954), p. 25.
[3] A. Michelson: *Phil. Mag.*, **31**, 256 (1891).
[4] H. Gebbie: *Nature*, **178**, 432 (1956).
[5] J. Connes: *Journ. Phys.*, **21**, 615 (1960); *Rev. Opt.*, **40**, 45, 116, 171, 231 (1961).
[6] H. Gebbie: *Nature*, **191**, 264 (1961).

High-Resolution Interferometric Spectroscopy.

P. CONNES
C.N.R.S. - Bellevue

1. – Introduction.

Before describing the present possibilities of high-resolution interferometric spectroscopy, it is necessary to recall the *needs* of spectroscopists. With the light sources used for measuring hyperfine structure or isotope shift, it is fundamentally the Doppler effect which sets a limit to the linewidth and, as a consequence, to the useful resolving power. The most frequently used source is the hollow cathode cooled in liquid nitrogen hydrogen, or even helium; it shows no Stark effect and the pressure-broadening is negligible. But the need to dissipate internally a certain amount of power causes an appreciable temperature rise, and the measured line widths are never less than $10\cdot10^{-3}$ cm for visible lines, even for the heaviest elements. Atomic beams used in emission or absorption can give Doppler widths going down to $2\cdot10^{-3}\,\text{cm}^{-1}$, but are useful only with a very limited number of lines. Corresponding relative linewidths, for $\lambda = 0.5\,\mu\text{m}$ are respectively 2.10^6 and 10^7.

It can be shown that, with all methods of spectroscopy, the resolution σ_r or instrumental linewidth is approximately equal to $1/\Delta_{\text{max}}$, Δ_{max} being the maximum path difference between interfering beams. With the largest gratings, of width 25 cm, used in Littrow mounting, and with a large incidence, Δ_{max} can be of the order of 40 cm which gives $\sigma_r = 25\cdot10^{-3}\,\text{cm}^{-1}$. But, it is easy in principle to build Fabry-Perot etalons for which Δ may well be more than 10 times larger; their resolving power will be more than enough to study the sharpest existing lines.

But this is only a part of the problem. In a great number of cases, the spectroscopist will have to deduce the intensities and positions of various spectral components from an imperfectly resolved profile. If $B(\sigma)$ is the spectrum as it would be observed without Doppler broadening (considered to be constant in a small spectral range), and $A(\sigma)$ the instrumental profile, the recorded spectrum will be the result of a triple convolution

$$B'(\sigma) = B(\sigma) * D(\sigma) * A(\sigma) .$$

In theory, the inverse operation of « deconvolution », *i.e.*, the reconstruction of profile $B(\sigma)$ knowing the other three functions, is mathematically definite; it is often done by successive approximations. In practice, if the structure is very narrow the recorded profile differs very little from the Doppler or instrumental profile and the required accuracy in all measurements increases enormously. Since noise is the only *fundamental* limitation to the accuracy (and quite often the practical one), an instrument which presents a higher light gathering power offers a fundamental advantage. This is one of the interesting aspects of the Fabry-Perot etalon.

2. – Essential properties of the Fabry-Perot spectrometer.

A Fabry-Perot spectrometer (Fig. 1) is made with a Fabry-Perot etalon, a circular diaphragm isolating the central portion of the ring system in the focal plane of a lens, and a receiver. Scanning of the spectrum is achieved by varying the optical thickness of the etalon, in most cases by varying the gas pressure inside. The receiver output is recorded and gives a representation of the spectrum which is linear both in abscissae and ordinates — a great advantage over the Fabry-Perot spectrograph in which the rings are photographed. The classical theory of the Fabry-Perot etalon illuminated by an incoherent source, which neglects both diffraction and the loss of oblique rays, is fully sufficient to explain all results because the thickness of the etalon is seldom greater than its diameter.

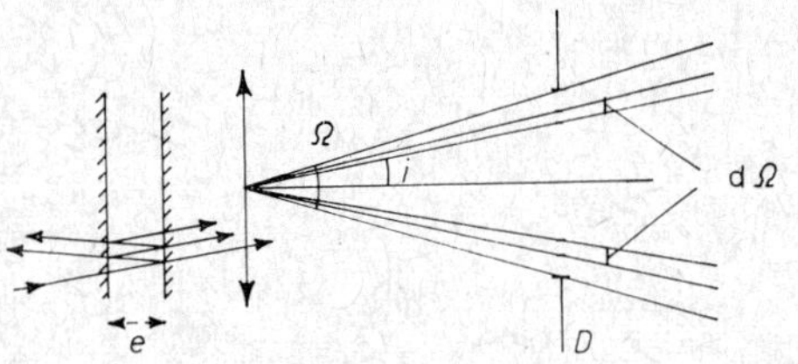

Fig. 1.

2·1. *Theoretical resolving power and instrumental function.* – If the instrument is perfectly adjusted and the incident angle constant (which supposes a beam of negligible solid angle), the classical calculation shows that the instrumental function is an Airy function (Fig. 2). The interval between two consecutive peaks, or free spectral range, is $\Delta\sigma = \frac{1}{2}e$, e being the plate separation; the width of a peak at half height, or resolution, is $\sigma_r = \Delta\sigma/N$, N being the finesse which depends only on the reflectivity R:

$$N = \frac{\pi\sqrt{R}}{1-R} .$$

It is also possible to write $\sigma_r = \frac{1}{2}Ne = 1/\Delta_{max}$ where Δ_{max} is the « equivalent » maximum path difference between interfering rays. Of course, there is an infinite number of rays of decreasing intensity, but the instrumental function would not be very different if one considered N rays of equal intensity. The theoretical resolving power is $R_0 = \sigma/\sigma n = 2Ne/\lambda$. It coincides with the Q factor of the etalon considered as a resonant cavity.

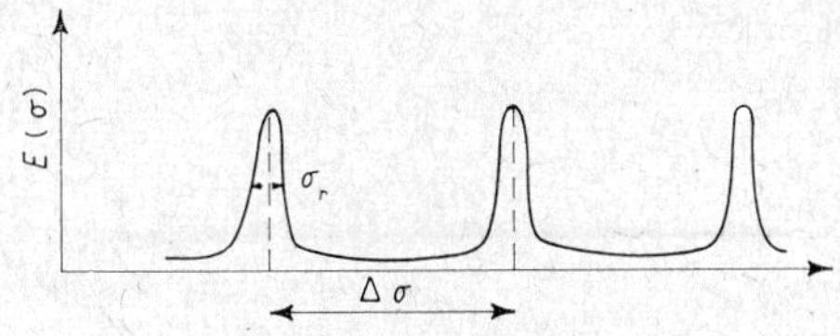

Fig. 2.

The most important limitation to the use of a Fabry-Perot etalon arises from the fact that while it is possible to increase R_0 without limit by increasing e, it is almost impossible to obtain $N > 50$ (if the area of the plates is of the order of a few cm²). Indeed, while it appears that multidielectric layers should permit to reach much higher values (with $R = 0.995$, $N = 600$), imperfections of the figure of the plates limit the value of N whatever the reflecting power. An etalon made with imperfect plates acts as a large number of etalons in parallel of different thicknesses which give slightly shifted Airy functions. The limiting finesse is an essential property of an etalon; it is equal to the maximum number of independent pieces of information one can get out of a Fabry-Perot recording. If there are too many components in the hyperfine structure of the studied line, one has to use a double etalon made of two successive etalons whose thickness ratio is an integer k; the double etalon has the same R_0 as the thickest etalon and the same $\Delta\sigma$ as the thinnest etalon; the total finesse is kN.

2·2. *Effective resolving power and light gathering power.* – In practice, the etalon is illuminated by an extended beam limited by a circular diaphragm whose solid angle is Ω (Fig. 1). This beam can be looked upon as the sum of elementary beams of solid angle $d\Omega$, of incidence (i) to which we can apply the previous results. Each gives a slightly shifted instrumental line shape. Altogether, the effective instrumental function $A(\sigma)$ will be the convolution of the Airy function $E(\sigma)$ by a function $H(\sigma)$ describing the lack of planeity of the etalon and by a rectangular function $K(\sigma)$ of width $r = \sigma(\Omega/2\pi)$ describing the diaphragm.

The experimenter has to choose the value of Ω according to what he wants; if Ω is increased, the resolving power decreases and the light flux increases. In most cases the most favorable compromise is reached when the product light flux × resolving power is a maximum; this happens when $\sigma_r = r$ which gives us the important relationship; $\Omega R = 2\pi$. This relationship shows that, compared to a grating spectrometer giving the same resolving power and the slits of which have an angular height $\beta_{rad.}$, the Fabry-Perot spectrometer gives a gain in light gathering power $G = 2\pi/\beta$. Since β lies generally between 10^{-1} and 10^{-2} rad, one sees that this gain is very large and makes the Fabry-Perot useful even for low resolving-power problems.

2˙3. *Applications.* – We shall only describe rapidly those in which the highest resolving powers have been obtained. With an Hg 198 emission atomic beam and the line 2537 Å, KESSLER [1] using an etalon of thickness 21 cm with a free spectral range $23 \cdot 10^{-3}$ cm^{-1} has measured a line width equal to $5 \cdot 10^{-3}$ cm^{-1}. Also, MEISSNER and KAUFMAN [2] were able to get visible fringes with an etalon of 100 cm thickness and the resonance line of natural calcium (containing 96% of Ca 40) emitted by an atomic beam. They deduced a line width of $3 \cdot 10^{-3}$ cm^{-1} approximately.

Obviously even very large Fabry-Perot etalons like these cannot be used to measure the intrinsic linewidth of a laser. Nevertheless, they can be useful to study side effects. For instance, STOICHEFF and HANES [3] obtained time-resolved spectra from a ruby laser. They showed that each spike has a different wavelength and also the existence of a wavelength drift due to thermal effects. They used a spherical Fabry-Perot etalon (to be described later on) of thickness 40 cm and an image converter with linear time scan.

3. – Fabry-Perot with internal emission or absorption.

3˙1. *Internal emission.* – It has been suggested by KASTLER [4] that much advantage could be gained by putting an emission source inside the Fabry-Perot. Although the idea was formulated after the appearance of the laser, it is, in fact, completely independent of it. This procedure should lead to an increase in source brightness by a factor of the order N if the line is neither self-absorbed nor self-amplified. In the latter case of course, the system becomes a laser; in the former, little or no gain can be obtained.

If a source emitting isotropic and monochromatic radiation is placed *in front* of the Fabry-Perot, one observes on the opposite side the classical phenomenon of multiple beam interference by transmission, *i.e.*, sharp, bright rings, and on the source side, sharp, dark rings. If the absorption of the reflecting layers is negligible, both systems are complementary. The interferometer acts as a half reflecting mirror, the transmission of which would be equal to 1 for discrete values of the incidence angle and very small for other values. Total energy emitted by the source is conserved; the illumination in the bright transmission rings is the *same* one would get without the etalon. Now, if the source is put *inside* the etalon, Kastler's reasoning shows that the total energy emitted, which stays the same as before, is now concentrated into the sharp rings. Since they occupy a fraction $1/N$ of the total solid angle, their illumination is multiplied by the same factor N. The etalon acts by modifying the emission diagram of the source which is no longer isotropic. In the privileged directions, one obtains the black-body brightness corresponding to the discharge temperature for the particular transition.

If the line has hyperfine structure, it can be scanned in the usual way by varying the thickness of the etalon.

3·2. *Internal absorption.* – When an atomic beam is used in absorption and if the amount of matter available is limited (which often happens in the important case where enriched isotopes are used), the absorption can be very small and it is useful to increase it by multiple passage of the optical beam through the atomic beam. JACKSON [5] has proved experimentally that the most efficient method consists in putting the beam inside the etalon. In this way, he was able to detect a component of the resonance line of barium (5535 Å) at less than $2\cdot10^{-3}$ cm^{-1} distance of the main component. The etalons were spherical ones with thicknesses between 6 and 12 cm.

The theory of this method is rather complex and has not yet been worked out since the Fabry-Perot no longer acts as a perfectly linear spectrometer which modifies the spectrum by simply convolving it with an instrumental function. If the beam absorption is very small, it can be said very roughly that the apparent absorption is increased by a factor of N and that the lines are slightly broadened.

4. – The spherical Fabry-Perot etalon.

This is a variant of the classical etalon which gives a greater light gathering power when extremely high resolving power is wanted. It consists of two spherical mirrors (fig. 3) of radius of curvature p making an afocal system. Half of each plate is fully reflecting and the other half is partially transparent. Any incident ray gives an infinite number of outgoing rays; neglecting aberrations, they all coincide and their path difference is equal to $4p$. If one takes aberrations into account, one finds a path difference variation

$$\delta\Delta = -\frac{r_1^2 r_2^2}{p^3}\cos 2\theta$$

for two outgoing rays arising from one which went through the plates at points M_1, M_2.

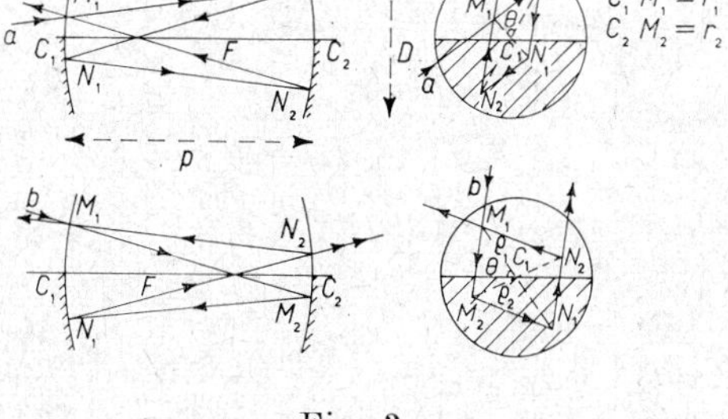

Fig. 3.

If used in a Fabry-Perot spectrometer, the spherical etalon has the following properties: the finesse N (and also the maximum trasmission) would be the same as that of the plane Fabry-Perot if the reflectivity of the fully reflecting parts were equal to 1; in practice, it is slightly less. The free spectral range is $\Delta\sigma = \frac{1}{4}\varrho$. The theoretical resolving power R_0 and the free spectral range are thus identical to those of a plane Fabry-Perot of thickness $e = 2p$ so both instruments can be interchanged to study a given problem. However, the product of cross-section times solid angle (or « étendue ») of the useful beam will be very different in each case. With the plane Fabry-Perot, this étendue is $U_p = S\Omega$, S being the area of the plate, which is theoretically unlimited but in practice, cannot be more than a few cm². Ω, as we have seen, is fixed by the resolving power since

$$\Omega = 2\pi/R .$$

With the spherical Fabry-Perot using the same criterion of maximum value for the product of light flux by resolving power, one gets the value $U_s = (\pi^2/4N^2)\lambda^2 R$ which shows that light gathering power is *proportional* to resolving power instead of being *inversely proportional* to it. This means that, if we replace a plane Fabry-Perot of thickness e and diameter D by the equivalent spherical Fabry-Perot whose thickness is $p = e/2$, we shall get a gain in light output $G = U_s/U_p = 2(e/D)^2$. This gain is large only for problems in which the use of a plane etalon with a thickness appreciably larger than the diameter of available plates is justified. Only atomic beams and lasers give sharp enough lines to be in this category and we have seen that the number of problems that can be studied in this way are rather small.

The spherical Fabry-Perot has another important practical advantage; adjustment is easy because only thickness has to be varied, and accuracy is not too strict. This, in turn, means it is not difficult to build a permanently adjusted etalon. This last property was very important in the internal atomic-beam experiment described earlier because the oven gives large temperature gradients and the adjustment of a plane Fabry-Perot could not have been made stable enough.

Nevertheless, the use of the spherical Fabry-Perot should be rather exceptional in spectroscopy. An entirely different application seemed at one time to be this: the Fabry-Perot etalon considered as an interference filter could be used to fabricate artificial lines by isolating a small portion of a continuous spectrum. In principle their width could be made infinitesimally small. However, with a plane etalon, the available energy soon becomes too small (because of the decrease in the etendue) while with a spherical Fabry-Perot, the energy can be made practically constant down to linewidths of the order of 1 MHz. Two simple experiments have been made [7] in order to illustrate this possibility. In the first one, the light issuing from a high-pressure mercury lamp travels through a first spherical etalon, then a Kerr cell and then a second etalon identical to the first. With $p = 250$ cm, one gets $\Delta\sigma = 10^{-3}$ cm^{-1}, or $\Delta\nu = c\Delta\sigma = 30$ MHz, and since $N = 30$, the width of the lines generated by the first etalon is about 1 MHz. The Kerr cell is fed by a HF voltage whose frequency is a few MHz. It modulates the light, splits the line and sidebands appear with the expected positions and intensity.

The second experiment showing the same experimental arrangement can be used to detect very small Doppler effects. The Kerr cell is replaced by a diffusing disk revolving around its axis. By looking at the disc, it is possible to see linear equidistant fringes; the distance between two fringes decreases when the speed of rotation increases. These fringes can be looked upon as a kind of Brewster fringes between the two etalons. With etalons a few meters in length and photoelectric detection, it can be shown that speeds of the order of 10^{-12} c could be detected. The sensitivity of these experiments is almost comparable to that obtained with the Mössbauer effect.

Of course, today lasers give sharper lines with far greater intensity and so the idea of using a multiple beam interferometer as a *passive* resonant cavity excited by an external source has completely lost interest.

On the other hand, the use of two spherical mirrors forming an afocal system has become frequent as a laser cavity [8], but for different reasons (except for the ease of adjustment). Indeed, an ideal laser oscillates on a single mode which means the emitted beam has an étendue of the order of λ^2. This is much smaller than the étendues U_p and U_s computed earlier. The useful diameter of the plates for oscillation on the axial mode is of the order of $\sqrt{\lambda p}$. It is much smaller than the plate diameter giving the étendue U_s and is determined by totally different considerations. Of course, the remarkable properties of the afocal system, both as a high-resolving-power interferometer and as a laser cavity, arise from the same reason—each mirror is imaged upon itself by the other.

5. – Comparison with heterodyne spectroscopy.

It is interesting to try to compare the possibilities of heterodyne spectroscopy, as described by FORRESTER [9], to those of the classical methods we have just reviewed and to look whether any improvement can be obtained in this way.

We are considering here the study of a classical source of light, both temporally and spatially incoherent. Its power spectrum $B(\nu)$ can be obtained in two ways. In the first scheme (« low-level detection »), the light falls on a photoelectric receiver which acts as a quadratic mixer. For each pair of

Fourier components of frequencies ν_2, ν_1, a beat signal is generated with frequency $N = \nu_2 - \nu_1$. If the power spectrum of the photoelectric current is scanned by an harmonic analyser with bandpass ΔN, one gets a recording of the autocorrelation function:

$$A(N) = \int_0^\infty B(\nu) \cdot B(\nu - N)\, d\nu$$

of the spectrum. With some limitations, $B(\nu)$ can be deduced from $A(N)$. These limitations are the same as one encounters in Michelson's fringe-visibility method. For instance, if the spectrum consists of two component lines of unequal intensities, it is possible to deduce the absolute value of their frequency difference but not its sign.

In the second scheme (« superheterodyne detection »), a laser is used as a local oscillator. The spectrum of the signal contains mostly beats between the local-oscillator frequency and the source frequencies. In this way, the *true* spectrum can be obtained.

In both cases, the frequency resolution is about equal to the bandpass ΔN. The resolving power $\nu/\Delta N$ is as large as permitted by the uncertainty principle, that is to say T/t, where T is the measurement time and t is the period of the light vibration.

However, the signal-to-noise ratio to be expected in the best possible circumstances is extremely poor. Neglecting many numerical factors of the order of unity in both methods, the ratio can be written as $S/N = \sqrt{\varrho \bar{n}}$ where ϱ is the photoelectric efficiency and $\bar{n}$ is the degeneracy parameter of the light [10]. It is the average number of photons in one cell of phase-space, or again, the average number of photons emitted by the source into an étendue equal to λ^2 per second and per unit bandpass in the neighborhood of fre quency ν. If the source is a black-body at temperature θ, then $\bar{n} = \{\exp[h\nu/k\theta] - 1\}^{-1}$.

In the $\lambda = 0.5$ µm region where photoelectric detectors still have a reasonable efficiency ($\varrho = 10^{-1}$), one gets $\bar{n} = 10^{-2}$ with $\theta = 6\,000$ °K. Thus, the S/N ratio is always much smaller than unity. In order to be able to measure something, one has to lengthen considerably the measurement time T over the minimum possible value $1/\Delta N$. This is equivalent to making $(T \cdot \Delta N)$ independent successive determinations and the final signal-to-noise ratio is then $(S/N)_{\text{het}} = \sqrt{\varrho \bar{n} T \Delta N}$. Let us compare this result with the one we get with a classical method of spectroscopy giving the same resolving power and frequency resolution ΔN and using the same amount of measuring time T (per spectral element). The light goes through some kind of optical filter or monochromator whose band pass is ΔN and which admits a beam of étendue U. It then falls on a receiver with photoelectric efficiency ϱ, the *direct* current of which is averaged during time T. The resulting signal-to-noise ratio is

$(S/N)_{\text{class}} = \sqrt{\varrho \bar{n} T \Delta N (U/\lambda^2)}$. Comparison of these two results gives

$$\frac{(S/N)_{\text{class}}}{(S/N)_{\text{het}}} = \sqrt{U/\lambda^2} = \sqrt{m}\,,$$

where we have set $U/\lambda^2 = m$.

This result is not very surprising. In the classical method the optical filter acts directly upon the light beam which has m degrees of freedom and is able to transmit m distinct pieces of information—one averages the results of m independent simultaneous measurements. In heterodyne spectroscopy, the receiver and transmission line after it are only able to pick up the information content of a single optical mode.

For the plane Fabry-Perot $m = (2\pi/R)(S/\lambda^2)$; for the spherical one $m = (\pi^2/4)(r/N^2)$. For a slit monochromator m can be written as

$$m = \frac{R_0}{R} \cdot \frac{\beta}{\alpha}\,,$$

where R_0/R is the ratio of theoretical to effective resolving power and β/α is that of slit length to slit width. In all three cases with any reasonable value of R one gets $m \gg 1$ and the heterodyne method suffers a great disadvantage. In principle, this could be overcome by using m identical systems (receiver, transmission line, filter) in parallel, and averaging results, but this would be far too complex in practice.

Only in the case where the étendue of the available beam is of the order of λ^2 or smaller, are the two methods theoretically equivalent. This should be the case in stellar spectrometry. Unfortunately, due to the limited bandwidth of photoelectric receivers (a few GHz at best) and the small tuning range of present lasers, heterodyne spectroscopy would be suitable only for extremely-high-resolving-power spectroscopic studies of very narrow spectral ranges. It is likely that no absorption or emission feature in the spectrum of any star is sharp enough to warrant that kind of study. If broadly tunable lasers were to become available, then the method could be a practical possibility.

REFERENCES

[1] K. G. Kessler: *Journ. Opt. Soc. Am.*, **51**, 827 (1961).
[2] K. W. Meissner: *Journ. Opt. Soc. Am.*, **49**, 942 (1959).
[3] B. P. Stoicheff: *Nature*, **195**, 587 (1962).
[4] A. Kastler: *App. Opt.*, **1**, 17 (1962).
[5] D. A. Jackson: *Proc. Prog. Soc.*, **263**, 289 (1961).
[6] P. Connes: *Journ. Phys.*, **19**, 262 (1958).
[7] P. Connes: *Journ. Phys.*, **23**, 173 (1962).
[8] G. O. Boyd and J. P. Gordon: *Bell. Syst. Techn. Jour.*, **60**, 489 (1961).
[9] A. T. Forrester: *Phys. Rev.*, **99**, 1291 (1955); *Journ. Opt. Soc. Am.*, **51**, 253 (1961).
[10] L. Mandel: *Journ. Opt. Soc. Am.*, **51**, 797 (1961).

Ions in Crystals (*).

W. Low

The Hebrew University of Jerusalem - Jerusalem

1. – Introduction.

The optical information required for materials useful in laser operation are very similar to those in ordinary spectroscopy. One measures the position of the energy levels by means of absorption or fluorescence spectroscopy, the line width and lifetime of the emitting states, and the intensity or *f* number of these lines. The theoretical interpretation of these spectra is somewhat more complicated. The interaction of the relatively localized valence electrons of the usual paramagnetic ions with the cristalline lattice affects both static phenomena, such as the position of the energy levels, as well as dynamic phenomena such as the decay times and line width. The degeneracy of the energy levels is usually partially or fully removed, the lines are split into a crystal fine structure. The interaction with the surroundings often reduces the degree of « forbiddeness » of a given transition to an extent that such levels can be observed.

The optical requirements of solid-state laser materials are usually stated as:

1) Narrow fluorescent lines.

2) Efficient way of populating the fluorescent level.

3) Preferably a lower level which is not the ground state and which can be populated rapidly.

In these lectures we shall deal with some of the materials which fulfil requirements 1 and 3. The second requirement is interpreted to mean that

(*) The research reported in this document has been sponsored in part by the United States National Bureau of Standards and the Cambridge Research Laboratories, O.A.R. through the European Office Aerospace Research, U.S.A.F.

there are strong absorption bands which store energy and filter it selectively to the fluorescent levels. In effect one desires a high quantum efficiency, that is to say a high ratio of the number of photons emitted to those absorbed. Requirement 3) implies that the level should be sufficiently removed from the ground state so that at the operating temperature it is essentially depopulated, but not too far removed so that nonradiative or radiative transitions can establish thermal equilibrium rapidly. Essentially one wants to short-circuit these two levels.

Since this is not a course on solid-state spectroscopy we shall not go into the various methods of calculating the energy levels. We shall briefly summarize these, and illustrate the more salient features of these spectra.

2. – Energy levels in the iron and rare-earth groups.

1) The nonrelativistic Hamiltonian for a complex atom may be written (1)

$$H = H_0 + H_{so} , \tag{1}$$

where

$$H_0 = \sum_i \left(\frac{p_i^2}{2m} - \frac{Ze^2}{r_i}\right) + \sum_{i>j} \frac{e^2}{r_j} \tag{2}$$

and

$$H_{so} = \frac{1}{2m^2c^2} \sum_i \frac{1}{r}\frac{\partial U}{\partial r} \boldsymbol{s}_j \boldsymbol{l}_j .$$

Here U gives the central field potential.

2) The Coulomb interaction in eq. (2) accounts for the configurations and the various term values. The spin-orbit interaction gives rise to a fine structure.

The lowest configuration for the iron group elements in their divalent or trivalent states is given by $1s^2 2s^2 2p^6\ 3s^2 3p^6 3d^n$. It starts with Ti^{3+} and ends with Cu^{2+} (d^9). The spectroscopy information is contained in N.B.S. tables [1, 2].

The next configuration is $3p^6 4s$ followed by $3p^6 4p$ at about 100 000 cm^{-1}. The d^n configuration and the following configuration essentially do not overlap. For example for Ti^{3+} (Ti IV) $3d^1$, $^2D_{\frac{3}{2}}$ the next configuration occurs at 80 000 cm^{-1}, followed by the $3p^6 4p$ at 128 000 and $3p^6 4d$ at 194 000 cm^{-1}.

The next ion after Ti^{3+} is $V^{3+}\ 3d^2$, $^3F_2$. The two electrons give rise to triplets and singlets which are $^3F(0)$, $^3P(13000)$, $^1D(11000)$, $^1G(18387)$, $^1S(2)$ cm^{-1}.

The spin-orbit coupling is usually a few hundred cm^{-1}.

An important ion for laser action is Cr^{3+}, $3d^3\ {}^4F_{\frac{3}{2}}$. Here there are quartets and doublets at ${}^4F(0)$, ${}^4P(14\,000)$, ${}^2P(14\,000)$, ${}^2G(15\,000)$, ${}^2D_a(20\,000)$ and ${}^2D_b$, ${}^2H$, ${}^2F$.

The next configuration is at about 100 000 cm^{-1}. Because of the large separation and the small spin-orbit coupling there is not much configuration interaction.

The calculations of the energy levels of the iron group elements have been perfected by RACAH and his students and they are able today to predict levels sometimes within a few cm^{-1}.

One usually expands the (e^2/r_{ij})-term into multipoles

$$\frac{1}{r_{ji}} = \sum_k \frac{r_i^k}{r_j^{k+1}} P_k(\cos\theta)\,, \tag{4}$$

where $r_i > r$; and θ is the angle between the two radius vectors. One operates now on the angular part and on the radial part. The angular part can be treated by means of Racah's vector coupling methods [3, 4].

The radial part is expressed as parameters F^k where

$$F^k = e^2 \int_0^\infty \int_0^\infty \frac{r_i^k}{r_j^{k+1}} [R(i)R(j)]^2 \,\mathrm{d}r_i \,\mathrm{d}r_j\,. \tag{5}$$

For the iron group one can terminate the series at $k = 4$.

RACAH and his students have established interpolation formulae to high accuracy between the configurations d^n, $d^{n-1}s$, $d^{n-2}s^2$. They found it necessary to introduce in addition to the three parameters F_0, F_2 and F_4 also a correction term α, the Trees' correction [5, 6, 7].

The coefficient α multiplies the operator $\sum_{i>j} l_i \cdot l_j$ which has the form $L(L+1)$. Recently it has been found necessary to add another correction term.

The spin-orbit coupling splits the various terms into levels to which can be assigned the quantum number J.

For equivalent electrons the spin-orbit coupling can be written

$$H_{so} = \xi \sum s \cdot l \tag{6}$$

with

$$\xi = \frac{1}{2m^2e^2} \int_0^\infty R^2 \frac{1}{r} \frac{\partial V}{\partial r} \,\mathrm{d}r\,. \tag{7}$$

The spin-orbit coupling connects states of the same J but different L and S and this may produce deviations from the interval rule.

In the Russell-Saunders approximation these off-diagonal elements are neglected. In this approximation we can write

$$\sum \xi s \cdot l \rightarrow \lambda L \cdot S \tag{8}$$

and the Landé interval rule is

$$E_j - E_{j-1} = \lambda L \,. \tag{9}$$

Summarizing we can say that the three electrostatic parameters F_0, F_2, F_4, the spin-orbit coupling, two smaller correction terms permit the calculations of the energy levels of the various configurations of the iron group to a fair accuracy. Table I summarizes some of the properties of the iron-group elements.

TABLE I. – *Parameters of the iron group.*

No. of electrons	1	2	3	4	5	6	7	8	9
Ions	Ti^{3+}	V^{3+}	Cr^{3+}	Cr^{2+}	Fe^{3+}	Fe^{2+}	Co^{2+}	Ni^{2+}	Cu^{2+}
Ground state	${}^2D_{\frac{3}{2}}$	${}^3F_2$	${}^4F_{\frac{3}{2}}$	${}^5D_0$	${}^6S_{\frac{5}{2}}$	${}^5D_4$	${}^4F_{\frac{9}{2}}$	${}^3F_4$	${}^5D_{\frac{5}{2}}$
Spin orbit coupling	154	104	87	57	420	-100	-180	-335	-852

3. – Rare-earth group.

Here the experimental data are not as readily available and the calculations more complicated. It has been known for a long time that in the rare-earth series there are a number of competing configurations, with energies not very different from one another. It is now established that for the trivalent ions the lowest configuration is $4f^n 5s^2 6p^6$ followed by the $4f^{n-1} 5d$ configuration. In Fig. 1 is shown the separation of the centers of gravity of the near configurations both for the trivalent and divalent ions. At the beginning of the shell, Ce^{3+} and Pr^{3+}, the next configuration is at about $(50\,000 \div 60\,000)\ \text{cm}^{-1}$ and at the end Yb^{3+} much further at about $100\,000\ \text{cm}^{-1}$. On the whole the $4f^n$ and $4f^{n-1} 5d$ configurations do not overlap. In the case of the divalent rare-earth ions the position of the next configuration is in the visible range and is as close as $10\,000\ \text{cm}^{-1}$ in the case of Ce^{3+}. At the end of the shell near Yb^{3+} the $4f^{n-1} 6s$ configuration which has the same parity as the $4f^n$ configuration becomes important. The $4f^{n-1} 5d$ configuration has opposite parity and electric dipole transitions between this and the f^n configurations are permitted.

The closeness of the many configurations results in departure from R.S. coupling. This may shift levels as much as 1000 cm^{-1}. An example of such a shift is Pr^{3+} where the $^1I_6$ level seems to be shifted by about 350 cm^{-1}. The many configurations and the large number of levels make the calculations rather complex.

The calculations of the energy levels, that is to say the matrices of the electrostatic and spin-orbit interaction, even in the absence of configuration interaction, are more complicated. These matrices have been constructed [8].

Since one is dealing with f electrons one can expand eq. (4) until $k=6$ and one needs 4 electrostatic parameters. One usually uses linear combinations of the F^k called ε

(10) $$\varepsilon = \sum e_k F^k .$$

RACAH has shown that one has to introduce two additional quantum numbers, W and U respectively, to specify a given level. An eigenfunction has to be written

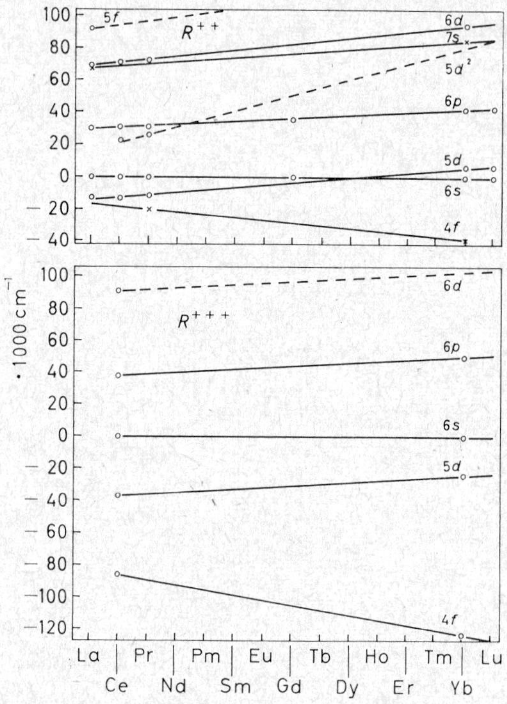

Fig. 1. – Position of center of gravity of various configurations for divalent and trivalent ions (taken from C. H. DICKE and H. M. CROSSWHITE: *Applied Optics*, **2**, 675 (1963)).

(11) $$\psi(f^n \tau W U S L S_z L_z)$$

where $W(w_1 w_2 w_3)$ takes on 3 integral numbers w_1, w_2, w_3 with $w_1 \geqslant w_2 \geqslant w_3$ and $w \leqslant 2$. The quantum number $U = (u_1 u_2)$ is another integral number.

One can show that one may introduce 3 additional correction terms, one of which is the Trees correction.

The largest Slater parameter F_2 follows a nearly linear relation with Z

$$F_2 = a(Z - \sigma), \qquad a = 12.4, \qquad \sigma = 34 - 35, \quad \text{for trivalent ions.}$$

Similarly the spin-orbit coupling shows a linear shift with Z [9]:

(12) $$\xi = a'(Z - \sigma') + b/(\sigma'' - Z)$$

with

$$a' = 77.4\,, \qquad \sigma' = 66.28\,, \qquad b = 28720\,, \qquad \sigma'' = 8078\,.$$

The more significant parameters of the trivalent rare-earth ground configuration are listed in Table II.

If the spin-orbit coupling is taken into account the density of levels in the optical range can become quite high for ions near the middle of the shell.

A summary of the experimental knowledge is contained in the paper of DICKE and CROSSWHITE [8] and of the theoretical calculation is given in a recent paper by WYBOURNE [10].

TABLE II. – *Optical properties of trivalent ions.*

	No. of electrons	Ground and state	No. of levels	Spin-orbit coupling in cm^{-1}	F_2
Ce	1	$^2F_{5/2}$	2	640	—
Pr	2	$^3H_4$	13	730	305
Nd	3	$^4I_{5/2}$	41	876	337
Pm	4	$^5I_4$	107	1070	346
Sm	5	$^5H_{5/2}$	198	1200	370
Eu	6	$^7F_0$	295	1320	401
Gd	7	$^8S_{7/2}$	327	1581	405
Tb	8	$^7F_6$	295	1705	434
Dy	9	$^6H_{15/2}$	198	1900	420
Ho	10	$^4I_8$	107	2163	450
Er	11	$^4I_{15/2}$	41	2445	425
Tm	12	$^3H_6$	13	2656	451
Yb	13	$^2F_{7/2}$	2	2882	—

Summarizing we may say that the energy levels can be calculated using 4 electrostatic parameters, the spin orbit coupling and probably up to 3 correction terms. The mean deviation of the calculated parameters is still quite large but one may expect higher accuracy in the near future.

4. – Crystal field calculations.

4·1. – There are a number of textbooks which are dealing with this field which is of importance both to physics and chemistry [11, 12*a*, 12*b*].

Briefly the main assumptions of this theory are as follows:

a) We may use the same Hamiltonian as in eq. (1).

b) Acting on the ions are a distribution of charges setting up a « crystalline field potential ». The symmetry of the distribution will determine the number and the degeneracy of the split levels. The strength of the interaction of the charge distribution with the valence electrons will determine the overall splitting.

c) The same crystal field acts on all the electronic levels.

The first assumption although an approximation, is well born out in the rare-earth series. The $4f$ electrons do not participate to first order in chemical bonding. The electrons are well localized.

Still one finds, in more detailed analysis, that the center of gravity of the Stark-split levels is not the same in different crystal hosts and differs also from the free ion values. These deviations are of a few hundred cm^{-1} and can be associated with a « chemical effect ». Precision measurements of the Zeeman splitting confirm that one has to take into account covalent bonding [13] to a small degree.

In the iron group such shifts are much larger. They may be of the order of 20% in some crystalline hosts. Essentially this amounts to a reduction of the value of the Slater integrals and the effective spin-orbit coupling.

The reasons for this difference between the iron group and rare-earth group is that the d^n electrons participate extensively in the bonding, the $4f$ electrons are shielded by the $5s$ and $5p$ electrons. This will be discussed later.

With these assumptions in mind we add to the Hamiltonian (1) a term

$$V(r, \theta, \varphi) = \sum_j \frac{q_j}{d_j - r}, \tag{13}$$

where d_j is the distance of the charge q_j from the origin.

The expansion can be easily performed and is indicated for the octahedral cubic symmetry. Consider charges of the corners $(\pm a, 0, 0)$, $(0, \pm a, 0)$, $(0, 0, \pm a)$.

The potential at a point (x, y, z) is

$$V = q\left[\frac{1}{\sqrt{r^2 + a^2 - 2ax}} + \frac{1}{\sqrt{r^2 + a^2 + 2ax}}\right], \qquad x_j = x, y, z, \quad r^2 = x^2 + y^2 + z^2. \tag{14}$$

Expanding the square root and collecting terms

$$V(x, y, z) = \frac{6q}{a} - \frac{21q}{4a^5}(x^2 + y^2 + z^2)^2 + \frac{35}{4}\frac{(x^4 + y^4 + z^4)}{a^5} + \tag{15}$$
$$+ \frac{90}{8}\frac{(x^2 + y^2 + z^2)^3}{qj} + \frac{231}{8}\frac{(x^6 + y^6 + z^6)}{a^7} - \frac{315}{8}\frac{(x^2 + y^2 + z^2)(x^4 + y^4 + z^4)}{q^7}.$$

This is written more conventionally as

(16) $$V(x, y, z) = V_0 + D_4 \left[x_j^4 - \frac{3r^4}{5} \right] + D_6 \left[\frac{15}{4} (x_i^2 x_j^4) - \frac{15r^6}{14} \right].$$

Similar potentials can be derived for other symmetries. Some of these are listed in ref. [12].

It is more convenient for matrix calculations to expand the potential (13) in spherical harmonics

(17) $$V(r, \theta, \varphi) = \sum_j q_j \sum \frac{r^n}{d_j^{n+1}} \left(\frac{4\pi}{2n+1} \right) \sum_{m=n}^{n} (-1)^n Y_n^m(\theta, \varphi) Y_n^{-m}(\theta, \varphi) = \sum V_n^m .$$

In this case the potential in octahedral symmetry takes the form

(18) $$V(r, \theta, \varphi) = Y_0' + D_4' \left[Y_4^0 + \sqrt{\frac{5}{14}} (Y_4^4 + Y_4^{-4}) \right] + \\ + D_6' \left[Y_6^0 + \sqrt{\frac{7}{2}} (Y_6^4 + Y_6^{-4}) \right].$$

In view of some confusion regarding signs we list in Table III the coefficients of the various D_i's for some of the cubic symmetries.

TABLE III.

	D_4	D_6	D_4'	D_6'	B_4^0	B_6^0
units: $qq' \times$	$\frac{1}{d^5}$	$\frac{1}{d^7}$	$\frac{\sqrt{\pi} r^4}{d^5}$	$\sqrt{\frac{\pi}{13}} \frac{r^6}{d^7}$	$\frac{\beta_j \langle r^4 \rangle}{d^5}$	$\frac{\gamma_j \langle r^6 \rangle}{d^7}$
6-fold co-ordination	35/8	$-$ 21/2	+ 7/3	3/2	$-$7/16	$-$3/64
8-fold co-ordination	$-$70/9	$-$224/9	$-$56/27	32/9	+7/18	$-$1/9
4-fold co-ordination	$-$35/9	$-$112/9	$-$28/27	16/9	+7/36	$-$1/18

The coefficients are proportional to $1/d^{n+1}$. The angular part determines the type of matrix elements involved. In case of lower symmetry there will be many more parameters. For the rare-earth ions the main parameters are for C_{3v}:

$$V_2^0,\ V_4^0,\ V_6^0,\ V_4^3,\ V_6^3,\ V_6^6;$$

for axial distortion

$$V_2^0,\ V_4^0,\ V_6^0,\ V_4^4,\ V_6^4.$$

For the d^n system often three parameters V_2^0, V_4^0, V_4^4 may be sufficient.

The number of parameters is limited by 3 rules:

a) Restriction on n: $n \geqslant 2l$ where l is the orbital angular momentum.

b) Restriction on n: Matrix elements are different from zero only for even n, *i.e.*, $n = 2p$. This holds true for matrix elements within a configuration. Odd potential terms can admix configurations of the opposite parity [15].

c) Restriction on m: $m = m' - m''$, where m' and m'' are the two unperturbed levels. Hence the off-diagonal elements Y_n^m couple states differing by $\Delta J_z = \pm m$.

To calculate these matrix elements it is convenient to use the operator equivalent method [16].

In this method one goes from single-electron wave function to levels specified by a definite J or L:

$$H_c = \sum_{nm} [A_n^m \langle r^n \rangle \theta_n] O_n^m = B_n^m O_n^m , \tag{19}$$

where the A_n^m are numerical factors, $\langle r^n \rangle$ are the average values of r^n, θ_n a multiplication factor called the operator equivalent (α, β, γ) and are listed in various tables [12*a*, 14].

O are the operators whose values are also listed in tables corresponding to the various symmetries.

$$B_n^m = [A_n^m \langle r^n \rangle] \theta_n .$$

We list the values of B_n^m in Table III. The cubic field potential may then be written as

$$H_c = B_4^0 [O_4^0 + 5 O_4^4] + B_6^0 [O_6^0 - 21 O_6^4] . \tag{20}$$

It should be noticed that experiment determines the products $A_n^m \langle r^n \rangle$. These are measured from the crystal fine-structure splitting.

4·2. *Application on the rare-earth and the iron group.* – In the rare-earth group it is found that the values of the crystal field strength $A_n^m \langle r^n \rangle$ are relatively small compared with the spin-orbit coupling. The splitting effected by these potentials is usually only a few hundred cm^{-1}. To first order we can take each LSJ level separately and calculate the expected splitting from the crystal field potential. Refined calculations take into account the effects of the off-diagonal elements connecting different J levels.

The reasons for the small values of $A_n^m \langle r^n \rangle$ are the following.

a) The «natural» symmetry in which rare-earth compounds tend to crystallize is such an arrangement that minimizes the value of the potential. If a lattice sum calculation is performed the resultant potential is small [17, 18].

b) The parameter A_n^m depend on $1/d^{n+1}$. The radius of the rare-earth ions and the distance to the nearest neighbours is relatively large. On the other hand the $4f$ electron density is quite close to the nucleus.

c) The polarization of the outer shells $5s$ and $5p^6$ by the surroundings leads to shielding and antishielding giving rise to smaller parameters. This shielding is expected to be a function of n; the smaller n the larger the shielding [19-22]. In general one may write

$$A_n^m \langle r^n \rangle_{\text{exp}} = \{A_n^m \langle 4f | r^n | 4f \rangle\}_{\text{true}} (1 - P_n^m), \tag{24}$$

where P_n^m measures the shielding effect.

The combination of all these reasons gives relatively small splittings for the rare-earth ions in symmetric C_{3i} and C_{3h}. In CaF_2 in which the ions see a combination of cubic and axial fields the splitting seems to be larger. It should be noticed that the close spacing of some of these Stark levels may give level schemes of potential use for lasers in the infra-red or for infra-red.

This small interaction with the surroundings results in line widths which are relatively sharp, many of the lines at low concentration having a width of a fraction of a cm^{-1}.

In the iron group the crystal field splitting is as large as the separation between the term values. The result is that the crystal field mixes the wave functions of the various levels to a degree that they cannot be classified anymore according to their parent L, S, J. It is more convenient to classify the levels according to their irreducible representation Γ_i. An example how the levels change as a function of the crystal field strength is given in Fig. 2.

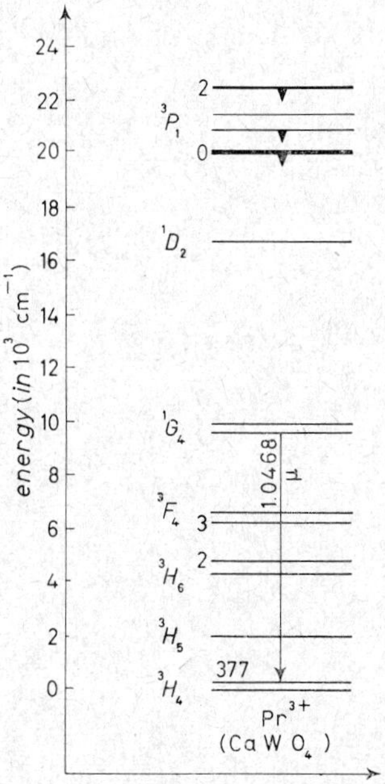

Fig. 2. – Position of electronic levels of Pr^{3+} in $LaCl_3$ as determined by X-ray excitation.

The calculations of the various levels in this moderately strong field can be made along two lines. One may use a weak field representation in which one utilizes the spin-orbit and electrostatic matrices available in the literature. This has been used extensively by RACAH and his students [23, 24], as well as by other scientists.

The other method uses a strong field representation. A cubic field splits the electron into two groups of e and t orbitals (sometimes called $d\gamma$ and $d\varepsilon$, or e and t). The splitting $E_e - E_t$ is known conventionally as $10Dq$. The electronic configuration is then written as $e^m t^n$ with $m+n=N \leqslant 10$. This method has been used extensively by TANABE and SUGANO [25].

For the iron group the spin-orbit coupling is smaller than the crystal field and, therefore, only a small perturbation.

The effects of such a moderate strong field can be briefly summarized.

a) In octahedral complexes $10Dq$ is of the order of 8000 to 9000 cm^{-1} for divalent ions and 15000 to 18000 cm^{-1} for trivalent ions.

b) In eight co-ordinates compounds such as CaF_2 the crystal field is about $\frac{1}{2}$ or less than that of octahedral compounds.

c) The Slater integrals F_k are reduced by as much as 20% compared with the free ions in octahedral complexes. There is a correlation between this reduction and the strength of the crystal field as well as the amount of covalent bonding.

d) The majority of the absorption lines consists of wide bands with only very few sharp lines. There is a correlation between the width of the bands and the strength of the crystalline field.

Two examples will be used to illustrate.

A) The spectrum of Cr^{3+} (d^3) in a cubic and axial field.

The experimental data are taken from ruby which has a trigonal symmetry. The ground state ^4F is split by the strong cubic field into $^4\Gamma_2(t^2)$, a triplet $^4\Gamma_4(t^2e)$ which experimentally is found at about 17000 cm^{-1} in ruby and is a broad band (called the U band), a triplet at about 25000 cm^{-1} (called the Y band) and identified as $^4\Gamma_4(^4F)(t^2e)$. In addition there is another weaker wide band about 39500 cm^{-1} which corresponds to a $^4\Gamma_4(^4P)(te^2)$ band. These three bands show polarization effects and are split into a doublet and a singlet (^4E and ^4A) levels through the axial field with a splitting of about 800, 500 and 450 cm^{-1}. In addition there are the R_1 and R_2 lines at 14418 and 14437 belonging to the $^2G\,^4\Gamma_3$ level which is split by the trigonal field and G another set of sharp lines at about 21000 cm^{-1}. Other wider lines appear in the region of about 15000 cm^{-1} and 21000 cm^{-1}. In Table IV we have listed the position of the free ion values and those of the computed energy levels for a cubic field. It is seen that these bear no relation to one another. Furthermore many of the lines show very large admixtures. The agreement of the cubic field approximation as applies to the spectrum of ruby is excellent. This shows that the cubic field is strongest when followed by a trigonal field which

TABLE IV. – *Calculated spectrum of* Cr^{3+} *in cubic fields.*

Free ion			Ion in crystal			
designation	$J=$	position (cm^{-1})	designation			position (cm^{-1})
^4F	3/2	0	^4F	$^4\Gamma_2$	Γ_8	0
	5/2	244	^2G	$^4\Gamma_3$	Γ_8	14 845
	7/2	561	47% ^2H + 41% ^2G	$^2\Gamma_4$	Γ_6	15 438
	9/2	956			Γ_8	15 837
^4P	1/2	14 072	^4F	Γ_5	Γ_7	17 909
	3/2	14 217			Γ_8	17 950
	5/2	14 481			Γ_8	18 055
^2P	3/2	14 185			Γ_6	18 066
	1/2	14 317	49% ^2D + 32% ^2H	Γ_5	Γ_8	21 822
^2G	7/2	15 064			Γ_6	22 081
	9/2	15 414	49% ^4F + 45% ^4P	Γ_4	Γ_8	25 710
^2D	3/2	20 218	56% ^4F + 45% ^4P		Γ_7	25 712
	5/2	20 667	48% ^4F + 46% ^4P		Γ_8	25 767
^2H	9/2	21 078	52% ^4F + 47% ^4P		Γ_6	25 787
	11/2	21 328	^2G	Γ_1	Γ_6	30 238
^2F	7/2	36 480	58% ^2G + 35% ^2H	Γ_5	Γ_7	33 114
	5/2	37 062			Γ_8	33 170
			41% ^2H + 28% ^2G	Γ_4	Γ_8	33 433
					Γ_6	33 558
			51% ^2H + 48% ^2D	Γ_3	Γ_8	34 874
			48% ^2P	Γ_4	Γ_6	38 782
					Γ_8	38 919
			55% ^4P + 45% ^4F	Γ_4	Γ_7	40 162
			55% ^4P + 41% ^4F		Γ_8	40 170
			57% ^4P + 47% ^4F		Γ_6	40 226
			52% ^4P + 41% ^4F		Γ_8	40 230

is not much stronger than the spin-orbit coupling. It is to be noticed that the sharp line $^2G\,^2\Gamma_3$ is hardly admixed with any other state to first order and is not affected to this order by changes in the cubic crystalline field strength. The admixture will be of the order of

$$\frac{\lambda}{E_{2\Gamma_3} - E_{4\Gamma_2}}$$

and other higher-order terms. Only the trigonal field combined with the spin-orbit coupling removes this degeneracy.

B) The spectrum of Pr^{3+} in the field of C_{3h}. The ion Pr^{3+} is probably the most studied in the rare-earth series. The position of the energy levels as determined from the fluorescence and absorption spectra in single crystals of

$LaCl_3$: Pr^{3+} is shown in Fig. 3. It is to be noticed that there is a gap between the $^1S_0$ and the $^3P_2$ levels. Now each of these levels are split through the crystal field. An example of such a splitting is shown for the $^1G_4$ and $^3P_1$ levels in Fig. 4. The ground state $^3H_4$ is split into levels at 0, 33.2, 96.1, 133 cm^{-1}.

The divalent rare-earth ions have been studied by KISS [26]. Figure 5 shows a summary of his results.

One notices the very strong bands in the near infra-red and visible range. Presumable these bands are from the $f^{n-1}d$ configurations. In the solid state these configurations may not necessarily fall at the same place as in the free ion, because the constant term in the potential in eq. (16) may differ for different configurations. Because of these strong bands the number of observable sharp lines of transition within the $4f^n$ configuration is limited. An example of this is the more carefully studied spectrum of Tm^{2+} in CaF_2 and is shown in Fig. 6. Here two fluorescent lines

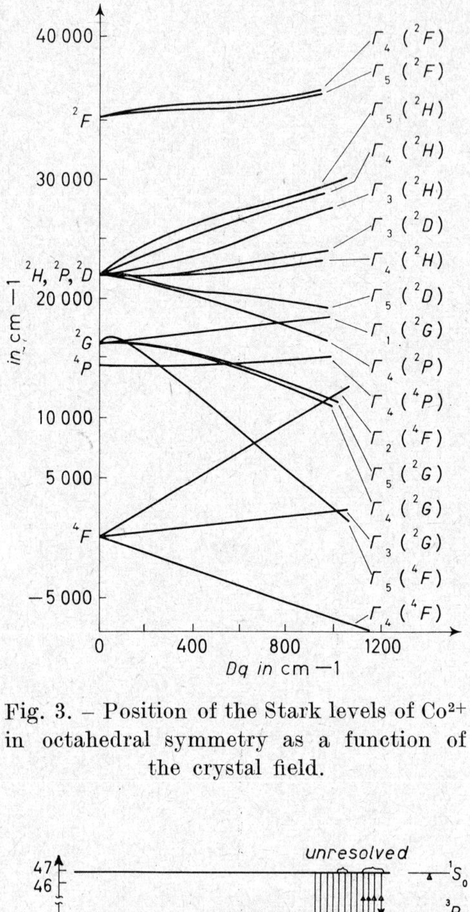

Fig. 3. – Position of the Stark levels of Co^{2+} in octahedral symmetry as a function of the crystal field.

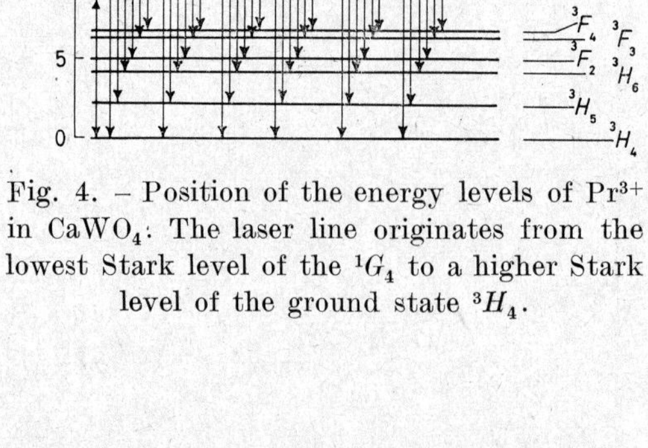

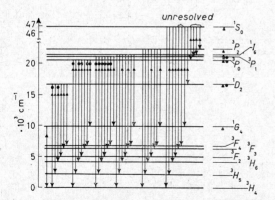

Fig. 4. – Position of the energy levels of Pr^{3+} in $CaWO_4$. The laser line originates from the lowest Stark level of the $^1G_4$ to a higher Stark level of the ground state $^3H_4$.

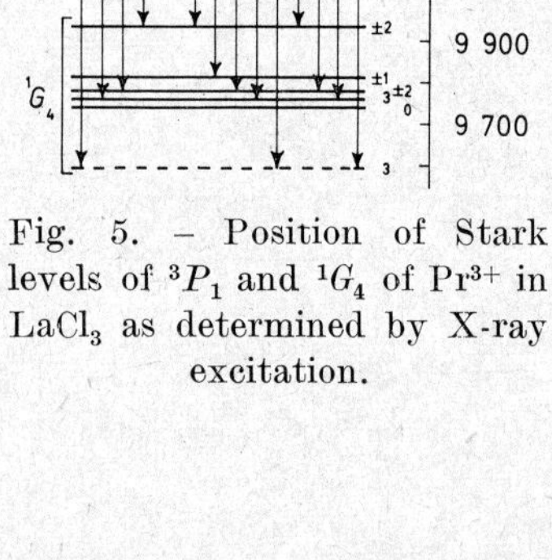

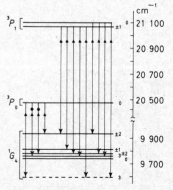

Fig. 5. – Position of Stark levels of $^3P_1$ and $^1G_4$ of Pr^{3+} in $LaCl_3$ as determined by X-ray excitation.

at 8966 and 8410 cm^{-1} are observed corresponding to transition from the upper $\Gamma_7(^2F_{\frac{5}{2}})$ to the Γ_7 and Γ_8 levels of the Stark-split $^2F_{\frac{7}{2}}$ level. The f number of these transitions is about 10^{-8} and the line width less than 0.02 cm^{-1}. The transition to the Γ_6 $^2F_{\frac{7}{2}}$ is supposedly forbidden. The absorption bands at (15 000 ÷ 20 0000) cm^{-1} are with the large f number of 10^{-2} caused by the next configuration. This system has been successfully operated as laser.

Similarly the spectra of CaF_2:Sm^{2+} have been studied in detail [27, 28]. It has been shown that near the pumping band at (15 000 ÷ 16 000) cm^{-1} these are sharp lines. These have been identified by Zeeman effect and by unaxial strain studies and shown to belong to the f^5d configuration and not to the f^6 configuration. In particular the large shifts and splittings under strain indicate that the upper level contains an unshielded d electron. It is not understood why the line is so sharp since most of the d transitions usually consist of wide bands.

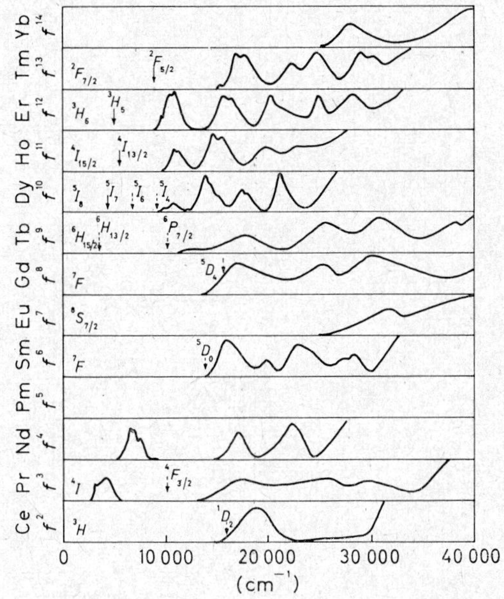

Fig. 6. – Sharp energy levels and wide absorption bands for divalent rare-earth ions (according to Kiss, R.C.A. Laboratories, Princeton, N. J.).

5. – Some special features and special techniques.

The usual method of obtaining the position of the energy levels is to measure the absorption and the fluorescence spectrum. In many cases the absorption spectrum above 25 000 cm^{-1} becomes very weak. The fluorescence spectrum of most rare earths and even more so that of the iron group is of negligible intensity in the U.V. In part this is caused by inadequate light sources in the U.V. which could profitably be used for populating these levels. It is of great interest to have energy levels in this region since at present most optical masers generate near infrared or visible light.

Recently Makovsky, Low and Yatziv [29, 30] have used X-rays to excite the fluorescence of rare-earth ions. Stevenson [31] has used with success this method on iron group elements. This method has the advantage that one does not have to filter the exciting light. In many cases the resultant fluorescent light is very rich and yields fluorescence from many and to many levels. Many of these fluorescent lines could not be observed with conventional techniques. An example of this is shown in Fig. 7, with Pr^{3+} in $LaCl_3$. The transitions marked with a triangle are those observed with X-ray technique and those with a circle observed with U.V. excitation. It is to be noticed that we find fluorescence even from the $^1S_0$ level to the ground state, a transition which falls in the U.V. In short we can find fluorescence from all the energy levels of the configurations. This method promises to be important in establishing the level schemes including some of the complicated Stark patterns. The method of excitation is not quite understood at present. Probably photo-electrons are being released and scattered inelastically. Probably a photo-electron will give rise to a number of secondary electrons of lower energy which may excite many of the electronic levels. The possibility of using this technique for the excitation of a visible or U.V. laser is being explored. It has of course the difficulties which have been mentioned by some of the speakers as one goes to higher frequencies in maser generation. In addition there are likely to be bands at twice the frequency, and also the absorption of the crystal host itself. Other difficulties may arise because of the increased line width of the fluorescent lines at higher frequencies and radiation damage.

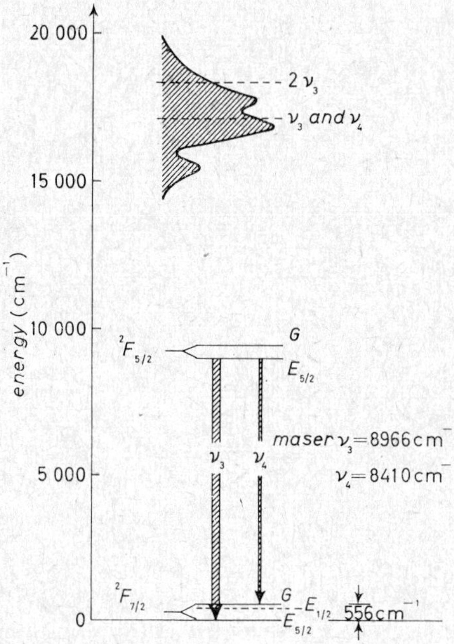

Fig. 7. – Pumping bands and sharp energy levels, as well as the maser transition Tm^{2+} in CaF_2 (according to KISS).

Another method of finding some of the Stark levels has been used by a Canadian group [32]. They have used a strong mercury discharge lamp and found side-bands at well-defined frequencies, with frequency differences corresponding to the frequencies of the various positions of the Stark levels in $PrCl_3$. In a sense this is similar to Raman scattered radiation. This experiment should be repeated with laser sources.

In general the line spectra of the iron group and rare earth elements are even more complex and are only partially understood. There are usually many more lines than can be accounted for even if all selection rules were broken.

In the iron group two types of additional line spectra can be identified:

a) Vibrational series of lines often seen superimposed on wide bands. This is clearly seen in the U-band in ruby and also well-resolved in V^{3+} in corundum. Usually the origin of these vibrational series starts at the beginning of the band, but there are also cases where the more intense lines are on the top of a band. One is tempted to consider these lines to be local modes of vibration of the Cr_2O_3 molecule. However the full details are not understood as yet.

b) Sharp lines flanking some of the electronic transitions. The intensity of these lines is usually dependent on the concentration of the iron group element. These lines have been identified to belong to pairs of ions [33]. The exchange interaction between close-lying chromium ions sets up additional series of lines.

In the rare-earth group there are to be found many additional lines. One may hope to understand these better since the $4f^n$ series is so shielded. I should mention here only a few of the main observations.

a) VARSANYI and DIEKE [34, 35] have shown that there is absorption at well-defined frequencies, in regions where one knows that the single rare-earth ion has no absorption line. These frequencies coincide with the sum of two transitions $h\nu = h\nu_1 + h\nu_2$, where ν_1, and ν_2 are the absorption frequencies from the ground state to definite energy levels. This two ion-pair absorption has been found for many levels. This is usually detected by monitoring the fluorescence ν_1, of a given level, while exciting with a variable monochromatic light source at frequency $\nu_1 + \nu_2$. DEXTER [36*a*] has discussed the mechanism giving rise to this pair absorption.

b) In Jerusalem YATSIV [36*b*] found new fluorescent and absorption lines for various gadolinium salts. YATSIV will discuss these new lines here and I shall only briefly comment on this. The frequencies of the fluorescent light are lower and fall again in regions where it is known that there are no absorption or emission lines of Gd^{3+}. These frequencies correspond to $h\nu = h\nu_1 - h\nu_{vib}$ where $h\nu_{vib}$ is the characteristic vibration energy of an isolated complex surrounding the gadolinium complex. For example in $Gd(SO_4)_3 \cdot 8H_2O$ one observes that the difference in frequency between the « parent » and strong emission and the weaker emission line corresponds to the vibrational frequency of the SO_4^{--} or H_2O molecule. In the case of Gd^{3+} this frequency falls in the U.V., but other ions have shown similar phenomena. Essentially the photon is split into a new photon of lower frequency and a phonon is given to the radiation field. This is similar to a 3-level maser in which the second level decays rapidly to the ground state. This may prove to be a suitable mechanism for the U.V. laser although many difficulties will have to be overcome. It is also a useful tool for « Raman spectroscopy ». The mechanism is probably similar to that elucidated by DEXTER. It should be noticed however that MARSHALL and STUART [37] have shown that the orbital wave function of the water molecule overlaps that of the $4f$ orbital.

c) As in the iron group so the rare-earth group shows many discrete vibrational lines spreading over several hundreds of cm^{-1} and making the identification of some of these lines difficult. This is true in particular in CaF_2 and $CaWO_4$. In CaF_2 a series of lines separated by 250 cm^{-1} has been identified in the fluorescence spectrum of Ce^{3+} [38]. In addition there are many other lines, some very sharp and separated only a fraction of a cm^{-1} to a few cm^{-1} and are so-called « satellite lines ». These may arise from many other point symmetries, from defects near rare-earth ions, from clustering of the rare-earth ions, etc. It is likely that these lines will shed light on the nature of some of the crystalline imperfections.

6. – Line width and lifetime.

6·1. *Introduction.* – The transitions in the iron and rare-earth groups are relatively weak. This arises because they are transitions in the main within the d^n or f^n configuration and electric dipole transitions are forbidden. In the case when transitions are between configurations of opposite parity these are indeed quite strong.

VAN VLECK [39] was the first to point out that the interaction with the surroundings affects the transition probability. Some measurements and solutions were made by Hoogenschagen and Gorter [40] indicating that many of the transition are of the electric dipole type. This can be explained if the configuration is admixed with the $4f^{n-1}5d$ configuration or other configurations of opposite parity.

We shall give some qualitative results and also some partial explanations of these results. Unfortunately the solutions to the problems of intensities and line width are still not complete.

6·2. *Experimental evidence.* – There is no systematic study of line width, and line shape. A number of generalizations may be made from the scattered information available. Like all generalizations they should be treated with great caution. There are many exceptions to these rules.

6·2.1. Iron group.

1) For most ions in octahedral complexes the spectrum consists of several wide bands and only a few narrow lines.

2) The width of these bands may be several thousand cm^{-1}. The width seems to be a function of the interaction of the valence electrons with their surroundings. In ionic crystals there is a correlation between the strength of the crystal field and the band width. For example Co^{2+} in MgO shows wide bands, however in CaF_2 which has a smaller crystal field the bands are narrower and permit the measurement of the spin split levels. The width of the band is not strongly temperature-dependent.

3) Only very few lines fluoresce.

4) The narrow absorption of emission lines occurs between levels whose energy separation is only effected to a small degree by the crystal field.

5) The narrow lines belong usually to spin-forbidden transitions ($\Delta S \neq 0$) and to transitions within the same cubic configuration, *i.e.*, $e^n t^m \rightarrow e^n t^m$.

6) The f number of the bands is usually of the order of $10^{-4} \div 10^{-3}$, that of the lines 10^{-6} (example Cr^{3+} in Al_2O_3). Spin-forbidden transitions are less intense by about a factor of a hundred. In crystals of cubic symmetry the f number of the lines is about 10^{-8} (see Cr^{3+} in MgO, magnetic dipole transition).

7) Decay time of fluorescence is usually short. (In the case of Cr^{3+} it is, however, several ms.)

6.2.2. Rare-earth group.

1) The majority of the lines are fairly sharp, some of these have width as little as 0.01 cm^{-1}. Bands are sometimes found in trivalent ions in the U.V. (Ce^{3+}, Yb^{3+}), and in divalent ions in the visible region.

2) The line width in different crystal hosts differs. Usually in those in which the Stark splitting is smallest the lines are sharp and fluoresce strongly.

3) In a group of Stark levels of a given electronic level the lowest-lying level is the sharpest level. The higher Stark levels are more diffuse.

4) In vibrational series the higher vibrational lines have larger line width.

5) The f number of many of the narrow lines in C_{3v} and C_{3h} systems is of the order of $10^{-6} \div 10^{-8}$ for trivalent ions [41]. The f number is of the order of 10^{-8} for divalent ions. For some of the bands in divalent ions in CaF_2 the f number is $10^{-2} \div 10^{-4}$ [26].

6) The decay lines of the fluorescence are from a fraction of a μs to ms [42].

Table V gives some characteristic decay times for Pr^{3+} in $LaCl_3 \cdot Sm^{2+}$ in CaF_2 for example has a decay time of $2 \cdot 10^{-6}$ s but is very long in SrF_2 ($2 \cdot 10^{-2}$ s).

TABLE V. – *Decay time of some of the fluorescent transitions measured with an X-ray pulse.*

Host crystal	Transition	Wavelength in Å	Temperature in °K	Decay time in μs
$LaCl_3$	${}^3P_0 \to {}^3H_4$	4 890	370	16 ± 2
	${}^3P_1 \to {}^3H_5$	5 290	300	4.5 ± 0.5 and 15 ± 2
	${}^3P_1 \to {}^3H_5$	5 290	77	3.5 ± 0.2
	${}^1D_2 \to {}^3F_4$	10 050	300	60 ± 5
CaF_2	${}^1S_0 \to {}^3P$	4 070	300	0.7 ± 0.1

6'3. *Some definitions.* – The oscillator strength of an absorption line is defined as

(22) $$f = \frac{mc}{\pi e^2 N}\int k_\nu \, d\nu$$

and k_ν is defined through an intensity measurement

(23) $$I = I_0 \exp[-k_\nu x]$$

where x is the width of the absorption path. The f number is also related to the lifetime τ

(24) $$f \sim \frac{mc}{\pi e^2}\left(\frac{\lambda_0^2}{8\pi}\right)\frac{g_2}{g_1}\frac{1}{\tau} = \frac{G}{\tau},$$

g_2, g_1 are the statistical weights of the excited and ground states.

For emission the f number is given by

(25) $$f = \frac{8\pi^2 m\nu}{n}|\langle i|M|j\rangle^2|,$$

where $|\langle i|M|j\rangle|^2$ is the square of the matrix element. It is usually difficult to evaluate these matrix elements. One needs to know the wave-function admixture. This can be inferred to some extent from the position of the energy levels. However the energy levels are not too sensitive to small changes in the wave-functions. However intensity calculations, being by one order lower in the perturbation, are more sensitive to the exact composition of the wave-functions. It is because of this that calculations have not been too successful.

6'4. *Possible explanations.* – The factors which contribute to the line width and lifetime can be divided into dynamic and static effects.

A) Equation (25) indicates that the f number depends on the matrix element. One conventionally classifies electric-dipole, magnetic-dipole and electric-quadrupole transitions. Experimentally it has been shown that by far the majority of the transitions are of electric-dipole character. The magnetic-dipole transitions are expected to have an f number of the order of 10^{-8}. In some cases when the ion is in a center of symmetry and in a cubic crystal, magnetic-dipole transitions have been observed. Examples of these are Cr^{3+} in MgO ($f \sim 10^{-8}$) and Sm^{2+} in SrF_2 or Tm^{2+} in CaF_2 ($f \sim 10^{-8}$).

Electric-dipole transitions may become permitted if opposite configurations are admixed. Crystal field potentials with odd indices can admix such configurations. This precludes ions which are located at a center of symmetry. Another mechanism are certain odd vibrations coupled to the electronic energy. Finally the electron transfer states may be admixed to the ground-state configuration. Presumably the last mechanism is of importance in the iron group elements.

Let us consider this a little more in detail. The multipole transition M_q^n can be expanded in spherical harmonics:

$$M_q^k \propto \sum_j r_j^k Y_q^k(\theta, \varphi) . \tag{27}$$

For example the electric dipole transition is $M^{(1)} = ex$; q denotes here the polarization.

We have, to calculate now the matrix element. In the case of electric-dipole transitions, transitions within the configuration are strictly forbidden. This can be seen as follows. Let us denote the ground-state wave function and the wave function of any excited states as

$$\left\{ \begin{aligned} \langle A | &= \sum_M \langle f^n \tau J M | a_M , \\ | A' \rangle &= \sum_{M'} a'_{M'} | f^n \tau' J' M' \rangle , \end{aligned} \right. \tag{28}$$

where JM and τ are quantum numbers designating the given state. Let us assume that the a_M and $a'_{M'}$ are not time-dependent. Now we interchange

$$x \to -x, \qquad M_q^1 \to -M_q^1.$$

Hence

$$\langle A | M'_q | A' \rangle = 0 . \tag{29}$$

We therefore need a mechanism which will admix a wave function of an opposite parity to A' or A. There may be several such mechanisms.

6.4.1. Odd crystal field potential. Consider the crystal field potential to be composed of

$$V_c = V_{\text{odd}} + V_{\text{even}} . \tag{30}$$

This will be so in cases where the ion is not in a position of center of symmetry.

We can now write the new wave functions as

$$\begin{cases} \langle B| \equiv \sum_M \langle f^n \tau J M | a_M + \sum_S \langle f^{n-1}(n'l')\,\tau'' J'' M''| b(n'l'\tau' J' M') , \\ |B'\rangle \equiv \sum_{M'} a'_M |f^n \tau' J' M'\rangle + \sum_S b'(n'l'\,\tau'' J'' M'')\,|f^{n-1}(n'l')\,\tau'' J'' M''\rangle , \end{cases} \tag{30}$$

where n' and l' are the principal and radial quantum numbers of the outer electron in the new configuration.

b measures the amount of admixture and is given by

$$b(n'\,l'\,\tau''\,J''\,M'') = \sum_M \frac{a\langle f^n\,\tau\,J\,M\,|\,V_{\text{odd}}\,|\,f^{n-1}(n'\,l')\tau''\,J''\,M''\rangle}{E(\tau J) - E(n'\,l'\,\tau''\,J'')} \tag{31}$$

and a similar expression for b'.

Note that S stands for the sum over all the quantum numbers $\tau'' J'' M'' l'$ for each n' of an excited configuration.

Obviously now

$$\langle B\,|\,M'_q\,|B'\rangle \neq 0 ,$$

i.e.,

$$\langle B\,|\,M'_q\,|B'\rangle = \sum a_M\,a_{M'}\,\langle f^n\,|\,M'_q\,|\,f^{n-1}(n'\,l')\rangle \cdot \frac{\langle f^{n-1}(n'\,l')\,|\,V_{\text{odd}}\,|\,f^n\rangle}{E(\tau'\,J') - E(n'\,l'\,\tau''\,J'')} + \\ + \frac{\langle f^n\,|\,V_{\text{odd}}\,|\,f^{n-1}(n'\,l')\rangle\,\langle f^{n-1}(n'\,l')\,|\,M'_q\,|\,f^n\rangle}{E(\tau J) - E(n'\,l'\,\tau''\,J'')} . \tag{32}$$

The sum now extends over all the odd potential terms, and over s. For brevity's sake we have left out the quantum numbers $\tau J M$ in this notation.

This sum is very difficult and laborious to evaluate. In the iron group such a calculation has been attempted by LOW and WEGER [15]. They consider the admixture of the configuration $3d^{n-1}4f$ and $3d^{n-1}4p$ to the $3d$ configuration. Even with only two configurations this sum is still formidable. It turns out that one may neglect the splitting of the various levels by the crystal field in the excited configuration and only evaluate the effect of the ionic levels of the next configurations on the various Stark-split levels of the ground configuration.

JUDD [44] has recently applied this quite successfully to the calculation of the optical absorption intensity of rare-earth ions. He assumes that we can take a center of gravity, of which the $Ef^{n-1}5d$ is the most important of the various excited configurations. In a sense he collapses all the levels of different crystal field splitting, of different M, J, τ, of the configuration into one highly degenerate level. He then calculates the matrix element. His absolute and relative intensities are in good agreement with those found in rare earth solutions ($f \sim 10^{-6}$).

6'4.2. Vibrationally induced transitions. It should be noticed that one may get nonvanishing matrix elements even if the ion is at a site of center of symmetry. Consider the normal modes of vibration of the complex. Let us denote the value of the crystal field potential at equilibrium as $A_n^m \langle r^n \rangle$. Then for small vibrations [44]

$$V = \sum_{m,n} \left[A_n^m + \sum_i \frac{\partial A_n^m}{\partial Q_i} Q_i \right] \langle r^n \rangle Y_n^m \,. \tag{33}$$

Let the totality of the quantum numbers be q. The eigenfunctions to a first approximation can be taken as the product of the harmonic oscillator function and the electronic eigenfunction. Hence

$$\langle B, \eta | M'_q | B, \eta' \rangle = \sum_i \langle \eta | Q_i | \eta' \rangle \frac{\partial}{\partial Q_j} \langle B | M'_q | B' \rangle \,. \tag{34}$$

The matrix elements have a similar form as in (32). In the first case the intensity is proportional to $\sum |A^m_{\text{odd}}|^2$ and in the second case

$$\sum_\eta \frac{\partial A_n^m}{\partial Q_j} |\langle \eta | Q_i | \eta' \rangle|^2 \,.$$

In the first case we have a « pure » electronic transition and in the second a vibrationally shifted transition. In some cases both mechanisms are operative.

The oscillator strength of some of these forced electric dipole transitions in the rare-earth group are about 10^{-6} [43].

Transitions between different configurations have f numbers of the order of 10^{-2} similar to ordinary electric-dipole transitions. Examples of this are the bands found in Sm^{2+} in CaF_2.

B) The measured lifetime τ_{exp} is related to τ by

$$\eta = \tau_{\text{exp}}/\tau \tag{35}$$

where η is the quantum efficiency, *i.e.*, the number of photons emitted in the line to the number of photons absorbed.

For example Sm^{2+} in CaF_2 has $\tau_{exp} \approx 2\cdot 10^{-6}$ s and in SrF_2 about $8\cdot 10^{-4}$s for the strong emitting line near 14 000 cm^{-1}.

The quantum efficiency in the former case is 10^{-1} and in the latter case $3\cdot 10^{-2}$ yielding $\tau = 2\cdot 10^{-5}$ and $2.7\cdot 10^{-7}$, respectively. This gives a calculated f number of $4\cdot 10^{-4}$ and 10^{-7} respectively identifying the transition in CaF_2 as electric dipole and in SrF_2 as magnetic dipole.

For chromium $\eta \sim 1$ and τ_{exp} is $2\cdot 10^{-3}$ s, f is of the order of 10^{-6}.

C) Additional broadening and shortening of lifetime may occur for higher Stark levels because of rapid thermalization among these levels. Some of these levels have spin-lattice relaxation times which are very short. The relaxation will depend on the temperature, on the matrix elements connecting these levels and in particular on the energy gap between these levels. For large gaps the process of multi-phonon emission and absorption is not very effective and the relaxation therefore is slow. Similarly, Stark levels near or even coinciding with vibrational overtones from a different Stark level can cause the broadening. The line shape at temperatures where relaxation is effective is Lorentzian.

D) The static phenomena are even more difficult to estimate. We have so far assumed that the electrostatic and crystal field parameters have sharp values. This is probably not true in the crystal. It is found experimentally that the centers of gravity of various electronic levels differ by as much as several hundred cm^{-1} in the rare-earth ions, say one part in 10^3. This is connected with variations in the amount of covalent bonding, differences in polarization of the shell, and differences in the amount of configuration interaction. We may assume that within a crystal, slight misorientation, dislocation, different strains and faults, clustering of impurities will also change the amount of these shifts. A reasonable estimate is that these changes may be at most of several percent of the differences observed between different crystal hosts. This would mean a distribution of values in the Slater integral of not more than in 10^{-5} or 10^{-6}, or about $(1 \div 0.1)$ cm^{-1} in the visible range. It would imply that the higher the frequency the wider the line and this seems to be borne out by experiment.

In the iron group these effects are by far more pronounced. One may expect these shifts in the F_k value to be of the order of 10^{-4} or higher.

Similar considerations prevail for the crystal field parameters $A_n^m\langle r^n\rangle$. In the rare-earth ion this splitting is of the order of a few hundred cm^{-1}. A small change say in the lattice parameters changes both the magnitude and the symmetry. In high symmetries this may give rise to additional splittings.

A simple point-charge model will give changes up to 1% in the crystal field parameters for changes of 10^{-3} Å. Again a line width of 0.1 cm^{-1} can then be expected. Well-annealed crystals show indeed a smaller line width.

In the iron group these changes are much stronger since the crystal field is much larger. Here a significant parameter is the derivative $d(h\nu)/d(A_n^m\langle r^n\rangle)$ which in some cases may be quite large. In the case of the *R*-lines in ruby these are negligible.

E) Random magnetic fields by surrounding magnetic moments of nuclei or other paramagnetic ions may give rise to line widths of $(10^{-3} \div 10^{-4})$ cm^{-1} in the iron group and about $(10^{-4} \div 10^{-5})$ cm^{-1} in dilute rare-earth crystals.

F) The nature of the wide bands, however, despite of all what has been enumerated is only partially understood at present.

REFERENCES

[1] E. U. Condon and G. H. Shortley: *Introduction to Atomic Spectra* (Cambridge, 1953).
[2] C. E. Moore: *Atomic Energy Levels* (U. S. Dept. of Commerce, N.B.S.).
[3] G. S. Racah: *Phys. Rev.*, **76**, 1352 (1949).
[4] U. Fano and G. S. Racah: *Irreducible Tensorial Sets* (New York, 1959).
[5] R. E. Trees: *Phys. Rev.*, **83**, 756 (1961).
[6] G. Racah: *Phys. Rev.*, **85**, 381 (1952).
[7] R. E. Trees and C. K. Jorgensen: *Phys. Rev.*, **123**, 1278 (1961).
[8] G. H. Dieke and H. M. Crosswhite (*Applied Optics*, **2**, 675 (1963)) have a list of references of the theoretical and experimental status of the spectra of these ions.
[9] G. B. R. Judd and I. Lindgren: *Phys. Rev.*, **122**, 1802 (1961).
[10] B. G. Wybourne: *Journ. Chem. Phys.*, **36**, 2295 (1962).
[11] J. S. Griffith: *The Theory of Transition Metal Ions* (Cambridge, 1961).
[12*a*] W. Low: *Paramagnetic Resonance in Solids*, Suppl. II (New York, 1960).
[12*b*] D. S. McClure: *Solid State Physics*, vol. **9** (New York, 1961).
[13] W. Low and R. S. Rubins: *Phys. Rev.*, **131**, 2527 (1963).
[14] M. T. Hutchins: Techn. Note 13, A. F. Contract (1963).
[15] W. Low and M. Weger: *Phys. Rev.*, **118**, 1119 (1960).
[16] K. W. H. Stevens: *Proc. Phys. Soc.*, A **65**, 209 (1952).
[17] G. Burns: *Phys. Rev.*, **128**, 2121 (1962).
[18] M. T. Hutchins and D. K. Ray: *Proc. Phys. Soc.*, **81**, 663 (1963).
[19] B. R. Judd: *Proc. Roy. Soc.* (*London*), A **241**, 414 (1957).
[20] R. A. Satten: *Journ. Chem. Phys.*, **27**, 286 (1957).
[21] C. J. Lenander and E. Y. Wong: *Journ. Chem. Phys.*, **38**, 2750 (1963).
[22] A. J. Freeman: private communication.
[23] G. Schonfeld: *M. Sc. Thesis*, Jerusalem 1959: (d^2, d^3) cubic field. G. Rosengarten: *M. Sc. Thesis*, Jerusalem 1962: (d^4, d^5) cubic field. S. Plato: *M. Sc. Thesis*, Jerusalem 1962: (d^2, d^3) trigonal field.

[24] W. Low and G. Rosengarten: *Journ. Molec. Spect.*, **12**, 319 (1964).
[25] Y. Tanabe and S. Sugano: *Journ. Phys. Soc. Japan*, **9**, 273 (1954).
[26] Z. A. Kiss: *Divalent rare earth in* CaF_2 *as optical maser material*, be to published.
[27] W. A. Runciman and C. V. Stager: *Journ. Chem. Phys.*, **37**, 196 (1962).
[28] C. G. B. Garrett, W. Kaiser and D. L. Wood: *Phys. Rev.*, **123**, 766 (1961).
[29] J. Makovsky, W. Low and S. Yatziv: *Phys. Lett.*, **2**, 186 (1964).
[30] W. Low, J. Makovsky and S. Yatziv: *Proc. of 3rd Quantum Electronics Conference* (Paris, 1963).
[31] R. H. Stevenson: unpublished.
[32] J. T. Hougen and S. Singh: *Phys. Rev. Lett.*, **10**, 406 (1963).
[33] A. L. Schawlow, D. L. Wood and A. M. Clogston: *Phys. Rev. Lett.*, **3**, 271 (1959).
[34] F. Varsanyi and G. H. Dieke: *Phys. Rev. Lett.*, **7**, 442 (1961).
[35] G. H. Dieke and E. Dorman: *Phys. Rev. Lett.*, **17**, 11 (1963).
[36*a*] R. Dexter: *Phys. Rev.*, **126**, 1962 (1962).
[36*b*] S. Yatsiv, A. Goren and I. Adato: *Phys. Rev. Lett.*, **11**, 108 (1963).
[37] W. Marshall and R. Stuart: *Phys. Rev.*, **123**, 2048 (1961).
[38] D. Kiro: *M. Sc. Thesis* (Jerusalem, 1962).
[39] J. H. Van Vleck: *Journ. Phys. Chem.*, **41**, 67 (1937).
[40] J. Hoogschaygen and C. J. Gorter: *Physica*, **14**, 197 (1948).
[41] F. Varsanyi and G. H. Dieke (*Journ. Chem. Phys.*, **36**, 835 (1962)) have made precision measurements in the infrared for Sm^{3+}, Dy^{3+}, Ho^{3+} and Er^{3+}.
[42] G. H. Dieke and L. A. Hall: *Journ. Chem. Phys.*, **27**, 465 (1957).
[43] D. L. Wood and W. Kaiser: *Phys. Rev.*, **126**, 2079 (1962).
[44] B. R. Judd: *Phys. Rev.*, **127**, 750 (1962).

Vibronic Spectra in Gadolinium Compounds (*).

S. YATSIV

Hebrew University - Jerusalem

1. – Introduction.

The appearance of vibronic structure is quite common in the absorption spectra of transition-element ions in condensed materials [1]. The relative intensity of such transitions grows with the strength of interaction of the ion with the surrounding medium.

On the other hand, ions that are strongly coupled to the lattice do not emit strongly so that, in the past, vibronic structure was observed mostly in absorption spectra. In crystals grown from solutions, the ions of Eu, Gd and Tb have strong fluorescence and were believed to possess very weak, if any, vibronic structure.

In 1937, TOMASCHEK and MEHNERT [2] observed in gadolinium sulphate two conspicuous lines that are now known as vibronic transitions accompanying the « parent » line at 3116 Å. However, at that time and much more so in later works [3], such long-wavelength emissions in gadolinium were attributed to impurity effects (**).

In a recent study of the role of molecular groups in excitation-transfer mechanisms, we happened to detect new emission lines at the long wavelength side of the strong 3116 Å emission in a number of gadolinium compounds. In all cases the frequencies of these lines were in good fit with Stokes-shifted vibronic emission. The transitions are compiled in Table I. The wavelengths

(*) The work represented here was done in co-operation with A. GOREN and I. ADATO.

(**) *Note added in proof*. - Prof. ZAIDEL has called our attention to the publication in the *Bulletin of the Academy of Sciences U.S.S.R.*, **26**, no. 1, 74 (1962), where the right assignment for the emission vibronics was made by him and his group prior to the present work. The absorption vibronics and the theoretical interpretation were not accounted for in that work.

were determined from low resolution (16 Å/mm) spectrograms obtained by a Bausch and Lomb grating monochromator. A typical spectrogram of $GdCl_3 \cdot 6H_2O$ is reproduced in Fig. 1. A few of the transitions, denoted by a star, are determined by a higher-resolution double-grating instrument.

TABLE I. – *Emission and absorption vibronics.*

Compound	Gd^{3+} parent transition (Å)	Fluorescence		Absorption		Molecular group	Infra-red or Raman frequency (cm^{-1}) (**)
		Vibronic transition (Å)	Vibration frequency (cm^{-1})	Vibronic transition (Å)	Vibration frequency (cm^{-1})		
$GdCl_3 \cdot (6H_2O)$	3115 (*)	3283 (*) 3480 (*)	1634 (*) 3315 (*)	2820	3390	H_2O	1650 3210
$GdCl_3 \cdot (6D_2O)$	3118	3238 3377	1190 2460	2886	2580	D_2O	1220 2512
$Gd_2(SO_4)_3 \cdot (8H_2O)$	3113 (*)	3213 (*)	1000 (*)			SO_4	1105
		3281 (*) 3476 (*)	1635 (*) 3225 (*)			H_2O	1650 3210
$Gd_2(SeO_4)_3 \cdot 8H_2O$	3120	3207 3483	870 3340			SeO_4 H_2O	875 3210
$Gd(C_2H_5)SO_4 \cdot (9H_2O)$	3112	3233	1200			SO_4	1105
		3280 3478	1640 3380			H_2O	1630 3210
$GdPO_c$	3117	3233	1200			PO_4	1080

(*) Numbers obtained from high-resolution data.
(**) R. MECHE and F. KERKHOF: *Landolt-Bornstein, Zahlenwerte and Funktionen U.S.A. 2. Teil* (Berlin, 1951).

In some cases, absorption vibronics are found at the same distance to the short-wavelength side of the parent transition.

Gadolinium is particularly favourable for studying emission vibronics since its energy-level scheme does not yield emission lines longer than 3116 Å. Thus, lines observed at longer wavelength are either vibronics or impurity effects. The latter alternative was ruled out by the following observations:

a) In each of the investigated crystals there is a close fit between the decay-time of the electronic parent transition (3116 Å) and those of the accompanying vibronics. This is an indication that the lines are emitted from the same level.

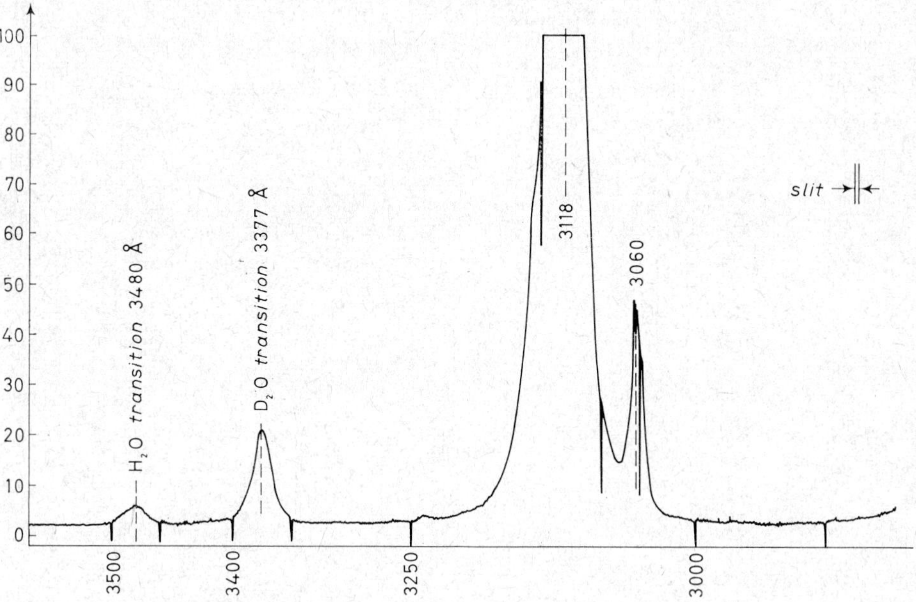

Fig. 1. – Fluorescence spectrogram of $GdCl_3 \cdot 6D_2O$ (+trace H_2O).

b) In each case, the frequency difference between the parent and a particular vibronic closely matches the vibration frequency of a molecular group in the vicinity of the emitting ion. This is illustrated in columns four and eight of the Table where the vibration frequencies can be compared with infra-red data.

c) The frequencies of the absorption vibronics appear as a mirror image of the emission vibronic frequencies with respect to the parent transitions.

d) At high resolution, the vibronic bands contain replicas of the Stark patterns in the parent group. The number of sub-components was equal and the energy spacing was very close in the two cases.

The assignment of emission vibronics in other ions such as Eu and Tb is more difficult because of the proximity of pure electronic transitions. In a recent study we were able to detect vibronic emission in terbium nitrate.

2. – Preliminary results of high resolution work.

Some of the spectra were taken in a dual grating spectrograph (linear dispersion of 4 Å/mm) with the following results:

a) The electronic 3116 Å line revealed its well-known Stark pattern which in the sulphate and chloride consisted of four narrow lines.

b) Each of the vibronic transitions consisted of one or more replicas of this Stark pattern.

c) The distance between corresponding components of two different Stark groups was proportional to the intensity of the particular vibronic transition. Thus, weak vibronics contain only one Stark group whose sub-components are broad possibly indicating unresolved structure. The stronger vibronics are well split into two or more groups of Stark replica. The energy spacing between different groups in these lines is of the order of $(20 \div 100)\ \text{cm}^{-1}$.

3. – Theoretical interpretation.

There is a distinction between vibronic transitions involving « external » or « internal » vibrations. The former involve a lattice mode, the properties of which are determined by inter-ionic forces. An « internal » vibration corresponds to an internal motion of a molecular group in the crystal. This can always be correlated to a corresponding vibration in the gaseous phase. The rare-earth ion does not belong to these molecular groups and does not participate in the motion of an « internal » vibration.

An example which illustrates well the distinction between an « internal » vibronic and the well-known molecular vibronics in the spectra of free molecules is furnished by the emission spectra of the uranil ion $(UO_2)^{++}$ in solids [4]. Here the emission spectra contain two kinds of vibronics; the first involves the vibrations modes of the UO_2^{++} ion and the second corresponds to vibrations of molecular groups such as NO_3^-, SO_4^{--} and CO_3^{--} as separate entities in the same crystal. The latter group corresponds to « internal » vibronics in the context of the present work.

The following assumptions will be made for explaining the « internal » vibronics:

a) Since the electronic transitions are between $4f^n$-$4f^n$ levels, the interionic or ion-molecule forces are independent of the state of excitation of the rare-earth ion.

b) An « internal » vibronic in absorption or emission will be considered as a two-site process, where site stands for the geometrically separate ion or molecule.

c) The interaction of the two sites with the radiation field is proportional to the square of the matrix element of the operator $M_e + M_v$ where M_e

is the electronic dipole moment of the ion and M_v is the molecular dipole moment due to its vibrational motion.

The transitions involved in emission and absorption vibronics are schematically drawn in Fig. 2 and Fig. 3, respectively.

The letters I and M stand for ion and molecule. A circle and cross denote initial and final states respectively. It is seen that an «internal» vibronic

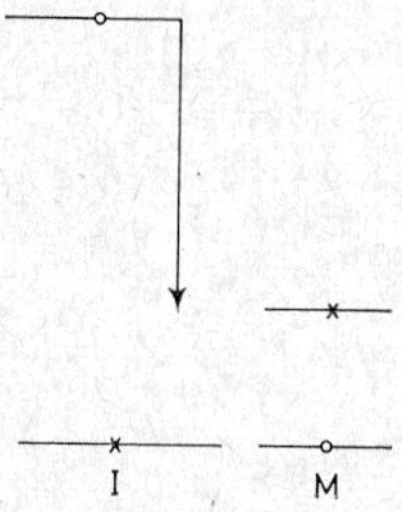

Fig. 2.

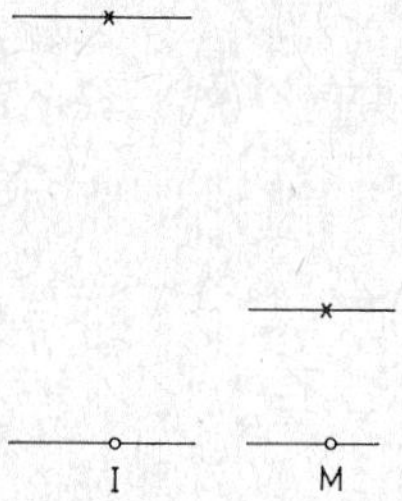

Fig. 3.

always involves a simultaneous transition in the ion and its adjoining molecule. Theoretically, the operator M_e+M_v, responsible for the transition probability, cannot achieve such a double jump unless the states of the ion and molecule are suitably modified.

A similar problem has recently come up in connection with co-operative absorption due to pairs of rare-earth ions [5].

DEXTER [6] has shown that the required state mixing is due to the interaction between the pair of ions. A similar interaction between the ion and the molecular group is responsible for the transition probability of the vibronics. The essential point in this state mixing is that the ion-molecule interaction introduces into the final state of the system a portion of the initial state so that the operator M_e+M_v connects the two modified states.

4. – Emission vibronics as laser transitions.

Considering Fig. 2 it is seen that the final state of an emission vibironc involves an excited vibration state of a molecular group. These excited states are almost unoccupied at room temperature or lower. From the point of view of laser action, the energy-level scheme described in Fig. 2 corresponds to a four-level scheme which is favourable in its low threshold.

The use of crystals for laser action is unattractive since the crystals grown from solution are usually hygroscopic, brittle and difficult to machine. Recently, we have obtained vibronic emission in a solution of $GdCl_3$. The solution freezes as glass and has encouraging optical properties. Considering a 20 cm long tube of frozen solution, the threshold-inverted population was found to be only a few percent of the overall concentration of Gd ions in the solution. Further work is now proceeding to investigate threshold requirements.

REFERENCES

[1] E. Fick und G. Joos: *Encyclopedia of Physics*, vol. **28** (Berlin, 1957), p. 260.
[2] R. Tomaschek and E. Mehnert: *Ann. d. Phys.*, **29**, 306 (1937).
[3] G. H. Dieke and L. Leopold: *Journ. Optical Soc. Am.*, **47**, 944 (1957).
[4] P. Pringsheim: *Phosphorescence and Fluorescence* (New York, 1949), p. 480.
[5] F. Varsanyi and G. H. Dieke: *Phys. Rev. Lett.*, **7**, 442 (1961).
[6] D. L. Dexter: *Phys. Rev.*, **126**, 1962 (1962).

Nonlinear Optics.

N. BLOEMBERGEN

Division of Engineering and Applied Physics, Harvard University - Cambridge, Mass

1. - Introduction.

The high intensity available in laser beams has made possible the observation of nonlinear effects at optical frequencies. FRANKEN [1] was the first to observe the second-harmonic generation of light by a ruby-laser beam in a crystal of quartz. A typical experimental arrangement is shown in Fig. 1.

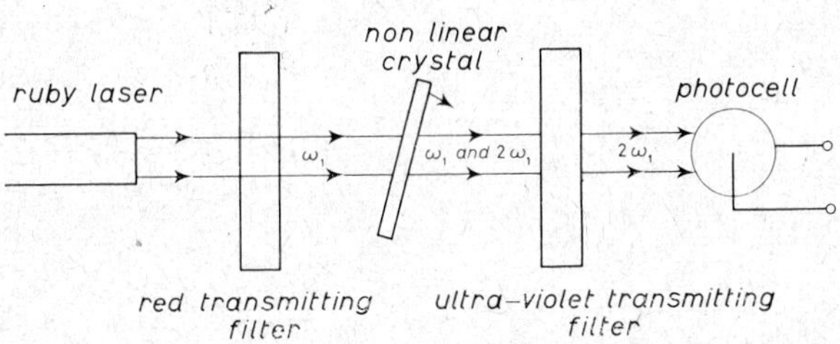

Fig. 1. - Experimental arrangement to observe the production of light harmonics

A simple classical description of the phenomenon is possible by considering the electrons in the crystal as anharmonic oscillators. If the system lacks inversion symmetry, there will be a potential term $\frac{1}{3}\alpha^1 x^3$, where x is the deviation from equilibrium. The anharmonic oscillator is driven by a periodic force

$$m\ddot{x} + m\omega_0^2 x + \alpha^1 x^2 + \Gamma\dot{x} = \mathrm{Re}\,\{eE \exp[i\boldsymbol{k}\cdot\boldsymbol{r} - i\omega t]\}\,. \tag{1.1}$$

The resonant frequency of the linear oscillator is ω_0 and a phenomenological damping term has also been introduced. It is a simple matter to calculate the dipole moment induced at the frequency 2ω, by substituting a Fourier series for x into eq. (1.1). One finds

$$\mathscr{P}(2\omega) = ex(2\omega) = \mathrm{Re}\,\frac{\frac{1}{2}(e/m)^3 \alpha^1 E^2 \exp[2i\boldsymbol{k}\cdot\boldsymbol{r} - 2i\omega t]}{(\omega_0^2 - \omega^2 + i\omega\Gamma)^2(\omega_0^2 - 4\omega^2 + 2i\omega\Gamma)}\,. \tag{1.2}$$

The polarization induced at 2ω is the source for the second-harmonic generation. In a similar manner sum and difference frequencies can be generated if the oscillator is driven by fields at two different frequencies. This has also been observed. In a similar manner higher harmonics will appear. The second harmonic vanishes in the electric dipole approximation in crystals with inversion symmetry. TERHUNE has observed third-harmonic generation in such crystals. The anharmonic potential then has the form $\frac{1}{4}\alpha'' x^4$.

It should be noted that the spatial distribution of the harmonic polarization is determined by twice the wave vector of the fundamental wave. The harmonic wave to be generated will propagate with $\boldsymbol{k}(2\omega)$. Due to natural dispersion one has in general no match of the phase velocities, $\boldsymbol{k}(2\omega) \neq 2\boldsymbol{k}(\omega)$. Therefore alternate layers of the crystal platelet in Fig. 1 will interfere destructively in the harmonic generation as the phase $[\boldsymbol{k}(2\omega) - 2\boldsymbol{k}(\omega)] \cdot \boldsymbol{r}$ alternates. As the platelet is changed in thickness or, for experimental expediency, rotated, maxima and minima in the harmonic generation occur as shown in Fig. 2. Analysis of such a curve permits a determination of the phase mismatch and the nonlinear polarizability, which is the ratio between $\mathscr{P}(2\omega)$ and $E^2(\omega)$ in eq. (1.2).

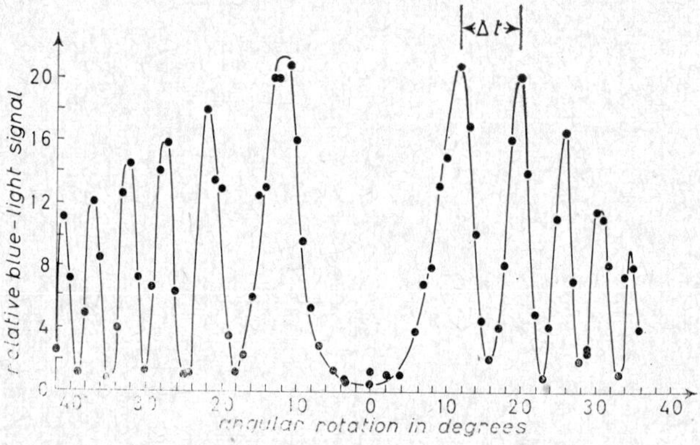

Fig. 2. – Second-harmonic generation as a function of the inclination of a 0.0308 in. thick quartz platelet with respect to the ruby-laser beam [3]. $\Delta t_{\text{theor}} = 13.9\ \mu\text{m}$, $\Delta t_{\text{exp}} = 14\ \mu\text{m}$.

Perfect phase matching is possible in noncubic crystals if one uses combinations of ordinary and extraordinary rays at the different frequencies. This was first shown by GIORDMAINE [2] and TERHUNE [3], who obtained the curves in Fig. 3. Since in this case the second-harmonic waves produced by all volume elements in the crystal are in phase, the harmonic generation can be observed from CW neon lasers operating in a single mode with a power density of less than one milliwatt/cm². The power density in unfocused beams of giant pulsed lasers lies between $(1 \div 50)$ megawatt/cm². The power density can be increased further by focusing of the beam or by maser light amplifiers. In a focused beam electric light fields of about 10^7 V/cm have beén obtained, corresponding to a power density of $0.3 \cdot 10^{12}$ W/cm². Nonlinear phenomena of a wide variety can thus be observed. Besides the parametric generation of power at new combination frequencies, the Raman laser effect discovered by WOODBURY [4] constitutes another interesting example of the nonlinear response of a medium. It should be emphasized that the nonlinear response in the radiofrequency and microwave region of the electromagnetic spectrum was well known before the optical nonlinearities were discovered.

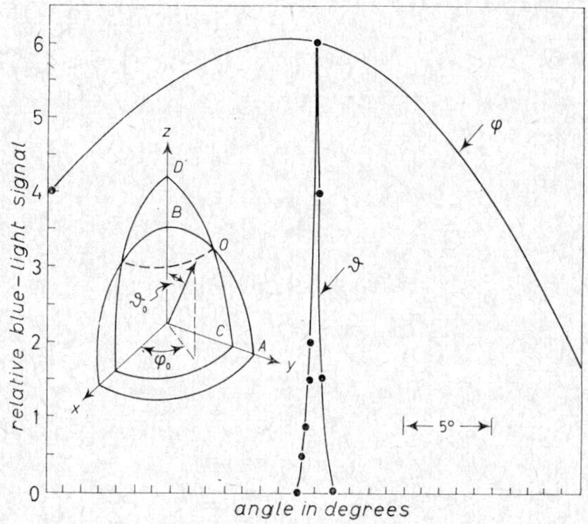

Fig. 3. – Second-harmonic generation as a function of angle between the light beam and the crystallographic axes in KDP. At $\theta = 52°$ the harmonic extraordinary ray has the same phase velocity as the fundamental ray at $\lambda = 6\,943$ Å.

A general theoretical framework will be presented in Part A of this review. The linear and nonlinear responses of a medium, with loss mechanisms incorporated, are described in terms of a hierarchy of linear and nonlinear complex susceptibilities. After the quantum-mechanical calculation of the combined saturation, maser, Raman maser and parametric effects in terms of susceptibilities has been performed, they can be incorporated in Maxwell's equations. The macroscopic phenomenological description in terms of these classical field equations is outlined in Part B, where wave propagation in nonlinear media is discussed.

A. – Quantum Theory of Nonlinear Susceptibilities.

2. – Steady-state response in the density matrix formalism.

The problem of the steady-state response of a material system subjected to periodic perturbations at several frequencies simultaneously occurs in a wide variety of situations and has been treated by many authors. It includes as special cases the combined optical pumping and radiofrequency experiments described by KASTLER and coworkers [5], double nuclear resonance treated by BLOCH [6], the Overhauser effect [7], three-level maser [8], frequency doubling by magnetic resonance [9, 10], and, more recently, optical parametric [11] and stimulated Raman effects [12]. We shall follow closely the treatment of BLOEMBERGEN and SHEN [13], where many other references to earlier work may be found.

In addition to the periodic perturbations the system is subjected to random fields. These include interactions with black-body radiation and lattice vibrations. Our knowledge about these fields is incomplete. They can be described statistically as damping. The use of the density-matrix formalism is indicated to take account of these random perturbations. The discussion here will be limited to dilute isotropic systems in the limit of rapid motion. This language, borrowed from magnetic resonance where most of the formalism was first developed [6], means that the width of the spectral density of the perturbation is large compared to the width of the resonance lines and the interaction energy between particles may be ignored. Under these conditions the influence of the random hamiltonian on the diagonal elements is described by the rate equations

$$\left(\frac{\partial}{\partial t}\right)_{\text{random}} \varrho_{aa} = \sum_n w_{an}\varrho_{nn} - \sum_n w_{na}\varrho_{aa}\,. \tag{2.1}$$

It should be emphasized that a random pump field, which is used in the optical pumping of solid-state lasers, or electron-collision pumping in gas discharges, is included in the random hamiltonian. Consequently the ratio w_{an}/w_{na} need not be equal to $\exp[\hbar\omega_{na}/kT]$, which ratio obtains if the only random perturbation is caused by the interaction with a single thermal reservoir at temperature T.

If no approximately equal spacings in the energy levels occur, each off-diagonal element of the density matrix relaxes accordingly

$$\left(\frac{\partial}{\partial t}\right)_{\text{random}} \varrho_{ab} = -\Gamma_{ab}\varrho_{ab}\,. \tag{2.2}$$

The equation of motion is then written in the form

$$i\hbar\dot{\varrho} = [\mathscr{H}_A, \varrho] + [\mathscr{H}_{\text{coh}}, \varrho] + i\hbar\left(\frac{\partial}{\partial t}\right)_{\text{random}} \varrho\,. \tag{2.3}$$

$\mathscr{H}_A$ is the unperturbed Hamiltonian of the isolated material system, $\mathscr{H}_{\text{coh}}$ represents the interaction with periodic fields. Although the following procedure would be valid for any type of periodic perturbation, the explicit form of the interaction of a single electron with applied electromagnetic fields will be used,

FIUTAK [14] has shown that the usual Hamiltonian form for this interaction in terms of momentum or current-density operators may be canonically transformed into an equivalent Hamiltonian multipole expansion

$$\mathscr{H}'_{\text{coh}} = -\boldsymbol{\mathscr{P}}\cdot\boldsymbol{E} - \boldsymbol{M}\cdot\boldsymbol{H} - \tfrac{1}{2}e\boldsymbol{rr}:\nabla\boldsymbol{E} + \dots \tag{2.4}$$

This form has definite advantages if expectation values of electric and magnetic dipoles have to be evaluated, because commutation rules of operators $\boldsymbol{p}$ and $\boldsymbol{r}$ in the usual formulation become very cumbersome. $\mathscr{H}_{\text{coh}}$ consists of a number of periodic terms corresponding to the number of applied periodic fields.

A steady-state solution for the density matrix in ascending powers of the coherent perturbations may be found from the following hierarchy of equations:

$$\begin{cases} i\hbar\dot{\varrho}^{(0)} = [\mathscr{H}_A, \varrho^{(0)}] + i\hbar\left(\dfrac{\partial}{\partial t}\right)_{\text{random}} \varrho^{(0)}, \\ i\hbar\dot{\varrho}^{(1)} = [\mathscr{H}_A, \varrho^{(1)}] + i\hbar\left(\dfrac{\partial}{\partial t}\right)_{\text{random}} \varrho^{(1)} + [\mathscr{H}'_{\text{coh}}, \varrho^{(0)}], \\ i\hbar\dot{\varrho}^{(n)} = [\mathscr{H}_A, \varrho^{(n)}] + i\hbar\left(\dfrac{\partial}{\partial t}\right)_{\text{random}} \varrho^{(n)} + [\mathscr{H}'_{\text{coh}}, \varrho^{(n-1)}]. \end{cases} \tag{2.5}$$

The first equation gives the density matrix in thermodynamic equilibrium for $\dot{\varrho}^{(0)} = 0$. The linear response of the system is determined by the second equation; $\varrho^{(1)}$ contains the same frequencies as $\mathscr{H}'_{\text{coh}}$. In second approximation the steady-state response $\varrho^{(2)}$ contains sum, difference and second-harmonic frequencies, as well as d.c. terms. The latter are a first approximation to incipient saturation effects and arise as the beat between positive and negative frequency terms in $\mathscr{H}'_{\text{coh}}$ and $\varrho^{(1)}$ respectively. Insertion of $\varrho^{(2)}$ into the equation for $\varrho^{(3)}$ gives the Fourier components in the next approximation, etc. Note that in the steady state the time differentiation on the left side is replaced by $-i\sum_j(\pm n_j\omega_j)$ where the $(+\omega_j)$ component has a time-dependence $\exp[-i\omega_j t]$ and the $(-\omega_j)$ component varies as $\exp[+i\omega_j t]$. Each successive step corresponds therefore to a very simple algebraic operation relating Fourier components in each approximation to those of the preceding one.

The lowest-order nonlinear term in a system that lacks inversion symmetry is the electric-dipole moment proportional to a quadratic function of the electric-field amplitudes. Consider explicitly the Fourier component of the dipole moment at the sum frequency $\omega = \omega_1 + \omega_2$, induced by an electric field with components at ω_1 and ω_2. The Hamiltonian for this problem is

$$\mathscr{H}'_{\text{coh}} = -\boldsymbol{\mathscr{P}}\cdot\tfrac{1}{2}(\boldsymbol{E}_1^*\exp[i\omega_1 t] + \boldsymbol{E}_1\exp[-i\omega_1 t]) - \\ -\boldsymbol{\mathscr{P}}\cdot\tfrac{1}{2}(\boldsymbol{E}_2^*\exp[i\omega_2 t] + \boldsymbol{E}_2\exp[-i\omega_2 t]).$$

It will be assumed that the electric-dipole moment operator has only off-diagonal elements. (A case where diagonal elements are important will be discussed in the next Section.) A typical off-diagonal element of the density matrix obeys the equation

$$i\hbar\dot{\varrho}_{nn'} = (+\,\omega_{nn'} - i\Gamma_{nn'})\varrho_{nn'} + \sum_{n''}(\mathscr{H}_{nn''}\varrho_{n''n'} - \varrho_{nn''}\mathscr{H}_{n''n'})\,. \tag{2.6}$$

The first or linear approximation to these off-diagonal elements is

$$\{\varrho^{(1)}_{n''n'}\}^{(\omega_1)} = \frac{\frac{1}{2}\boldsymbol{\mathscr{P}}_{n''n'}\boldsymbol{E}_1}{\omega_1 - \omega_{n''n'} + i\Gamma_{n''n}}(+\,\varrho^{(0)}_{n''n''} - \varrho^{(0)}_{n'n'}) \tag{2.7}$$

and similar expressions for frequency components at $-\omega_1$ and $\pm\omega_2$.

In second approximation one finds

$$\{\varrho^{(2)}_{nn,}\}^{(\omega_1+\omega_2)} = \sum_{n''\neq n,n'} \frac{\frac{1}{4}\hbar^{-2}(\boldsymbol{\mathscr{P}}_{nn''}\cdot\boldsymbol{E}_2)(\boldsymbol{\mathscr{P}}_{n''n,}\cdot\boldsymbol{E}_1)}{\omega_1+\omega_2-\omega_{nn'}+i\Gamma_{nn'}}\cdot \tag{2.8}$$
$$\cdot\left[\frac{\varrho^{(0)}_{n'n} - \varrho^{(0)}_{n''n''}}{\omega_1 - \omega_{n''n'} + i\Gamma_{n''n'}} + \frac{\varrho^{(0)}_{nn} - \varrho_{n''n''}}{\omega_2 - \omega_{nn''} + i\Gamma_{nn''}}\right] +$$
$$+\sum_{n''\neq n,n'} \frac{\frac{1}{4}\hbar^{-2}(\boldsymbol{\mathscr{P}}_{nn''}\cdot\boldsymbol{E}_1)(\boldsymbol{\mathscr{P}}_{n''n'}\cdot\boldsymbol{E}_2)}{\omega_1+\omega_2-\omega_{nn'}+i\Gamma_{nn'}}\left[\frac{\varrho^{(0)}_{n'n'} - \varrho^{(0)}_{n''u''}}{\omega_2 - \omega_{n''n'} + i\Gamma_{n''n'}} + \frac{\varrho^{(0)}_{nn} - \varrho^{(0)}_{n''n''}}{\omega_1 - \omega_{nn''} + i\Gamma^{nn''}}\right].$$

The expectation value of the dipole moment at ω_3 proportional to the product of the field amplitudes at ω_1 and ω_2 may be calculated. A third-rank nonlinear polarizability tensor may be defined. Its component β_{ijk} is given by the following relationship

$$\langle\mathscr{P}^{(2)}_i(\omega_3 = \omega_1+\omega_2)\rangle = \tfrac{1}{4}\beta_{ijk}\{E_j(\omega_1)E_k(\omega_2) + E_k(\omega_2)E_j(\omega_1)\} = \tag{2.9}$$
$$= \sum_n\sum_{n'}(\mathscr{P}_i)_{nn'}\{\varrho^{(2)}_{n'n}\}^{(\omega_1+\omega_2)}\,.$$

The factor $\frac{1}{4}$ is inserted so that for real β and real fields $E_1\cos\omega_1 t$ and $E_2\cos\omega_2 t$, the real polarization is given by $\mathscr{P}_i\cos\omega_3 t$. The expression is symmetrical in the components $E_j(\omega_1)$ and $E_k(\omega_2)$. This follows immediately from the detailed form of eq. (2.8). The permutation symmetry relations, introduced by Armstrong *et al.* [11], remain valid in the presence of damping.

If the damping is negligible, the terms $i\Gamma_{nn'}$ in the denominators of eq. (2.8) can be omitted. This situation is important in the harmonic generation of light, when all optical resonances are far removed. When the denominators are real and contain only frequency differences, the terms in eq. (2.8) can be re-arranged and relabeled. The ijk component of the third-rank polarizability tensor can be written in the absence of damping as

$$(2.10)\qquad \beta_{ijk} = \sum_{g}\sum_{n,n'\neq g}\{(\mathscr{P}_i)_{gn}(\mathscr{P}_j)_{n'g}(\mathscr{P}_k)_{nn'}A_{nn'} + (\mathscr{P}_i)_{gn}(\mathscr{P}_j)_{nn'}(\mathscr{P}_k)_{n'g}A'_{nn'} +$$
$$+ (\mathscr{P}_i)_{n'g}(\mathscr{P}_j)_{nn'}(\mathscr{P}_k)_{gn}B_{nn'} + (\mathscr{P}_i)_{n'g}(\mathscr{P}_j)_{gn}(\mathscr{P}_k)_{nn'}B'_{nn'} +$$
$$+ (\mathscr{P}_i)_{n'n}(\mathscr{P}_j)_{gn'}(\mathscr{P}_k)_{ng}C_{nn'} + (\mathscr{P}_i)_{n'n}(\mathscr{P}_j)_{ng}(\mathscr{P}_k)_{gn'}C'_{nn'}\}\,\varrho^{(0)}_{gg}$$

with

$$A_{nn'} = (2\hbar^2)^{-1}[(\omega_3 - \omega_{ng})^{-1}(\omega_1 - \omega_{n'g})^{-1}]\,,$$
$$A'_{nn'} = (2\hbar^2)^{-1}[(\omega_3 - \omega_{ng})^{-1}(\omega_2 - \omega_{n'g})^{-1}]\,,$$
$$B_{nn'} = (2\hbar^2)^{-1}[(\omega_3 + \omega_{n'g})^{-1}(\omega_2 + \omega_{ng})^{-1}]\,,$$
$$B'_{nn'} = (2\hbar^2)^{-1}[(\omega_3 + \omega_{n'g})^{-1}(\omega_1 + \omega_{ng})^{-1}]\,,$$
$$C_{nn'} = -(2\hbar^2)^{-1}[(\omega_1 + \omega_{n'g})^{-1}(\omega_2 - \omega_{ng})^{-1}]\,,$$
$$C'_{nn'} = -(2\hbar^2)^{-1}[(\omega_2 + \omega_{n'g})^{-1}(\omega_1 - \omega_{ng})^{-1}]\,.$$

When the additional assumption is made that the matrix elements $\mathscr{P}_{nn'}$ are real, the expression eq. (2.10) is identical with eqs. (2.13) and (2.14) of Armstrong *et al.* [11].

In a similar manner, higher-order nonlinear electric and magnetic susceptibilities may be determined. Not only parametric effects, but also saturation, maser and Raman maser action are described by these nonlinear complex susceptibilities. Far away from all resonance transitions the parametric effects dominate. In this case, the hierarchy in terms of ascending powers of the field amplitudes is especially useful. In case of resonance, one often wishes to retain all powers of the fields for the Fourier components of the density matrix at resonance to take complete cognizance of saturation effects. One decides in this case, *a priori*, which Fourier components in each of the matrix elements of ϱ are to be retained and which are to be truncated off as small nonsecular terms. Sorting out the terms on the left and right with the same frequency-dependence in the equations of motion (1.4) leads to a set of simultaneous linear algebraic equations. In principle, the Fourier components of the density matrix elements and, therefore, of expectation values of the dipole moments can be determined in a straightforward algebraic manner. In practice, the number of unknowns is large even in relatively simple situations with only two or three energy levels. Computer solutions are indicated, but they tend to obscure the basic physical processes in the high-order interference of parametric, maser, Raman maser and other multiple photon processes.

The general methods outlined in this Section will be applied and illustrated for a two-level and a three-level system. In these cases, the basic nonlinear mechanisms can be unraveled. The analysis will show when parametric and when maser effects are dominant and how they interfere.

If the applied electric or magnetic fields contain a d.c. component, *i.e.*, if one of the applied frequencies is zero, this formalism contains, as special cases, the Pockels and quadratic electro-optic effect, as well as the Faraday and quadratic magnetic effects. In the case of applied d.c. fields, some care must be taken to correct the relaxation terms as well. The paramagnetic part of the Faraday effect [27] is, *e.g.*, due to the change in population of states by the application of the d.c. magnetic field. The relaxation is towards thermal equilibrium for the instantaneous values of the applied fields as mentioned earlier.

3. – Parametric and Raman effects in a two-level system.

Consider as a simple example the case of a two-level system, for which we may adopt without loss of generality the language and notations of magnetic resonance. The Raman effect for such a system has already been discussed by BLOCH [6], WINTER [15] and JAVAN [16]. The parametric response has been treated in classical manner by AYRES, VARTANIAN and MELCHOR [10].

In our example it will be assumed that there is a rotating transverse field applied at frequency ω_1 and a longitudinal field at frequency ω_3. The Hamiltonian of the coherent perturbation has the form

$$\text{(3.1)}\qquad \begin{cases} \mathscr{H}_{ba} = -\mu_{ba} H_1 \exp[-i\omega_1 t] = \mathscr{H}^*_{ab}\,, \\ \mathscr{H}_{aa} = -\mathscr{H}_{bb} = -\tfrac{1}{2}\mu_0 (H_3 \exp[-i\omega_3 t] + H_3^* \exp[+i\omega_3 t])\,. \end{cases}$$

The equations of motion for the density matrix are in this case

$$\text{(3.2)}\qquad \begin{cases} i\hbar\dot{\varrho}_{ba} = -\mu_{ba} H_1 \exp[-i\omega_1 t](\varrho_{aa} - \varrho_{bb}) - \hbar(\omega_{ab} + i/T_2)\varrho_{ba} - \\ \qquad\qquad - \mu_0 (H_3 \exp[-i\omega_3 t] + H_3^* \exp[+i\omega_3 t])\varrho_{ba}\,, \\ \dot{\varrho}_{bb} - \dot{\varrho}_{aa} = -2i\hbar^{-1}(\mu_{ba} H_1 \exp[-i\omega_1 t]\varrho_{ab} - \mu_{ab} H_1^* \exp[+i\omega_1 t]\varrho_{ba}) - \\ \qquad\qquad - (\varrho_{bb} - \varrho_{aa} - \varrho_{bb}^{(0)} + \varrho_{aa}^{(0)})/T_1\,. \end{cases}$$

The lowest-order nonlinear response consists of a familiar saturation correction $\{\varrho_{bb}^{(2)} - \varrho_{aa}^{(2)}\}^{dc}$ proportional to $|H_1|^2$ and a parametric beat for the transverse components of magnetization at the frequencies $\omega_1 \pm \omega_3$. The off-diagonal elements of the density matrix have Fourier components such as

$$\text{(3.3)}\qquad \{\varrho_{ba}^{(2)}\}^{\omega_1-\omega_3} = \frac{-\hbar^{-2}\mu_0\mu_{ba} H_1 H_3^* (\overset{0}{\varrho}_{aa} - \overset{0}{\varrho}_{bb})}{(\omega_1 - \omega_{ba} + i/T_2)(\omega_1 - \omega_3 - \omega_{ba} + i/T_2)}\,.$$

In the next higher nonlinear approximation the components at the original frequencies ω_1 and $\pm\omega_3$ receive corrections proportional to the intensity of the applied fields,

$$(3.4)\qquad \{\varrho_{ba}^{(3)}\} = -\frac{\hbar^{-3}\mu_0^2\mu_{ba}H_1|H_3|^2(\overset{0}{\varrho}_{aa}-\overset{0}{\varrho}_{bb})}{(\omega_1-\omega_{ba}+i/T_2)^2}\cdot\left[\frac{1}{\omega_1-\omega_3-\omega_{ba}+i/T_2}+\right.$$

$$\left.+\frac{1}{\omega_1+\omega_3-\omega_{ba}+i/T_2}\right]+\text{terms proportional } H_1|H_1|^2\,,$$

$$(3.5)\qquad \{\varrho_{bb}^{(3)}-\varrho_{aa}^{(3)}\}^{(\omega_3)} = -\frac{2\hbar^{-3}|\mu_{ab}|^2\mu_0H_3|H_1|^2(\overset{0}{\varrho}_{bb}-\overset{0}{\varrho}_{aa})}{(\omega_3+i/T_1)(\omega_1-\omega_{ba}-i/T_2)(\omega_1-\omega_3-\omega_{ba}-i/T_2)}+$$

$$+\frac{2\hbar^{-3}|\mu_{ab}|^2\mu_0H_3|H_1|^2(\overset{0}{\varrho}_{bb}-\overset{0}{\varrho}_{aa})}{(\omega_3+i/T_1)(\omega_1-\omega_{ba}+i/T_2)(\omega_1+\omega_3-\omega_{ba}+i/T_2)}\,.$$

Consider the case $\omega_1-\omega_3=\omega_{ba}$. A two-quantum Raman transition is possible as indicated in Fig. 4 *a*). Exclude single-quantum transitions,

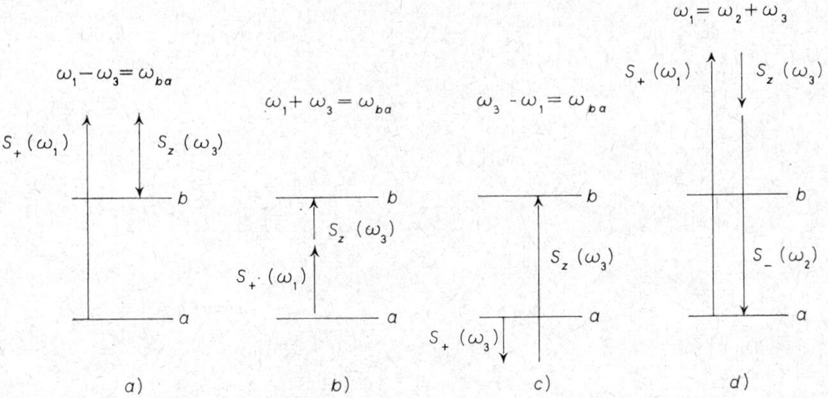

Fig. 4. – Nonlinear processes in a two-level system: *a*) Raman process, in which a « transverse » quantum is emitted and a « longitudinal » quantum absorbed; *b*) two quanta absorption; *c*) Raman process, in which a « transverse » quantum is absorbed and a « longitudinal » quantum emitted; *d*) illustration of a parametric process. It should not be interpreted literally as a three-photon scattering process, as explained in the text.

$|-\omega_1+\omega_{ba}|\gg T_2^{-1}$. This implies $\omega_3\gg T_2^{-1}\geqslant T_1^{-1}$. Under these circumstances the first term on the right-hand side of eqs. (3.4) and (3.5) are dominant and the nonlinear susceptibilities become pure imaginary:

$$(3.6)\qquad \{\varrho_{ba}^{(3)}\}^{(\omega_1)}/H_1 = +2iT_2\hbar^{-3}\omega_3^{-2}\mu_0^2\mu_{ba}|H_3|^2(\varrho_{aa}^{(0)}-\varrho_{bb}^{(0)})\,,$$

$$(3.7)\qquad \{\varrho_{aa}^{(3)}-\varrho_{bb}^{(3)}\}^{(\omega_3)}/H_3 = -2iT_2\hbar^{-3}\omega_3^{-2}\mu_0|\mu_{ba}|^2|H_1|^2(\varrho_{aa}^{(0)}-\varrho_{bb}^{(0)})\,.$$

For normal populations $\varrho_{aa}^{(0)}-\varrho_{bb}^{(0)}>0$, the sign of the susceptibility is such, that there is positive absorption at ω_1 proportional to the intensity $|H_3|^2$, but there is negative absorption at ω_3, proportional to the intensity $|H_1|^2$. This is just what could be expected for the Raman effect. In a similar manner the two-photon absorption of Fig. 4 *b*), and the Raman process with negative absorption at ω_3 of Fig. 4 *c*), are described by the same eqs. (3.4) and (3.5).

The parametric process described by eq. (3.3) is illustrated in Fig. 4 *d*). The atomic system is purely reactive and makes no real transition to a state with different energy. The visualisation of the parametric process as a three-photon scattering process should, however, not be taken literally. In such a scattering process with a well-defined number of photons phase information is not involved. The phase of the induced polarization of the combination frequencies $\omega_1 \pm \omega_3$ is, however, determined by the phases of the applied fields at ω_1 and ω_3. The number of quanta is not precisely known and the fields should be described quantum-mechanically by « coherent states » of the field oscillator.

4. – Nonlinear susceptibility of a three-level system.

The steady-state response of a system with a lower energy state $|a\rangle$, a middle state $|b\rangle$, and an upper state $|c\rangle$ to three applied fields at the frequencies ω_1, ω_2, and $\omega_3=\omega_1+\omega_2$ can be calculated with the general Fourier power series expansion method. If the three applied frequencies are close to the resonant frequencies, *i.e.*, $|\omega_1-\omega_{ba}|\ll\omega_{ba}$, $|\omega_2-\omega_{cb}|\ll\omega_{cb}$, and, consequently, $|\omega_3-\omega_{ca}|\ll\omega_{ca}$, the Fourier series can be truncated in an unambiguous fashion. Only the following matrix elements of the periodic perturbations are retained, so that the truncated Hamiltonian becomes:

$$\mathscr{H}_{\text{coh}} = \begin{Bmatrix} 0 & V_{ab}\exp[i\omega_1 t] & V_{ac}\exp[i\omega_3 t] \\ V_{ba}\exp[-i\omega_1 t] & 0 & V_{bc}\exp[i\omega_2 t] \\ V_{ca}\exp[-i\omega_3 t] & V_{cb}\exp[-i\omega_2 t] & 0 \end{Bmatrix}. \tag{4.1}$$

For electric dipole transitions, one has, for example, $V_{ab}=-\hbar^{-1}\mathscr{P}_{ab}\cdot\mathbf{E}_1$, etc. Note that this truncated Hamiltonian can be made time-independent by a diagonal unitary transformation $\mathscr{H}'=U^\dagger\mathscr{H}U$,

$$U = \begin{Bmatrix} \exp[i\omega_1 t] & 0 & 0 \\ 0 & 1 & 0 \\ 0 & 0 & \exp[-i\omega_2 t] \end{Bmatrix}. \tag{4.2}$$

WILCOX and LAMB [22] have solved the three-level problem with two applied fields in the transformed representation. The steady-state solution is, however, more directly obtained in the laboratory frame. The fact that the problem can be reduced to a time-independent problem in which each matrix element in the steady state is time-independent, suggests that only one Fourier component for each element of the density matrix will occur in the laboratory frame. This is, indeed, the case. Only d.c. components of the diagonal elements of the density matrix are retained, together with the following six off-diagonal Fourier components: $\varrho_{ba}^{(\omega_1)}$ and $\varrho_{ab}^{(-\omega_1)}$, $\varrho_{ca}^{(\omega_3)}$ and $\varrho_{ac}^{(-\omega_3)}$, $\varrho_{cb}^{(\omega_2)}$ and $\varrho_{bc}^{(-\omega_2)}$. The equations of motion reduce to nine algebraic linear equations with nine unknowns. One of these equations is the inhomogeneous normalization condition $\varrho_{aa}^{dc} + \varrho_{bb}^{dc} + \varrho_{cc}^{dc} = 1$. With the abbreviations

$$(4.3)\qquad \begin{cases} \Delta_{ba} = \omega_1 - \omega_{ba} + i\Gamma_{ba} = -\Delta_{ab}^{*} \\ \Delta_{cb} = \omega_2 - \omega_{cb} + i\Gamma_{cb} = -\Delta_{bc}^{*} \\ \Delta_{ca} = \omega_3 - \omega_{ca} + i\Gamma_{ca} = -\Delta_{ac}^{*} \end{cases}$$

the equations of motion are expressed in matrix form

$$(4.4)\qquad \begin{pmatrix} 1 & 1 & 1 & 0 & 0 & 0 & 0 & 0 & 0 \\ w_{ba} & w_{ab}-w_{cb} & w_{bc} & V_{ba} & -V_{ab} & -V_{cb} & V_{bc} & 0 & 0 \\ w_{ca} & w_{cb} & -w_{ac}-w_{bc} & 0 & 0 & V_{cb} & -V_{bc} & V_{ca} & -V_{ac} \\ -V_{ab} & V_{ab} & 0 & \Delta_{ab} & 0 & 0 & V_{ac} & -V_{cb} & 0 \\ V_{ba} & -V_{ba} & 0 & 0 & \Delta_{ba} & -V_{ca} & 0 & 0 & V_{bc} \\ 0 & -V_{bc} & V_{bc} & 0 & -V_{ac} & \Delta_{bc} & 0 & V_{ba} & 0 \\ 0 & V_{cb} & -V_{cb} & V_{ca} & 0 & 0 & \Delta_{cb} & 0 & -V_{ab} \\ -V_{ac} & 0 & V_{ac} & -V_{bc} & 0 & V_{ab} & 0 & \Delta_{ac} & 0 \\ V_{ca} & 0 & -V_{ca} & 0 & V_{cb} & 0 & -V_{ba} & 0 & \Delta_{ca} \end{pmatrix} \begin{pmatrix} \varrho_{aa}^{dc} \\ \varrho_{bb}^{dc} \\ \varrho_{cc}^{dc} \\ \varrho_{ab}^{(-\omega_1)} \\ \varrho_{ba}^{(\omega_1)} \\ \varrho_{bc}^{(-\omega_2)} \\ \varrho_{cb}^{(\omega_2)} \\ \varrho_{ac}^{(-\omega_3)} \\ \varrho_{ca}^{(\omega_3)} \end{pmatrix} = \begin{pmatrix} 1 \\ 0 \\ 0 \\ 0 \\ 0 \\ 0 \\ 0 \\ 0 \\ 0 \end{pmatrix}.$$

The solution for the density-matrix elements from this array of linear equations gives them as functions of all powers of the amplitudes of the three applied fields. The solution contains, therefore, all possible interference effects between single and multiple quantum absorption and emission processes and parametric scattering processes, as well as all saturation effects of successive absorption and re-emission of quanta.

There are schemes to unravel the complexity of the 9×10 matrix problem. It is helpful to eliminate first ϱ_{ab}, ϱ_{bc}, and ϱ_{ca}, and write the remaining six variables as two vectors, $\boldsymbol{\rho} = (\varrho_{aa}, \varrho_{bb}, \varrho_{cc})$ and $\boldsymbol{\mu} = (\varrho_{ba}, \varrho_{cb}, \varrho_{ac})$. The remaining six equations can then be expressed as two vector equations multiplied by 3×3 matrices. This procedure was used by WILCOX and LAMB [22], who solved the case of two large applied fields, as did YATSIV [13]. It allows for the arrangement of the various terms according to the powers of the field amplitudes. The expressions are too complicated for reproduction here, and are not particularly useful or illuminating. If all three fields are very large $|V/\Gamma| \gg 1$, a «heat death» of the system results, $\varrho_{aa} = \varrho_{bb} = \varrho_{cc} = \frac{1}{3}$. In the intermediate situation when several (V/Γ) and (w/Γ) are of the order of unity, peculiar inversions may occur, and even the possibility that $\varrho_{cc} - \varrho_{aa} > 0$ cannot be excluded in a limited range of field values and relaxation parameters. It appears, however, that the price for generality of the system (4.4) is too high in terms of algebraic complexity.

It is more useful to consider the more specialized case in which all powers of one large field amplitude, say at ω_3, are retained, but a power series expansion is used for the two smaller field amplitudes at ω_1 and ω_2. This approach was already used by CLOGSTON [15], whose calculation we shall follow. We shall not make the unnecessary assumption $\omega_3 = \omega_{ca}$, and shall arrange the various terms so that a physical identification is possible. First consider the zero-order solution independent of the field amplitudes at ω_1 and ω_2. Consider the first, second, third, and last row of the matrix eq. (4.4) together, with the terms in V_{ab}, V_{ba}, V_{bc}, and V_{cb} omitted. One thus obtains the terms which are independent of the fields at ω_1 and ω_2. The solution consists of the well-known populations for a pumped three-level maser, $\varrho_{aa}^{(0)}$, $\varrho_{bb}^{(0)}$, and $\varrho_{cc}^{(0)}$, and the response of the off-diagonal elements at the pump frequency,

$$\{\varrho_{ca}^{(0)}\}^{(\omega_2)} = \{\varrho_{ac}^{(0)}\}^{(-\omega_3)*} = \Delta_{ca}^{-1} V_{ca} (\varrho_{aa}^{(0)} - \varrho_{cc}^{(0)}) \, .$$

Consider next the two simultaneous equations for ϱ_{ba} and ϱ_{bc}, *i.e.*, the fifth and sixth rows of the matrix (4.4),

$$V_{ba}(\varrho_{aa}^{(0)} - \varrho_{bb}^{(0)}) + \Delta_{ba}\varrho_{ba}^{(1)} - V_{ca}\varrho_{bc}^{(1)} + V_{bc}\varrho_{ca}^{(0)} = 0 \, , \tag{4.4a}$$

$$V_{bc}(\varrho_{cc}^{(0)} - \varrho_{bb}^{(0)}) + \Delta_{bc}\varrho_{bc}^{(1)} - V_{ac}\varrho_{ba}^{(1)} + V_{ba}\varrho_{ac}^{(0)} = 0 \, . \tag{4.4b}$$

The solution gives the first approximation to ϱ_{ba} and ϱ_{bc}, correct to linear terms in the field amplitudes at ω_1 and ω_2:

$$\{\varrho_{ba}^{(1)}\}^{(\omega_1)} = \left[\Delta_{ba}^{-1} V_{ba}(\varrho_{aa}^{(0)} - \varrho_{bb}^{(0)}) + \frac{V_{ba}|V_{ca}|^2(\varrho_{aa}^{(0)} - \varrho_{cc}^{(0)})}{\Delta_{ac}\Delta_{ba}\Delta_{bc}} + \right.$$
$$\left. + \frac{V_{bc}V_{ca}(\varrho_{aa}^{(0)} - \varrho_{cc}^{(0)})}{\Delta_{ba}\Delta_{ca}} + \frac{V_{bc}V_{ca}(\varrho_{bb}^{(0)} - \varrho_{cc}^{(0)})}{\Delta_{ba}\Delta_{bc}}\right] \frac{\Delta_{ba}\Delta_{bc}}{\Delta_{ba}\Delta_{bc} - |V_{ac}|^2} \, . \tag{4.5}$$

This expression contains the same terms as eq. (25) of CLOGSTON's paper [15].

There is a similar equation for $\varrho_{cb}^{(1)} = \varrho_{bc}^{(1)*}$. The terms have been rearranged to facilitate their identification.

The factor outside the square bracket is always of the order unity, if the frequencies are adjusted to maximum response for a given value of the pump amplitude. If the pump field is small compared to linewdith $|V_{ac}/\Gamma| \ll 1$, it is obvious that the factor may be replaced by unity. If, however, $|V_{ac}/\Gamma| \gg 1$, the term has a dip at the resonant frequencies $\omega_1 = \omega_{ba}$, $\omega_2 = \omega_{bc}$. It causes a characteristic splitting of the response. This behavior is well known from the resonance condition in the rotating co-ordinate system. If the frequency is adjusted outside the dip at the center for maximum response, the factor has again a magnitude of about unity.

The first term inside the square bracket of eq. (4.5) has the appearance of a linear response term. The population difference $\varrho_{aa}^{(0)} - \varrho_{bb}^{(0)}$ does not have the thermal equilibrium value, but is a function of the pump power $|V_{ac}|^2$. This term represents the maser action, when $\varrho_{bb}^{(C)} - \varrho_{aa}^{(0)} > 0$.

The second term has the appearance of a Raman maser effect. A transition from level $|b\rangle$ to $|c\rangle$, while a quantum $\hbar\omega_3$ is absorbed and a quantum $\hbar\omega_1$ is emitted, would be proportional to $\varrho_{bb} - \varrho_{cc}$. The second term includes also the process proportional to $\varrho_{aa} - \varrho_{bb}$ which has to be added to the Raman transition. It represents the single-quantum absorption associated with a transition from $|a\rangle$ to $|b\rangle$ modified by the simultaneous scattering of one or more quanta $\hbar\omega_3$.

The third and fourth terms between the square brackets look like parametric terms. A polarization at ω_1 is created by fields applied at frequencies ω_3 and ω_2. These terms, however, do not only represent scattering processes in which three quanta take part. They also describe interference terms between single-photon and Raman processes in the transition probability between levels $|a\rangle$ and $|b\rangle$ which are connected by a matrix element of the form $cV_{ab} + c'V_{ac}V_{cb}$. This gives rise to an absorption proportional to $V_{ab}V_{bc}V_{ca}$.

The interpretation in terms of elementary quantum processes is already quite complex in this approximation. The illustrations in Fig. 5 should not be taken too literally. The macroscopic behavior is, however, described by complex susceptibilities of the parametric or the Raman type. The former describe a polarization induced at a combination frequency by fields applied at other frequencies. The complex value of the susceptibility determines the phase of the polarization with respect to these applied fields. One cannot decide whether or not absorption occurs, until the phase of a field at the combination frequency is known. The Raman-type susceptibility describes a complex change in the linear index of refraction proportional to the intensity of a field at another frequency. Its imaginary part corresponds to positive or negative absorption.

The solutions (4.5) for $\varrho_{ab}^{(1)} = \varrho_{ba}^{(1)*}$ and $\varrho_{bc}^{(1)} = \varrho_{cb}^{(1)*}$ can be substituted back into the equations for the populations and $\varrho_{ac}=\varrho^*_{ca}$. One finds in second approximation terms quadratic in the small fields, $|V_{ab}|^2$, $|V_{bc}|^2$, $V_{ab}V_{bc}$ and $V_{cb}V_{ba}$. In third approximation one may use the eqs. (4.4a) and (4.4b) to obtain a relationship between $\varrho^{(3)}_{ba}$ and $\varrho^{(2)}_{bb}-\varrho^{(2)}_{aa}$ etc. The labor involved is large, and one might as well solve the complete matrix (4.4), if the fields at ω_1 and ω_2 become comparable to the damping parameters, $|V_{ab,bc}/\Gamma_{ab,bc}|\sim 1$.

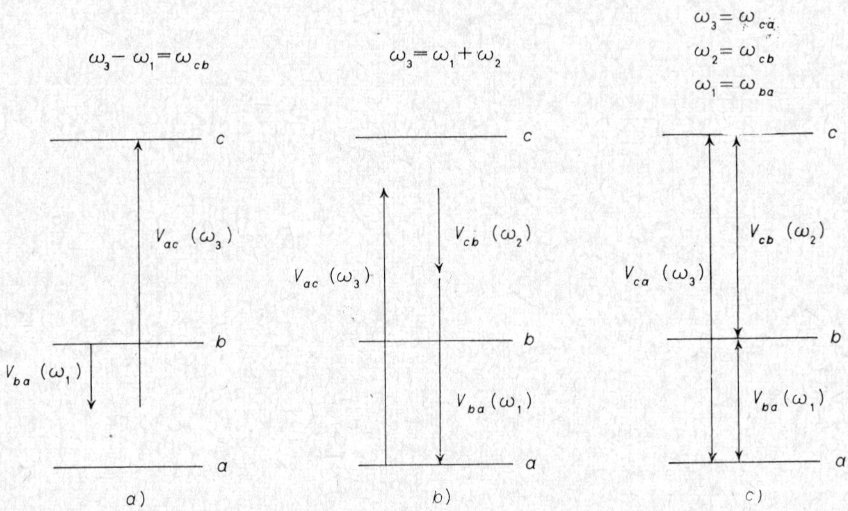

Fig. 5. – Nonlinear processes in a three-level system. The text should be consulted for a correct interpretation of these illustrations: a) illustration of a Raman process; b) illustration of a parametric process; c) combination of saturation, maser, Raman maser and parametric processes.

The relative importance of the various terms in eq. (4.5) will now be discussed in some detail. If the pumping field is small compared to the linewidth and all frequencies are near resonance, the first term is dominant. The well-known case of the solid-state three-level maser results.

The second or Raman-type term will not necessarily be larger than the first term, if $|V_a|$ is chosen very large, because the population difference $\varrho^{(0)}_{aa}-\varrho^{(0)}_{cc}$ itself approaches zero. It should be remembered that the superscript (0) refers to zero power in the small fields only. In fact, the optimum response, *i.e.*, the largest value of $\varrho^{(1)}_{ba}$ is obtained for $|V^2_{ac}/\Delta^2|\sim 1$, as explained previously. In that case, the Raman term has the same order of magnitude as the maser term, and precise values for $|V_{ca}/\Delta_{ac}|$ and $|V_{ca}/\Delta_{bc}|$ must be known for a detailed comparison in this case.

There is, however, a situation in which the Raman term will always dominate. This occurs when only the frequency $\omega_2=\omega_{cb}$ is at resonance and the applied field at this frequency is very small, $V_{bc}=0$. Because of this last condition, the parametric terms vanish. Since the frequency ω_1 is off resonance, $|\omega_1-\omega_{ba}|>\Gamma_{ba}$, and so is the pump field at ω_3,

$$|\omega_1-\omega_{ba}|=|\omega_3-\omega_{ca}|>|V_{ca}|>\Gamma_{ca}\,,$$

the imaginary part of the first term, corresponding to linear absorption, is $\Gamma_{ba}|\Delta_{ba}|^{-2}V_{ba}(\varrho_{aa}^{(0)}-\varrho_{bb}^{(0)})$. The ratio of the Raman-type term to the linear absorption can easily be made larger than unity,

$$\frac{|V_{ca}|^2(\varrho_{aa}^{(0)}-\varrho_{cc}^{(0)})}{\Gamma_{bc}\Gamma_{ba}(\varrho_{aa}^{(0)}-\varrho_{bb}^{(0)})}>1\,.$$

Since the pump field is off resonance, the populations have essentially their thermal equilibrium value. If the applied pump field is larger than the natural widths Γ_{bc} and Γ_{ba}, the Raman process is dominant. This situation is shown schematically in Fig. 5 *a*). The conditions set forth are, of course, precisely those under which optical Raman laser action has been observed [4].

The paramagnetic terms in eq. (4.5) can always be made dominant, if all three frequencies are well removed from resonance. The ratios of the parametric term to the linear absorption is, in that case, larger than unity, if

$$\left|\frac{V_{bc}V_{ca}\Delta_{ba}}{V_{ca}\Gamma_{ba}\Delta_{bc}}\right|>1\,.$$

This can be achieved, even if the pump amplitude is smaller than the linewidth. If the amplitude V_{ba} is initially very small, a polarization at the frequency ω_1 will be created by the larger applied fields at ω_3 and ω_2. This « pure parametric » case is illustrated as a three-photon scattering process in Fig. 5 *b*), although important reservations about this pictorial representation must be made, as discussed previously. If the applied frequencies are far removed from resonance, the truncation procedure which led to eq. (4.5) becomes invalid. Eventually, one should return to the general Fourier expansion method of Sect. **2**.

Thus far, the field amplitudes are assumed to be applied externally as given fixed quantities. This is the proper procedure in calculating macroscopic susceptibilities. If the applied field at ω_1 vanishes, $V_{ab}=0$, the parametric terms in eq. (4.5) are the only ones left. They create a polarization at ω_1, which, in turn, will generate a field at ω_1: The assumption $V_{ab}=0$ is not self-consistent. This extreme example clearly shows that the question should be considered, how the magnitude of the fields is in turn determined by the reaction of the material system on the fields.

B. – Macroscopic Description of Electromagnetic Field in Nonlinear Media.

5. – Wave propagation in nonlinear media.

The question of the reaction of the material system on the electromagnetic modes was treated very early by BLOEMBERGEN and POUND [17]. They considered the precessing magnetization in a magnetic-resonance experiment in turn as a source for the electromagnetic field. This scheme has been developed further by several authors [10, 18, 19] both for cavity modes and for traveling waves. The reaction of the nonlinear polarization can be treated in the same way as a nonlinear source term. ARMSTRONG *et al.* [11, 20] have considered such terms as sources of plane waves traveling in homogeneous, anisotropic, lossless, nonlinear, optical media. Their treatment will be followed here with the more general complex polarizabilities developed in Part A.

Consider a medium with dielectric constant ε (and $\mu = 1$), exclusive of that part of the polarization which is explicitly considered for maser, Raman maser and/or parametric action. For simplicity it will be assumed that the medium is not dense in the optical sense. The difference between the macroscopic Maxwell field and the local field acting on the atomic system may then be ignored. The more general case of dense media requires modifications, which have been given elsewhere [11]. The total electric polarization is given by

$$\boldsymbol{P} = \frac{\boldsymbol{\epsilon} - 1}{4\pi}\,\boldsymbol{E} + N\langle\mathscr{P}\rangle\,. \tag{5.1}$$

Here N is the number of particles per cm³ and $\langle\mathscr{P}\rangle$ is the expectation value of the dipole moment per particle calculated explicitly in terms of the applied fields according to the methods of Part A.

The constitutive equation for the dielectric displacement becomes

$$\boldsymbol{D} = \boldsymbol{E} + 4\pi\boldsymbol{P} = \boldsymbol{\epsilon}\boldsymbol{E} + 4\pi N\langle\mathscr{P}\rangle \tag{5.2}$$

and Maxwell's equations may be written as

$$\left\{\begin{aligned} \nabla\times\boldsymbol{H} &= \frac{1}{c}\frac{\partial\boldsymbol{D}}{\partial t} = \frac{1}{c}\frac{\partial(\boldsymbol{\epsilon}\boldsymbol{E})}{\partial t} + \frac{4\pi}{c}\frac{\partial\langle N\mathscr{P}\rangle}{\partial t}\,,\\ \nabla\times\boldsymbol{E} &= -\frac{1}{c}\frac{\partial\boldsymbol{B}}{\partial t}\,. \end{aligned}\right. \tag{5.3}$$

The resulting wave equation takes the form

$$\nabla\times\nabla\times\boldsymbol{E}+\frac{1}{c}\frac{\partial^2(\boldsymbol{\epsilon}\boldsymbol{E})}{\partial t^2}=-\frac{4\pi}{c^2}\frac{\partial^2\langle N\mathscr{P}\rangle}{\partial t^2}\,. \tag{5.4}$$

When three monochromatic waves are considered, as in the example of the preceding section, one has

$$\begin{cases}\dfrac{c^2}{\omega_1^2}\nabla\times\nabla\times\boldsymbol{E}^{(\omega_1)}-\boldsymbol{\epsilon}(\omega_1)\boldsymbol{E}^{(\omega_1)}=+\,4\pi N\langle\mathscr{P}^{(\omega_1)}\rangle\,,\\ \dfrac{c^2}{\omega_2^2}\nabla\times\nabla\times\boldsymbol{E}^{(\omega_2)}-\boldsymbol{\epsilon}(\omega_2)\boldsymbol{E}^{(\omega_2)}=+\,4\pi N\langle\mathscr{P}^{(\omega_2)}\rangle\,,\\ \dfrac{c^2}{\omega_3^2}\nabla\times\nabla\times\boldsymbol{E}^{(\omega_3)}-\boldsymbol{\epsilon}(\omega_2)\boldsymbol{E}^{(\omega_3)}=+\,4\pi N\langle\mathscr{P}^{(\omega_3)}\rangle\,.\end{cases} \tag{5.5}$$

The dipole moments on the right-hand side have been calculated as functions of the three applied fields. These equations show how the nonlinear polarization couples the waves together. The system of eqs. (5.5) is difficult to solve if the general expression for the Fourier components of $\langle\mathscr{P}\rangle=\mathrm{Tr}\,(\mathscr{P}\varrho)$ from the solution of eqs. (4.4) is substituted.

Consider instead the simpler situation where the parametric effect dominates. If one lumps the linear part of $\langle\mathscr{P}\rangle$ with ε and retains only the lowest order nonlinear approximation,

$$\begin{cases}\langle\mathscr{P}^{(\omega_1)}\rangle=\boldsymbol{\beta}(\omega_1=\omega_3-\omega_2):\boldsymbol{E}_1\boldsymbol{E}_2^*\exp[i(\boldsymbol{k}_3-\boldsymbol{k}_2)\cdot\boldsymbol{r}]\,,\\ \langle\mathscr{P}^{(\omega_2)}\rangle=\boldsymbol{\beta}(\omega_2=\omega_3-\omega_1):\boldsymbol{E}_3\boldsymbol{E}_1^*\exp[i(\boldsymbol{k}_3-\boldsymbol{k}_1)\cdot\boldsymbol{r}]\,,\\ \langle\mathscr{P}^{(\omega_3)}\rangle=\boldsymbol{\beta}(\omega_3=\omega_1+\omega_2):\boldsymbol{E}_1\boldsymbol{E}_2\exp[i(\boldsymbol{k}_1+\boldsymbol{k}_2)\cdot\boldsymbol{r}]\,,\end{cases} \tag{5.6}$$

the coupled equations become more tractable. Since the nonlinear coupling is small, the relative variation of amplitude and phase per wavelength is quite small. With

$$\left|\frac{\partial^2 E_1}{\partial z^2}\right|\ll|k_1|\left|\frac{\partial E_1}{\partial z}\right|,$$

and similar expressions for the complex wave amplitudes E_2 and E_3, a set of coupled amplitude equations results for the three coupled plane polarized waves all propagating in the z-direction,

$$\begin{cases}\mathrm{d}E_1^*/\mathrm{d}z=i\omega_1^2(K/k_1)E_3^*E_2\exp[+i\Delta kz]\,,\\ \mathrm{d}E_2^*/\mathrm{d}z=i\omega_2^2(K/k_2)E_3^*E_1\exp[+i\Delta kz]\,,\\ \mathrm{d}E_3/\mathrm{d}z=i\omega_3^2(K/k_3)E_1\,E_2\exp[+i\Delta kz]\,,\end{cases} \tag{5.7}$$

where $\Delta k = k_1 + k_2 - k_3$ is a measure for the mismatch of the propagation vectors.

The constant K is defined by

$$K = \frac{2\pi}{c^2} N \hat{e}_3 \cdot \boldsymbol{\beta}(\omega_3) : \hat{e}_1 \hat{e}_2 = \frac{2\pi}{c^2} N \hat{e}_2 \cdot \boldsymbol{\beta}(\omega_2) : \hat{e}_1 \hat{e}_2 = \frac{2\pi}{c^2} N \hat{e}_1 \cdot \boldsymbol{\beta}(\omega_1) : \hat{e}_3 \hat{e}_2 . \tag{5.8}$$

The three unit vectors give the direction of polarization of the three waves. The equalities in eq. (5.8) are valid because of the permutation symmetry property [11]. The indices for the tensor components may be interchanged if the frequencies are also interchanged, so that the field at each frequency keeps the same orientation with respect to the crystallographic axes. This property follows immediately from the detailed expression for the nonlinear polarizability (eq. (2.9)), and also from energy considerations. One may consider the change in time-averaged free energy of a volume element of the nonlinear medium [11, 21] due to the simultaneous presence of three electromagnetic waves at ω_1, ω_2 and $\omega_3 = \omega_2 + \omega_1$. An important physical consequence is that the electric Kerr effect, describing the change in index of refraction of a light wave at ω on application of a d.c. field, is determined by the same constant as the d.c. rectification voltage which appears across a nonlinear crystal, when a light wave ω passes thru the crystal. This has been verified by FRANKEN [22]. It also follows that the d.c. Kerr effect is but a special case of the general parametric nonlinearity with $\omega_1 = 0$ and $\omega_2 = \omega_3$. In a similar way microwave modulation of light is described by this formalism if ω_1 is taken to lie in the microwave region. Second-harmonic generation is described for $\omega_1 = \omega_2 = \frac{1}{2}\omega_3$.

A general solution of eqs. (5.7) has been given and is rather involved. Two integrals can, however, be written down by inspection:

$$\begin{cases} \dfrac{(E_1 \times H_1)_z}{h\omega_1} + \dfrac{(E_3 \times H_3)_z}{h\omega_3} = \text{constant} , \\[2ex] \dfrac{(E_2 + H_2)_z}{h\omega_2} + \dfrac{(E_3 \times H_3)_z}{h\omega_3} = \text{constant} . \end{cases} \tag{5.9}$$

They are known as Manley-Rowe relations and describe the fact that a quantum $h\omega_3$ can only be added to the sum wave, if one takes simultaneously a quantum out of each of the waves at ω_1 and ω_2.

Some solutions for second-harmonic generation for varying degrees of phase mismatch are shown in Fig. 6. Except when the phase match is nearly perfect over a very long distance the power generated at the sum frequency will be small. In that case the amplitudes E_1 and E_2 can be considered as constant and the last of eqs. (5.7) gives a sinusoidal variation of the power at the sum frequency

$$|E(\omega_3)|^2 = (\omega_3^4 K^2/k_3^2)\left(\frac{\sin\frac{1}{2}\Delta k z}{\frac{1}{2}\Delta k}\right)^2 |E(\omega_1)|^2 |E(\omega_2)|^2 .$$

This behavior is responsible for the oscillations in Fig. 2.

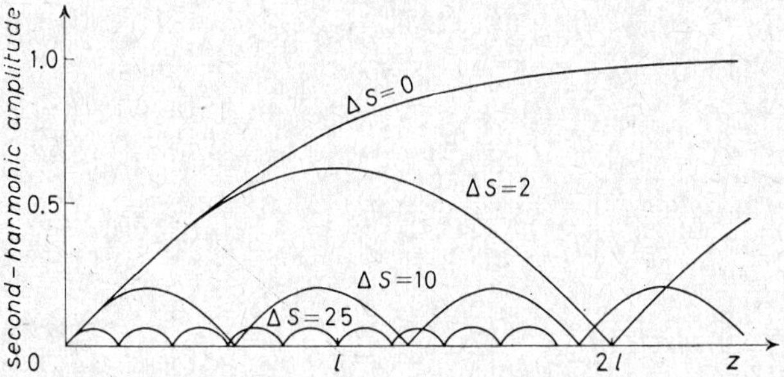

Fig. 6. – Theoretical growth curves for the second-harmonic amplitude for varying degrees of phase mismatch.

For perfect matching $\Delta k = 0$, it is in principle possible to convert all power from the fundamental to the second harmonic frequency. An interaction length l' may be defined, in which about 70% of the power is transferred. It is inversely proportional to the initial amplitude of the fundamental,

$$l' = \frac{\varepsilon \lambda_{\text{med}}}{8\pi^2 E(\omega)} \quad (\chi^{NL} = N\beta) .$$

TERHUNE [23] has converted more than 20% of the fundamental power to second harmonic KDP, using a giant pulsed beam focused by a lens with long focal length.

Phase matching over a distance l' is difficult to obtain. There is one direction at an angle θ_M from the optic axis, shown in Fig. 3, where the fundamental ordinary ray and the second harmonic extraordinary ray in KDP are matched. The beam divergence must be very small to meet the matching requirement. Focusing increases the fundamental field strength, but also increases the beam divergence. Ideally, a well-collimated beam traversing a long optically perfect crystal carefully oriented for matching would give the best results. The reason that harmonic generation from low-intensity gas laser beams is observable [24, 25], is due to the fact that a long coherence length is possible for the CW beam with a single spatial mode. BOYD [24] obtained $8.1 \cdot 10^{-14}$ watt second-harmonic power for a fundamental power of $1.48 \cdot 10^{-3}$ watt in a crystal-length of 1.23 cm. The yield is shown for various modes in Fig. 7. He determines the nonlinear tensor component in KDP,

$$\chi_{36}(\omega_3 = 2\omega_1) = N\{\beta_{zxy}(\omega_3 = \omega_1 + \omega_1) + \beta_{zyx}(\omega_3 = \omega_1 + \omega_1)\} = 3\cdot 10^{-9}\ \text{e.s.u.}$$

for $\lambda = 2\pi c/\omega_1 = 1.1526\cdot 10^{-4}$ cm, whereas previous estimates with a less well-defined ruby-laser beam were almost one order of magnitude smaller. With $\chi = 3\cdot 10^{-9}$ e.s.u. an interaction length $l' = 1$ cm would obtain for a field strength $E(\omega) = 120$ kV/cm, corresponding to a power flux density of 50 megawatt/cm².

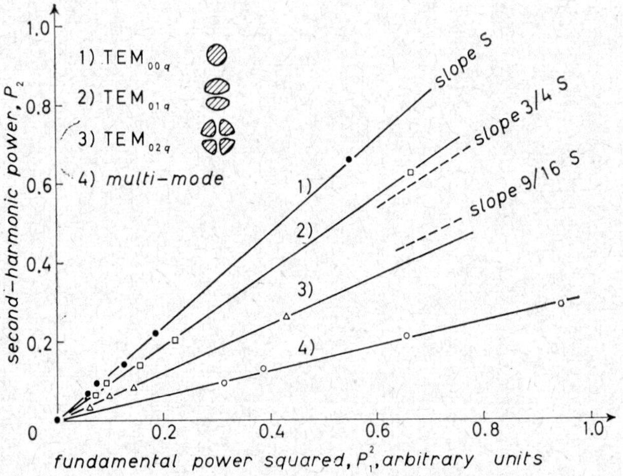

Fig. 7. – Harmonic power generation in KDP *vs.* fundamental power squared, for different CW transverse modes of a helium neon maser. The theoretical ratio is 1:0.75:0.56. Curve 4) is a combination of different modes, indicating the deleterious effects of multi-mode operation [24].

The tensorial character of the nonlinear susceptibility describing second-harmonic generation has the same symmetry properties as the piezo-electric tensor. For the tetragonal symmetry $\bar{4}\ 2\ m$ of KDP one has

$$\chi_{14}(\omega_3 = 2\omega_1) = \chi_{25}(\omega_3 = 2\omega_1) \neq \chi_{36}(\omega_3 = 2\omega_1)\,.$$

If there were no dispersion, as postulated by KLEINMAN [26], χ_{36} would be equal to χ_{25}. In a cubic medium with tetrahedral $\bar{4}\ 3\ m$ symmetry, this last relation holds rigorously. Measurements by MILLER [27] indicate that this equality holds, but data by VAN DER ZIEL [28] yield the result $\chi_{14}(\omega_3 = 2\omega_1) = (0.75 \pm 0.05)\,\chi_{36}(\omega_3 = 2\omega_1)$ for second-harmonic generation of ruby light in KDP. There is of course a large dispersion in the infra-red for the nonlinear as well as for the linear dielectric constant. At microwave and lower frequencies the ionic motion contributes to the nonlinearity [26]. The d.c. Kerr constant or light rectification constant is [22] $\chi_{36}(0 = \omega_1 - \omega_1) = 12\cdot 10^{-8}$ e.s.u., or some forty times larger than $\chi_{36}(\omega_3 = 2\omega_1)$. The value at microwave frequencies is equal to the d.c. value within the experimental errors.

VAN DER ZIEL has also measured the components of the nonlinear susceptibility tensor in KDP in its orthorhombic ferro-electric phase with $mm\,2$ symmetry. Care has to be taken that the light passes through single domain regions of the crystal. It is cooled in the presence of an applied electric field through the transition temperature at 123 °K. The nonlinear tensor elements are referred to the orthorhombic crystallographic axes which are rotated by 45° around the c-axis with respect to the tetragonal axes:

$$\begin{pmatrix} P_x(2\omega) \\ P_y(2\omega) \\ P_z(2\omega) \end{pmatrix} = \begin{pmatrix} 0 & 0 & 0 & 0 & \chi'_{15} & 0 \\ 0 & 0 & 0 & \chi'_{24} & 0 & 0 \\ \chi'_{31} & \chi'_{32} & \chi'_{33} & 0 & 0 & 0 \end{pmatrix} \begin{pmatrix} E_x^2(\omega) \\ E_y^2(\omega) \\ R_2^2(\omega) \\ E_y E_z \\ E_z E_x \\ E_x E_y \end{pmatrix}.$$

The elemnts determined by VAN DER ZIEL from curves of the kind shown in Fig. 2 for KDP at 80 °K are related to « corresponding » values in the tetragonal phase at 300 °K by, $\chi'_{15}/\chi_{14} = 1.73 \pm 0.12$, $\chi'_{24}/\chi_{14} = 0.63 \pm 0.05$, $\chi'_{31}/\frac{1}{2}\chi_{36} = 3.6 \pm 0.4$, $\chi'_{32}/\frac{1}{2}\chi_{36} = 0.16 \pm 0.06$, $\chi'_{33}/\frac{1}{2}\chi_{36} < 0.05$. The relative signs are not known.

In the next higher nonlinear approximation one obtains source terms for the third harmonic, and terms describing the variation of the index of refraction with the intensity of the light. The Raman effect is also contained in this formalism as the imaginary part of the fourth-rank susceptibility tensor. A typical element may be written as

$$\mathscr{P}^{(\omega_1)}_{x\,\text{Raman}} = i\chi''_{xxyy}(\omega_1 = \omega_1 + \omega_2 - \omega_2) E_x(\omega_1) \,|E_y(\omega_2)\,|^2 .$$

The coupled amplitude equations can again be solved in this approximation. For lack of space and time details of theory [12] and experiments [4, 23] are not discussed here.

6. – Optical laws of nonlinear reflection and refraction.

In this Section some recent experimental results are described which confirm a part of the detailed theoretical considerations of BLOEMBERGEN and PERSHAN [29]. Consider two waves at ω_1 and ω_2, respectively, incident on the plane boundary of a nonlinear medium. After refraction they will produce in the medium a Fourier component of polarization at the sum frequency $N\langle\mathscr{P}^{(\omega_3)}\rangle$. This polarization acts as an inhomogeneous source term for a wave at ω_3. One has a homogeneous solution of the wave equation propagating with wave vector $\boldsymbol{k}_3$, and an inhomogeneous solution of eq. (5.5) with the same spatial distribution as $\langle\mathscr{P}^{(\omega_3)}\rangle$, *i.e.*, with a source wave vector $\boldsymbol{k}_1^T+\boldsymbol{k}_2^T$, equal to the vector sum of the wave vectors of the incident waves after refraction. There is another homogeneous solution of the wave equation at ω_3 in the linear medium on the other side of the boundary. The coefficients of the homogeneous solutions must be so chosen that the boundary conditions are satisfied, *i.e.*, the tangential components of $\boldsymbol{E}$ and $\boldsymbol{H}$ must be continuous everywhere on the boundary between the linear and nonlinear media. In this way reflected and transmitted second-harmonic waves are obtained. Their direction is determined by the fact that the spatial variation of the fields along the boundary is determined by the variation of $\langle\mathscr{P}^{(2\omega)}\rangle$ which varies as $\exp[2i\boldsymbol{k}(\omega)\cdot\boldsymbol{r}]$. Therefore the angle of reflection of the reflected harmonic wave is related to the angle of the incident fundamental beam by

$$\sin\vartheta_2=\frac{k_T(2\omega)}{k(2\omega)}=\frac{n(\omega)}{n(2\omega)}\frac{k_T(\omega)}{k(\omega)}=\frac{n(\omega)}{n(2\omega)}\sin\vartheta_i\,, \tag{6.1}$$

where $n(\omega)$ is the index of refraction for the linear medium. Figure 8 shows the reflection from a nonlinear mirror of GaAs immersed in benzene. The angle between the reflected fundamental and harmonic beam of 2.1° corresponds well to the known dispersion of benzene. If the benzene is not present, the second harmonic coincides with the reflected fundamental.

If the incident laser beam is split into beams of approximately equal intensity and the beams are made to coincide at the surface of the nonlinear mirror, as shown in Fig. 9, three harmonic beams appear in reflection. The one in the middle is the « cross beat »

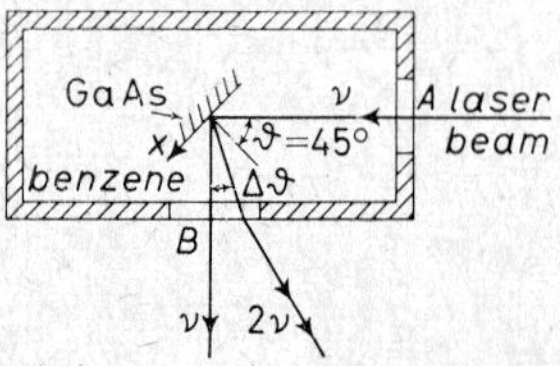

Fig. 8. – The law of reflection, when a nonlinear mirror is inserted in a dispersive linear medium.

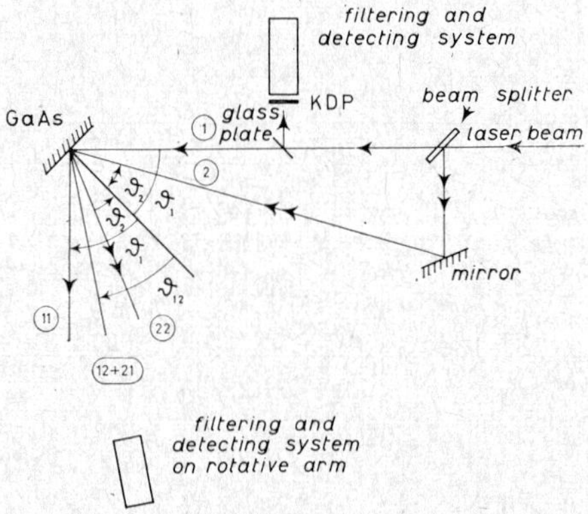

Fig. 9. – Harmonic generation by two incident light beams at frequency ν, in the same plane of incidence and with electric fields normal to the plane. Three second-harmonic beams emerge.

between the two incident beams and emerges at an angle ϑ_{12} given by

$$\sin\vartheta_{12} = \tfrac{1}{2}(\sin\vartheta_1 + \sin\vartheta_2)\,. \tag{6.2}$$

The polarization and intensity of the second harmonic beams reflected from GaAs has also been measured [31] in the geometry of Fig. 10. The incident light beam is polarized normal to the plane of incidence. The mirror is rotated in its own [1 −1 0] plane, so that the fundamental $\boldsymbol{E}_1(\omega)$ vector can be made parallel to the [0 0 1], [1 1 0] and [1 1 1] crystallographic directions. The components of second-harmonic polarization in tetrahedral symmetry referred to the cubic axes are given by

$$P_x^{(2\omega)} = \chi_{14} E_y E_z\,,$$

$$P_y^{(2\omega)} = \chi_{14} E_z E_x$$

and

$$P_z^{(2\omega)} = \chi_{14} E_x E_y\,.$$

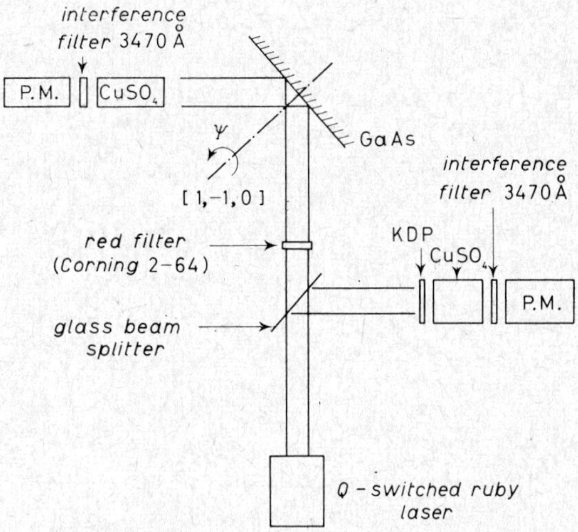

Fig. 10. – Diagram of experimental arrangement to measure polarization properties of reflected second harmonics. A Glan-Thomson analyser is inserted between the GaAs mirror and the $CuSO_4$ filter.

There is no second harmonic generation, when $E(\omega_1)$ is parallel to [0, 0, 1]. When $E(\omega_1)$ is along [1 +1 0], the second-harmonic polarization is at right angles to the incident field. Consequently the second-harmonic reflected beam has an electric field in the plane of reflection, normal to the fundamental electric field. Finally, when $E(\omega_1)$ is along [1, 1, 1] $E(2\omega_1)$ is parallel to $E(\omega_1)$. These and other features are strikingly confirmed by the experimental results [31]. The polarization of the reflected harmonic is determined by the bulk symmetry properties of the GaAs crystal, even though the second harmonic is generated in a layer of approximately 400 Å, because of the strong absorption of GaAs at the second-harmonic frequency. Many other theoretical predictions about nonlinear generalizations of optical laws [29] can also be tested.

7. – Fluctuation in second-harmonic production.

The second-harmonic production in each laser pulse is a random function. The proportionality constant between the second-harmonic intensity and the square of the fundamental intensity fluctuates by a factor three or more from pulse to pulse. If the primary laser-beam intensity is calibrated by means of a quadratic effect, *i.e.*, if two similar nonlinear effects from the same fundamental beam are compared with each other, the fluctuations disappear [32]. The experimental arrangement which eliminates the fluctuations in the relative measurement of the second-harmonic intensity, is shown in Fig. 10. The explanation for the fluctuation rests in the multimode structure of the primary laser beam. They should not occur with a single fundamental mode.

Let a_m represent the complex amplitude of m-th fundamental mode with wave vector $\boldsymbol{k}_m$ and frequency ω_m.

If the fundamental intensity is averaged over a time, long compared to the inverse of all difference frequencies, $t \gg (\omega_m - \omega_{m'})^{-1}$, and over the area of the photocathode, one obtains

$$(7.1) \qquad \langle \mathscr{I}_1 \rangle = \sum_m \sum_{m'} a_m a^*_{m'} \exp[-i(\omega_m - \omega_{m'})t] \exp[i(\boldsymbol{k}_m - \boldsymbol{k}_{m'}]\cdot \boldsymbol{r}] = \\ = \sum_m \sum_{m'} a_m a^*_{m'} \delta(\boldsymbol{k}_m - \boldsymbol{k}'_m) = \sum_m |a_m|^2 .$$

The three-dimensional δ-function occurs because the frequencies must be equal and the spatial variation over the photocathode must be the same. This leads to the well-known result that the intensity is equal to the sum of the intensities in the individual modes.

The amplitude of the n-th second harmonic mode is given by

$$b_n \exp[i\boldsymbol{k}_n\cdot \boldsymbol{r} - i\omega_n t] = \chi \sum_m \sum_{m'} a_m a_{m'} \exp[i(\boldsymbol{k}_m + \boldsymbol{k}_{m'})\cdot \boldsymbol{r} - i(\omega_m + \omega_{m'})t],$$

where χ is the nonlinear susceptibility.

The energy and momentum conservation laws require

$$\boldsymbol{k}_n = \boldsymbol{k}_m + \boldsymbol{k}_{m'} \qquad \text{and} \qquad \omega_n = \omega_m + \omega_{m'} .$$

The total second-harmonic intensity, averaged over space and time, is correspondingly given by

$$\langle \mathscr{I}_2 \rangle = \chi^2 \sum_m \sum_{m'} \sum_{m''} \sum_{m'''} a_m a_{m'} a^*_{m''} a^*_{m'''} \delta(\omega_m + \omega_{m'} - \omega_{m''} - \omega_{m'''}) \delta(\boldsymbol{k}_m + \boldsymbol{k}_{m'} - \boldsymbol{k}_{m''} - \boldsymbol{k}_{m'''}).$$

The last δ-function is two-dimensional, for the transverse components of the momentum:

$$(7.2) \qquad \langle \mathscr{I}_2 \rangle = \chi^2 \sum_m |a_m|^4 + 2\chi^2 \sum\sum_{m \neq m'} |a_m|^2 |a_{m'}|^2 + \\ + \chi^2 \sum_m{}' \sum_{m'}{}' \sum_{m''}{}' \sum_{m'''}{}' a_m a_{m'} a^*_{m''} a^*_{m'''} \delta(\boldsymbol{k}_m + \boldsymbol{k}_{m'} - \boldsymbol{k}_{m''} - \boldsymbol{k}_{m'''}) .$$

The last term depends on the relative phases of the four different modes, m, m', m'', m''', which should satisfy the vector relationship $\boldsymbol{k}_{m'''} = \boldsymbol{k}_m + \boldsymbol{k}_{m'} - \boldsymbol{k}_{m''}$. If there is no definite phase relationship between the modes, the average second-harmonic intensity is given by the first two terms on the right-hand side. It is interesting to compare this with the square of the fundamental intensity

$$\langle \mathscr{I}_1 \rangle^2 = \sum_m |a_m|^4 + \sum_{m \neq m'}\sum |a_m|^2 |a_{m'}|^2 . \tag{7.3}$$

If there is only one mode, the usual relationship $\langle \mathscr{I}_2 \rangle = \chi^2 \langle \mathscr{I}_1 \rangle^2$ is obtained. If there is a very large number of modes with random phases, one obtains $\langle \mathscr{I}_2 \rangle = 2\chi^2 \langle \mathscr{I}_1 \rangle^2$. If there are definite phase relationship between the different modes the last term may add or subtract and the determination of χ becomes a hazardous matter. Fluctuations in the relative phases and random variations in the amplitude of the individual fundamental modes may lead to large fluctuations in the harmonic production, even for a fixed value of $\langle \mathscr{I}_1 \rangle$.

The observation of these fluctuations [32] and the measurement of higher moments, such as $\langle \mathscr{I}_2^2 \rangle$, $\langle \mathscr{I}_3 \rangle$, etc. leads in principle to a determination of the higher-order correlation functions which describe the fundamental incident field. This combination of the theory of coherence and nonlinear phenomena shows how actual multimode lasers can produce results that are very different from those calculated for an ideal coherent oscillator.

REFERENCES

[1] P. FRANKEN, A. E. HILL, C. W. PETERS and G. WEINREICH: *Phys. Rev. Lett.*, **7**, 118 (1961).

[2] J. A. GIORDMAINE: *Phys. Rev. Lett.*, **8**, 19 (1962).

[3] P. D. MAKER, R. W. TERHUNE, M. NISENOFF and C. M. SAVAGE: *Phys. Rev. Lett.*, **8**, 21 (1962).

[4] G. ECKHARDT, R. W. HELLWARTH, F. J. MCCLUNG, S. E. SCHWARZ, D. WEINER and E. J. WOODBURY: *Phys. Rev. Lett.*, **9**, 455 (1962).

[5] See, for example, papers by A. KASTLER, J. BROSSEL, C. COHEN-TANNOUDJI and J. M. WINTER in *Rendiconti S.I.F.*, Corso XVII (New York, 1962).

[6] F. BLOCH: *Phys. Rev.*, **102**, 104 (1956).

[7] See, for example, A. ABRAGAM: *Principles of Nuclear Magnetism* (Oxford, 1960).

[8] See, for example, the following papers: A. JAVAN: *Phys. Rev.*, **107**, 1579 (1957); A. M. CLOGSTON: *Phys. Chem. Solids*, **4**, 271 (1958); S. YATSIV: *Phys. Rev.*, **113**, 1538 (1959); L. R. WILCOX and W. E. LAMB: *Phys. Rev.*, **119**, 1915 (1960); P. L. KELLEY: *Journ. Chem. Phys. Sol.*, **24**, 607 (1963).

[9] W. P. Ayres, P. H. Vartanian and J. L. Melchor: *Journ. Appl. Phys.*, **27**, 188 (1956).
[10] P. W. Anderson: *Journ. Appl. Phys.*, **28**, 1049 (1957).
[11] J. A. Armstrong, N. Bloembergen, J. Ducuing and P. S. Pershan: *Phys. Rev.*, **127**, 1918 (1962).
[12] R. W. Hellwarth: *Phys. Rev.*, **130**, 1850 (1963).
[13] N. Bloembergen and Y. R. Shen: *Phys. Rev.*, **133**, A 37 (1964).
[14] J. Fiutak: *Can. Journ. Phys.*, **41**, 12 (1963).
[15] J. M. Winter: *Journ. de Phys. et Rad.*, **19**, 802 (1958).
[16] A. Javan: *Journ. de Phys. et Rad.*, **19**, 806 (1958).
[17] N. Bloembergen and R. V. Pound: *Phys. Rev.*, **96**, 8 (1954).
[18] E. T. Jaynes and F. W. Cummings: *Proc. I.E.E.E.*, **51**, 89 (1963); L. W. Davis *Proc. I.E.E.E.*, **51**, 89 (1963).
[19] H. Haken and H. Sauermann: *Zeits. f. Phys.*, **173**, 261 (1963).
[20] N. Bloembergen: *Proc. I.E.E.E.*, **51**, 124 (1963).
[21] P. S. Pershan: *Phys. Rev.*, **130**, 919 (1963).
[22] M. Bass, P. A. Franken, J. F. Ward and G. Weinreich: *Phys. Rev. Lett.*, **9**, 446 (1962).
[23] R. W. Terhune: *Proc. of the Third Conference on Quantum Electronics* (Paris, 1963).
[24] A. Ashkin, G. D. Boyd and J. M. Dziedzic: *Phys. Rev. Lett.*, **11**, 14 (1963).
[25] N. I. Adams and P. B. Schoefer: *App. Phys. Lett.*, **3**, 19 (1963).
[26] D. A. Kleinman: *Phys. Rev.*, **126**, 1977 (1962).
[27] R. C. Miller: *Phys. Rev.*, **131**, 95 (1963).
[28] J. van der Ziel: *Phys. Rev.* (to be published).
[29] N. Bloembergen and P. S. Pershan: *Phys. Rev.*, **128**, 606 (1962).
[30] N. Bloembergen and J. Ducuing: *Phys. Lett.*, **6**, 5 (1963).
[31] J. Ducuing and N. Bloembergen: *Phys. Rev. Lett.*, **10**, 474 (1963).
[32] N. Bloembergen: *Proc. of the Brooklyn Polytechnic Institute Symposium on Lasers* (April 1963). J. Ducuing and N. Bloembergen, *Phys. Rev.* **133**, A 1493 (1964).

The Intensity-Dependence of Optical Absorption in Semiconductors.

O. KROKHIN

P. N. Lebedev Physical Institute of the Academy of Sciences of the USSR - Moscow

The problem of saturation effects in light absorption by semiconductors is of interest in connection with semiconductor lasers. The solution of this problem in detail is difficult but the essential results can be obtained by a very simple method.

The absorption coefficient in a semiconductor is caused by the creation of electron-hole pairs and its frequency-dependence is connected with the band structure.

In the case of direct transitions the absorption coefficient for low light intensity has the following form:

$$k_0 = \text{const}\, \omega^{-1} (\hbar\omega - \Delta)^{\frac{1}{2}} ,$$

where Δ is energy gap.

It is well known now that in the presence of high light intensity the absorption (or emission) must depend on the radiation density.

Let us consider a semiconductor illuminated by light. If the light intensity is small the pairs which were produced will recombine and therefore the nonequilibrium density of pairs will be small. If the light intensity is high the density of pairs will be large and it is necessary to take into account the process of stimulated recombination.

In this case the absorption coefficient may be written in the following form

$$k = k_0[f_v(1 - f_c) - f_c(1 - f_v)] , \tag{2}$$

where f_c and f_v are distribution functions in conduction and valence band, respectively. In the case of small intensity $f_v \approx 1$, $f_c \approx 0$ and $k \approx k_0$.

There are three relaxation processes which take place in semiconductors,

1) The fast process of electron-electron collisions with a time constant of about $(10^{-12} \div 10^{-13})$ s for electron densities near $(10^{15} \div 10^{16})/\text{cm}^3$.

2) The process of establishing temperature equilibrium between lattice and carriers with time constant of about $(10^{-9} \div 10^{-10})$ s.

3) The process of recombination of pairs with time constant usually longer than 10^{-9} s.

If the intensity of light is not too high so that probability of pair creation is smaller than $10^{12}\,\text{s}^{-1}$ then the distribution of carriers can be described by the Fermi function

$$f = \frac{1}{\exp[(\varepsilon - \mu)/\varkappa T] + 1} . \tag{3}$$

In this case the saturation means that with increasing intensity f_c increases, f_v decreases and $f_v - f_c \to 0$. It means in turn that

$$\mu_c - \mu_v \to \hbar\omega , \tag{4}$$

where μ_c and μ_v are the corresponding quasi-Fermi levels. Thus the process of saturation in semiconductors means that splitting between quasi-levels approaches the energy of the photon.

It is possible to obtain the dependence of absorption coefficient on intensity of light in the case of strong saturation.

We can write the rate equations for the quasi-levels

$$\begin{cases} \dfrac{d\mu_c}{dt} = \left(\dfrac{dn}{d\mu_c}\right)^{-1} (Ik - R) , \\[2ex] \dfrac{d\mu_v}{dt} = -\left(\dfrac{dp}{d\mu_v}\right)^{-1} (Ik - R) , \end{cases} \tag{5}$$

where I is the intensity in quanta/s·cm², and R, the number of recombination pairs per second in the unit volume. One can expand the absorption coefficient and recombination rate in a power series in I.

Keeping only the linear terms:

$$\begin{cases} k = -k_0 \dfrac{\partial f_c}{\partial \varepsilon} [\hbar\omega - (\mu_c - \mu_v)] , \\[2ex] R = R_0 + A[\hbar\omega - (\mu_c - \mu_v)] . \end{cases} \tag{6}$$

If we put the time derivatives equal to zero, then we can obtain equations for $\mu_c - \mu_v$

$$\begin{cases} \hbar\omega - (\mu_c - \mu_v) = \dfrac{+R_0}{A - k_0(\partial f_c/\partial\varepsilon)I}, \\ k = k_0 \dfrac{\partial f_c}{\partial\varepsilon} \dfrac{-R_0}{A - k_0(\partial f_c/\partial\varepsilon)I}. \end{cases} \tag{7}$$

These expressions are valid at strong saturation,

$$A = \left(\frac{\partial R_0}{\partial n} + \frac{\partial R_0}{\partial p}\right)\left[\left(\frac{\partial n}{\partial\mu_c}\right)^{-1} - \left(\frac{\partial p}{\partial\mu_v}\right)^{-1}\right]^{-1}.$$

This result is also interesting if we consider the possibility of converting the energy of a coherent light beam into electric current by means of diodes. Practically speaking it means operation of the laser diode in reverse way. As it may be seen from the formula the voltage can approach the value of the quantum energy and the efficiency of this transformation can be very high.

Photomixing in Semiconductors.

O. SVELTO

Istituto di Fisica del Politecnico - Milano

1. – Introduction.

The phenomenon which is responsible for photomixing in a semiconductor can be summarized as follows. When a light wave is absorbed in a semiconductor electron-hole pairs are produced at a rate n which is proportional to the incident light power, *i.e.*, to the square of the electric field E at optical frequency. Therefore if the light wave is composed of two frequencies ω_1 and ω_2, due to this quadratic relationship between n and E, the rate of pair production n will be modulated at the difference frequency $\omega_1 - \omega_2$. If now a d.c. bias voltage is applied to the semiconductor, the resulting photocurrent will contain a component at the difference frequency $\omega_1 - \omega_2$ and therefore power can be delivered at this frequency to an external load.

The semiconductors so far used for photomixing fall in the following two classes: 1) *p-i-n* or *p-n* junctions [1-3], and bulk photoconductors [4, 5]. In the first case the junction is reverse-biased and the mixing mostly occurs in the *i*-layer for the *p-i-n* diode and in the depletion layer for the *p-n* diode. The purpose of the p and n materials is to provide electric contacts to the active region. The light is incident on the junction in the way shown in Fig. 1 *a*).

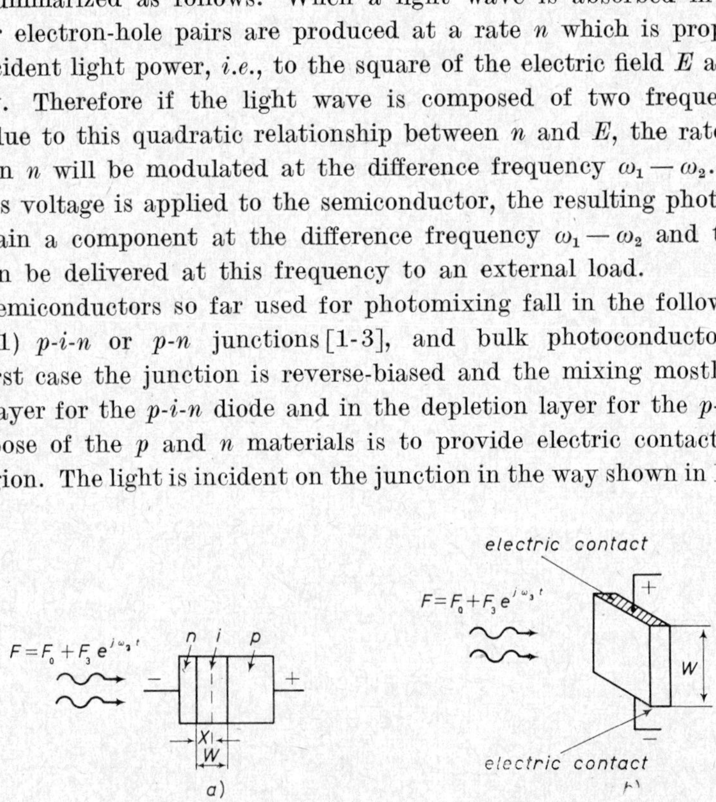

Fig. 1. – Schematic diagrams of semiconductor photodetectors: *a*) *p-i-n* photodiode, *b*) bulk photodonductor.

In the case of the bulk photoconductor the arrangement is as shown in Fig. 1 *b*). Of course, for both cases, the semiconducting device is connected to a suitable load to which it delivers power at the difference frequency $\omega_1 - \omega_2$.

In next Section we discuss the performances of the previous devices as photomixers both from a theoretical and experimental basis.

2. – Performances of semiconductors as photomixers.

2·1. *General considerations.* – We first discuss in more detail the mixing phenomenon. For this purpose we write the total electric field E_t of the incident light wave as

$$E_t = E_1 \cos \omega_1 t + E_2 \cos \omega_2 t \,, \tag{1}$$

where ω_1 and ω_2 are the two frequency components of the incident light. The square of E_t can then be written as

$$E_t^2 = E_1^2 \cos^2 \omega_1 t + E_2^2 \cos^2 \omega_2 t + \\ + E_1 E_2 \cos(\omega_1 - \omega_2) t + E_1 E_2 \cos(\omega_1 + \omega_2) t \,. \tag{2}$$

Now, as shown by PERSHAN and BLOEMBERGEN [6], there is a certain time uncertainty τ in the process of generation of electron-hole pairs in a semiconductor, and this time τ is generally given by the correlation time of the electron-photon interaction. Therefore we can say that the rate of pairs generation n is proportional to the average of the incident light power, *i.e.*, to the average of E_t^2 over the time τ. Since this time is of the order of 10^{-12} s, then in the case $(\omega_1 - \omega_2)\tau \ll 1$ the rate n is seen to be proportional to

$$n \propto \left(\frac{E_1^2 + E_2^2}{2}\right) + E_1 E_2 \cos(\omega_1 - \omega_2) t \,. \tag{3}$$

Hence, as previously stated, n is modulated at the difference frequency $\omega_1 - \omega_2$. In view of this result we shall assume for what follows that the incident light flux F (photons/cm² s) can be expressed in a complex notation as

$$F = F_0 + F_3 \exp[j\omega_3 t] \,, \tag{4}$$

where $\omega_3 = \omega_1 - \omega_2$. The ratio between F_3 and F_0 is seen by eq. (3) to be given by

$$\frac{F_3}{F_0} = \frac{2E_1 E_2}{E_1^2 + E_2^2} \,. \tag{5}$$

Note that eq. (4) may as well represent a light wave which is amplitude-modulated at ω_3. In this case the ratio F_3/F_0 is given by the index of modulation of the signal. Therefore what follows applies to the case of mixing of two optical frequencies as well as to the case of demodulating an amplitude-modulated light signal.

We now proceed to evaluate the current and the corresponding available power at frequency ω_3 for the devices shown in Fig. 1 when a light flux F of the form shown in eq. (4) is incident.

2'2. *Case of a p-i-n diode.* – Since the p and n regions are made up of heavily doped material, if the diode is reverse biased (as in Fig. 1 *a*)), most of the applied voltage will drop across the i-region which becomes a region of nearly constant electric field [7]. The electrons and holes photogenerated in the i-region are rapidly separated by this electric field, they travel across the i-region and finally they are collected by the n and p regions, respectively. Since the thickness of the i-region is normally very small (a few μm), the transit time across the i-region is, with the bias voltages commonly used (a few volts), of the order of 10^{-10} s [8]. Under these conditions, recombination between holes and electrons in the i-region can be complitely neglected.

The short circuit a.c. photocurrent $I_3(t)$ due to the term $F_3 \exp[j\omega_3 t]$ in eq. (4) is given by the average of the conduction current $I_{\text{cond}}(x, t)$ over the thickness of the i-region [9], *i.e.*,

$$I_3(t) = \frac{1}{W}\int_0^W I_{\text{cond}}(x, t)\,\mathrm{d}x\,, \tag{6}$$

where W is the thickness of the i-region (see Fig. 1 *a*)). To calculate now $I_{\text{cond}}(x, t)$ one must consider the contributions of all the carriers which are generated at some other place in the i-region at an earlier time t^* and which cross the plane at position x at time t. All these contributions have to be added up with their appropriate phase which is given by $\omega_3(t - t^*)$. The detailed calculation performed in this way gives the following expression for the amplitude I_3 of the a.c. photocurrent $I_3(t)$ [10, 11]:

$$I_3 = \eta q F_3 A\,|f(\omega_3 t_n)|\,, \tag{7}$$

where q is the electron charge, A is the cross-sectional area of the i-region and η is an effective quantum efficiency given by the product of the true quantum efficiency times the fraction of the light flux $F \exp[j\omega_3 t]$ which actually enters the i-region. The factor $|f(\omega_3 t_n)|$ is a dimensionless quantity always <1 which depends upon the product of the frequency ω_3 times the transit time t_n of the charges across the i-region, and also depends upon the fraction of the light flux which is absorbed within the i-region. If the light flux is completely absorbed within the i-region then the function $|f(\omega_3 t_n)|$ simply reduces to $\sin(\omega_3 t_n/2)/(\omega_3 t_n/2)$. The physical meaning of eq. (7) is easily understood when one notes that the factor $\eta F_3 A$ represents the total number of electron-hole pairs which are generated per second in the i-region while the factor $|f(\omega_3 t_n)|$ takes into account the differences in phase between the various contributions of carriers, as previously discussed.

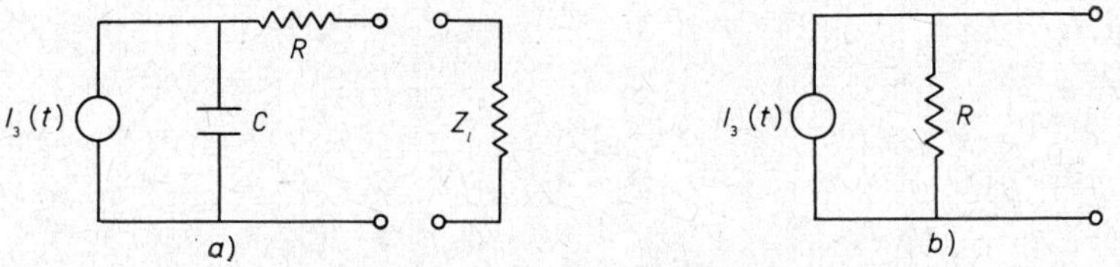

Fig. 2. – Microwave equivalent circuit of semiconductor photodetectors: *a*) *p-i-n* photodiode, *b*) bulk photodonductor.

To calculate the power available at frequency ω_3 one must know the equivalent circuit of a *p-i-n* diode at this frequency. Measurements performed by ANDERSON [12] have shown that, if ω_3 is a microwave frequency, the equivalent circuit can be approximated as shown in Fig. 2 *a*), where C is the capacity and R is the series resistance of the diode. Typically C and R are respectively of the order of $C \simeq 2$ pF and $R \simeq 2\ \Omega$. The power delivered to an external load Z_l will be a maximum when Z_l is the conjugate match of the internal impedance of the diode, *i.e.*,

$$Z_l = R + J\omega_3 L\,, \tag{8}$$

where $L = 1/\omega_3^2 C$. The power P_3 delivered in this case to the load is given by

$$P_3 = \frac{1}{4}\left(\frac{I_3}{\sqrt{2}}\right)^2 \frac{R}{(\omega_3 RC)^2}\,. \tag{9}$$

One sees that P_3 has a $1/\omega_3^2$ roll off with frequency due to the RC time constant of the diode. Note that P_3 further depends upon the frequency through I_3

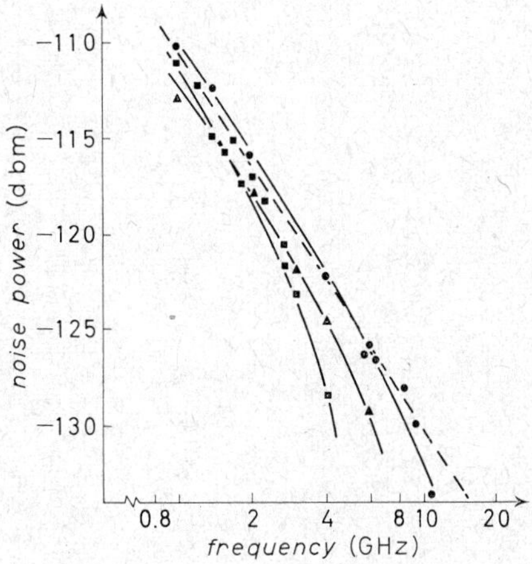

Fig. 3. – Noise power as a function of the frequency for a p-i-n photodiode: -●-●- Riesz 9/11/62 no. 1, $I_{\text{d.c.}} = 30\ \mu\text{A}$; -▲-▲- Philco L 4501, $I_{\text{d.c.}} = 7\ \mu\text{A}$; -■-■- Philco L 4500, $I_{\text{d.c.}} = 50\ \mu\text{A}$.

since $|f(\omega_3 t_n)|$ in eq. (7) is frequency-dependent as previously discussed. However if $\omega_3 t_n \ll 1$ then $|f(\omega_3 t_n)| \simeq 1$ and P_3 should be proportional to $1/\omega_3^2$. This has been verified by ANDERSON [11] by looking at the behavior of the shot noise of the diode as a function of the frequency. In fact the shot noise undergoes the same frequency limitation as the signal does. The results of his measurements are shown in Fig. 3.

The noise power of the diode can also be easily calculated by observing that there are two main sources of noise: 1) shot noise of the d.c. photocurrent produced by the term F_0 in eq. (4), and 2) thermal noise of the series resistance R of the diode. Since the shot noise originates in the i-region this noise power undergoes the same frequency limitations as the signal does (see eq. (9)). In this way one can calculate the signal-to-noise ratio, which results to be [13-15]

$$\left(\frac{S}{N}\right)_{\text{power}} = \frac{\eta}{4B}\left(\frac{F_3}{F_0}\right)^2 F_0 A \left[1 + \frac{2kT}{q}\,\frac{(\omega_3 RC)^2}{RI_0\,|f(\omega_3 t_n)|^2}\right]^{-1}, \tag{10}$$

where B is the bandwidth, k is the Boltzmann's constant, T the absolute temperature, and I_0 is the d.c. photocurrent. All the other symbols have been previously defined.

2·3. *Case of a bulk photoconductor.* – Three main features differentiate a bulk photoconductor mixer from a p-i-n diode: 1) In the case of a photoconductor the distance W (see Fig. 2 *b*)) between the electrodes is much bigger, hence the carrier transit time much longer than in the case of a p-i-n diode (typically about 3 to 4 orders of magnitude longer [4]). Therefore, for a photoconductor, it is not correct to neglect carrier recombinations, which actually play an important role. 2) Depending upon the nature of the electric contacts to the photoconductor, the carriers may or may not be replenished at the electrodes [16]. For a p-i-n replenishment is made automatically negligible by the nature of the *contacts* (*i.e.*, the p and n materials). 3) The direction of the incident light is orthogonal to the direction of the d.c. electric field for the case of a photoconductor, while for the case of a p-i-n diode the two directions are parallel.

These differences make the calculation and the final formula for a photoconductor to be somewhat different from a photodiode, although the starting point (*i.e.*, eq. (6)) is still the same. Furthermore the final formula for the a.c. photocurrent is different depending on whether the charges are or are not replenished at the electrodes. If replenishment occurs, the magnitude I_3 of the short-circuit a.c. photocurrent is given by [17-20]

$$I_3 = \left[\eta q F_3 A \frac{\tau_n}{t_n}\right][1 + \omega_3^2 \tau_n^2]^{-\frac{1}{2}}, \tag{11}$$

where τ_n is the carrier lifetime, t_n is the carrier transit time and all the other symbols have the same meaning as in eq. (7). Note that eq. (11), in the limit case $\omega_3 = 0$, gives the correct formula for the d.c. photocurrent in a photoconductor, the ratio τ_n/t_n being usually referred to as the gain of the photoconductor [21]. The factor $[1+\omega_3^2\tau_n^2]^{-\frac{1}{2}}$ in eq. (11) (which is always <1) is therefore understood to be a frequency limitation factor due to the differences in phase between the various contributions of the a.c. photocurrent. This factor is the analogue of the $|f(\omega_3 t_n)|$ factor in eq. (7) for the *p-i-n* diode. Note however that there is a basic difference between the two factors since the former depends upon the lifetime τ_n while the latter depends upon the transit time t_n. This is because, in a photoconductor, if replenishment occurs, the charges do not disappear when they reach the electrodes but only when recombination takes place, and therefore it is certainly not surprising that the frequency limitation factor in eq. (11) depends only on the lifetime. On the contrary, for a *p-i-n*, since the transit time is much shorter than the lifetime and since replenishment does not occur, the charges disappear only when they reach the electrodes. It is therefore not surprising that the frequency limitation factor in eq. (7) depends only on the transit time t_n.

If replenishment does not occur, the expression for I_3 for the photoconductor is a bit more complicated than eq. (11) because the frequency limitation factor depends both on the transit time and lifetime [17].

The calculation of the power available at frequency ω_3 is now a simple matter since the equivalent circuit of a photoconductor at microwave frequency is, with a good approximation, a pure resistance [17] (see Fig. 2 *b*)). Therefore the available power P_3 is simply given by

$$P_3 = \frac{1}{4}\left(\frac{I_3}{\sqrt{2}}\right)^2 R\,, \tag{12}$$

where I_3 is given by eq. (11) in the case of charge replenishment. At microwave frequencies eq. (11) can be semplified since it is $\omega_3\tau_n \gg 1$ for most semi-

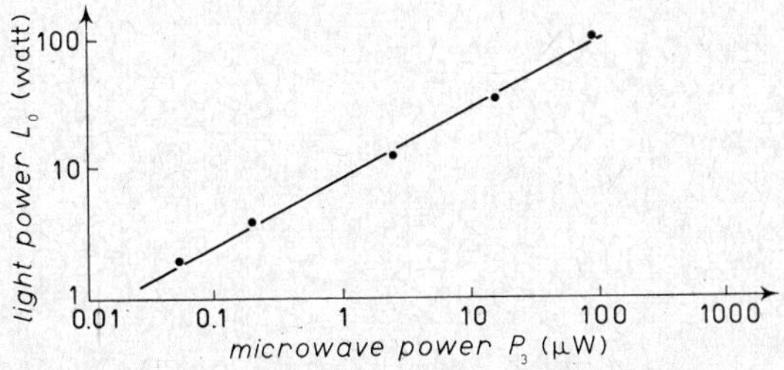

Fig. 4. – Power P_3 at the difference frequency $f_3 = \omega_3/2\pi$ as a function of the incident light power L_0. Bias voltage $V = 90$ V, frequency $f_3 = 1.327$ GHz.

conductors, and P_3 reduces to

$$P_3 = \frac{1}{8}[\eta q F_3 A]^2 \frac{R}{(\omega_3 t_n)^2} \tag{13}$$

and hence becomes independent from the lifetime τ_n. Since the transit time t_n is inversely proportional to the d.c. voltage V applied to the photoconductor, eq. (13) predicts for P_3 to be proportional to the square of the light intensity (to which F_3 is proportional) to V^2 and to $1/\omega_3^2$. This has been experimentally verified in the case of CdSe bulk photoconductor by using for the two optical frequencies ω_1 and ω_2 to be mixed two axial modes of a ruby laser [17]. The results are shown in Fig. 4, 5 and 6 and are in good agreement with eq. (13).

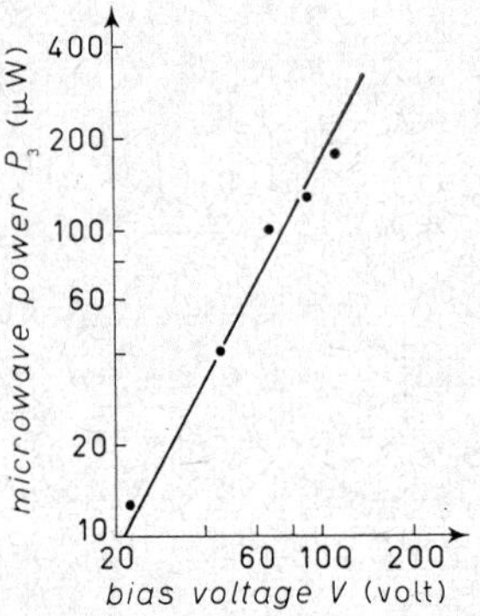

Fig. 5. – Power P_3 at the difference frequency $f_3 = \omega_3/2\pi$ as a function of the d.c. bias voltage V applied to the photoconductor. Light intensity $L_0 = 100$ W, frequency $f_3 = 1.327$ GHz.

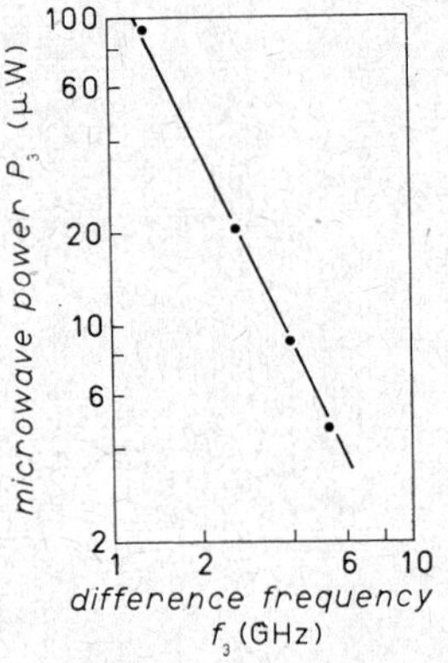

Fig. 6. – Power P_3 at the difference frequency $f_3 = \omega_3/2\pi$ as a function of the frequency. Light intensity $L_0 = 100$ W, bias voltage $V = 90$ V.

The noise of a photoconductor can also be easily calculated by observing that there are three main sources of noise [22]: 1) noise in the process of photogeneration of carriers, 2) noise in the process of recombination of carriers, and 3) thermal noise in the resistance R. In this way, with the help of eq. (12), one can calculate the signal-to-noise ratio, which results to be [13]

$$\left(\frac{S}{N}\right)_{\text{power}} = \frac{\eta}{8B}\left(\frac{F_3}{F_0}\right)^2 F_0 A \left[1 + \frac{kT}{q}\frac{t_n}{\tau_n}\frac{(1+\omega_3^2\tau_n^2)}{RI_0}\right]^{-1}, \tag{14}$$

where B is the bandwidth, k is the Boltzmann's constant, T the absolute temperature, and I_0 is the d.c. photocurrent. Equations (14) and (10) are rather similar. Note the factor $\frac{1}{8}$ which occurs in eq. (14) instead of the factor

$\frac{1}{4}$ in eq. (10). This comes about because in a photoconductor both generation *and* recombination noises are present, whereas in a photodiode only generation noise is present since the carriers do not recombine inside the *i*-region.

The performances of a photoconductor can now be theoretically compared with those of a photodiode by comparing eqs. (12) and (14) with eqs. (9) and (10) respectively. Without entering in too many details we merely wish to point out here that this comparison shows that a photodiode is a superior detector for low-level light intensities whereas at high light intensities (such as those, for instance, of a ruby laser) the two systems give comparable performances [13].

REFERENCES

[1] R. P. Riesz: *Rev. Sci. Instr.*, **33**, 994 (1962).
[2] H. Inaba and A. E. Siegman: *Proc. I.R.E.*, **50**, 1823 (1962).
[3] G. Lucovsky, M. E. Lasser and R. B. Emmons: *Electrochem. Soc. Electronics Division Abstracts*, **2**, 284 (1962).
[4] M. Di Domenico jr., R. H. Pantell, O. Svelto and J. N. Weaver: *Appl. Phys. Lett.*, **1**, 77 (1962).
[5] A. W. Smith: *Bull. Am. Phys. Soc.*, **8**, 381 (1963).
[6] P. S. Pershan and N. Bloembergen: *Appl. Phys. Lett.*, **2**, 115 (1963).
[7] W. T. Read: *Bell. Syst. Tech. Journ.*, **35**, 1239 (1956).
[8] H. Inaba and A. E. Siegman: Tech. Rep. No. 177-2 (June 1962), Stanford El. Labs, Stanford University (Stanford, Cal.).
[9] W. W. Gaertner: *Phys. Rev.*, **116**, 84 (1959).
[10] R. P. Riesz: *BTL Memorandum* (unpublished).
[11] L. K. Anderson: *Proc. I.E.E.E.*, **51**, 846 (1963).
[12] L. K. Anderson: *BTL Memorandum* (unpublished).
[13] M. Di Domenico jr. and O. Svelto: *Proc. I.E.E.E.*, **52**, 136 (1964).
[14] H. S. Sommers jr.: *Proc. I.E.E.E.*, **51**, 140 (1963).
[15] G. Lucovsky, M. E. Lasser and R. B. Emmons: *Proc. I.E.E.E.*, **51**, 166 (1963).
[16] R. H. Bube: *Photoconductivity of Solids* (New York, 1960), first ed., p. 75.
[17] O. Svelto, P. D. Coleman, M. Di Domenico jr. and R. H. Pantell: *J. Appl. Phys.*, **34**, 3182 (1963).
[18] G. Lucovsky, R. F. Schwarz and R. B. Emmons: *Proc. I.E.E.E.*, **51**, 613 (1963).
[19] G. J. Lasher and A. H. Nethercot: *Journ. Appl. Phys.*, 34, 2122 (1963).
[20] R. H. Pantell, M. Di Domenico jr., O. Svelto and J. N. Weaver: Quantum Electronics III, Vol. 2, (New York, 1964), p. 1811.
[21] See ref. [16] p. 60.
[22] A. van der Ziel: *Fluctuation Phenomena in Semiconductors* (New York, 1959), chap. 6.

Stimulated Raman Effect (*).

A. JAVAN

Physics Department, Massachusetts Institute of Technology - Cambridge, Mass.

1. – Introductory remarks.

The process of Raman scattering involves a double-quantum atomic transition in which one photon is absorbed from an incident radiation field at a frequency Ω_0 while a second photon is emitted simultaneously at a different frequency, ω. From energy conservation, $\hbar|\Omega-\omega|=|E_1-E_2|$, where E_1 and E_2 refer to the energies of the initial and the final states of the atom. Thus, at least one of the two photons is required to have a frequency larger than the resonance frequency of the atom, ω_{21}, given by $|E_2-E_1|\hbar$ (see Fig. 1). Furthermore, in the Raman process, the absorption and emission of the two photons, together with simultaneous transition of an atom from its initial to the final state, all take place in one single act of transition. In such an act, the phase memory of an atom is generally destroyed only after transition to the final state has been accomplished. Thus, the Raman process may be distinguished from stepwise transitions involving absorption and emission of photons through two consecutive single-quantum transitions via a third atomic energy level (see Fig. 2). Such a stepwise transition is accompanied by complete disruption

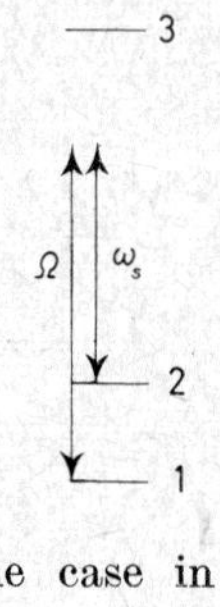

Fig. 1. – Three-level system. The Raman transition takes place between levels 1 and 2. Ω is the pump frequency and ω_s is the Stokes frequency. There are two special cases in which the Raman term is particularly enhanced. One is the case in which ω_{31} is close to ω_s. The other is the case in which ω_{31} is close to Ω. For the last case, see Fig. 2.

(*) Work supported by NASA, NsG-330.

of the phase of an atom after each act of emission or absorption of a single light quantum.

In an ordinary Raman-scattering experiment, an atomic system is subject to an intense light beam at a frequency $\Omega > |E_1 - E_2|/\hbar$. This light beam will be referred to as the pump field. If an atom is initially in the lower energy state, E_1, the Raman transition to the state E_2 will result in absorption of one photon at the pump frequency, Ω, and emission of one photon at a frequency $\omega_s = \Omega - |E_2 - E_1|/\hbar$, where ω_s is the well-known Stokes frequency. In the case where an atom is initially in the excited state, E_2, a transition may take place by absorption of one photon from the pump field and emission of one photon at a frequency $\omega_a = \Omega + |E_2 - E_1|/\hbar$, where ω_a is the well-known anti-Stokes frequency. In these two cases, initial presence of a light beam at the Stokes or anti-Stokes frequency is not necessary. The main requirement is the presence of the pump field which provides the absorbed photon. In the presence of the pump field alone, the act of emission of a Stokes or an anti-Stokes photon occurs through a spontaneous process. This may be referred to as the « spontaneous Raman effect ». However, if, in addition to the pump field, the system is simultaneously subjected to an additional light beam at the Stokes or at the anti-Stokes frequency, an act of emission will be stimulated further by the presence of the light quanta at the corresponding frequency. In the case where the majority of atoms are in the ground energy state, E_1, the stimulated Raman transition leads to coherent amplification of the Stokes field. This occurs at the expense of an attenuation of the pump field. Conversely, if somehow the majority of atoms are in the excited energy state, E_2, the light beam at the frequency ω_s will be attenuated while that at the frequency Ω is simultaneously amplified.

Fig. 2. – A three-level system in which, in addition to the Raman resonance, ω_{31} and ω_{32} resonate with the pump and the Stokes fields.

According to the above, the process of stimulated Raman effect may be used in achieving coherent amplification of an electromagnetic radiation. A maser system operating on this principle, does not require the presence of an inverted population. With a normal distribution of population where a lower energy level is more densely populated as compared to an upper energy level, a Raman-active transition is capable of coherently converting energy from a pump field into an applied field at the Stokes frequency.

The principle of stimulated Raman effect as a way of obtaining maser oscillation was initially considered [1] prior to the advent of optical masers. This principle has now been applied and further extended [2-4] into the optical range of frequency. In the present paper, the type of Raman transitions which are most common in the optical range of frequency will be particularly emphasized. These transitions are generally of the electrical dipole type. In the microwave region, however, paramagnetic levels in solids form an important class of levels for application of the principle of stimulated Raman effect. The details of the quantum-mechanical formulation of a magnetic-dipole Raman transition is similar to that of the electrical-dipole transitions considered in the following discussions.

In a Raman maser, once a self-sustained oscillation is achieved, additional interesting effects occur due to nonlinear mixing of the pump and the Stokes fields [5-7]. A quantum-mechanical treatment of these effects is given later in this paper.

2. – Induced polarization.

In this Section, we will be primarily concerned with the stimulated Raman effect and we shall not deal with the spontaneous process. This being the case, it will be best to formulate the problem without the use of a quantized electromagnetic field. For this, the interaction of a classical electromagnetic field with the bulk of the scatterer will be treated by evaluating the induced macroscopic polarization resulting from the presence of the field.

Consider an atomic system with a center-of-inversion symmetry, interacting through electrical-dipole coupling with two applied e.m. fields at the frequencies Ω and ω_s. In such a system, a Raman transition between two nondegenerate levels, E_1 and E_2, may be accounted for, by considering at least a third atomic energy level, E_3. The level E_3 will be required to be connected by electrical-dipole matrix elements to the levels 1 and 2. In this case, the presence of an inversion symmetry rules out the possibility of existence of an electrical-dipole matrix element between levels 1 and 2.

The effects arising from the presence of the third level, such as the induced Raman effect which is under our present discussions, become larger when the frequency $\omega_{31}=(E_3-E_1)/\hbar$ approaches the value of Ω (see Fig. 2). Thus, the existence of additional levels, other than E_1, E_2, and E_3, may be ignored only if

$$|\Omega-\omega_{31}|\ll|\Omega-\omega_{q1}|,$$

where $\omega_{q1}=(E_q-E_1)/\hbar$ with E_q as the energy of the q-th additional level. We shall assume in the following that such a condition is satisfied. Under this assumption, one needs to deal only with three energy levels. This enables one to attempt solving the quantum-mechanical equations in almost a closed form without resorting to an approximate perturbation calculation. Such a solution gives additional information on the effect of very intense fields on the line shape of the induced Raman effect. However, if one is interested in an approximate solution valid for weak fields, a restriction to three levels is not essential. In this case, the solution of the problem for more than three levels may be obtained by a trivial extension of the approximate solution of a three-level system.

We shall now proceed to estimate the induced polarization in a three-level system as described in the above. In terms of the elements of the density matrix, ϱ_{nk}, a component, p, of the electric polarization in a given direction may be written as

$$p = \sum \mu_{nk}\varrho_{kn} = \mu_{31}\varrho_{13} + \mu_{23}\varrho_{32} + \text{c.c.}\,, \tag{1}$$

where μ_{nk} is the corresponding component of the dipole moment matrix element connecting levels n and k. Furthermore, it is assumed that the diagonal elements of the density matrix are normalized according to $\sum \varrho_{nn} = N$, where N is the total density of the atoms. Thus, ϱ_{nn} represents directly the population of the n-th level.

Let us now consider the equations of motion for the off-diagonal elements of the density matrix in a representation in which the unperturbed Hamiltonian is diagonal:

$$\left(\frac{\mathrm{d}}{\mathrm{d}t} + i\omega_{nk} + \frac{1}{T}\right)\varrho_{nk} = \frac{1}{i\hbar}\sum_m (H'_{nm}\varphi_{mk} - \varrho_{nm}H'_{mk}) \tag{2}$$

with

$$\omega_{nk} = (E_n - E_m)/\hbar\,.$$

Notice that $\omega_{nk} = -\omega_{kn}$. The term $(\varrho_{nk})/T$ has been introduced in the eq. (2) in order to allow for the effects of random thermal relaxation processes. H'_{nk} in (2) is the matrix element of the perturbation Hamiltonian.

For the sake of definiteness, let us assume the two applied light waves at the frequencies Ω and ω_s to be plane polarized with their electric field vectors lying in the same direction. For an electric dipole interaction, the matrix element of the perturbation Hamiltonian is given by

$$H'_{nk} = -\mu_{nk}E\,,$$

where μ_{nk} is the dipole moment matrix element in the direction of the E-field and E is given by

$$E = E_0\cos(\Omega t + \varphi_0) + E_s\cos(\omega_s t + \varphi_s) = \tag{3}$$

$$= \tfrac{1}{2}(A_0\exp[i\Omega t] + A_s\exp[i\omega_s t]) + \text{c.c.}$$

with

$$A_0 = E_0 \exp[i\varphi_0], \qquad A_s = E_s \exp[i\varphi_s].$$

In the above equation, E_0 and φ_0 are the amplitude and the phase of the pump field, respectively. E_s and φ_n are the corresponding quantities for the Stokes field. Furthermore, the Raman transition will be assumed to be near resonance, namely, $\Omega - \omega_s \approx \omega_{21}$.

Applying (2) to our three-level system, we obtain for ϱ_{13}, ϱ_{32} and ϱ_{12}, the following equations:

$$\left(\frac{\mathrm{d}}{\mathrm{d}t} - i\omega_{31} + \frac{1}{T}\right)\varrho_{13} = \frac{\mu_{13}E}{i\hbar}(\varrho_{11} - \varrho_{33}) + \frac{\mu_{23}E}{i\hbar}\varrho_{12}, \tag{4a}$$

$$\left(\frac{\mathrm{d}}{\mathrm{d}t} + i\omega_{32} + \frac{1}{T}\right)\varrho_{32} = \frac{-\mu_{32}E}{i\hbar}(\varrho_{22} - \varrho_{33}) - \frac{\mu_{31}E}{i\hbar}\varrho_{12}, \tag{4b}$$

$$\left(\frac{\mathrm{d}}{\mathrm{d}t} - i\omega_{21} + \frac{1}{T}\right)\varrho_{12} = \frac{-E}{i\hbar}(\mu_{13}\varrho_{32} - \mu_{32}\varrho_{13}). \tag{4c}$$

In these equations, the matrix elements of the electric-dipole moment are assumed to be nonzero only for the off-diagonal elements, μ_{13} and μ_{23}. The order of energy levels is that given in the Fig. 1. Thus, ω_{31}, ω_{32}, and ω_{21} are all positive frequencies.

The eqs. (4) may be solved for ϱ_{13}, ϱ_{32}, and ϱ_{12} in terms of the population differences, $(\varrho_{11} - \varrho_{33})$ and $(\varrho_{22} - \varrho_{33})$. If the effect of saturation of population is not sizable, the population differences are essentially the same as that in the absence of the applied fields. In what follows immediately, we need not to be concerned about the saturation effect. Later below, the effect of saturation will be discussed separately.

We note from (4) that, ϱ_{13} and ϱ_{32} are coupled together through ϱ_{12}. The oscillatory components of ϱ_{13} and ϱ_{32} are responsible for induced radiative properties of our three-level system. This arises due to dependence of electric polarization on ϱ_{13} and ϱ_{32} given by (1). However, since $\mu_{12} = 0$, ϱ_{12} does not contribute directly to the value of electric polarization. Instead, it serves to drive ϱ_{13} and ϱ_{32} at the frequencies of the two applied fields.

Inserting (3) in (4) and inspecting various oscillatory terms in the resulting equations, we note that a nearly complete solution may be obtained by taking

$$\begin{cases} \varrho_{13} = (\lambda_{13}^- \exp[-i\omega_s t] + \Lambda_{13}^+ \exp[i\Omega t]) + (\lambda_{13}^+ \exp[i\omega_s t] + \Lambda_{13}^- \exp[-i\Omega t]), \\ \varrho_{32} = (\lambda_{32}^- \exp[-i\omega_s t] + \Lambda_{32}^+ \exp[i\Omega t]) + (\lambda_{32}^+ \exp[i\omega_s t] + \Lambda_{32}^- \exp[-i\Omega t]), \\ \varrho_{12} = D^+ \exp[i(\Omega - \omega_s)t] + D^- \exp[-i(\Omega - \omega_s)t]. \end{cases} \tag{5}$$

It should be emphasized that (5) applies only to situations where, in the presence of a pump field at the frequency Ω, one only allows the build-up of radiation at the Stokes frequency, ω_s. An inspection of (4) shows, however, that there always exists additional components of ϱ_{31} and ϱ_{32} at new frequencies such as at $2\Omega-\omega_s$. These components originate due to nonlinear mixing of oscillatory terms at the frequencies Ω and ω_s. There exists actual cases in which one allows build-up of radiation at these new frequencies leading to sizable amplitudes of ϱ_{13} and ϱ_{32} at the corresponding frequencies. These cases will be treated separately later below. At the moment, however, we shall treat the presence of these terms as small perturbations and, hence, ignore their existence in the first order.

Let us now substitute (5) in (4) and allow for the explicit form of E as given by (3). We may then proceed collecting the coefficients of each oscillatory terms separately. In doing so, however, in accordance to the above discussions, we shall ignore in (4*a*) and (4*b*), the presence of oscillatory terms other than those at the frequencies ω_s and Ω. This leads immediately to two sets of linear equations. One set contains only $(\lambda_{13}^-, \lambda_{32}^-, \Lambda_{13}^+, \Lambda_{32}^+, D^+)$ and the other contains the rest of the coefficients, $(\lambda_{13}^+, \lambda_{32}^+, \Lambda_{13}^-, \Lambda_{32}^-, D^-)$. The equations of the first set are obtained as follows:

The coefficients of $\exp[-i\omega_s t]$ in (4*a*) and (4*b*) give

$$(7)\quad \begin{cases} \left[(\omega_{31}+\omega_s)+\dfrac{i}{T}\right]\lambda_{13}^- = \dfrac{\mu_{13}A_s^*}{2\hbar}(\varrho_{11}-\varrho_{33})+\dfrac{A_0^*\,\mu_{23}}{2\hbar}D^+\,, \\[2ex] \left[-(\omega_{32}-\omega_s)+\dfrac{i}{T}\right]\lambda_{32}^- = -\dfrac{\mu_{32}A_s^*}{2\hbar}(\varrho_{22}-\varrho_{33})-\dfrac{\mu_{31}A_0^*}{2\hbar}D^+\,. \end{cases}$$

The coefficients of $\exp[i\Omega t]$ in (4*a*) and (4*b*) give

$$(8)\quad \begin{cases} \left[(\omega_{31}-\Omega)+\dfrac{i}{T}\right]\Lambda_{13}^+ = \dfrac{\mu_{13}A_0}{2\hbar}(\varrho_{11}-\varrho_{33})+\dfrac{\mu_{23}A_s}{2\hbar}D^+\,, \\[2ex] \left[-(\omega_{32}+\Omega)+\dfrac{i}{T}\right]\Lambda_{32}^+ = -\dfrac{\mu_{32}A_0}{2\hbar}(\varrho_{22}-\varrho_{33})-\dfrac{\mu_{31}A_s}{2\hbar}D^+\,. \end{cases}$$

The coefficients of $\exp[i(\Omega-\omega_s)t]$ in (4*c*) give

$$(9)\quad \left[\omega_{21}-(\Omega-\omega_s)+\frac{i}{T}\right]D^+ = \frac{A_0}{2\hbar}(\mu_{32}\lambda_{13}^- - \mu_{13}\lambda_{32}^-)+\frac{A_s^*}{2\hbar}(\mu_{32}\Lambda_{13}^+ - \mu_{13}\Lambda_{32}^+)\,.$$

Accordingly, $\lambda_{13}^-, \lambda_{32}^-, \Lambda_{13}^+, \Lambda_{32}^+$ are coupled together through D^+. These coefficients may be determined by solving simultaneously (7), (8) and (9). An inspection of (9) reveals a resonance behavior when $\Omega > \omega_s$ and $(\Omega-\omega_s)$ approach the value of ω_{21}. This corresponds to the resonance of the Raman transition. As a reminder of this resonance behavior, let us define

$$R = \frac{1}{\omega_{21} - (\Omega - \omega_s) + i/T}. \tag{10}$$

We note from (9) that D^+ is proportional to R. It will be seen below that this leads to resonance behavior of the Raman terms in λ_{13}^-, λ_{32}^-, Λ_{13}^+ and Λ_{32}^+.

A second set of equations involving the rest of the terms (λ_{13}^+, λ_{32}^+, Λ_{13}^-, Λ_{32}^-, D^-) may be obtained by collecting the coefficients of $\exp[i\omega_s t]$, $\exp[-i\Omega t]$ and $\exp[-i(\Omega - \omega_s)t]$. The resulting equations are similar to (7), (8) and (9). However, for $\Omega > \omega_s$ and $\Omega - \omega_s$ close to ω_{21}, the resonance behavior mentioned above does not occur in this second set. As a result of this, it will be seen later below that with the exception of some special circumstances, the contributions of these terms to the Raman effect will be negligible. We may now proceed solving (7), (8) and (9). Substituting (9) in (7) and (8), we obtain four linear equations in four unknowns (λ_{13}^-, λ_{32}^-, Λ_{13}^+ and Λ_{32}^+). An inspection of the resulting equations reveals the presence of considerable symmetry in the forms of various terms which may be taken to advantage in obtaining a complete solution with ease.

Let us introduce the following simplifying notation:

$$L_{ij}(\omega) = (\omega_{ji} - \omega) + \frac{i}{T}, \tag{11}$$

with $\omega_{ji} = (E_j - E_i)/\hbar$ interpreted algebrically as before. According to this notation, the coefficients of λ_{13}^- and λ_{32}^- in the left-hand sides of eqs. (7) are $L_{13}(-\omega_s)$ and $L_{32}(-\omega_s)$, respectively. Similarly, the coefficients of Λ_{13}^+ and Λ_{32}^+ in the left-hand sides of (8) are $L_{13}(\Omega)$ and $L_{32}(\Omega)$, respectively. Specifically, we have

$$\begin{cases} L_{13}(-\omega_s) = (\omega_{31} + \omega_s) + \dfrac{i}{T}, \\ L_{32}(-\omega_s) = -(\omega_{32} - \omega_s) + \dfrac{i}{T}, \\ L_{13}(\Omega) \quad = (\omega_{31} - \Omega) + \dfrac{i}{T}, \\ L_{32}(\Omega) \quad = -(\omega_{32} + \Omega) + \dfrac{i}{T}. \end{cases} \tag{12}$$

In order to simplify our present discussions, let us assume, for the moment, a population distribution where essentially all of the atoms occupy the lowest energy state. This will correspond to $\varrho_{22} = \varrho_{33} = 0$ and $\varrho_{11} = N$, with N as the density of the atoms. With this assumption, the complete solution of (7),

(8) and (9) for λ_{13}^- and λ_{32}^- will be

$$(13) \qquad \lambda_{13}^- = \frac{\varrho_{11}\mu_{13}A_s^*}{2\hbar L_{13}(-\omega_s)} + \frac{\varrho_{11}|\mu_{23}|^2\mu_{13}|A_0|^2A_s^*}{8\hbar^3\Delta} R \left\{\frac{L_{13}(-\omega_s)+L_{13}(\Omega)}{[L_{13}(-\omega_s)]^2 L_{13}(\Omega)}\right\}$$

and

$$(14) \qquad \lambda_{32}^- = \frac{-\varrho_{11}|\mu_{13}|^2\mu_{32}|A_0|^2A_s^*}{8\hbar^3\Delta} R \left\{\frac{L_{13}(-\omega_s)+L_{13}(\Omega)}{L_{32}(-\omega_s)L_{13}(-\omega_s)L_{13}(\Omega)}\right\}.$$

In the above equations, R gives the Raman resonance and is defined by (10), L_{ij} are given in (12) and Δ is given by

$$(15) \qquad \Delta = 1 - \frac{|A_0|^2}{4\hbar^2} R \left[\frac{|\mu_{23}|^2}{L_{13}(\Omega)} + \frac{|\mu_{13}|^2}{L_{32}(\Omega)}\right] - \frac{|A_s|^2}{4\hbar^2} R \left[\frac{|\mu_{23}|^2}{L_{13}(-\omega_s)} + \frac{|\mu_{13}|^2}{L_{32}(-\omega_s)}\right].$$

Note that, at the limit of small field intensities, Δ will reduce to unity. However, for very large fields, Δ introduces considerable distortions in the Raman response which needs to be considered. It should also be noted that the above expressions hold if the energy separations of level 3 from levels 1 and 2 are such that new resonances are introduced with respect to the frequencies Ω and ω_s. For instance, if ω_{31} approaches the value of Ω, (13) and (14) still hold.

Before we proceed further, let us discuss the behavior of the second set of coefficients (λ_{13}^+, λ_{32}^+, Λ_{13}^- and Λ_{32}^-). As it was pointed out earlier, the equations governing these quantities are similar to (7), (8) and (9). In fact, the final expressions for λ_{13}^+ and λ_{32}^+ may be obtained from the explicit solutions of λ_{13}^- and λ_{32}^- given above. For this, one needs to substitute Ω and ω_s in (13) and (14) by $-\Omega$ and $-\omega_s$, respectively, and also substitute A_0 and A_s by their complex conjugates, A_0^* and A_s^*, respectively. The same operation may be used to transform Λ_{13}^+ and Λ_{32}^+ to Λ_{13}^- and Λ_{32}^-. An inspection of (13) and (14) shows immediately that the resonance form of R, which is evident from (10), will disappear if the signs of Ω and ω_s are reversed. Thus, the Raman terms in λ_{13}^+ and λ_{32}^+ are anti-resonant and in general, they contribute negligibly to the actual value of polarization. An exception will occur, however, if ω_{31} happens to be on resonance with respect to ω_s. Under this condition, new resonances will appear through the presence of the terms in $L_{13}(\omega_s)$ in the denominators of the Raman terms of λ_{13}^+ and λ_{32}^+. In this case, the contributions of the λ_{13}^+ and λ_{32}^+ to the Raman terms will be in excess of those of λ_{13}^- and λ_{32}^-. However, if ω_{31} approaches the value of Ω (see Fig. 2), λ_{13}^+ and λ_{32}^+ will remain small and the main terms contributing to the Raman effect will originate from λ_{13}^- and λ_{32}^-. These two cases differ in that, for $\Omega > \omega_s$ and $\Omega - \omega_s \approx \omega_{31}$, the condition $\omega_{31} \approx \omega_s$ introduces only one additional resonance, while the resona ce condition $\omega_{31} \approx \Omega$ implies a simultaneous presence of an additional resonance given by $\omega_{32} \approx \omega_s$ (see Fig. 2). An inspection of various terms in $\lambda_{ij}^\pm$ shnow that the presence of each additional resonance introduces an enhancement of the Raman terms. Accordingly, this enhancement is larger for $\omega_{31} \approx \Omega$ as compared to the case in which $\omega_{31} \approx \omega_s$.

In the following discussions, we shall assume that ω_s is considerably removed from the resonance of the (3, 1) transition; namely, $|\omega_{31}-\omega_s| \gg 1/T$. In this way, we may ignore entirely the contributions of λ_{13}^+ and λ_{32}^+ to the Raman terms. However, in doing so, we will not be inhibited in allowing ω_{31} to become comparable to Ω for which (13) and (14) give the main contributions to the Raman terms.

In the above discussions, we were primarily concerned with the behavior of the Raman terms in $\lambda_{ij}^{\pm}$. From (13) and (14), we note that the contribution λ_{ij}^- to the linear polarization arises from the first term in the right-hand side of (13). This term is responsible for absorption of power due to direct (1, 3) transition. The absence of a linear term associated with the (2, 3) transition in (13) and (14) is due to our simplifying assumption on the population distribution; namely, $\varrho_{22} = \varrho_{33} = 0$. Let us now consider the linear terms in λ_{ij}^+. Applying the prescription given in the above for transforming λ_{ij}^- to λ_{ij}^+, we obtain for the linear terms

$$(16) \qquad \begin{cases} \lambda_{13}^+ = \dfrac{\varrho_{11}\mu_{13}A_s}{2\hbar L_{13}(\omega_s)}, \\ \lambda_{32}^+ = 0 . \end{cases}$$

Unlike the Raman terms, the linear term of λ_{13}^+ may not be ignored in the presence of the corresponding term in λ_{13}^-. Accordingly, subject to the conditions $\varrho_{22} = \varrho_{33} = 0$ and $|\omega_{31}-\omega_s| \gg 1/T$, (13), (14) and (16) describe completely the interaction of our Stokes field with the three-level system.

At this point, we need various expressions describing the exchange of power between the induced polarization and electromagnetic field. For this, let us write the polarization at the Stokes frequency in the complex notation, $p_s = \chi A_s^* \exp[-i\omega_s t]$. In this form, the actual value of polarization is the real part of p_s. The Stokes field is $E_s =$ real part of $A_s^* \exp[-i\omega_s t]$, and χ is the usual definition of suceptibility. The imaginary part of χ is responsible for absorption or induced emission of power and the real part introduces a phase shift in polarization. Let us write the real and imaginary parts of χ in the form

$$\chi = \chi' - i\chi'' .$$

The increase of power, ΔP, across a small thickness of the sample, ΔZ, may be written in terms of χ'' as

$$(17) \qquad \Delta P = \frac{\omega_s}{2} \chi'' |A_s|^2 \Delta Z .$$

From this, we may define a gain (or attenuation) coefficient per unit length, γ, given by

$$\gamma = \frac{\Delta P}{\Delta Z P} = \frac{4\pi\omega_0}{c}\chi'' . \tag{18}$$

Thus, for $\chi'' > 0$ we obtain a power gain, while for $\chi'' < 0$ we obtain an attenuation.

The expression for susceptibility may be written in terms of λ_{ij}^* by considering the above definition of p_s and making note of the eqs. (1) and (3). This gives

$$\chi A_s^* = 2[(\mu_{31}\lambda_{13}^-) + (\mu_{23}\lambda_{32}^-) + (\mu_{31}\lambda_{13}^+)^* + (\mu_{23}\lambda_{32}^+)^*] . \tag{19}$$

From (13), (14) and (16), we find that χ consists of two parts, $\chi = \chi_0 + \chi_s$. The first part, χ_0, is the ordinary susceptibility which does not depend on the presence of the pump field. The second part, χ_s, is proportional to $|A_0|^2$ and is the Raman susceptibility.

Let us now consider various limiting cases separately. Assume first that the applied fields are not very large so that Δ given by (15) may be approximated as unity. Under this condition, the Raman susceptibility obtained from 19), (13) and (14), may be written as

$$\chi_s = \frac{\varrho_{11}|\mu_{23}\mu_{13}|^2|A_0|^2}{4\hbar^3} R\left[\frac{1}{L_{13}(\Omega)} + \frac{1}{L_{13}(-\omega_s)}\right]\left[\frac{1}{L_{13}(-\omega_s)} - \frac{1}{L_{32}(-\omega_s)}\right], \tag{20}$$

where L_{ij} are given by (12) and R is responsible for the Raman resonance and is given by (10). Let us now assume the absence of all possible resonances other than the Raman resonance; *i.e.*, $|\omega_{31} - \Omega| \gg 1/T$ and $\omega_{21} \approx \Omega - \omega_s$. In this case, the imaginary parts of the terms in the square brackets of (20) become much smaller then the real parts and contribute only a small phase angle which may be ignored. Under this condition, (20) may be written as

$$\chi_s = \frac{\alpha|A_0|^2}{\delta + i}, \tag{21}$$

where

$$\alpha = \frac{\varrho_{11}|\mu_{23}\mu_{13}|^2 T}{4\hbar^3} \frac{(\omega_{31} + \omega_{32})^2}{(\omega_{32} - \omega_s)^2(\omega_{31} + \omega_s)} \tag{22}$$

and

$$\delta = [\omega_{21} - (\Omega - \omega_s)]T .$$

δ gives the detuning of the Raman transition in unit of angular frequency width, $1/T$. In α, we have assumed a near resonance Raman condition and accordingly the deviation $\omega_{21}-(\Omega-\omega_s)$ is ignored compared to ω_{32}.

If we separate the real and imaginary parts of (21) in the form of $\chi_s'-i\chi_s''$, it becomes immediately evident that χ_s'' is positive. Accordingly, the Raman susceptibility gives rise to a net gain of power at the Stokes frequency. The gain factor may be obtained from χ_s'' and (18).

It should be pointed out that, if ω_{31} is not far different from Ω, the imaginary parts of the square brackets in eq. (20) may no longer be ignored. In this case, the Raman resonance will be distorted and asymmetrical, as is evident from (20).

For the sake of completeness, let us also write down the expression for linear susceptibility χ_0. From (19), (13) and (16), we obtain

$$\chi_0 = \frac{\varrho_{11}|\mu_{13}|^2}{\hbar}\left[\frac{1}{L_{13}^*(-\omega_s)}+\frac{1}{L_{13}^*(\omega_s)}\right]. \tag{23}$$

If we write χ_0 in the form $\chi_0'-\chi_0''$, we note that χ_0'' is negative leading to an absorption of power as expected.

In order to achieve a net amplification of power at the Stokes field, we need to have $\chi_0''+\chi_s''>0$. Comparing the imaginary parts of (21) and (23), we note immediately that $\chi_0''+\chi_s''>0$, if

$$\left|\frac{\mu_{23}A_0}{2\hbar}\right|^2 T^2 > \frac{4\omega_s\omega_{31}(\omega_{32}-\omega_s)}{(\omega_{31}-\omega_s)^2(\omega_{31}+\omega_{32})^2} \approx \frac{\omega_s}{\omega_{31}}.$$

In the above, we have assumed that $\omega_{21}\ll\omega_{32}$. Thus, unless ω_s is considerably smaller than ω_{31}, a net gain may only be obtained when the quantity $|\mu_{23}E_0/\hbar|$ is comparable or larger than $1/T$. It should, however, be remembered that the linewidth parameter, $1/T$, refers to the homogeneous part of the broadening of the resonance, namely, the width of the individual atoms. In many instances, this width may be considerably smaller than the full observed widths due to presence of inhomogeneous broadening.

For purposes of quick calculations, the gain at the Raman frequency defined by $G_s=\Delta P_s/P_s$, may be written in terms of the ordinary absorption coefficient of (1, 3) transition, $A=|\Delta P|/P$, measured at a frequency resonating with ω_{31}. This relationship is

$$G_s \approx \left|\frac{\mu A_0}{\hbar(\omega_{31}-\Omega)}\right|^2 A.$$

In the presence of feedback, self-sustained oscillation at the Stokes frequency will result if G_s is larger than the loss of the medium.

3. – Distortion of Raman line shape at large field intensities.

Let us now consider the limit in which the intensities of the applied fields are so large that the term in Δ appearing in (13) and (14) and given by (15), may no longer be approximated by unity. In this case, the full expression for Raman susceptibility, χ_r, may be obtained from (20) by multiplying it by $1/\Delta$. Let us rewrite the expression for Δ given by (15) in the following abbreviated form:

$$\Delta = 1 - \frac{a}{\delta + i}, \tag{23}$$

where

$$a = \frac{T|A_0|^2}{4\hbar^2}\left[\frac{|\mu_{23}|^2}{L_{13}(\Omega)} + \frac{|\mu_{13}|^2}{L_{32}(\Omega)}\right] + \frac{T|A_s|^2}{4\hbar^2}\left[\frac{|\mu_{23}|^2}{L_{13}(-\omega_s)} + \frac{|\mu_{13}|^2}{L_{32}(-\omega_s)}\right] \tag{24}$$

and, as before, δ is the Raman detuning parameter given by $\delta = [\omega_{21} - (\Omega - \omega_s)]T$. The terms L_{ij} appearing in (24) are defined by (12).

Let us assume off-resonance condition for separation of (1, 3) levels; namely $|\omega_{31} - \Omega| \gg 1/T$. In this case, we may utilize eq. (21) and by dividing it by Δ, we obtain

$$\chi_s = \frac{\alpha|A_0|^2}{\delta - a + i}, \tag{25}$$

where α is given by (22). Accordingly, the real part of a gives a frequency shift while its imaginary part is responsible for broadening of Raman resonance. An inspection of (24) shows, however, that under the condition $|\omega_{31} - \Omega| \gg 1/T$, the real part of a is considerably larger than its imaginary part. Thus, the presence of a leads predominantly to a frequency shift unless $|\omega_{31} - \Omega|$ approaches the value of $1/T$, in which case the broadening will also become appreciable. In order to give an order-of-magnitude estimate of this shift, let us continue assuming $|\omega_{31} - \Omega| \gg 1/T$ and also take $|A_s|^2 \ll |A_0|^2$. Furthermore, let us take a case in which $(\omega_{31} - \Omega)$ is the smallest frequency term appearing in various denominators of the square brackets of (24). With these assumptions, we obtain

$$a = \frac{|\mu_{23} A_0|^2}{4\hbar^2} \frac{T}{(\omega_{31} - \Omega)}. \tag{26}$$

According to (25), the peak frequency of the Raman resonance occurs at

$$\delta - a = 0,$$

This gives a frequency shift, $\Delta\nu_s$ given by

$$\Delta\nu_s = -\frac{|\mu_{23} A_0|^2}{8\pi\hbar^2(\omega_{31} - \Omega)} . \tag{27}$$

This shift is a manifestation of high-frequency Stark effect produced by the applied fields. The magnitude of the shift is particularly sizable if $(\omega_{31} - \Omega)$ is not very large. In order to give a numerical example, let us take a case in which ω_{31} is in the ultra-violet while Ω is in the visible region. (This is, for instance, the case of nitrobenzene excited by ruby-maser light, which, by the way, is not a particularly favorable example for achieving a large frequency shift.) Furthermore, assume $\mu = 4 \cdot 10^{-18}$ e.s.u. For a Q-switched ruby maser with 20 megawatt power focussed to an area corresponding to dimensions of the order of 0.25 mm, we obtain a shift of the Stokes emission towards the violet by about $\Delta\nu_s = 1\ \text{cm}^{-1}$. STOICHEFF has detected the presence of a frequency shift in his studies of stimulated Raman effect [9]. At the present, however, it is not clear whether the frequency shift discussed in this paper accounts for those observed by STOICHEFF. In fact, spurious distortions of the line shape due to sources other than those considered in this paper and connected, perhaps, with the kinematics of the growth of radiation, may possibly be present in some cases. However, the frequency shift due to high-frequency Stark effect as discussed in this paper, appears to be a sizable effect which should be detectable in favorable circumstances.

If Ω approaches the values of ω_{31}, the distortions of the Raman line shape becomes more sizable. In this case, the full expression for χ_s given by (20) divided by Δ, should be used. For $|\omega_{31} - \Omega| \approx 1/T$ the Raman effect will be mixed with the direct single-quantum transition given by the linear part of the susceptibility. This problem has been treated previously by the author [10] and by CLOGSTON [11]. The only additional effect which may become sizable for $|\omega_{31} - \Omega| \approx 1/T$, is that of the saturation of population.

4. – Parametric amplification at the anti-Stokes frequency.

In this Section, we consider the effect of nonlinearities of the three-level system which lead to oscillatory components of the radiating elements of the density matrix, ϱ_{13} and ϱ_{32}, at frequencies other than those of the applied fields. The resulting polarization at a new frequency may radiate coherently if its propagating phase allows constructive interference of the radiated field. In this case, the radiated power will grow as a function of the depth of penetration of the fields within the sample. A characteristics of this type of growth of the radiated wave is that, the increase of power, ΔP, over a thickness of the sample, ΔZ, is proportional to the amplitude of the wave within this thickness. This may be seen by noting that, ΔP is given by the time average of $\langle (\mathrm{d}p_m/\mathrm{d}t) E_m \rangle \Delta Z$, where p_m is the driven polarization at the new mixed frequency and E_m is the radiation field at the corresponding frequency. Considering that, to the first order, p_m is independent of E_m, the resulting increase of power, ΔP, is hence proportional to the amplitude of E_m. This type of gain is characteristics of « parametric amplification » which differs from normal maser gain where the induced polarization is proportional to the field amplitude leading to an increase of power proportional to the square of the field amplitude. (Such a distinction is, however, an artificial one in that both parametric and maser gain originate from the induced processes.) Let us now consider parametric gain in a material which presents a background loss at the mixed frequency. The attenuation of a propagating field due to normal type of losses gives a decrease of power, ΔP, proportional to the square of the field amplitude. Thus the parametric increase of power has a lower-order dependence on the field amplitude as compared to the decrease of power due to normal losses. Accordingly, regardless of the extent of lossiness of the material, the parametric generation of power leads to a growth of power at the limit of low field intensity where quantities of the order of E_m^2 may be ignored. This growth will take place until the background absorption becomes comparable to the parametric increase of power.

The problem of parametric generation at the anti-Stokes frequency, arising from the presence of the pump and the Stokes fields, has been discussed by TOWNES in his lecture [5]. In the discussions which follow, we shall treat this problem quantum-mechanically by evaluating additional oscillatory components of the radiating elements of the density matrix, ϱ_{13} and ϱ_{32}.

In the presence of the pump and the Stokes fields at the frequencies Ω and ω_s, the lowest-order mixing terms in ϱ_{13} and ϱ_{32}, occurs at the frequency $2\Omega - \omega_s$. This may be seen by noting that, according to discussions of the previous Section, the pump and the Stokes fields give rise to a component of ϱ_{12} oscillating at the frequency $\Omega - \omega_s$ and given by $D^+ \exp[i(\Omega - \omega_s)t]$. This term, in turn, mixes with the pump field to produce an oscillatory component of the product $E\varrho_{12}$ at the frequency $2\Omega - \omega_s$. The presence of $E\varrho_{12}$ in the eqs. (4a) and (4b) of the master equations subsequently drives ϱ_{13} and ϱ_{32} at the frequency $2\Omega - \omega_s$. Since $\Omega - \omega_s$ is assumed to be close to ω_{21}, we note that $2\Omega - \omega_s \approx \Omega + \omega_{21}$. Thus, in the presence of the pump and the Stokes fields, the radiating elements of the density matrix, ϱ_{13} and ϱ_{32}, oscillate at a new frequency $\omega_a = 2\Omega - \omega_s$, which happens to fall within the anti-Stokes resonance of the pump field. These components of the density matrix may subsequently radiate at the corresponding frequency, ω_a. The resulting field, in turn, interacts further with the three-level system. Accordingly, in addition to the pump and the Stokes fields given by (3), we shall assume the presence of an additional field at the anti-Stokes frequency, ω_a, given by

$$E_a(t) = \tfrac{1}{2}(A_a \exp[i\omega_a t] + A_a^* \exp[-i\omega_a t]) \,, \tag{28}$$

where

$$A_a = E_a \exp[i\varphi_a] \quad \text{and} \quad \omega_a = 2\Omega - \omega_s \,.$$

We now proceed solving (4*a*), (4*b*) and (4*c*) in the presence of three fields given by (28) and (3). The components of the density matrix may now be written as

$$\varrho_{13} = \sum_{+,-} \{\lambda_{13}^{\pm} \exp[\pm i\omega_s t] + \Lambda_{13}^{\pm} \exp[\pm i\Omega t] + l_{13}^{\pm} \exp[\pm i\omega_a t]\} \,, \tag{29}$$

$$\varrho_{32} = \sum_{+,-} \{\lambda_{32}^{\pm} \exp[\pm i\omega_s t] + \Lambda_{32}^{\pm} \exp[\pm i\Omega t] + l_{32}^{\pm} \exp[\pm i\omega_a t]\} \,, \tag{30}$$

where, in taking $\sum_{+,-}$ the plus sign in an exponent is to be taken with the plus sign in the coefficient which multiplies it, and similarly the minus signs are to be taken together. An inspection of (4*c*) in the master equations for the density matrix shows that, if the only important fields are those at the frequencies ω_s, Ω and ω_a, ϱ_{12} has the same form as given in (5), namely

$$\varrho_{12} = D^+ \exp[-i(\Omega - \omega_s)t] + D^- \exp[-i(\Omega - \omega_s)t] \,, \tag{31}$$

here it should be remembered that according to our assumptions, $\Omega - \omega_s = \omega_a - \Omega$. In the present case, the equations describing D^+ and D^- are different than those considered in the previous Section.

Using (29), (30), and (31) in (4*a*), (4*b*), and (4*c*), we may proceed separating various oscillatory terms. Unlike the case discussed in the previous Section, we note that, in its most general form, all of the coefficients ($\lambda_{ij}^{\pm}$, $\Lambda_{ij}^{\pm}$ and $l_{ij}^{\pm}$) are coupled together. The resulting equations are, however, simple in their features and a complete solution may readily be obtained without approximation. In the following, however, we shall first proceed in giving a solution which is valid only at the limit of low field intensities. A more complete solution will be given later below.

To the first order, $l_{ij}^{\pm}$, $\Lambda_{ij}^{\pm}$, $\lambda_{ij}^{\pm}$ depend linearly on the field intensities. These linear terms are responsible for linear susceptibility describing the ordinary single-quantum transitions between various levels. They may be obtained from (4*a*) and (4*b*) by ignoring the term in ϱ_{12}; the element ϱ_{12} being nonlinear in its dependence on the field intensities. Assuming, as before, $\varrho_{22} = \varrho_{33} = 0$, we obtain to the first order

$$(32)\quad \begin{cases} l^+_{13} = \dfrac{\varrho_{11}\mu_{13}A_a}{2\hbar L_{13}(\omega_a)}\,, & l^+_{32} = 0\,, \\[2ex] \lambda^-_{13} = \dfrac{\varrho_{11}\mu_{13}A^*_s}{2\hbar L_{13}(-\,\omega_s)}\,, & \lambda^-_{32} = 0\,, \\[2ex] \Lambda^+_{13} = \dfrac{\varrho_{11}\mu_{13}A_0}{2\hbar L_{13}(\Omega)}\,, & \Lambda^+_{32} = 0\,, \\[2ex] \Lambda^-_{13} = \dfrac{\varrho_{11}\mu_{13}A^*_0}{2\hbar L_{13}(-\,\Omega)}\,, & \Lambda^-_{32} = 0\,, \end{cases}$$

where, $L_{ij}(\omega)$ are defined by eq. (11).

Let us now consider the complete equations for $l^\pm_{ij}$ by keeping the term in ϱ_{12} in (4*a*) and (4*b*). Remembering that $\omega_a = 2\Omega - \omega_s$, the coefficients of the terms in $\exp[i\omega_a t]$ give

$$(33)\quad \begin{cases} L_{13}(\omega_a)l^+_{13} = \dfrac{\varrho_{11}\mu_{13}A_a}{2\hbar} + \dfrac{\mu_{23}A_0}{2\hbar}D^+\,, \\[2ex] L_{32}(\omega_a)l^+_{32} = -\dfrac{\mu_{31}A_0}{2\hbar}D^+\,. \end{cases}$$

The equations describing D^+ may be obtained similarly from (4*c*) by collecting the coefficients of the oscillatory terms in $\exp[i(\Omega - \omega_s)t]$ keeping in mind that $\Omega - \omega_s = \omega_a - \Omega$:

$$(34)\quad \left[\omega_{31} - (\Omega - \omega_s) + \frac{i}{T}\right] D^+ = \frac{A^*_0}{2\hbar}(\mu_{32}l^+_{13} - \mu_{13}l^+_{32}) + \\ + \frac{A_a}{2\hbar}(\mu_{32}\Lambda^-_{13} - \mu_{13}\Lambda^-_{32}) + \frac{A_0}{2\hbar}(\mu_{32}\lambda^-_{13} - \mu_{13}\lambda^-_{32}) + \frac{A^*_s}{2\hbar}(\mu_{32}\Lambda^+_{13} - \mu_{13}\Lambda^+_{32})\,.$$

Inserting the first-order terms (32), in (34), we obtain

$$(35)\quad D^+ = \frac{\varrho_{11}\mu_{32}\mu_{13}}{4\hbar^2} R\left\{A_0 A^*_s\left[\frac{1}{L_{13}(-\,\omega_s)} + \frac{1}{L_{13}(\Omega)}\right] + \right. \\ \left. + A^*_0 A_a\left[\frac{1}{L_{13}(-\,\Omega)} + \frac{1}{L_{13}(\omega_a)}\right]\right\}\,,$$

where R describes the Raman resonance as before, and is given by (10).

Substitution of D^+ from (35) in (33) gives immediately the Raman and the nonlinear mixing terms for l_{13}^+ and l_{32}^+.

Following a procedure as in the above, we may estimate the expressions for l_{13}^- and l_{32}^-. We note, however, that the nonlinear part of these terms are anti-resonant in Raman detuning and they may hence be ignored. Accordingly, the polarization at the frequency ω_a may be written as the real part of the following expression:

$$p_a = 2[(\mu_{31}l_{13}^+)^* + (\mu_{23}l_{32}^+)^*] \exp[-i\omega_a t]\,. \tag{36}$$

Considering only the nonlinear parts of l_{13}^+ and l_{32}^+, we obtain from (33)

$$2[\mu_{31}l_{13}^+ + \mu_{23}l_{32}^+] = \mu_{31}\mu_{23}\frac{A_0 D^+}{\hbar}\cdot\left[\frac{1}{L_{13}(\omega_a)} - \frac{1}{L_{32}(\omega_a)}\right]. \tag{37}$$

The coefficient of $\exp[-i\omega_a t]$ in the eq. (36) is the complex conjugate of (37). From the expression for D^+ given by (35), we note that p_a may be expressed as sum of two terms each having a different origin. The first term is the Raman anti-Stokes polarization which is proportional to $A_0 A_0^* A_a^*$. The second terms is independent of the amplitude of the anti-Stokes field and is proportional to $A_0^* A_0^* A_s$. This term originates purely from the nonlinear mixing of the pump and the Stokes field. Accordingly, we may write

$$p_a = (\chi_a A_a^* + \psi A_s) \exp[-i\omega_a t]\,. \tag{38}$$

The expressions for χ_a and ψ may be expressed as follows:

$$\chi_a = \frac{f|A_0|^2}{\delta - i}\,, \tag{39}$$

$$\psi = \frac{g A_0^* A_0^*}{\delta - i}\,, \tag{40}$$

where

$$f = \frac{\varrho_{11}|\mu_{31}\mu_{32}|^2 T}{4\hbar^3}\left[\frac{1}{L_{13}^*(\omega_a)} - \frac{1}{L_{32}^*(\omega_a)}\right]\cdot\left[\frac{1}{L_{13}^*(-\Omega)} + \frac{1}{L_{13}^*(\omega_a)}\right] \tag{41}$$

and

$$g = \frac{\varrho_{11}|\mu_{31}\mu_{23}|^2 T}{4\hbar^3}\left[\frac{1}{L_{13}^*(\omega_a)} - \frac{1}{L_{32}^*(\omega_a)}\right]\cdot\left[\frac{1}{L_{13}^*(-\omega_s)} + \frac{1}{L_{13}^*(\Omega)}\right]. \tag{42}$$

In (39) and (40), δ expresses the Raman detuning and, as before, is given by

$\delta = [\omega_{21} - (\Omega - \omega_s)]T$. It should be remembered that in the present case $\Omega - \omega_s = \omega_a - \Omega$.

Let us now consider a restricted case in which $|\omega_{31} - \Omega| \gg 1/T$ and $|\omega_{31} - \omega_a| \gg 1/T$. With these conditions, the imaginary parts of (41) and (42) will be small and may be ignored. Assuming a near Raman resonance condition, the resulting expressions for f and g will be reduced to

$$f = \frac{\varrho_{11}|\mu_{31}\mu_{23}|^2 T}{4\hbar^3(\omega_{31} - \omega_a)^2} \frac{(\omega_{32} + \omega_{31})^2}{(\omega_{32} + \omega_a)(\omega_{31} + \Omega)}, \tag{43}$$

$$g = \frac{\varrho_{11}|\mu_{31}\mu_{23}|^2 T}{4\hbar^3(\omega_{31} - \omega_a)(\omega_{31} - \Omega)} \frac{(\omega_{32} + \omega_{31})^2}{(\omega_{32} + \omega_a)(\omega_{31} + \Omega)}. \tag{44}$$

From (43) and (44), we note that

$$\frac{f}{g} = \frac{(\omega_{31} - \Omega)(\omega_{31} + \Omega)}{(\omega_{31} - \omega_a)(\omega_{31} + \omega_s)}.$$

We note from the above that, in general, the value of f may be different from the value of g and, they may even have different signs. However, for $\omega_{21} \ll \omega_{31}$, the ratio of f/g will be close to unity; this ratio deviating from unity by a quantity of the order ω_{21}/ω_{31}.

The growth of the anti-Stokes field may be obtained from (38). For this, we note that the increase of anti-Stokes power, ΔP_a, within a thickness of the sample, ΔZ, is given by

$$\Delta P_a = \tfrac{1}{2}\,\mathrm{Re}\,(-p_a A_a \exp[i\omega_a t])\,\Delta Z = \frac{\omega_a}{2}\,\mathrm{Re}\,(i\chi_a A_a A_a^* + i\psi A_s A_a)\,\Delta Z\,. \tag{44a}$$

Writing χ_a in the form $\chi_a' - i\chi_a''$, we observe from (39) that χ_a'' is negative. Accordingly, in (44a), the sign of the term in χ_a which is independent of the phases of various fields is negative; thus leading to an absorption of anti-Stokes field. The sign and magnitude of the second term in (45), however, depends on the phases of the pump, Stokes and anti-Stokes fields. This term becomes independent of the propagation phases of the input fields if their directions of propagations are such that, $2\boldsymbol{k}_0 - \boldsymbol{k}_s - \boldsymbol{k}_a = 0$. Furthermore, the relative phases of the applied fields may be adjusted so that $\mathrm{Re}\,(i\psi A_s A_a) > 0$, leading to increase of power at the anti-Stokes frequency. For details of this, the reader is referred to the lecture by TOWNES [5].

5. – The effect of high field intensities.

According to (31), D^+ is a function of $\Lambda^\pm_{ij}$, λ^-_{ij} and $l^\pm_{ij}$. In the presence of the pump, Stokes and anti-Stokes fields, with $\omega_a = 2\Omega - \omega_s$, we obtain:

$$(45)\qquad \begin{cases} L_{13}(\Omega)\Lambda^+_{13} = \dfrac{\mu_{13}A_0}{2\hbar}\varrho_{11} + \dfrac{\mu_{23}A_s}{2\hbar}D^+ + \dfrac{\mu_{23}A_a}{2\hbar}D^-\,, \\[2ex] L_{32}(\Omega)\Lambda^+_{32} = 0 \qquad\qquad - \dfrac{\mu_{31}A_s}{2\hbar}D^+ + \dfrac{\mu_{31}A_a}{2\hbar}D^-\,, \end{cases}$$

and

$$(46)\qquad \begin{cases} L_{13}(-\Omega)\Lambda^-_{13} = \dfrac{\mu_{13}A_0^*}{2\hbar}\varrho_{11} + \dfrac{\mu_{23}A_a^*}{2\hbar}D^+ + \dfrac{\mu_{23}A_s^*}{2\hbar}D^-\,, \\[2ex] L_{32}(-\Omega)\Lambda^-_{32} = 0 \qquad\qquad - \dfrac{\mu_{31}A_a^*}{2\hbar}D^+ + \dfrac{\mu_{31}A_s^*}{2\hbar}D^-\,. \end{cases}$$

The presence of the anti-Stokes field does not influence the form of the equations describing λ^-_{ij}. These equations are, therefore, the same as those given by (7) of the Section **2**.

From (45) and (46), we note that $\Lambda^\pm_{ij}$ are functions of D^+ and D^-. We, therefore, need to consider the equation describing D^-. This equation is

$$(47)\qquad \left[\omega_{21} + (\Omega - \omega_s) + \frac{i}{T}\right] D^- = \frac{A_0^*}{2\hbar}(\mu_{32}\lambda^+_{13} - \mu_{13}\lambda^+_{32}) + \frac{A_s}{2\hbar}(\mu_{32}\Lambda^-_{13} - \mu_{13}\Lambda^-_{32}) + \\ + \frac{A_0}{2\hbar}(\mu_{32}l^-_{13} - \mu_{13}l^-_{32}) + \frac{A_a^*}{2\hbar}(\mu_{32}\Lambda^+_{13} + \mu_{13}\Lambda^+_{32})\,.$$

From (47), we observe that D^- is anti-resonant in the Raman detuning. For the moment, we shall ignore the anti-resonant terms and hence, in (45) and (46) drop the dependence of $\Lambda^\pm_{ij}$ on D^-. Accordingly, from (45), (46), (33), and (7), we may express $\Lambda^\pm_{ij}$, l^+_{ij} and λ^-_{ij} in terms of D^+. Substituting the resulting expressions in (34), we obtain a linear equation in D^+ which may be solved immediately. The resulting expression for D^+ is

$$(48)\qquad D^+ = \frac{\varrho_{11}\mu_{32}\mu_{13}T}{4\hbar^2 D}\left\{A_0A_s^*\left[\frac{1}{L_{13}(-\omega_s)} + \frac{1}{L_{13}(\Omega)}\right] + \\ + A_0A_a\left[\frac{1}{L_{13}(-\Omega)} + \frac{1}{L_{13}(\omega_a)}\right]\right\},$$

where the expression for D appearing in the denominator is

$$D = \delta + i - \frac{T}{4\hbar^2}\{|A_0|^2(u_s^- + u_a^+) + |A_s|^2 u^+ + |A_a|^2 u^-\}\,. \tag{49}$$

In (49), u_s^-, u_a^+ and $u^\pm$ are

$$\left\{\begin{aligned} u_s^- &= \frac{|\mu_{23}|^2}{L_{13}(-\omega_s)} + \frac{|\mu_{13}|^2}{L_{32}(-\omega_s)}\,,\\ u_a^+ &= \frac{|\mu_{23}|^2}{L_{13}(\omega_a)} + \frac{|\mu_{13}|^2}{L_{32}(\omega_a)}\,,\\ u^+ &= \frac{|\mu_{23}|^2}{L_{13}(\Omega)} + \frac{|\mu_{13}|^2}{L_{32}(\Omega)}\,,\\ u^- &= \frac{|\mu_{23}|^2}{L_{13}(-\Omega)} + \frac{|\mu_{13}|^2}{L_{32}(-\Omega)}\,. \end{aligned}\right. \tag{50}$$

Comparing (48) with (35), we find that the only modification is the appearance of the frequency shift in the resonant denominator of D^+. Accordingly, the correct expression for χ_a and ψ may now be obtained by multiplying (39) and (40) of the previous Section by $(\delta - i)/D^*$, where D is given by (49). From the resulting expression, we note that the high field intensities influence the anti-Stokes line shape in a way which is analogous to that discussed in Section **3**. For instance, in the limit of $|\omega_{31} - \Omega| \gg 1/T$ and $|\omega_a - \omega_{31}| \gg 1/T$, the quantities $u^\pm$ and $u_a^\pm$ and u_s^- are essentially real leading primarily to a frequency shift, which is of the same order of magnitude as that estimated in Section **2**.

6. – Concluding discussions.

In the above discussions, it was assumed that the population distribution of the three-level systems is such that essentially all of the atoms occupy the lowest energy state. This assumption was made in order to simplify the presentations of various mathematical steps. For an arbitrary distribution of populations, the final results for Raman susceptibilities and the nonlinear mixing terms given by (20), (22), (41), (42) and (43), need only to be modified by substituting instead of ϱ_{11}, the population difference $(\varrho_{11} - \varrho_{22})$.

Let us now discuss the effect of saturation of population distribution due to transition induced by the applied fields. This effect becomes important if the rate of radiative transitions becomes comparable to the rates of thermal relaxations between various levels. Under this condition, the difference of population $(\varrho_{11}-\varrho_{22})$ will differ from that which exists in the absence of the applied fields. For a detailed account of this, the equations describing the diagonal elements of the density matrix need to be considered. In the present discussions, however, we will only give a brief account of the saturation effect.

Let us consider the case in which only the pump and the Stokes fields are present. The rate of Raman transition, $\mathscr{R}$, from level 1 to level 2, is proportional to the power gain per unit length at the Stokes frequency, ΔP_s, due to this transition. The relation between ΔP_s and $\mathscr{R}$ is

$$\Delta P_s = \varrho_{11}\mathscr{R}\hbar\omega_s\,,$$

ϱ_{11} being the density of the atoms in the level 1. From the discussions of Section **2**, we know that $\Delta P_s = \frac{1}{2}\omega_s\chi''_s|A_s|^2$, where χ''_s is the imaginary part of the susceptibility which may be obtained from eqs. (20) or (21). Accordingly, we obtain

$$\mathscr{R} = \frac{\chi''_s|A_s|^2}{2\varrho_{11}\hbar}\,.$$

Assuming $\delta = 0$, $|\omega_{31}-\Omega| \gg 1/T$ and $\omega_{21} \ll \omega_{31}$, and using (21) and the above equation we obtain

$$\mathscr{R} = \frac{1}{2}\left|\frac{\mu_{13}A_0}{\hbar(\omega_{31}-\Omega)}\right|^2\left|\frac{\mu_{13}A_s}{\hbar}\right|^2 T\,. \tag{51}$$

Let us indicate by $1/\theta_{ij}$, the rate of thermal decay from level i to level j. The effect of saturation due to Raman transition becomes appreciable if $\mathscr{R}$ approaches the value of $1/\theta$, where $1/\theta = \frac{1}{2}(1/\theta_{12}+1/\theta_{21})$. In fact, under the conditions for which (51) holds, we obtain

$$\varrho_{11}-\varrho_{22} = \frac{\varrho^0_{11}-\varrho^0_{22}}{1+\mathscr{R}\theta}\,, \tag{52}$$

where, $(\varrho^0_{11}-\varrho)^0_{22}$ is the difference of populations in the absence of the applied fields. The rate of Raman transition, $\mathscr{R}$, in its general form, is a function of the Raman detuning parameter, δ. When the detuning parameter is other than zero, the value of $\mathscr{R}$ is less than that given by (51). Accordingly, $(\varrho_{11}-\varrho_{22})$ given by (51), depends on δ, and hence, it introduces additional distortion in the Raman line shape. This distortion appears primarily in the form of broadening of the Raman line shape. This effect is identical to broadening due to saturation as is usually observed in resonance experiments involving single-quantum transitions.

Let us give a numerical estimate of the size of relevant quantities involved in the saturation effect. For this, we note that θ is always larger than, or at most equal to, T. Assume $\theta \simeq T \simeq 10^{-10}$ s, and $\mu_{ij} = 2\cdot 10^{-18}$ e.s.u. Furthermore, consider ω_{31} to be in the ultra-violet and ω_s in the red. For the pump field, consider a Q-switched ruby laser with 20 MW peak power focussed to an area corresponding to dimensions of the order of 0.25 millimeter. Lastly, consider a case in which the power in the Stokes field is a factor of thousand less than that in the pump field. Under these conditions, we obtain $\mathcal{R}\theta \simeq 3\cdot 10^{-3}$, which is negligibly small.

The effect of saturation may become sizable in cases where ω_{31} is not far removed from the pump frequency, Ω. In these cases, $\mathcal{R}$ should be estimated using the expression for susceptibility given by (20). Furthermore, for ω_{31} close to Ω, additional contributions to saturation effect will occur due to single-quantum transitions between various levels leading to the linear parts of the susceptibility. The case in which $|\omega_{31} - \Omega| \approx 1/T$ has been treated in detail by the author [10] and by CLOGSTON [11].

In the limit of very intense fields, in addition to saturation effect, the diagonal elements of the density matrix may also contribute, by a small amount, to nonlinear mixing of the pump and the Stokes fields, leading to a small correction term in generation of the anti-Stokes radiation. This is a higher-order effect and arises due to the fact that the off-diagonal elements of the density matrix are capable of mixing with the applied fields resulting in oscillatory components of the diagonal elements of the density matrix at the difference frequency $\Omega - \omega_s$. The presence of the terms in $E\varrho_{11}$ on the right-hand sides of (4*a*) and (4*b*) in turns is capable of driving the radiating components of the density matrix, ϱ_{13} and ϱ_{32}, at the anti-Stokes frequency $2\Omega - \omega_s$. This correction is however extremely small unless ω_{31} approaches the value of Ω.

REFERENCES

[1] A. JAVAN: *Journ. Phys. et Rad.*, **19**, 806 (1958); *Bull. Am. Phys. Soc.*, **3**, 213 (1958).

[2] G. ECKHARDT, R. W. HELLWARTH, F. J. MCCLUNG, S. E. SCHWARZ, D. WEINER and E. J. WOODBURY: *Phys. Rev. Lett.*, **9**, 455 (1962).

[3] H. J. ZEIGER and P. E. TANNENWALD: *Proc. of the Third Quantum Electronics Conference* (Paris, 1963).

[4] R. W. HELLWARTH: *Phys. Rev.*, **130**, 1850 (1963).

[5] R. Y. CHIAO, E. GARMIRE and C. H. TOWNES: this volume, p. 326.

[6] E. GARMIRE, F. PANDARESE and C. H. TOWNES: *Phys. Rev. Lett.*, **11**, 160 (1963).

[7] R. W. TERHUNE: *Bull. Am. Phys. Soc.*, **8**, 359 (1963).

[8] See also N. BLOEMBERGEN: this volume, p. 247.

[9] B. STOICHEFF: private communication.

[10] A. JAVAN: *Phys. Rev.*, **107**, 1579 (1957).

[11] A. M. CLOGSTON: *Journ. Phys. Chem. Sol.*, **4**, 271 (1958).

Stimulated Raman Scattering.

B. P. STOICHEFF

Division of Pure Physics, National Research Council - Ottawa

1. – Introduction.

Stimulated Raman emission has recently been observed by WOODBURY and NG [1], ECKHARDT *et al.* [2], and TERHUNE [3], using extremely intense ruby-maser radiation for excitation. They have shown that this emission possesses many of the properties characteristic of stimulated radiation, namely, a marked appearance threshold, high intensity, spectral-line narrowing and beam collimation. At the present time stimulated Raman emission has been observed at many different wavelengths from a number of liquids and compressed gases and is obviously an important source of coherent radiation in the red and blue regions of the spectrum.

The observation of stimulated Raman radiation has also created interest in the theory of Raman masers, particularly since population inversion is not a necessary condition for this class of masers. JAVAN [4] had already suggested in 1958 that two quantum processes such as the Raman effect could be used for amplification with atomic or molecular systems having higher populations in their lower states. Recently HELLWARTH [5], and ZEIGER and TANNENWALD [6] have discussed the threshold condition for stimulated emission of the Stokes radiation and BLOEMBERGEN *et al.* [7] have formulated a theory of nonlinear susceptibility which is applicable to Raman masers. More recently, GARMIRE, PANDARESE, and TOWNES [8] have discussed higher-order Raman effects which lead to the production of intense Stokes and anti-Stokes radiation of many orders and having many interesting properties.

The purpose of the present paper is to review the observed characteristics of the stimulated Raman radiation and to compare these with the known characteristics of the normal Raman scattering which are briefly summarized here. In doing so, I shall discuss some recent spectroscopic studies at high resolution carried out at the National Research Council Laboratories. It will be shown that while some of the properties of this radiation can be understood from the existing theories of stimulated Raman scattering, some features remain to be explained. It is to be hoped that the theories of Bloembergen, Javan, and Townes presented at this School may give us a further insight into the processes involved when stimulated Raman radiation is generated by intense coherent light.

2. – Résumé of the Raman effect.

The Raman effect [9] has its origin in atomic and molecular transitions which occur during the light scattering process. When a light quantum with any frequency ν_0 (wavelenght λ_0) and energy $h\nu_0$ interacts with a molecule in its ground state n or in any of its excited stationary states k (Fig. 1) the energy of the system is increased to $h\nu_0+E_n$ or $h\nu_0+E_k$. If the molecule does not possess a stationary state with this energy (*), the light quantum will be instantaneously scattered in any direction and the molecule either returns to its original state or goes to a different state. It the molecule returns to its original state, no energy has been taken from the light quantum nor has energy been given to it. Therefore, the frequency of the quantum remains unchanged and we have *Rayleigh scattering*. If the molecule goes over to another stationary state, it has either taken energy from the light quantum or given up part of its energy and the frequency of the light quantum is changed. As a consequence, the frequencies $\nu_0-\nu_{nk}$ and $\nu_0+\nu_{nk}$ appear in the scattered light and we have the *Raman effect*.

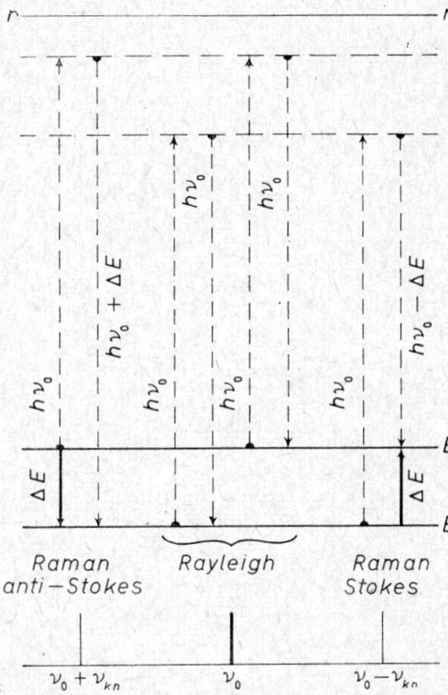

Fig. 1. – An energy level diagram representing the quantum theory of Raman and Rayleigh scattering. The solid arrows indicate the molecular transitions while the broken arrows represent virtual transitions. The resulting spectrum is shown at the bottom.

A very detailed theoretical discussion

(*) If the molecule does possess a starionary state with the energy $h\nu_0+E_n$ or $h\nu_0+E_k$, the incident light quantum is absorbed raising the molecule to this excited state. After a certain time, a quantum can be re-emitted with the same frequency ν_0 or a changed frequency, depending on whether the molecule returns to its original state or to a different state. This process is called fluorescence.

of the above process has been given by PLACZEK [10]. Here, only a brief outline of the theory will be presented.

The intensity of scattered light at $\nu_0 \pm \nu_{nk}$ is given by

$$I(\nu_0 \pm \nu_{nk}) = NI(\nu_0)h(\nu_0 \pm \nu_{nk})A_{nk} , \tag{1}$$

where the transition probability A_{nk} for a molecular transition $n \leftrightarrow k$ during the scattering process is defined as

$$A_{nk} = \frac{64\pi^4}{3} \frac{h}{c^3} (\nu_0 \pm \nu_{nk})^3 \mu_{nk}^2 , \tag{2}$$

with

$$\mu_{nk} = \frac{1}{h} \sum_r \left[\frac{M_{nr} M_{rk}}{\nu_{rn} - \nu_0} + \frac{M_{nr} M_{rk}}{\nu_{rk} + \nu_0} \right] E . \tag{3}$$

In these equations, c is the velocity of light, h is Planck's constant, r represents any one level of a complete set of electronic levels, M_{nr} is the matrix element of the transition $n \leftrightarrow r$, E is the electric field of the light wave, N is the number of molecules in the initial state and $I(\nu_0)$ the intensity of the incident radiation. For $k = n$ these equations apply to Rayleigh scattering. The angular dependence of the scattered light intensity is given by $I(\theta) = I(\nu_0)(1 + \cos^2 \theta)/2$ where θ is the angle between the incident and scattered light.

Equations (2) and (3) show that the probability for a Raman transition from a state n to a state k is determined by the sum over all states r of products of transition moments from the state n to some other state r and from the state r to the state k. Thus it can be seen that the Raman selection rules differ from the rules governing absorption and emission of dipole radiation: the former depend on the product of transition moments M_{nr} M_{rk}, and the latter depend only on the transition moments M_{nr} or M_{rk}. The explicit Raman selection rule is that only levels having eigenfunctions of the same symmetry can combine with one another.

While the evaluation of the scattering formula can be carried out in principle, our lack of knowledge of the excited states r, precludes the direct use of the above equations and necessitates some simplifying approximations. PLACZEK has simplified the scattering formula for molecules in their ground electronic states by showing that under certain conditions (which are generally always fulfilled in experiments) the induced dipole moment μ_{kn} in eq. (3) can be replaced by $\boldsymbol{\mu} = \alpha \boldsymbol{E}$ where $\boldsymbol{E}$ is the electric field vector of the light wave and α is the molecular polarizability tensor.

The transition probabilities and therefore intensity and selection rules are determined by integrals of the form

$$[\alpha_{XY}]^{kn} = \int \psi_n^* \alpha_{XY} \psi_k \, dt , \tag{4}$$

where ψ_n and ψ_k are the time-independent wave functions of the initial and final states, α_{XY} is one of the components of the polarizability tensor of the molecule referred to space-fixed axes and the integration is over all space. The simplification introduced by the polarizability theory is that $[\alpha_{XY}]^{kn}$ in eq. (4), and hence μ_{kn}, depend on a knowledge of the initial and final states only. According to eq. (4), it is necessary to know the form of the wave functions ψ_n, ψ_k and the dependence of the polarizability on the molecular structure.

It is evident that the polarizability will vary with the vibrational and rotational motions of a molecule. For vibrational motions of infinitesimal amplitudes, the polarizability can be represented by an expansion in terms of the $3N-6$ normal coordinates q_i

$$\alpha_{xy} = \alpha_{xy} + \sum_{i=1}^{3N-6} \left(\frac{\partial \alpha_{xy}}{\partial q_j}\right)_0 q_j + \text{higher terms} \tag{5}$$

where the six components α_{xy} are expressed in a molecule-fixed system (xyz).

Whether a particular vibration is Raman-active or inactive can be determined by considering the changes in the polarizability as the vibrating molecule goes through its equilibrium position. Also, an estimate can be made of whether the motion results in a change in the magnitude of the derivative of the polarizability (associated with totally symmetric vibrations) or in the anisotropy of the derivative of the polarizability (usually associated with antisymmetric vibrations). If the higher-order terms in the polarizability (eq. 5) or in the potential energy are considered, that is if anharmonicity is present, then overtone and combination frequencies can also occur (the second-order Raman spectrum). But these are usually very much weaker than the fundamentals. On the other hand, in some crystals, for example the alkali halides, the fundamental vibration (the first-order Raman spectrum) is forbidden by symmetry and only the very weak second-order spectrum is observed. Many types of vibrational bands can occur in the Raman effect (some of which may not occur in infra-red absorption) and their occurrence or nonocurrence in the Raman spectrum may be used to determine the molecular symmetry or point group of molecules. All totally symmetric vibrations are Raman-active. Since all molecules have at least one totally symmetric vibration, all molecules will exhibit a vibrational Raman spectrum. Detailed discussion of the vibrational modes and selection rules for polyatomic molecules are given by HERZBERG [11] and WILSON, DECIUS and CROSS [12]. The symmetry species for the vibrations of crystals are given by MATHIEU [13] and details of the theories of lattice dynamics by BORN and HUANG [14].

For rotational motions, the polarizability is expressed in a space-fixed co-ordinate system (XYZ) in terms of the polarizability components along the xyz axes fixed in the molecule. For example

$$\alpha_{XY} = \sum_{xy} \alpha_{xy} \cos(x, X) \cos(y, Y) . \tag{6}$$

The rotational selection rules are determined by the matrix elements $\int \psi^*_{r'} \alpha_{xy} \psi_{r''} \, dt$. PLACZEK and TELLER [15] have evaluated these integrals and derived the selection rules for linear, symmetric-top, spherical-top, and asymmetric-top molecules. The strict selection rule is that positive levels only combine with positive levels and negative only with negative. For the special case of the rigid nonlinear molecule the selection rules are $\Delta J = 0, \pm 2$. Moreover, transitions are only possible if the polarizability ellipsoid is anisotropic; this is a general condition for all molecules and holds for pure rotational transitions as well as for vibration-rotational transitions.

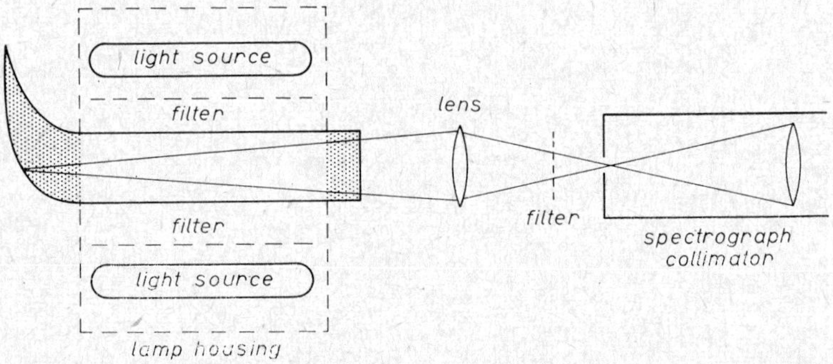

Fig. 2. – A typical experimental arrangement for the normal Raman effect (schematic).

A typical experimental arrangement for investigating the Raman effect is shown schematically in Fig. 2. The scattering substance is usually placed in a long glass or quartz tube (the Raman tube) and surrounded by several powerful lamps. These are a source of intense emission lines, usually of visible or ultra-violet wavelenghts. One or more of these lines may be selected (by means of suitable filters) to excite the Raman scattering. The light scattered at right angles to the incident radiation is then focused on a high-speed spectrograph and the resulting Raman spectrum is photographed or recorded photoelectrically.

A few examples of Raman spectra are given in Fig. 3, 4, 5. In each spectrum, the most intense feature is the exciting line. The Raman spectrum consists of several lines or bands on either side of the exciting line, those on the Stokes

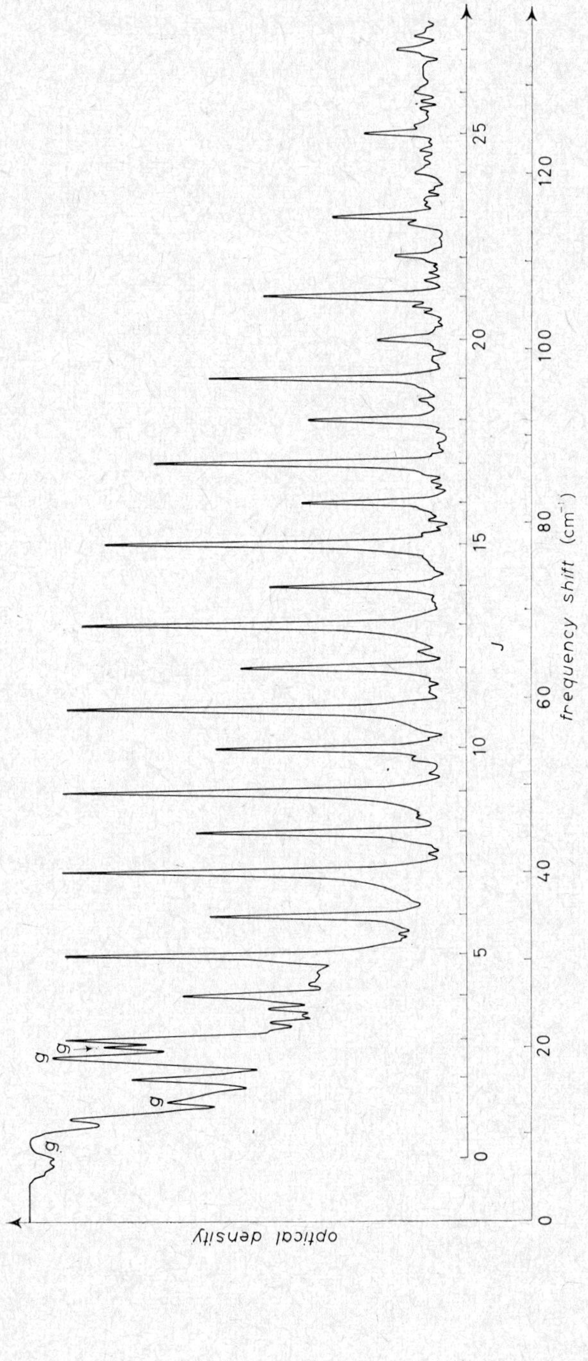

Fig. 3. – Microphotometer trace of the pure rotational Raman spectrum of the linear molecule acetylene, C_2H_2. Only the Stokes side of the spectrum is shown. (The lines marked *g* are grating ghosts.)

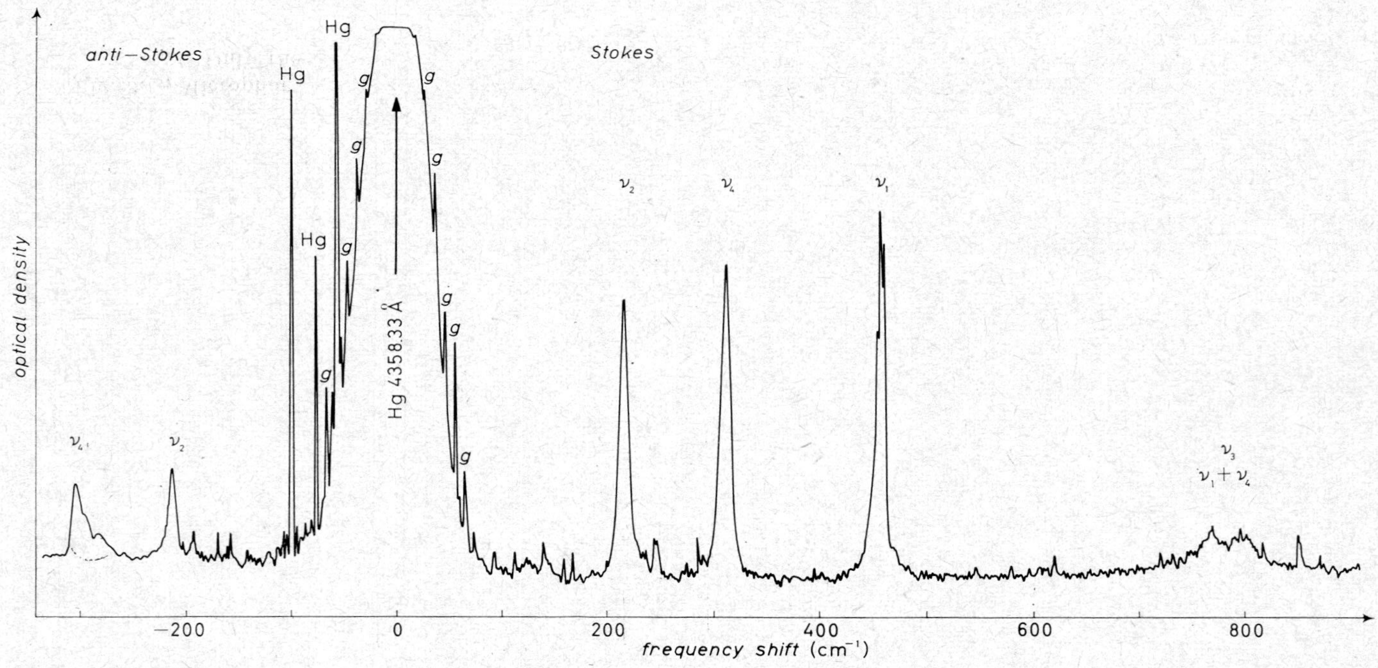

Fig. 4. – Microphotometer trace of the vibrational Raman spectrum of liquid carbon tetrachloride (CCl_4) showing the Stokes and anti-Stokes lines. (The lines marked *g* are grating ghosts.)

side being much more intense than those on the anti-Stokes side. The same pattern of lines is found for any given substance no matter what exciting line is used. That is, the frequency shifts of the Raman lines, or their displacements in

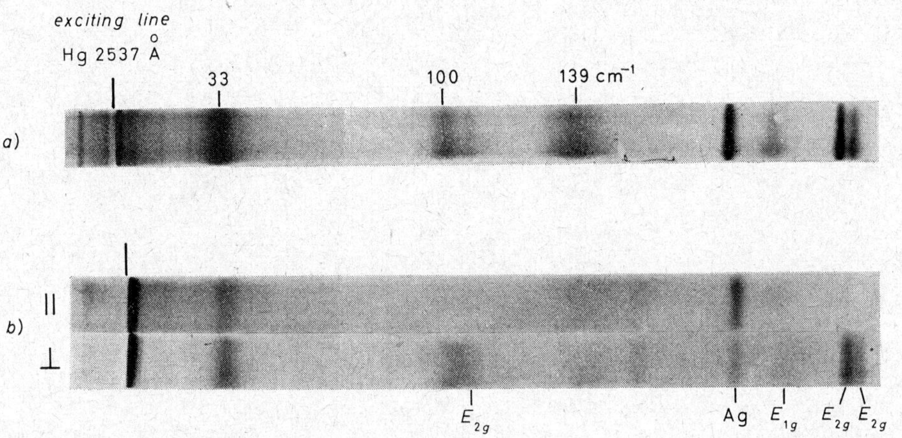

Fig. 5. – Raman spectrum of $PrCl_3$ at 77 °K showing the Stokes lines corresponding to: *a*) three electronic transitions of the Pr^{3+} ion in the vicinity of the λ 2537 exciting line and *b*) five vibrational transitions of the crystal. The vibrational spectra polarized parallel and perpendicular to the optic axis of the crystal with the exciting light traveling perpendicular to the optic axis are labeled $\parallel$ and $\perp$ [17].

units cm^{-1}, from any exciting line, are constant. These frequency shifts are found to equal the frequencies of rotational, vibrational, and electronic transitions of the scattering molecules.

Rotational transitions give rise to rotational lines in the spectra of gases close to the exciting line, usually within about 100 cm^{-1} (Fig. 3). At low resolution, these appear as a general broadening of the the exciting line or as rotational wings. At high resolution, the individual rotational lines may be observed. These rotational wings sometimes persist with reduced intensity and extent even in liquids, where (excepting liquid hydrogen) free rotation is not found. *Vibrational transitions* give rise to vibrational bands in the spectra of gases, liquids and solids, in the frequency range 100 to about 4 000 cm^{-1}. For all molecules, in general, strong line-like Q branches ($\Delta J = 0$) are observed for those vibrations which produce changes in the magnitude of the polarizability derivative, *i.e.*, for the totally symmetric vibrations (ν_1 in Fig. 4). On the other hand, considerable broadening (in liquids, *e.g.*, ν_2, ν_3, ν_4 in Fig. 4) or strong rotational wings ($\Delta J = \pm 1, \pm 2$) are observed for those vibration which produce changes in the anisotropy of the polarizability derivative. In some liquids and solids the Raman bands may be modified in frequency, intensity, or breadth from those in the gas phase because of intermolecular forces. Examples of *electronic transitions* in the Raman effect are rare. The only two known spectra include that of the molecule NO (RASETTI [16]) and of the ion Pr^{3+} in $PrCl_3$, Fig. 5 (HOUGEN and SINGH [17]). Along with the references already cited, the reader will find descriptions of esperimental techniques, examples of Raman spectra and tables of observed frequencies for many molecules in several texts and review articles on this subject [18].

Up to the present time, there have been several thousand investigations of the Raman effect, mainly in liquids but also in gases and solids, and these have been concerned with rotational and vibrational transitions of molecules in their ground electronic states. The measurement of frequencies, relative intensities, and optical polarization of vibrational bands has given valuable data on molecular symmetry, force constants, and thermodynamic quantities for a large number of molecules. The investigation of rotational spectra has led to the determination of internuclear distances and bond angles of simple molecules and to the evaluation of rotation-vibration interactions. From changes in the spectra with physical state, information on intermolecular forces has been obtained. From band intensities data on the rate of change of electronic polarizability with vibrational motion have been obtained. The Raman effect has also been very useful in chemical analysis.

To be sure, much of this information is similar to that obtained by infra-red spectroscopy and in part by microwave spectroscopy. However, according to theory (and practice) the information obtained from Raman spectra complements that obtained from infra-red and microwave spectra. This valuable property arises from the basically different mechanisms which produce the spectra: the Raman effect occurs because of a change in magnitude or direction of the electronic polarizability during the molecular motion, while infra-red and microwave absorption occur because of a change in magnitude or direction of the electric dipole moment during the motion. In addition, because of the vastly different experimental technique, the Raman effect has often been used to obtain information which was otherwise not easily obtainable. Accordingly, the investigation of the Raman effect has made valuable contributions to the development of molecular spectroscopy and to our present knowledge of molecular structure.

Another interesting type of light scattering is that due to thermal or elastic waves in liquids and solids and is known as Brillouin scattering. This may be considered as Raman scattering by acoustic phonons. It may be instructive to consider this scattering as a Doppler shift of the incident frequency due to the elastic waves (or acoustic phonons) of a specific wavelength travelling in a suitable direction to interact with the incident light waves (or incident photons). The frequency shifts are given by the equation [19]

$$\Delta\nu = \pm 2\nu_0 \frac{v}{c} n \sin\frac{\varphi}{2},$$

where ν_0 is the frequency of the incident wave, v is the acoustic velocity, c is the velocity of light, n is the refractive index and φ is the scattering angle. The shifts are relatively small, being less than 1 cm^{-1} for liquids and between about 1 and 10 cm^{-1} for solids. An example of a Brillouin spectrum is given in Fig. 6.

There have been relatively few studies of Brillouin scattering up to the present time [20], primarily because of the lack of a suitable source of high intensity and narrow line width. Nevertheless, these few experiments have confirmed the above equation and measurements of the small shifts have given information of the velocities of these high-frequency waves ($\sim 10^9$ to 10^{11} Hz) and the elastic constants of various solids. Also, measurements of the lines widths could lead to interesting information on the relaxation processes involved at these hypersonic frequencies.

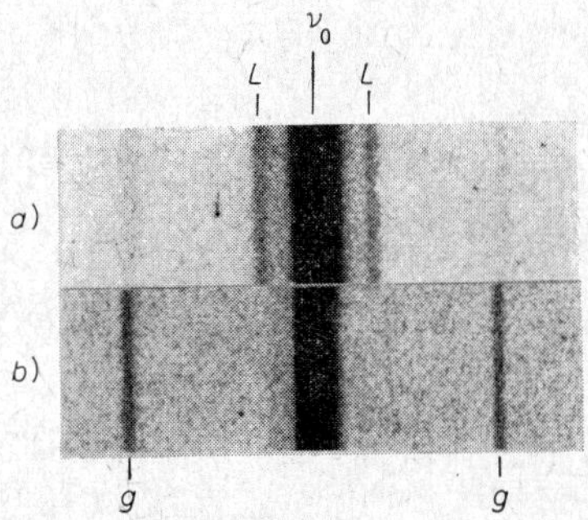

Fig. 6. – Brillouin spectrum from fused quartz *a*) showing the longitudinal components (*L*) shifted by 1.6 cm^{-1} and *b*) the ^{198}Hg 2 536.5 exciting line (ν_0) and grating ghosts (*g*) [20].

In concluding this review of the normal Raman effect, it may be mentioned that all of the remarkable properties of optical maser radiation, namely high intensity, directionality and narrow line make the maser an obvius source for the excitation of Raman and Brillouin spectra. Brief discussions of the use of the ruby maser in exciting Raman spectra of liquids have been given by Porto and Wood [21], and by Stoicheff [22] together with some preliminary results. With further developments, the optical maser may become an important excitation source for the Raman spectra of liquids and solids, of small crystalline samples and of gases, especially for studies at high resolution.

3. – Stimulated Raman scattering.

3·1. *Introduction.* – Since the theory of stimulated Raman scattering (including parametric and higher-order processes) will be covered in considerable detail in the papers by Townes [23] and Javan [24], only a brief outline will be presented here.

In eq. (1), an expression was given for the intensity of Raman-scattered radiation which may be considered as spontaneous emission. The intensity of scattered light is dependent on the intensity of the incident light and on the matrix elements μ_{nk} for two-photon processes. If the resulting Raman radiation is of extremely high intensity (or if radiation at a frequency $\nu_0 \pm \nu_{nk}$ is incident on the medium simultaneously with the original exciting light of frequency ν_0) then eq. (1) may be modified to include the possibility of stimulated Raman scattering. In analogy with the usual emission processes we can write

$$I(\nu_0 \pm \nu_{nk}) = N I_0 h(\nu_0 \pm \nu_{nk})[A_k + \varrho' B_{nk}]\,, \tag{7}$$

where ϱ' is the energy density of radiation at the Raman-shifted frequency $\nu_0 \pm \nu_{nk}$ and B_{nk} is the stimulated transition probability for a transition $n \leftrightarrow k$, given by

$$B_{nk} = \frac{c^3}{8\pi h(\nu_0 \pm \nu_{nk})^3} A_{nk}\,.$$

It is easily seen that, at normal temperatures where the population of the ground state is larger than that of the excited states, only Stokes radiation can occur as stimulated emission. Not only will ϱ' at the Stokes frequency be larger, but the net transitions will be $n \rightarrow k$ (Fig. 1). Thus, the intensity of stimulated radiation at the Stokes frequency will be given by

$$I(\nu_0 - \nu_{nk}) = (N_n - N_k)\, I_0 h(\nu_0 - \nu_{nk}) \varrho' B_{nk}\,. \tag{8}$$

We conclude, therefore, that population inversion is not required for stimulated (Stokes) Raman scattering; also that the stimulated scattering is only linearly dependent on the frequency $(\nu_0 - \nu_{nk})$ in contrast to the spontaneous scattering which is proportional to $(\nu_0 - \nu_{nk})$ [4].

The requirements for stimulated Raman scattering are therefore intense exciting radiation and intense spontaneous Raman radiation. It will be noted that an exciting source of coherent radiation has not been assumed and, in principle, is not necessary. Various estimates of the power required to generate stimulated Raman radiation give figures of the order of megawatts. Such intense radiation is now available from giant-pulse ruby masers and, as is well known has been successfully used to obtain stimulated Raman radiation.

WOODBURY and NG [1] first observed stimulated Raman emission while investigating the characteristics of a giant-pulse (or Q-switched) ruby maser using nitrobenzene as the fast Kerr-cell shutter. They found intense stimulated emission at 7 670 Å accompanying the maser line at 6 940 Å. Later, they showed that this additional radiation was stimulated Raman radiation from nitrobenzene, and along with ECKHARDT *et al.* [2] were able to produce such radiation at other wavelengths to the red of 6 940 Å from a number of other organic liquids. Their results are summarized in Table I. In this work, the nitrobenzene Kerr-cell was replaced by a KDP Pockel-cell which did not produce additional radiation, and the liquids were placed inside the ruby-maser cavity. The peak output power of the ruby radiation was approximately 0.2 to

2 MW of 20 to $70 \cdot 10^{-9}$ s duration. Briefly, their observations may be summarized as follows: many liquids (Table I) produced stimulated radiation of extremely high intensity, up to 10% of the incident maser radiation; a threshold

TABLE I. – *Comparison of frequencies observed in the stimulated and normal Raman spectra of some organic liquids* [2].

Liquid	Ruby frequency minus observed frequency (cm^{-1})	Frequency shift (cm^{-1}) of strongest Raman lines
Benzene	990 ±2 2× (990 ±2) 3064 ±4	992 — 3064
Nitrobenzene	1344 ±2 2×(1346 ±2) 3×(1340 ±5)	1345 — —
Toluene	1004 ±4	1002
1-Bromonaphthalene	1368 ±4	1363
Pyridine	992 ±2 2× (992 ±5)	991 —
Cyclohexane	2852 ±1	2853
Deuterated Benzene	944.3±1 2× (944 ±1)	945 —

was found for production of this radiation; beam collimation and spectral-line narrowing were observed; the spectrum revealed that this radiation was displaced from the ruby line at frequencies (in cm^{-1}) corresponding to those of the strongest lines in the normal Raman effect; in addition, lines at multiples of these frequencies were observed. There was no doubt that this new radiation was stimulated emission and that the underlying process was stimulated Raman scattering.

At the April 1963 American Physical Society Meeting, TERHUNE [3] reported further interesting results. In these experiments the liquids were external to the giant-pulse cavity with the ruby radiation focused in the liquid. He confirmed the findings of ECKHARDT *et al.* [1] with some organic liquids and with liquid nitrogen. In addition he observed intense radiation to wavelengths shorter than 6940 Å, that is, he observed anti-Stokes radiation. Moreover he found this radiation to be emitted not along the direction of the incident beam but in cones of a few degrees in the forward direction. Later, TERHUNE observed stimulated Raman radiation with compressed gaseous hydrogen at pressures of about 50 atm.

Now I shall describe the recent work on this subject carried out at the National Research Council.

3·2. *Experimental Procedure.* – A diagram of the apparatus is shown in Fig. 7. The exciting source was a giant-pulse ruby maser with the cavity formed by a spinning totally-reflecting prism at one end and at the other a

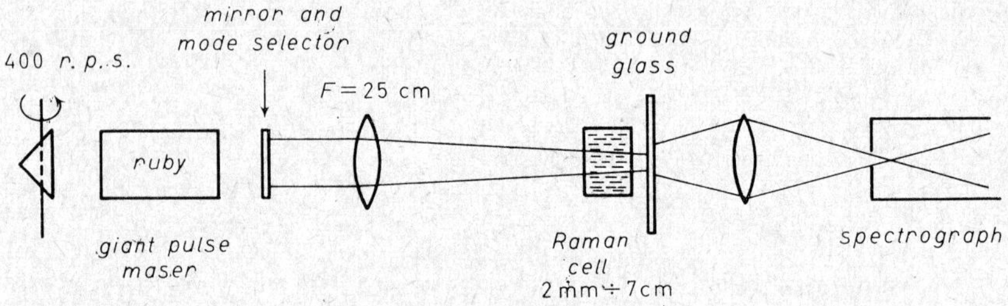

Fig. 7. – Experimental arrangement for generating stimulated Raman radiation external to the cavity of the giant-pulse ruby maser (schematic).

plane reflector ($\sim$ 25 % reflectivity) of Corning 2-58 glass 0.4 cm thick which also served as a mode selector and filter. The radiation was emitted in single bursts of duration $\sim$ 30 ns, of 0.1 to 0.8 joule energy and of spectral width $\sim$ 150 MHz. Various sample cells of lenght 2 mm to 7 cm were placed outside the maser cavity and near the focus of a lens ($f = 25$ cm) where the beam cross-section was about 0.1 cm^2, and the beam power density was upwards of 100 MW/cm^2. The liquids for which stimulated emission was observed include hydrogen, oxygen, nitrogen, and the following organic liquids: carbon disulphide, carbon tetrachloride, tetrachloroethylene, benzene, nitrobenzene, toluene, cyclohexane and a 1:1 mixture of carbon disulphide and benzene. Initially all of the spectra were photographed at low resolution [25], and later some were photographed with the high resolving power ($\sim 10^5$) of a 21 ft. grating spectrograph. For comparison the normal Raman spectra of some of these liquids were obtained with the 21 ft. grating using conventional techniques.

3·3. *Observations and Discussion* – Photographs of the stimulated Raman spectra of several liquids are shown in Fig. 8, 9, 10. A glance at any of these spectra taken at either low or high resolution shows them to have most remarkable properties when compared with the corresponding normal Raman spectra. The spectra are extremely intense; they consist of Stokes and anti-Stokes lines of almost equal intensity; the lines correspond to molecular vibrations of a particular symmetry only; each spectrum exhibits not only lines of the fundamental vibration frequency, but also lines of exact multiples of these frequencies. At high resolution, the lines for some liquids appear to be extremely sharp, but on occasion these same lines are several ångstroms in breadth, sometimes exhibiting fine structure and sometimes unusual intensity contours.

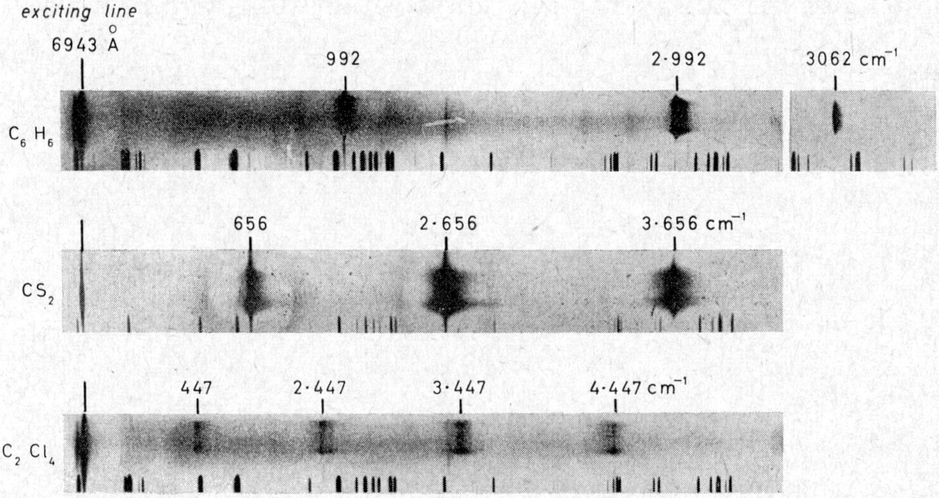

Fig. 8. – Stimulated Raman spectra of liquid C_6H_6, CS_2 and C_2Cl_4 showing the Stokes side only, photographed at low resolution.

A pronounced threshold was found both in beam power and in liquid path length for the appearance of the Raman spectra, in agreement with the earlier

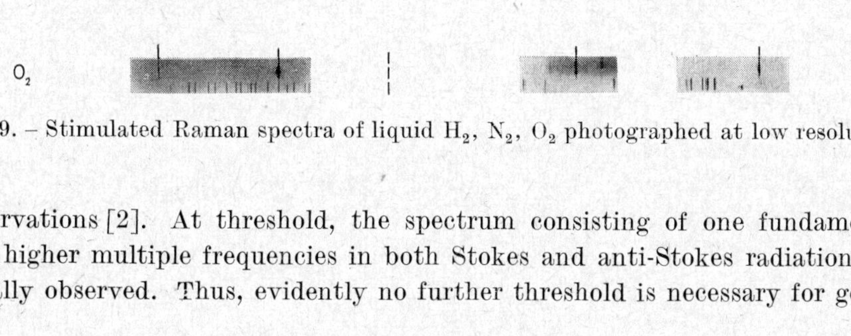

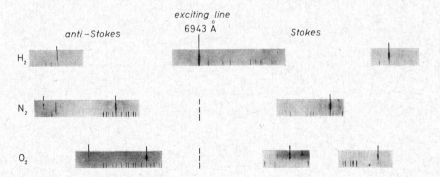

Fig. 9. – Stimulated Raman spectra of liquid H_2, N_2, O_2 photographed at low resolution.

observations [2]. At threshold, the spectrum consisting of one fundamental and higher multiple frequencies in both Stokes and anti-Stokes radiation was usually observed. Thus, evidently no further threshold is necessary for generation of the harmonic frequencies or the anti-Stokes lines. The threshold depends on the intensity per linewidth, as expected from maser theory. This was determined from a comparison of the normal and stimulated Raman spectra of

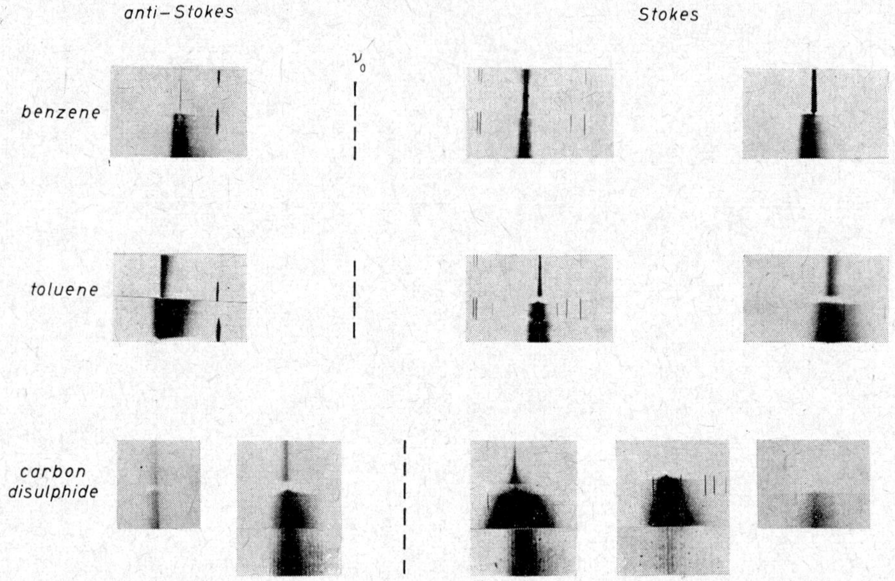

Fig. 10. – Stimulated Raman spectra of liquid C_6H_6, $C_6H_5CH_3$ and CS_2 photographed with resolving power of 10^5. (These photographs are representative of the unexpected differences observed in the spectra during consecutive experiments with all controllable experimental conditions seemingly constant.)

carbon disulphide, benzene and carbon tetrachloride. In the normal Raman spectra of these liquids the strongest lines have intensities in the ratio of 5:4:1 and half-widths of 1.0, 2.5, and 2.0 cm^{-1}, respectively. In the stimulated spectra carbon disulphide has the lowest threshold and carbon tetrachloride the highest.

For each liquid, the observed stimulated Ramam spectrum consists of only one or two of the lines found in the normal Raman spectrum, the frequencies being the same to within the experimental accuracy of ± 0.2 cm^{-1}. Every such line observed to date is a vibrational line corresponding to a totally symmetric vibration. This result is perhaps to be expected since it is these vibrations which usually give rise to the most intense and narrowest lines (of half-width 1 to 5 cm^{-1}) in the normal Raman spectra and would therefore be the first lines to appear in stimulated emission. Liquid parahydrogen (Fig. 9) was included in this study especially to look for stimulated Raman radiation corresponding to molecular rotations, but none was found. Only a single vibrational line was observed corresponding to the line $Q(0)$ in the normal Raman effect which arises from the transition $v=1 \rightarrow v=0$; $J=0 \rightarrow J=0$. These results suggest that isotropic scattering ($\Delta v = 1$, $\Delta J = 0$, $\Delta m = 0$) is dominant in the stimulated Raman effect.

In each spectrum the most striking features are: 1) the intense anti-Stokes lines and 2) the intense lines at multiples of the Raman frequencies (on both Stokes and anti-Stokes sides). In the normal Raman effect, anti-Stokes emission corresponds to transitions from a higher to a lower level, *e.g.*, $v = 1 \rightarrow v = 0$. At the low temperatures of liquid hydrogen and even liquid oxygen or nitrogen, vibrational levels other than $v = 0$ are not populated in these liquids and indeed no anti-Stokes radiation is found in the normal Raman spectra of liquid hydrogen, oxygen and nitrogen. Yet in the stimulated spectra (Fig. 9), anti-Stokes lines are present with appreciable intensity in all of these liquids. At the same time, it is significant that no Stokes lines have been observed corresponding to the transition $v = 2 \rightarrow v = 1$ which in the normal Raman effect has a slightly higher probability than the anti-Stokes transition originating from the same vibrational level. These results imply that even during the maser pulse the population in the $v = 1$ level is negligible and that the emission of Stokes and anti-Stokes radiation (*i.e.*, the molecular absorption and emission of radiation) must be considered not as independent processes, but rather as a single quantum process, the molecules remaining essentially in the $v = 0$ level.

The occurrence of Stokes and anti-Stokes radiation at multiples of the fundamental frequencies has already been noted. Measurements of these lines in the spectra of oxygen and nitrogen given in Table II show them to be indeed

TABLE II. – *Stimulated Raman spectra of liquid* N_2 *and* O_2.

	ν (cm^{-1})	$\Delta\nu$ (cm^{-1})
Liquid N_2	16 729.44	—
	ν_0 14 402.90	2 326.54
	12 076.39	— 2 326.51
	9 749.87	— 4 653.03
Liquid O_2	ν_0 14 402.86	—
	12 850.85	— 1 552.01
	11 298.84	— 3 104.02

exactly twice the frequency shifts of the fundamentals at 1 552.0 and 2 326.5 cm^{-1} respectively, the error in measurement being ± 0.05 cm^{-1} for these very sharp lines. Moreover, these measurements readily establish that the lines are not overtones of the molecular vibrations. The known anharmonicities of the vibrations of the oxygen and nitrogen molecules are large and give, for example for the first overtones, frequencies differing from twice the fundamentals by approximately 24 and 29 cm^{-1}, respectively.

Clearly, the observation of stimulated anti-Stokes radiation means that the simple theory represented by eq. (7) and (8) is not adequate. Furthermore, the observation of multiples of the Raman frequencies in Stokes and anti-Stokes radiation implies that, with excitation by coherent radiation, higher-order processes are important.

Experiments were also performed with a 1:1 mixture of benzene and carbon disulphide. The resulting spectra were then compared with those of the separated liquids placed in series in the path of the maser beam. In one experiment the maser beam traversed the benzene before the carbon disulphide and in a second experiment the order of the liquids was reversed. In the two experiments with the liquids separated, the spectrum due to carbon disulphide was dominant. Also, while intense lines of the harmonics of each liquid were present, only one weak line was observed at the sum ot the Raman frequencies of carbon disulphide and benzene. Several such lines at the sum and difference frequencies would be expected if the harmonics are produced by an iterative process [2]. In the mixture, however, a strikingly different spectrum was observed. Firstly, the benzene lines were dominant. Secondly, seven new lines appeared with appreciable intensity and they could all be accounted for (within the experimental error of 1 cm^{-1}) as sum and difference frequencies of the carbon disulphide and benzene frequencies. One may conclude, therefore, that molecular interactions are of general importance in the stimulated Raman effect.

The widths of the stimulated Raman lines of hydrogen, oxygen and nitrogen were very narrow and essentially determined by the instrumental width (~ 0.2 cm^{-1}). The Stokes lines of the organic liquids were found to be between 0.5 to 1 cm^{-1} in width, somewhat narrower than the lines in the normal Raman spectra. However, appreciable narrowing was observed in the anti-Stokes lines of these liquids. For example, in benzene (Fig. 10) the half-width of the fundamental anti-Stokes line measured with a Fabry-Perot interferometer was found to be ~ 0.05 cm^{-1} as compared with 0.5 cm^{-1} for the Stokes line and 2.5 cm^{-1} for these lines in the normal spectrum, This represents a narrowing by a factor of 5 for the Stokes line and of 50 for the anti-Stokes line.

Usually, the ruby-maser radiation was emitted in a single sharp line but on occasion in two sharp lines separated by 0.8 cm^{-1}. Under these conditions, the stimulated Raman spectra of carbon disulphide, benzene and toluene exhibited broad features at the Raman frequencies and their harmonics, with rather unusual intensity profiles. On the Stokes side, the Raman fundamental line was somewhat broader than usual. At the same time, the lines of the second and third harmonics were approximately two and three times the breadth of the fundamental: they were unsymmetrical in shape with the intensity maxima shifted by as much as 10 cm^{-1} to higher absolute frequencies. On the anti-Stokes side, the fundamental as well as the higher harmonic lines were similarly broadened asymmetrically and shifted to higher absolute frequencies.

A further unexpected feature of these spectra was the observation of a strong and extremely sharp (~ 0.2 cm^{-1}) absorption within the broadened anti-Stokes fundamental line (Fig. 10). This absorption line fell slightly to one side (~ 0.5 cm^{-1}) of the sharp emission line observed when the maser emitted only a single line. Also, this absorption was observed only at a specific angle to the direction of incidence, the angle being within 10′ of the direction of the anti-Stokes fundamental emission. Sometimes, under these same condition, the broad Raman lines consisted of long series of sharp maxima and minima having almost the spacing of the two maser lines and total widths of 10 to 50 cm^{-1}.

The angular dependence of the Stokes and anti-Stokes radiation was studied by simply allowing the beam of radiation from the cell to fall on a photographic plate placed ~ 30 cm from the cell, without the use of any imaging optics. Stokes radiation was isolated with Corning 5-57 filters and anti-Stokes radiation was isolated with a 1 cm thick $CuSO_4$ filter. The Stokes radiation was found to be most intense in the forward direction. Observations made to angles of 40° from the incident direction showed that this radiation fell off rapidly at angles larger tan 5°. Similarly, in the backward direction, the Stokes radiation was confined to small angles and was down in intensity by almost an order of magnitude from that in the forward direction. The anti-Stokes radiation, on the other hand, was only observed in sharply defined cones [3] having a spread of about 10′) within a few degrees of the direction of incidence (Fig. 11).

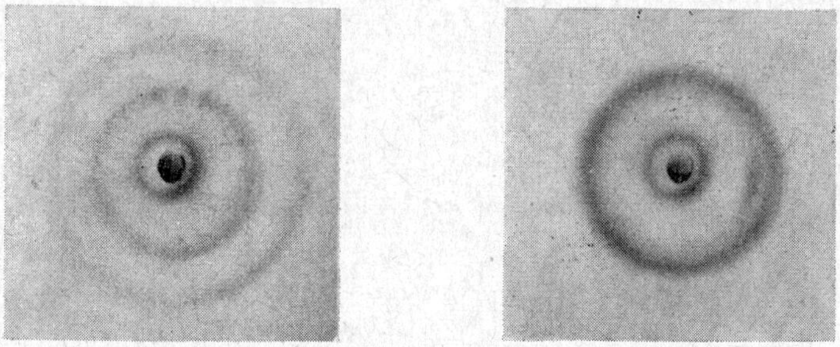

a) b)

Fig. 11. – Angular dependence of the anti-Stokes radiation *a*) in liquid benzene and *b*) liquid nitrobenzene.

For example, the following angles were measured: in benzene the first, second and third anti-Stokes cones have half-angles of 0,030, 0.048 and 0.079 radian; in toluene they are almost the same, being 0.032, 0.046, and 0,078 radian respectively: in carbon disulphide the second and third anti-Stokes cone have half-angles of 0.51 and 0.65 radian; in nitrogen and nitrobenzene, only the first anti- Stokes cones were observed, with half-angles of 0.020 and 0.054 radian, respectively. To test whether the measured values are in agreement with the predicted angles (from the wave-vector relation $2k_{\text{maser}} = k_{\text{Stokes}} + k_{\text{anti-Stokes}}$ required for gain in the anti-Stokes line), it is necessary to know the dispersion of these liquids with rather high accuracy.

4. – Conclusions.

Clearly, even these preliminary studies of the stimulated Raman radiation present new and interesting results not only in the field of stimulated emission but also in Raman spectroscopy. While some of these observations can be understood from existing theories of Raman masers, many details have yet to be explained. They may require higher-order interactions, as recently discussed by GARMIRE, PANDARESE and TOWNES [8] and perphaps interactions of intense elctric and acoustic fields generated in the medium.

As for the possible application of the effect to molecular spectroscopy, it has been shown that stimulated Raman scattering is exhibited by many liquids (and compressed gases [3]) consisting of either diatomic or simple as well as large polyatomic molecules. At present, for each liquid only one or at most two of the normally Raman-active vibrational bands have bene observed. However, in principle, it should be possible to observe the complete Raman spectrum including also rotational and electronic transitions. Also, investigations with mixtures may be useful in obtaining information on molecular interactions.

Although we do not have a complete understanding of the generation of this stimulated Raman radiation, we can already look forward to several immediate applications. For example, many new wavelenghts of intense stimulated radiation to the red and to the blue of the ruby maser can be produced readily. In fact, it would appear that any desired wavelenght can be obtained by the proper choice of liquid. This would be especially useful in fluorescence studies. Finally, it may even be possible to generate radiation in the infra-red by this process.

* * *

I am very grateful to Dr. W. J. JONES and Mr. E. PFITZER for valuable assistance during these experiments.

REFERENCES

[1] E. J. WOODBURY and W. K. NG: *Proc. I.R.E.*, **50**, 2367 (1962).
[2] G. ECKHARDT, R. W. HELLWARTH, F. J. MCCLUNG, S. E. SCHWARZ, D. WEINER and E. J. WOODBURY: *Phys. Rev. Lett.*, **9**, 455 (1962).
[3] R. W. TERHUNE: *Bull. Am. Phys. Soc.*, **8**, 359 (1963); see also A. L. SCHAWLOW: *Sci. Amer.*, **209**, 34 (1963).

[4] A. JAVAN: *Bull. Am. Phys. Soc.*, **3**, 213 (1958); *Journ. Phys. Rad.*, **19**, 806 (1958); see also J. WEBER: *Rev. Mod. Phys.*, **31**, 681 (1959).
[5] R. W. HELLWARTH: *Phys. Rev.*, **130**, 1850 (1963); *Applied Optics* (to be published).
[6] H. J. ZEIGER and P. E. TANNENWALD: *Proc. Third Quantum Electronics Conference* (Paris, 1963).
[7] N. BLOEMBERGEN *et al.*: *Proc. I.E.E.E.*, **51**, 124 (1963); J. A. ARMSTRONG, N. BLOEMBERGEN, J. DUCUING and P. S. PERSHAN: *Phys. Rev.*, **127**, 1918 (1962); N. BLOEMBERGEN and P. S. PERSHAN: *Phys. Rev.*, **128**, 606 (1962).
[8] E. GARMIRE, F. PANDARESE and C. H. TOWNES: *Phys. Rev. Lett.*, **11**, 160 (1963).
[9] Sir C. V. RAMAN: *Ind. Journ. Phys.*, **2**, 387 (1928).
[10] G. PLACZEK: in *Handb. d. Radiologie* (E. MARX, ed.), vol. **6**, part 2 (Leipzig, 1934), p. 205.
[11] G. HERZBERG: *Infrared and Raman Spectra of Polyatomic Molecules* (Princeton, N. J., 1945).
[12] E. B. WILSON jr., J. C. DECIUS and P. C. CROSS: *Molecular Vibrations* (New York, 1955).
[13] J. P. MATHIEU: *Spectre de vibration et symétrie des molécules et des crystaux* (Paris, 1945).
[14] M. BORN and KUN HUANG: *Dynamical Theory of Crystal Lattices* (London and New York, 1954).
[15] G. PLACZEK and E. TELLER: *Zeits. Phys.*, **81**, 209 (1933).
[16] F. RASETTI: *Zeits. Phys.*, **66**, 646 (1930).
[17] J. HOUGEN and S. SINGH: *Phys. Rev. Lett.*, **10**, 406 (1963); *Proc. Roy. Soc.*, A **277**, 193 (1964).
[18] See for example: J. BRANDMÜLLER and H. MOSER: *Einführung in die Ramanspektroskopie* (Darmstadt, 1962); S. BHAGAVANTAM: *Scattering of Light and the Raman Effect* (Brooklyn, N. Y., 1942); K. W. F. KOHLRAUSCH: *Der Smekal-Raman Effekt* (Berlin, 1931, 1938); *Ramanspektren, Hand- und Jahrbuch der Chemischen Physik*, vol. **9** (1943) (published in the U.S.A., Ann Arbor, 1945); L. A. WOODWARD: *Quart. Rev. (London)*, **6**, 1 (1952); **7**, 134 (1953); B. P. STOICHEFF in *Methods of Experimental Physics*, vol. **3** (New York, 1962), p. 11; in *Advances in Spectroscopy*, vol. **1** (New York, 1959), p. 91.
[19] L. BRILLOUIN: *Ann. Phys. (Paris)*, **17**, 88 (1922).
[20] R. S. KRISHNAN: *Proc. Ind. Acad. Sci.*, A **41**, 91 (1955); D. H. RANK, J. S. MCCARTNEY and G. J. SZASZ: *Journ. Opt. Soc. Amer.*, **38**, 287 (1948); D. H. RANK and J. P. MCKELVEY: *Journ. Opt. Soc. Amer.*, **39**, 762 (1949); P. FLUBACHER, A. J. LEADBETTER, J. A. MORRISON and B. P. STOICHEFF: *Journ. Phys. Chem. Solids*, **12**, 53 (1959).
[21] S. P. S. PORTO and D. L. WOOD: *Journ. Opt. Soc. Amer.*, **52**, 251 (1962).
[22] B. P. STOICHEFF: *Proc. X-th Colloquium Spectroscopicum Internationale* (Washington, 1963), p. 399.
[23] R. Y. CHIAO, E. GARMIRE and C. H. TOWNES: this volume, p. 326.
[24] A. JAVAN: this volume, p. 284.
[25] B. P. STOICHEFF: *Symposium on Molecular Structure and Spectroscopy*, Ohio State University (June 1963).

Raman and Phonon Masers (*).

R. Y. Chiao, E. Garmire and C. H. Townes

Massachusetts Institute of Technology - Cambridge, Mass.

Introduction.

When the very intense beams of light generated by optical masers interact with matter, they tend to excite various degrees of freedom of both the matter and the radiation field, and sometimes such excitations are quite large. This must be expected because the effective temperature of maser beams is in the range 10^{15} to 10^{30} °K, so that any interaction with cooler matter must tend to degrade the beam energy, and any equilibrium between the light beam and a small number of degrees of freedom must still correspond to enormously high temperatures. At certain threshold intensities, instabilities set in which transfer energy very rapidly from the beam to other electromagnetic or mechanical modes of the system. Some of these processes will be discussed here, in particular the generation of coherent molecular oscillations and phonons by interaction between intense maser beams and matter. Such instabilities produce the observed intense Raman radiation along with coherent molecular vibrations. They should also lead to generation of intense high-frequency sound waves and of infra-red radiation.

1. – Stimulated Raman effects, coherent molecular vibrations, and light modulation.

Normal Raman scattering, which has been known for some time [1], corresponds to spontaneous emission of Raman radiation. It can be described in terms of individual molecules and photons in which such Raman emission from one molecule is incoherent with that from a neighboring one. The process shows features of a distinctly quantum-mechanical nature.

(*) Work supported in part by the National Aeronautics and Space Administration under Research Grant NsG-330.

A Raman maser, or stimulated Raman emission, typically involves large numbers of molecules and photons. Except for details of molecular characteristics or initiation of the radiation by spontaneous emission, these processes may be discussed rather satisfactorily from a classical point of view.

The potential energy of a molecule with polarizability α in an electric field $\boldsymbol{E}(\boldsymbol{r}, t)$ is

$$W = -\tfrac{1}{2}\alpha(x)\,|\boldsymbol{E}(\boldsymbol{r}, t)|^2 .$$

The dependence of α on x, a molecular vibrational or rotational co-ordinate, results in nonlinear coupling of the molecule to the electromagnetic field and hence in scattered Raman radiation of shifted frequency. As an example we might consider a diatomic molecule for which x describes the deviation from the equilibrium internuclear distance during vibration; $\alpha = \alpha_0 + \alpha_1 x$ in the lowest-order approximation. The frequency-dependence and tensorial properties of α will be neglected. The force driving such vibrations will be

$$-\frac{\partial W}{\partial x} = \frac{1}{2}\alpha_1 E^2 .$$

A sinusoidally varying force, $F \cos \omega t$, will give the following differential equation for the vibrational co-ordinate:

$$m\ddot{x} + R\dot{x} + fx = F \cos \omega t .$$

R is a phenomenological damping coefficient given by the half-width $\Delta\nu$ of the resonance curve:

$$\Delta\nu = R/2\pi m .$$

It may be noted that in this approximation the molecular oscillator itself is, in the absence of an electromagnetic field, completely governed by a linear equation. The dielectric response of the molecules will also be assumed completely linear in the absence of molecular vibration. It is the coupling between the two motions which introduces a nonlinearity. The solution for x at frequencies very near the resonance frequency $\omega_r = \sqrt{f/m}$ is $x = (F/R\omega) \sin \omega t$. Thus the molecular vibration is 90° out of phase with the driving force.

The ratio of the dynamic stretch of the molecule near resonance to the static stretch for equal driving forces is

$$\frac{x_{\text{dyn}}}{x_{\text{stat}}} = \frac{f}{R\omega} = \frac{\nu_r}{\Delta\nu} .$$

In liquids this ratio is frequently as large as 10^3. The amplitude of vibration can thus become quite high, and nonlinear coupling effects associated with the vibration will show up much more prominently at this resonance than at nearby frequencies. Thus, the treatment below will consider only the resonant situation.

The generation of stimulated Raman emission requires the radiation field to contain radiation of Raman-shifted frequency as well as unshifted light. Thus consider $\boldsymbol{E}_0$, the electric field of the initial coherent radiation at frequency ω_0; and $\boldsymbol{E}'$, radiation of frequency $\omega' = \omega_0 \pm \omega_r$, initiated by spontaneous Raman emission. ω_r is the resonant vibrational frequency of the molecule. For traveling waves the total electric field is then

$$\boldsymbol{E} = \boldsymbol{E}_0 \cos(\omega_0 t - \boldsymbol{k}_0 \cdot \boldsymbol{r}) + \boldsymbol{E}' \cos(\omega' t - \boldsymbol{k}' \cdot \boldsymbol{r} + \varphi') .$$

The resonant vibration of the molecules produced by the beating of these two light waves through the force $\frac{1}{2}\alpha_1 E^2$ is, assuming E is coherent over times much larger than the inverse linewidth $1/\Delta\nu$,

$$x = \frac{\boldsymbol{E}_0 \boldsymbol{E}' \alpha_1}{2R(\omega_0 - \omega')} \sin[(\omega_0 - \omega')t - (\boldsymbol{k}_0 - \boldsymbol{k}') \cdot \boldsymbol{r} - \varphi'] .$$

The electric-dipole moment per unit volume induced by the field $\boldsymbol{E}$ is $\boldsymbol{\mu} = \alpha \boldsymbol{E}$. This oscillating-dipole moment may interact with the electric field

$$\boldsymbol{E}' \cos(\omega' t - \boldsymbol{k}' \cdot \boldsymbol{r} + \varphi')$$

to increase or decrease its amplitude continually, as long as the phase φ' is approximately constant. The time-averaged rate of energy flow per unit volume to the field $\boldsymbol{E}'$ is $N\langle \mathrm{d}\boldsymbol{\mu}/\mathrm{d}t \cdot \boldsymbol{E}' \rangle$. Here N is the effective number of molecules per unit volume which take part in this interaction or $N_0 - N_1$ where N_0 is the density of molecules in the ground state involved and N_1, the density in the upper state. Hence the power per unit volume delivered to E' from the input beam E_0 is

$$P' = \frac{N\alpha_1^2}{8R} \frac{\omega'}{\omega_0 - \omega'} (\boldsymbol{E}_0 \cdot \boldsymbol{E}')^2 .$$

For Stokes radiation in which $\omega' = \omega_0 - \omega_r$, $P' > 0$ so that any radiation E' is amplified. The phase φ' is arbitrary as long as it does not vary much during the molecular relaxation time $1/2\pi\Delta\nu$. For anti-Stokes radiation $\omega' = \omega_0 + \omega_r$, $P' < 0$ and any initial radiation E' will lose energy (*).

(*) Anti-Stokes radiation would be amplified and Stokes radiation deamplified if there were an inversion of population in the Raman material due to an additional excitation source, since then $N_0 - N_1$ would be negative.

Since P' is quadratic in E', there will be a threshold intensity required for E_0 before the instability takes place, allowing E' to build up. For build-up of the traveling wave $\boldsymbol{E}'$, the fractional power gain per unit length, assuming E_0 and E' have the same polarization, is

$$a = \frac{N\pi}{cR}\alpha_1^2 \frac{\omega_0 - \omega_r}{\omega_r} E_0^2 .$$

This must be greater than or equal to the fractional loss per unit length b which may, for example, be due to absorption. This leads to the requirement

$$E_0^2 \geqslant \frac{bcR}{\pi N \alpha_1^2} \frac{\omega_r}{\omega_0 - \omega_r} .$$

Once this threshold condition on intensity of the « pump » field E_0 is met, coherent Stokes radiation will increase from the spontaneous Raman emission with the exponential build-up usual in maser theory.

One might also ask whether there will always be an initial wave $\boldsymbol{E}'$ generated by spontaneous Raman emission. Usually, the spontaneous Raman emission will be sufficiently rapid to easily supply the initial field which is amplified. Consider a « plane » wave, defined in angular spread by necessary diffraction due to the finite dimensions of the space in which it exists. The time required for this plane wave to be doubled by stimulated emission is just equal to the average time required for a quantum to be emitted into it by spontaneous emission. The probability of spontaneous emission in any other « plane » wave of similar solid angle is identical, so that if a larger solid angle of waves can be amplified the effective spontaneous emission rate for initiation of the wave E' is correspondingly greater.

Gain in a Raman maser has been formulated several times previously [2-4], and ZEIGER and TANNENWALD [4] have noted that coherent molecular oscillations must exist in such a maser. Usually, the result is expressed in terms of a sum of matrix elements, which are separately very difficult to evaluate. In the above expression, these are replaced by the single quantity α_1: R may be evaluated from the half-width $\Delta\nu$ of the Raman resonance; for a diatomic molecule $R = 2\pi m \Delta\nu$, where m is the reduced mass. Here homogeneous broadening has been assumed, but extension to the inhomogeneous case is straightforward and gives the same final result when expressed in terms of the half-width $\Delta\nu$ of the Raman line. In typical cases the gain a due to stimulated emission in a pumping beam of power 100 megawatt per square centimeter is of the order of 10 cm^{-1}. If the absorption b is about 10 % per cm, this means that the threshold would be at about one megawatt/cm^2 of pump power. As is usual in masers, high gain results in an emission line which is appreciably narrower than that for spontaneously emitted Raman radiation.

Feedback, which may occur from scattering of emitted radiation, will produce still further line narrowing.

For a ruby pulse with the order of 100 MW/cm^2 in a single mode, molecules are stretched by about 10^{-4} of the bond distance. In planes defined by $(\boldsymbol{k}_0 - \boldsymbol{k}')\cdot\boldsymbol{r} = \text{const}$, vibrations of all molecules are in phase, and hence the molecules push each other apart. The resulting expansion in the planes $(\boldsymbol{k}_0 - \boldsymbol{k}')\cdot\boldsymbol{r} = \text{const}$ cannot, however, occur as rapidly as the molecular oscillation, since this would imply macroscopic motions of enormous kinetic energy. The gross expansion of the material occurs, instead, in a time as large as about 10^{-9} s, and is determined by the average value of E^2 over intervals of times as long as this. The resulting spatial variations in dielectric susceptibility are of the order 10^{-4}. In addition, there are variations in the susceptibility of the same order which oscillate at the molecular frequency, associated with the variation α_1 of molecular polarizability with molecular stretching. There is thus a slowly varying susceptibility and one varying synchronously with the molecular vibration, each periodic in $\boldsymbol{k}_0 - \boldsymbol{k}'$. These variations act like a three-dimensional phase grating and scatter light waves; those varying at molecular vibrational frequencies not only scatter, but also modulate light waves.

To be able to understand in detail the generation of anti-Stokes radiation, we consider the case where electromagnetic waves E_{-1} and E_1 of both Stokes and anti-Stokes frequencies are initially present:

$$\boldsymbol{E} = \boldsymbol{E}_0 \cos(\omega_0 t - \boldsymbol{k}_0\cdot\boldsymbol{r}) + \boldsymbol{E}_{-1}\cos[(\omega_0 - \omega_r)t - \boldsymbol{k}_{-1}\cdot\boldsymbol{r} + \varphi_{-1}] + \\ + \boldsymbol{E}_1 \cos[(\omega_0 + \omega_r)t - \boldsymbol{k}_1\cdot\boldsymbol{r} + \varphi_1]\,.$$

As in the treatment above [5], the vibration of the molecules and its oscillating dipole moment are calculated. The average power gain per unit volume of the Stokes radiation is

$$P_{-1} = \frac{N\alpha_1^2}{8R}\,\frac{\omega_0 - \omega_r}{\omega_r}\cdot \\ \cdot\{(\boldsymbol{E}_0\cdot\boldsymbol{E}_{-1})^2 + (\boldsymbol{E}_0\cdot\boldsymbol{E}_1)(\boldsymbol{E}_0\cdot\boldsymbol{E}_{-1})\cos[(2\boldsymbol{k}_0 - \boldsymbol{k}_1 - \boldsymbol{k}_{-1})\cdot\boldsymbol{r} + \varphi_1 + \varphi_{-1}]\}$$

and of the anti-Stokes wave

$$P_{+1} = \frac{N\alpha_1^2}{8R}\,\frac{\omega_0 + \omega_r}{\omega_r}\cdot \\ \cdot\{-(\boldsymbol{E}_0\cdot\boldsymbol{E}_1)^2 - (\boldsymbol{E}_0\cdot\boldsymbol{E}_1)(\boldsymbol{E}_0\cdot\boldsymbol{E}_{-1})\cos[(2\boldsymbol{k}_0 - \boldsymbol{k}_1 - \boldsymbol{k}_{-1})\cdot\boldsymbol{r} + \varphi_1 + \varphi_{-1}]\}\,.$$

From these expressions it is evident that there is a solution for power gain at the Stokes frequency when anti-Stokes radiation is absent, which is just that discussed above. However, there is no possibility of gain in the anti-

Stokes wave unless the Stokes radiation is present. Thus there is a phase-independent term which always gives gain for Stokes and loss for anti-Stokes. It is hence expected that $\boldsymbol{E}_{-1} > \boldsymbol{E}_1$, and when this is true there may be gain for anti-Stokes radiation if $2\boldsymbol{k}_0 = \boldsymbol{k}_{-1} + \boldsymbol{k}_1$ and the phase $\varphi_1 + \varphi_{-1}$ is suitable, $\varphi_1 + \varphi_{-1} = \pi$ giving the maximum gain.

If the phase $\varphi_1 + \varphi_{-1}$ is such that gain can occur for anti-Stokes radiation, the gain for the Stokes radiation is then always decreased at resonance by the presence of anti-Stokes waves. In this case the amplitude of the molecular vibration is proportional to $\boldsymbol{E}_{-1} - \boldsymbol{E}_1$; that is, the two fields drive the molecule in opposite phase.

The generation of the anti-Stokes wave E_1 may be interpreted as caused by a modulation of the input radiation E_0 due to the variations of index of refraction at frequency ω_r which result from the coherent molecular vibrations set up by E_0 and the existing E_{-1}. Such modulation produces sidebands on any radiation present, and hence if the threshold condition on E_0 for the generation of E_{-1} is met, many frequencies can be produced without a further threshold.

Since there is no condition on the wave vectors from the gain term for Stokes radiation, it will be radiated into all directions although under ideal conditions the gain would have an angular dependence $\cos^2\theta$, where θ is the angle between polarization of the pump and Stokes radiation. On the other hand, the wave vector relation, $2\boldsymbol{k}_0 = \boldsymbol{k}_1 + \boldsymbol{k}_{-1}$ required for gain in the anti-Stokes line confines this latter radiation to a cone in the forward direction, with half-angle θ_1, around the initial beam, and gives a unique direction for which the gain in the Stokes line is abnormally small. This vector relation has been also given by TERHUNE [6], although apparently on the basis of a 4-quantum interaction rather than the mechanism discussed here. For small angles one can show that the above relation gives

$$\theta_1^2 \approx \frac{1}{n}\frac{\omega_0 - \omega_r}{\omega_0 + \omega_r}\left[(\Delta n_1 - \Delta n_{-1}) + \frac{\omega_r}{\omega_0}(\Delta n_1 + \Delta n_{-1})\right].$$

Here $n = n(\omega_0)$ is the index of refraction at frequency ω_0;

$$\Delta n_1 = n(\omega_0 + \omega_r) - n(\omega_r)\,, \qquad \text{and} \qquad \Delta n_{-1} = n(\omega_0) - n(\omega_0 - \omega_r)\,.$$

Often the first term in the bracket of this expression predominates, so that the angle θ_1 is determined by the curvature of the dispersion curve. The Stokes radiation which interacts with the anti-Stokes wave occurs at an angle

$$\theta_{-1} = \frac{\omega_0 + \omega_r}{\omega_0 - \omega_r}\,\theta_1\,.$$

These angles are typically of the order of a few degrees. As was stated above, there is no additional threshold needed for the generation of E_1 beyond the existence of E_{-1} at the appropriate angle, since the gain is not quadratic in E_1.

Anti-Stokes radiation will not usually build up by the above mechanism in a Raman maser with plane-parallel reflectors perpendicular to the initial beam. Stokes radiation will build up by the first process discussed above in the direction of maximum gain which is parallel to the pump beam, at the expense of possible Stokes waves in other directions. Because of dispersion, the above wave vector relation required for the generation of anti-Stokes radiation cannot be satisfied by parallel E_0 and E_{-1} waves.

A field E_{-2} at frequency $\omega_0 - 2\omega_r$ can be emitted diffusely by a process generating power proportional to $E_1^2 E_{-2}^2$ essentially identical with that for the generation of E_{-1}. In addition, it may be produced through modulation of E_{-1} by the oscillations in dielectric constant due to E_0 and E_{-1}, giving a power generation proportional to $E_0(E_{-1})^2 E_{-2}$. The latter case, which has no threshold provided E_{-1} is present, is the more important in generation of Raman radiation by intense beams outside a cavity, since in any one direction $|E_{-2}| < |E_0|$. This process requires $\boldsymbol{k}_0 - \boldsymbol{k}_{-1} = \boldsymbol{k}'_{-1} - \boldsymbol{k}_{-2}$ where the wave vectors $\boldsymbol{k}_{-1}$ and $\boldsymbol{k}'_{-1}$ may be differently oriented but both correspond to frequencies $\omega_0 - \omega_r$. This equation cannot usually be satisfied in a dispersive medium if E_{-1} is in the same direction as E_0. Hence the former mechanism, which has a threshold, is probably the more important in a resonant cavity. Similar mechanisms can generate Stokes radiation of frequencies $\omega_0 - n\omega_r$. The strongest such radiation will usually be due to the modulation processes, which require no threshold condition, and will be diffusely emitted unless there is some feedback by reflection of the wave.

Radiation of frequency $\omega_0 + 2\omega_r$ is produced without threshold effects by vibrational modulation of $\omega_0 + \omega_r$ and is emitted in directions specified by $\boldsymbol{k}_0 - \boldsymbol{k}_{-1} = \boldsymbol{k}_2 - \boldsymbol{k}_1$. For normal materials, there is a $\boldsymbol{k}_{-1}$ and a $\boldsymbol{k}_2$ which will satisfy this equation, the angle between $\boldsymbol{k}_0$ and $\boldsymbol{k}_2$ being of the order of $2\theta_1$. Other anti-Stokes beams of frequency $\omega_0 + n\omega_r$ are similarly generated in cones about the original beam.

Although the build-up of Stokes radiation is exponential in the absence of anti-Stokes radiation, the interaction of the two fields produces a linear gain. If the fields E_{-1} and E_1 are initially $E_{-1}(0)$ and 0, respectively, and if each has a fractional power loss b per unit length in the medium due to other effects, the build-up thereafter of the two interacting waves in a distance L will have the form

$$E_1 = E_{-1}(0)\frac{aL}{2}\exp\left[-\frac{bL}{2}\right],$$

$$E_{-1} = E_{-1}(0)\left(\frac{aL}{2}+1\right)\exp\left[-\frac{bL}{2}\right].$$

Thus for $aL/2>1$, E_1 becomes comparable to E_{-1}. In this case, $E_{-1}(0)$ is understood to be not noise, as is often the case in masers, but Stokes light of sizeable intensity, perhaps scattered from other directions in which this radiation experiences an exponential build-up. If $E_{-1}(0)$ is large, the build-up of E_1 and E_{-1} in the directions specified by the wave vector equation may be considerable. Usually $bL/2 \ll 1$ for pertinent cases.

2. – Infra-red generation.

The molecules set into vibration in the crystal are all vibrating coherently over some spatial distribution. If these molecules have dipole moments, then their vibrating dipoles can coherently radiate infra-red radiation at the Raman frequency providing that the wave vector relation $\boldsymbol{k}_0-\boldsymbol{k}_{-1}=\boldsymbol{k}_r$ is satisfied. Here $\boldsymbol{k}_r$ is the wave vector of the infra-red radiation. From this relation, one finds that the angle θ_r between the generated infra-red beam and the incident radiation is given by

$$\cos\theta_r = 1 + \frac{\Delta n_r}{n}\,\frac{\omega_0-\omega_r}{\omega_0} + \frac{\Delta n_{-1}}{n}\,\frac{(\omega_0-\omega_r)^2}{\omega_0\omega_r}\,.$$

Here Δn_r is $n(\omega_0)-n(\omega_r)$. If both Δn_r and Δn_{-1} are positive, θ_r is no real angle, since $\cos\theta_r>1$. However, Δn_r will be negative for many substances if ω_r is an infra-red frequency and Δn_{-1} may on occasion be negative, so that θ_r can be real. When this condition is not met, infra-red radiation can still be radiated from surface layers of material of finite extent.

Consider now the origin of the dipole moment which is oscillating. Normally, the Raman transition is not thought of as involving an oscillating dipole moment, but this only holds when the molecules have a center-of-inversion symmetry. If they do not have such a center, then the transition can be both infra-red and Raman active. If a center of symmetry normally exists, it can be removed by applying a strong d.c. field which will then allow both infra-red and Raman activity in the molecules.

One might wonder whether the infra-red radiation will be strongly reabsorbed in traversing the material, since it corresponds to an active molecular transition. It will not be absorbed, but amplified, if it has the correct phase, since all the molecules are oscillating coherently. A wave with an arbitrary phase may be absorbed, but with just the correct phase it will receive energy from each molecule in turn as it propagates, as a result of the matching of wave vectors. The usual absorption then becomes an emission.

This is another example of amplification where there is no inversion of population. The numerical probability of finding a molecule in its upper state is typically only about 10^{-6}, corresponding to one part in 10^3 of the upper-state wave function mixed with the lower-state function. Amplification occurs not because of a population inversion, but because of phase coherence between the various oscillating systems, so that an infra-red wave of the correct phase and wave vector can receive energy from every oscillator.

3. – Phonon masers.

The phonon field is very similar in structure to the electromagnetic field, and hence one may expect maser-like phenomena in acoustic waves. The theory of a phonon maser quite analogous to a solid-state maser in the microwave region was discussed some time ago [7, 8] and has been realized by TUCKER [9]. He used impurity atoms in a crystalline lattice and inverted their population. Since the excited atoms in the lattice interact with the phonon field—as well as with the electromagnetic field—they can provide a phonon maser if the usual type of critical condition for amplification or oscillation is met.

Here a different type of phonon generation will be discussed, namely, one based on stimulated Brillouin scattering. In the normal Brillouin scattering [10], an incident light beam is scattered by thermally excited acoustic waves. The scattered light is shifted in frequency and the energy difference taken up by the acoustic wave just as in the usual Raman effect. However, because the scattering is produced by a large region of the crystal rather than by a localized molecule, as in the usual Raman effect, the scattered beam is highly directional. If the incident beam is sufficiently intense, this process can be made to produce coherent stimulated emission of both the scattered light and the acoustic wave. The process may be viewed as analogous to a Raman maser, or to parametric amplification of an extended wave.

The coupling of the light waves with the sound waves which will be considered is due to electrostriction, the compression or expansion of the material by electric fields in the light wave. For a quantitative measure of this effect, consider a condenser of volume V immersed in a compressible fluid. The change of electrical energy when the fluid in the condenser contracts by an amount ΔV is $(E^2/8\pi)V\Delta\varepsilon$ where $\Delta\varepsilon = (\mathrm{d}\varepsilon/\mathrm{d}V)\Delta V$ is the change in dielectric constant due to compression. This equals the work done on the fluid, $p\Delta V$, where p is the electrostrictive pressure. Since $\Delta\varrho/\varrho = -\Delta V/V$, this yields $p = (E^2/8\pi)\cdot$ $\cdot\varrho(\mathrm{d}\varepsilon/\mathrm{d}\varrho) = \gamma E^2/8\pi$ where $\gamma = \varrho(\mathrm{d}\varepsilon/\mathrm{d}\varrho)$. Usually $\varrho(\mathrm{d}\varepsilon/\mathrm{d}\varrho)$ is of order unity for liquids or solids, so that for a power flux of 300 MW/cm^2 the electrostrictive pressure p from this expression is about 10^5 dyn/cm^2.

Now consider two beams of light at slightly different frequencies in the medium. Since the electrostrictive pressure is proportional to E^2, the medium will be compressed at the beat frequency of the two beams (which may be anything up to the frequency of the light). So under certain conditions acoustic waves of high energy will build up. The whole crystal can be considered as one molecule and to vibrate analogously to a single molecule in the Raman effect discussed above. We are, in fact, considering a Raman effect of gross material. The crystal vibrates in modes, the wavelengths of which are characteristically short compared to the dimensions of the crystal. Since the susceptibility depends on the compression, the acoustic modes represent spatial phase gratings. The theory ot the interaction between light waves and the acoustic modes is similar to the above treatment of light waves interacting with vibrating molecules. Its quantitative behavior may be derived as follows.

The change in polarization per unit volume due to a pressure p in an isotropic material is given by

$$\boldsymbol{\mu} = \frac{\boldsymbol{E}}{4\pi}\frac{\mathrm{d}\varepsilon}{\mathrm{d}\varrho}\frac{\mathrm{d}\varrho}{\mathrm{d}p}\,p = \frac{1}{4\pi}\frac{\gamma}{B}\boldsymbol{E}p\,.$$

Hence, a nonlinear coupling between the electromagnetic field and the compressional waves is produced by the fluctuating dipole moment. Here B is the bulk modulus, or the inverse of the adiabatic compressibility, $1/B = (1/\varrho)\mathrm{d}\varrho/\mathrm{d}p$.

Only a general outline of the theory of build-up of coupled acoustic and electromagnetic waves will be presented. The polarization produced by the acoustic wave feeds energy into the electromagnetic wave. The power gain per unit volume of the electromagnetic wave is

$$(\text{Power})\ \text{e.m.} = -\boldsymbol{E}\cdot\frac{\mathrm{d}\boldsymbol{\mu}}{\mathrm{d}t} = -\frac{1}{4\pi}\frac{\gamma}{B}E\frac{\mathrm{d}}{\mathrm{d}t}(Ep)\,.$$

The power fed into the sonic wave per unit volume is

$$(\text{Power})\ \text{sonic} = \frac{-p_E}{V}\frac{\mathrm{d}V}{\mathrm{d}t} = \frac{\gamma E^2}{8\pi B}\frac{\mathrm{d}p}{\mathrm{d}t}$$

where p_E has been written for the pressure due to electrostriction and $\mathrm{d}v/\mathrm{d}t$ is the rate of change in volume due to pressure p in the sonic wave. Consider three electromagnetic waves of different frequencies present in the electrostrictive medium

$$\boldsymbol{E} = \boldsymbol{E}_0\cos(\omega_0 t - \boldsymbol{k}_0\boldsymbol{r}) + \boldsymbol{E}_{-1}\cos(\omega_{-1}t - \boldsymbol{k}_{-1}\cdot\boldsymbol{r} + \varphi_{-1}) + \boldsymbol{E}_1\cos(\omega_1 t - \boldsymbol{k}_1\cdot\boldsymbol{r} + \varphi_1)$$

and a sonic wave

$$p_s = p\cos(\omega_s t - \boldsymbol{k}_s\cdot\boldsymbol{r} + \varphi_s)\,.$$

Here

$$\omega_{-1} = \omega_0 - \omega_s \quad \text{and} \quad \omega_1 = \omega_0 + \omega_s \,.$$

The power fed into each one of these waves may now be calculated. It is easy to show that, as in stimulated Raman effects discussed above, waves of the upconverted frequency ω_1 are not amplified. But the E_{-1} wave and the sonic wave may be amplified. Thus one need consider in first approximation only three interacting waves in the system.

Amplification will take place only when the phase matching condition $\boldsymbol{k}_0 = \boldsymbol{k}_{-1} + \boldsymbol{k}_s$ is fulfilled. From this condition for the wave vectors the frequency of the sonic wave is found to be $\omega_s = (2v_s/c')\omega_0 \sin(\theta/2)$, where v_s is the velocity of sound in the medium, c' is the velocity of light in the medium, and θ is the angle between incident and scattered light waves with frequency difference ω_s. This expression is a valid approximation when $v_s \ll c'$. It was first derived by BRILLOUIN [10].

The velocity ratio v_s/c' is such that the sonic frequencies can go up to about 10^{11} Hz or even 10^{12} Hz for material with a very high velocity of sound. Thus the frequencies lie in the microwave frequency region. By calculating the power gain per unit length the threshold condition is found

$$\frac{E_c^2}{8\pi} \geqslant \frac{\varepsilon_0 B}{\gamma^2} \frac{1}{k_s L_s k_i L_i} \,.$$

Here L_i, L_s are the absorption lengths of light and sound waves, respectively. When the input radiation fulfills this condition, the sonic waves and the scattered electromagnetic wave field begin to build up. With absorption lengths $L_i \simeq 10^2$ cm and $L_s \simeq 10^{-2}$ cm (*e.g.*, quartz) and normal bulk moduli the necessary input power to meet this threshold is found to be about 1 MW/cm^2.

The maximum power which can go into the sound waves due to single Brillouin scattering is ultimately governed by the Manley-Rowe relations, that is, by the ratio of the optical to the sonic frequencies. Thus with 1 MW of power in the light beam there can be a maximum of about 1 kW of power in the sonic waves. It is particularly interesting that by this method acoustic energy can be fed into the interior of nearly every optical material. By the present known techniques, high-frequency acoustic power may be generated in quartz crystals, but cannot easily be coupled into many other materials.

4. – More general treatment of sonic waves.

So far we have treated the system in rather an elementary way. We have assumed that there are sonic and electromagnetic waves existing in the medium and have tried to find out under what conditions power is fed into them from the initial electromagnetic radiation or « pumping » wave. This approach is good in many cases, but it has its limitations. The fields E and p have been assumed to exist in the same space and to continue so. This is perfectly valid in a crystal when the fields E and p are standing waves reflected back and forth, that is, for a resonant type of structure. For two traveling waves, such an assumption is not adequate unless the sonic and electromagnetic waves are traveling in the same direction, in which case they tend to remain together and the above equations can be valid. However, the condition $\boldsymbol{k}_0 = \boldsymbol{k}_{-1} + \boldsymbol{k}_s$ requires that usually the sonic wave and scattered light waves travel in opposite directions. This is because $\omega_s \ll \omega$, even though k_s and k_0 may be comparable in magnitude. The vectors $\boldsymbol{k}_0$ and $\boldsymbol{k}_{-1}$ are therefore approximately equal in length, though usually different in direction. Hence the vector diagram has nearly the form of an isosceles triangle and the sound wave propagates at an angle greater than 90° with respect to the scattered light wave. If there is gain, the light wave and sound wave therefore build up in different directions, and hence one must treat this travelling wave case more carefully than we have done so far.

A more general approach is to start with the wave equations:

$$\ddot{\varrho} + \alpha_s \dot{\varrho} - v_s^2 \nabla^2 \varrho = - \frac{\gamma}{8\pi} \nabla^2 E^2 ,$$

$$\ddot{E} + \alpha \dot{E} - \frac{c^2}{\varepsilon_0} \nabla^2 E = - \frac{\gamma}{\varrho_0 \varepsilon_0} \frac{\partial^2}{\partial t^2} (\varrho E) .$$

The left-hand sides of each of these equations are the normal wave equations with damping constants α_s and α. The right-hand sides represent nonlinear driving or coupling terms. These equations have been given by KROLL [11], who has also obtained certain classes of solutions for them. They must be solved subject to boundary conditions appropriate to the system of interest. Details of this method are very similar to those in Kroll's discussion of parametric oscillation [12]. This approach allows, of course, appropriate discussion of either resonant or traveling-wave systems.

5. – Occurrence of such effects.

How fast does the acoustic wave build up in the crystal? For light pulses as short as 10^{-8} s the wave may not build up fast enough to be very important. For example, if one has an electric field strength just twice that required to overcome the threshold condition, then the rate of build-up of the acoustic wave is about equal to the rate of loss of the least lossy wave; this is usually that of the light wave, and represents a rather slow build-up. However, one can exceed the threshold field by factors of the order of 100 fairly easily and so obtain conditions in which the sound wave builds up importantly within the duration of a typical pulse.

A strong sound-wave field can also result if in the initial beam both of the fields E_0 and E_{-1} are present. This case is not uncommon, for usually one has the frequencies of several modes in the beam. We therefore start off with a pressure wave which gives an acoustic shock to the crystal as a result of the electrostriction. Some of the frequencies in the shock can be resonant in the system and so build up, or they may simply build up as traveling waves. In this case pressure in the sound wave begins to build up linearly with time, increasing approximately $2\pi\gamma E_0 E_{-1}$ in the reciprocal of the acoustic frequency. For frequencies near 10^{10} Hz, one sees that considerable build-up can be achieved within a pulse.

So far, we seem to have been limited by the phase matching condition to frequencies below about 10^{12} Hz. It is possible to go higher in frequency by, for example, the Raman effect, which can be viewed as Brillouin scattering from optical phonons. This is possible because of the anomalous dispersion suffered by the Raman wave, which leads to $\boldsymbol{k}_s$ taking on a wide range of values around resonance. Hence the condition $\boldsymbol{k}_0 = \boldsymbol{k}_{-1} + \boldsymbol{k}_s$ can be satisfied at very high frequencies. Any region of strong anomalous sound dispersion is likely to allow the phase matching condition, so that in such a region this type of interaction can generate acoustic frequencies considerably higher than those allowed by normal Brillouin scattering.

REFERENCES

[1] See, for example, G. HERZBERG: *Spectra of Diatomic Molecules* (New York, 1950).
[2] A. JAVAN: *Journ. Phys. et Rad.*, **19**, 806 (1958); *Bull. Am. Phys. Soc.*, **3**, 213 (1958).
[3] R. W. HELLWARTH: *Phys. Rev.*, **130**, 1850 (1963); *Applied Optics*, **2**, 847 (1963).
[4] H. J. ZEIGER and P. E. TANNENWALD: *Proc. of the Third Quantum Electronics Conference* (Paris, 1963).
[5] See also E. GARMIRE, F. PANDARESE and C. H. TOWNES: *Phys. Rev. Lett.*, **11**, 160 (1963).
[6] R. W. TERHUNE: *Bull. Am. Phys. Soc.*, **8**, 359 (1963).
[7] *Proc. of the Quantum Electronics Conference* (New York, 1960), p. 402, Discussion by C. H. TOWNES.
[8] C. KITTEL: *Phys. Rev. Lett.*, **6**, 449 (1961).
[9] E. B. TUCKER: *Phys. Rev. Lett.*, **6**, 547 (1961).
[10] L. BRILLOUIN: *Ann. de Phys.*, **17**, 88 (1922); M. BORN and K. WANG: *Dynamical Theory of Crystal Lattices* (Oxford, 1954), p. 373.
[11] N. M. KROLL: private communication.
[12] N. M. KROLL: *Proc. I.E.E.E.*, **51**, 110 (1963).

High-Intensity Flash Tubes (*).

J. L. Emmett

Department of Physics, Stanford University - Stanford, Cal.

With certain exceptions optically pumped optical masers place extreme requirements on the intensity of the pump light source. Consequently, most presently available solid-state materials are not operated continuously, but are pulsed for times on the order of one millisecond. The light source generally used is a high current discharge in rare gases at pressures of $(10\div 60)$ cm Hg. Xenon at a pressure of $(20\div 30)$ cm is often used because of the commercial availability of such flash tubes. It was chosen originally as a high-intensity white-light source for high-speed photography. Since it is of great interest to investigate other maser materials with absorption bands that are not necessarily in the visible or materials with short fluorescent lifetimes, the electrical and optical properties of these flash tubes should be investigated under widely varying conditions.

The optical radiation emitted by these sources is produced by three mechanisms. The first and most prominent at very low current densities is excitation of electronic spectra. While this mechanism is important at low current densities it is a negligible contribution to the total radiation at current densities above $5\cdot 10^3$ A/cm^2. The second mechanism is radiation by recombination. This forms a significant portion of the radiation in the wavelength region below 6500 Å in xenon discharges. The third mechanism which produces most of the red and near infra-red radiation is electron-ion bremsstrahlung. This is, of course, directly related to the degree of ionization and the current density in the plasma.

It was of interest to determine if the peak intensity and total output energy of a standard xenon flash lamp could be substantially increased in the violet and ultraviolet portion of the spectrum. The above considerations dictate that

(*) Portions of this paper describe work supported by the National Aeronautics and Space Administration, under grant NsG 331.

at a given gas pressure, the current density will have to be greatly increased if an increase in intensity in this portion of the spectrum is to be achieved. If the high voltage necessary to obtain a high current density is placed across the flash lamp prior to the triggering in the usual manner, when the flash tube is triggered a stable arc over the whole cross-section of the tube evidently does not form. The shockwave in the plasma generated in such an operation usually destroys the quartz envelope of the lamp. It has been found however, that high current densities can be obtained if a stable low-current discharge is first obtained. The flash tubes used in this work were commercial xenon flash tubes with a 7 mm inside diameter and 77 mm length between tungsten electrodes. These tubes were filled at a pressure of 30 cm of xenon. The flash tube is initially operated in the usual manner from a 300 μF capacitor at 1 000 V. Since the flash tube is to a first approximation a constant voltage device, a 150 μH inductor in series with the capacitor serves to limit the rate of rise of current thereby aiding the formation of a stable discharge. Approximately 225 μs after triggering the flash lamp, a peak current density of 2 000 A/cm² is obtained. At this time a 14 μF capacitor at 5 500 V is discharged, by a coaxial triggered gap, directly across the operating flash lamp. This portion of the circuit has very low impedance to allow high current and high rate of rise of current during the discharge. A minimum delay of 75 μs after initiation of the low-current discharge is required to avoid destruction of the tube by the high-current pulse. In this manner current densities of 25 000 A/cm² for several microseconds can be obtained. Figure 1 shows the circuit used for this work. Figure 2 shows

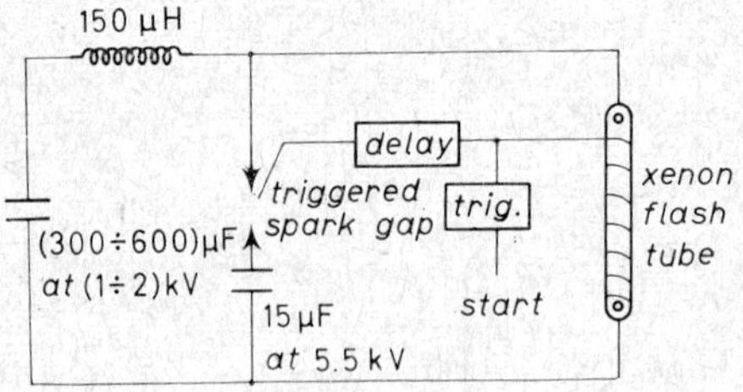

Fig. 1.

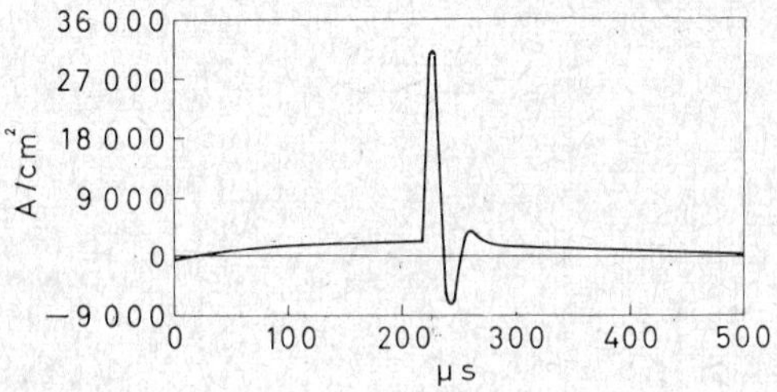

Fig. 2.

the current through the flash tube during this type of operation. The current through the flash tube was measured with a loop near the current carrying wire and an integrating amplifier. The critically damped risetime was 25 ns.

Figure 3 shows the spectral output of the flash tube for two different current densities. As can be readily seen, the peak intensity is greatly enhanced at high current densities. At 3 000 Å a factor of 100 is obtained in peak intensity. Measurements below 3 000 Å have been made with a filter which monitored the (2 500 ÷ 3 000) Å band. With this filter the ratio of peak intensities is a factor of 250 which indicates enhancement at wavelengths below 3 000 Å. Photographs of the spectrum show extreme broadening and self-absorption reversal of some of the xenon lines. In addition to the Xe I lines, many Xe II lines are easily seen. The presence of discrete lines shows that the discharge is not a black-

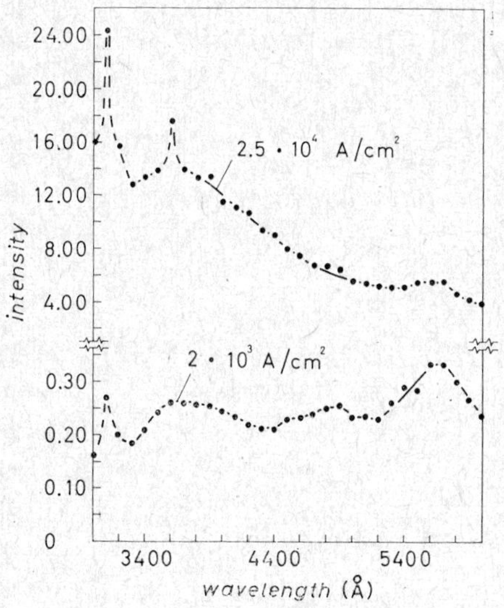

Fig. 3.

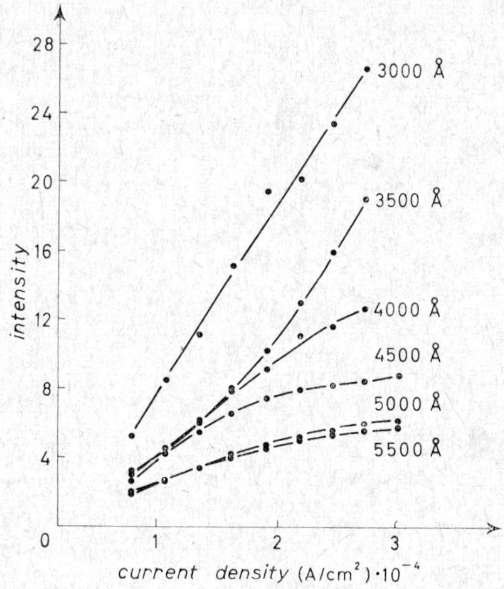

Fig. 4.

body radiator, and indicates that still greater intensities might be obtained from thicker discharge tubes. Figure 4 is a plot of peak intensity as a function of current density for various wavelengths. It can be seen that above 5 000 Å there is little improvement above 20 000 A/cm². However, at the shorter wavelengths the peak intensity increases rapidly with current density. The decay time of the light pulse falls from 8 μs at 6 000 Å to 4 μs (same as current pulse) at 3 000 Å.

Several conclusions can be drawn from the spectral curves. At current densities of 2 000 A/cm² the discharge does not radiate like a black-body. Approximate measurements of the ionization indicate that 2 % of the xenon has been ionized and an electron temperature of 6 000 °K exists. At 25 000 A/cm² the spectral curve more nearly approximates a black-body distribution and about 10 % of the xenon is ionized with and electron temperature of approximately 13 000 °K. In a partially ionized plasma the optical absorption coefficient, considering both absorption and stimulated emission, is proportional to the square of the electron density. Since the plasma column measured was 7 mm thick, we might conclude that at $2.5 \cdot 10^4$ A/cm² a plasma thickness of 2 cm should radiate like a black-body in the visible portion of the spectrum,

Therefore at 2 000 A/cm^2 a plasma thickness of possibly 50 cm would be required for black-body radiation in the same region to be achieved. Direct measurements presently being carried out indicate a large photon mean free path in the visible portion of the spectrum at 2 000 A/cm^2. The dependence of the optical absorption coefficient on frequency is to a first approximation $(\exp[h\nu/kT]-1)/\nu^3$, if an appropriate cut-off is assumed. For temperatures assumed above, this function reaches a minimum in the visible portion of the spectrum and rises very rapidly in the near infra-red. A slow rise is also noted in the far ultra-violet portion of the spectrum.

It should be noted that the radiation in the red and infra-red portion of the spectrum increases very slowly with increasing input *power*. Therefore, for efficiently pumping materials with infra-red absorption bands such as neodymium-glass, large area discharge tubes should be used so that the current density may be kept low even if the total energy is large, and the discharge time is quite short. The saturation of light output in the region of the spectrum above 5 000 Å can be partially offset by increasing the xenon pressure and thereby the recombination radiation. However, at higher pressures, the shock wave generated is more energetic and the flash tube is more easily destroyed for a given input energy and power. It is advantageous in certain cases, however, to operate at pressures from 50 to 130 cm. The total light output of a flash-tube in a particular portion of the spectrum as function of gas pressure and input inergy is shown in Fig. 5.

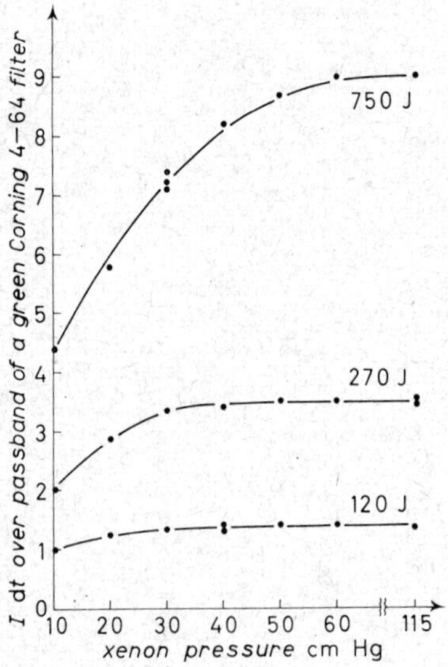

Fig. 5. – Total light output as a function of gas pressure and input energy. Flash tube bore (5 × 75) mm; constant pulse length.

Extremely high temperatures can be obtained in shocked gases and also in various types of high-current pinch discharges. In the case of the pinched discharge electron temperatures of 0.1 to 1.0 keV represent about the lower-current regions of operations; at such electron temperatures the bremsstrahlung radiation peak is below 1 000 Å. It should be noted that at high temperatures black-body radiation in the visible portion of the spectrum increases approximately as the first power of the temperature whereas the total radiation increases as T^4. Therefore, it can be easily seen that the attainment of a very-high-temperature pump source is quite inefficient unless use can be made of the far ultra-violet radiation.

Several applications of the double-pulse technique itself immediately present themselves. The most obvious is the pumping of materials with ultra-violet absorption bands, such as terbium, europium, and gadolinium ions. This technique would also be quite valuable for pumping materials in which the fluorescent lifetime is quite short. Another interesting application is to the giant pulse operation of ruby lasers. At high levels of inversion the effective fluorescent lifetime is considerably reduced. This occurs because spontaneous emission from the interior of the crystal is amplified by stimulated emission as it escapes. If a large increase in intensity for a short time could be obtained just before the Q of the optical cavity is switched to a high value, a considerable improvement in the energy of the giant pulse should be obtained.

Some Properties of a Small Gas Laser.

J. Haisma

Philips Research Laboratories, N. V. Philips' Gloeilampenfabrieken - Eindhoven

The announcement of inverted population and continuous optical maser oscillation in a gas discharge containing a helium-neon gas mixture [1], has led to an enormous increase of activities in the quantum-electronics field.

A one-meter Fabry-Perot interferometer construction with flat mirrors is not an easily manageable device and it was our aim to reduce its dimensions and thus construct a simpler, but fully comparable gas laser [2]. We succeeded in reducing the length of the gas discharge tube by about a factor of 10 (from 100 to 12 cm) by simultaneously changing the inner diameter from 15 to 3 mm and increasing the total gas pressure, with a He-Ne ratio of 85 to 15, from about 1 to 3 Torr. With these new dimensions it was possible to construct an « all glass » device using the positive column of a d.c. glow discharge as active medium. This gas laser construction and photograph of it are shown in Fig. 1 and 2. A channel, provided with side-channels for the electrodes, was drilled along the axis of a fused silica cylinder. Perpendicular to that channel the end faces were polished flat as well as parallel to a high degree of accuracy (flatness about $\frac{1}{10}$ of a wavelenth; the angle between the two end faces is less than one second of arc). Optical flats with dielectric coated mirrors were connected to the end faces by adhesion only, which appeared to be a very tight vacuum connection. No additional adjustment is needed in this stable construction, unlike the devices with flat mirrors described by others [1, 3, 4, 5].

The energy level diagram of He and Ne, given in Fig. 3, shows the possible transitions in Paschen notation. Our mirrors give selective amplification of the $2s_2$-$2p_4$ transition at a wavelenght of 1.153 μm (on the other hand, by using ordinary silver-coated mirrors it is possible to obtain laser action between the $3s_2$-$3p_4$ levels at a wavelength of 3.39 μm).

In the case of a small laser one of the questions is whether one can produce enough metastable He atoms without overpopulating the metastable 1s level

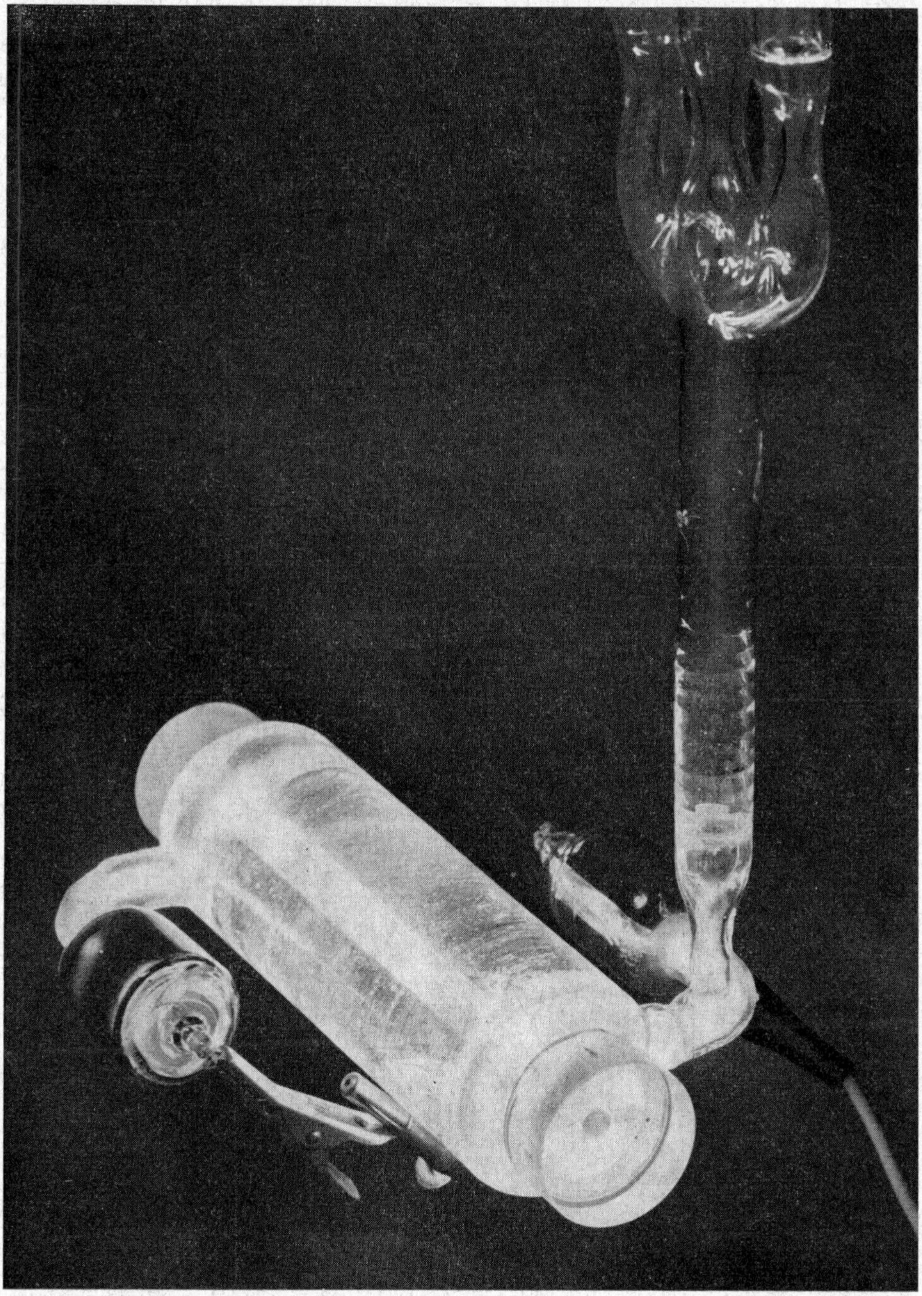

Fig. 1. – Construction of the gas laser.

of neon, because the excitation of this metastable level would fill the lower level of the laser transitions by trapping resonance radiation and so reduce or even prevent laser action. These considerations determine the discharge parameters, such as gas pressure, He to Ne ratio, diameter of the channel and the current. From our measurements the chosen value of E/p (E = electric field, p = total gas pressure) in the positive column appears to be favourable for maximum metastable He production.

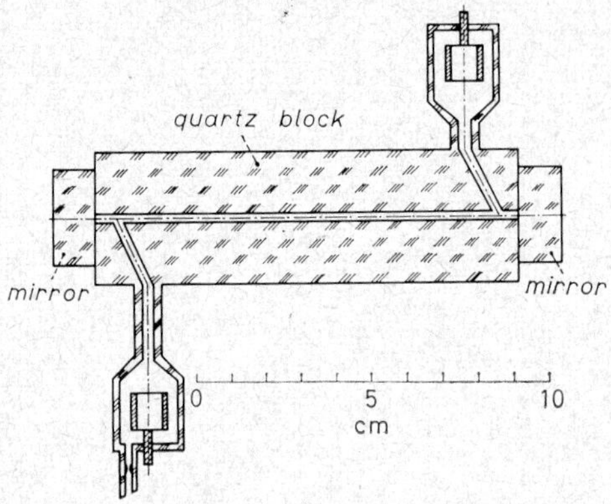

Fig. 2. – Photograph of the gas laser.

An important difference between a one-meter and a 10-cm interferometer lies in the frequency separation of two consecutive longitudinal interferometer resonances ($\nu_{n+1} - \nu_n = c/2l$, where c is the velocity of light and l the mirror separation). This is 10 times as large in the case of the small laser, being about 1500 MHz. Figure 4 shows, for both cases, the distribution of the resonance over the frequency scale compared with the Doppler profile which has a half-maximum width of 800 MHz. Consequently, in our small laser oscillation takes place in just one longitudinal mode.

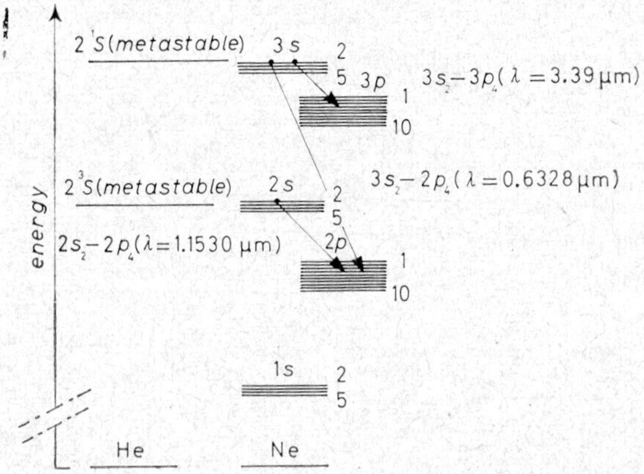

Fig. 3. – Energy level diagram of He and Ne (schematic).

On the other hand the output of the laser is divided over a number of transehrse electromagnetic modes of different order. A cycle of modes is produced by ʌeating the laser body [6]. It takes a dilatation of the channel by half a wavelength for the modes to run through a cycle. This cycle starts with the lowest axial mode and shifts towards superpositions of modes of higher order (Fig. 5).

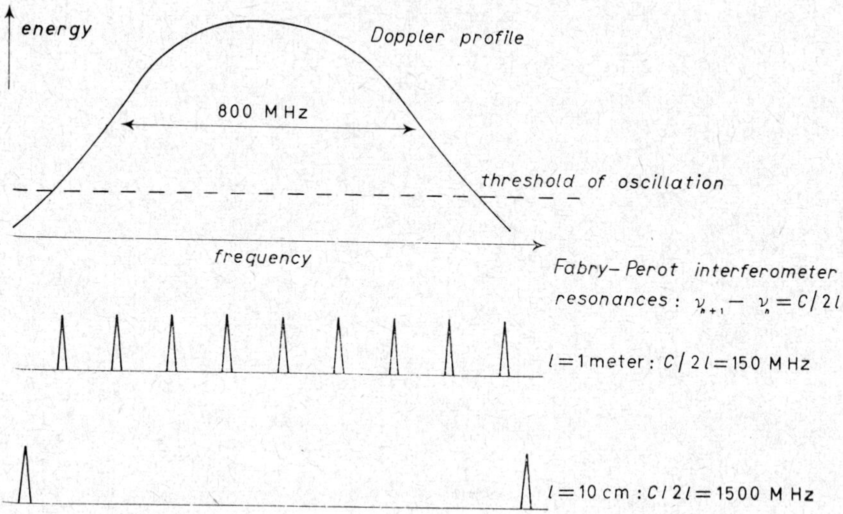

Fig. 4. – Comparison of one-meter and 10-cm Fabry-Perot interferometer resonances with regard to the Doppler width.

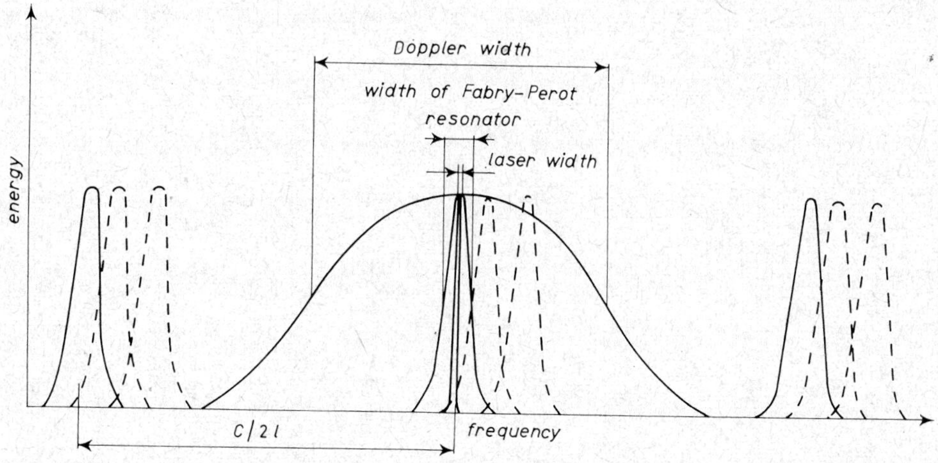

Fig. 5. – Outline of the resonance of various orders of modes in the case of the small gas laser; —— lower order; – – – subsequent higher orders.

A few of these superpositions are shown in Fig. 6. These are far-field patterns photographed by the use of an image converter (Fig. 7). After the cycle has come to an end a new cycle starts, corresponding to a standing wave with one more half-wavelength between the mirrors.

It is interesting to note the influence of the input power of the gas discharge on the cycle of mode patterns. At small imput power, lower- order modes predominantly occur, but at higher input power the lower orders give way to higher orders. The cause of this phenomenon is that the production of metastable

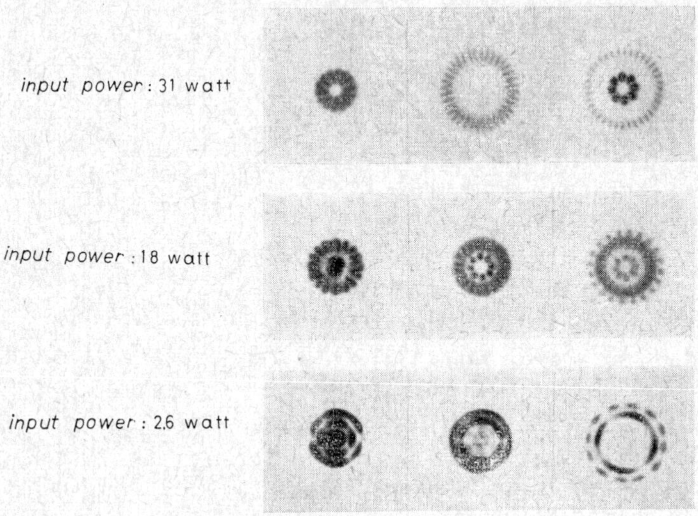

Fig. 6. – A few mode patterns from the same laser at different input power.

He atoms as well as their destruction by cumulative ionization varies across the diameter of the discharge tube. At high imput power, the metastable He atoms are preferentially destroyed in the centre of the discharge so that no central (axial) mode can appear; in the remaining area of the discharge a higher number of metastable atoms is created. At still higher imput power metastable atoms are destroyed over the whole cross-section of the disharge and no laser-action is possible at all.

Even for a fixed value of the input power, differences are observed between the mode cycles found for a number of lasers of identical construction. We

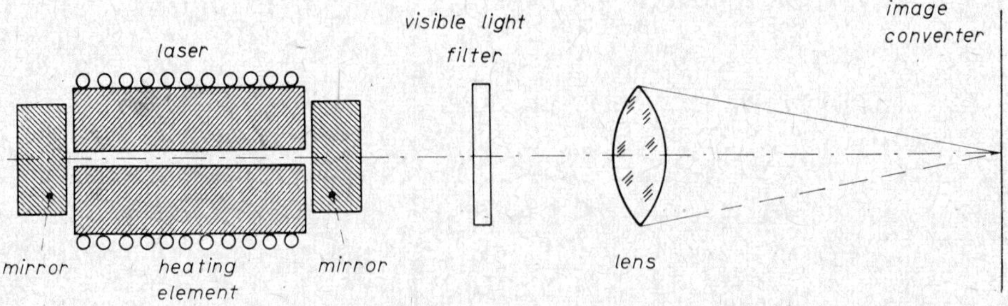

Fig. 7. – Experimental set-up of the tuning experiment.

relate this phenomenon to the fact that we use plane mirrors, whereas the wave fronts most likely have a slight curvature. The situation in our small laser may be compared to that in the centre of a large confocal interferometer (see Fig. 8). At the mirrors of such a larger device we have wave fronts which coincide with the mirror surface, while half-way between them we have a plane wave front. Near this plane the wave fronts are only slightly curved. Now the physical situation in our small laser can be imagined by putting plane mirrors at short distances on both sides of the central plane of the larger laser. The qualities of the small resonator thus made will depend on the phase errors between the plane mirrors and the slightly curved wave fronts nearby. Residual curvature of the mirrors can either improve or deteriorate the fitting of mirrors to wave fronts. As the curvature of the wave fronts is different for each mode, some are not found at all, others are nearly always found irrespective of the quality of the plane mirrors, but in between there are some modes with a near-critical phase error; whether or not these appear depends on the flatness of the mirrors, or even on imperfections of the polishing (*)

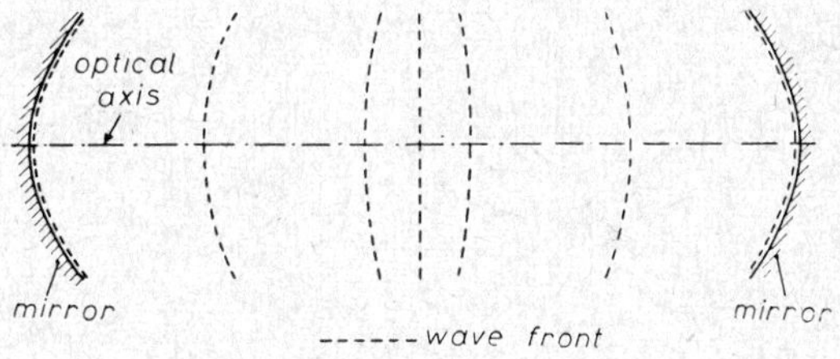

Fig. 8. – Behaviour of the wave fronts in a confocal resonator system.

In co-operation with the optical group a frequency analysis of the various modes has been made using a scanning confocal, passive interferometer; length about 1 m, separation of the resonances 73 MHz, bandwidth 0.5 MHz. In this experiment the small gas laser was tuned slowly and the output examined with the rapidly scanning interferometer.

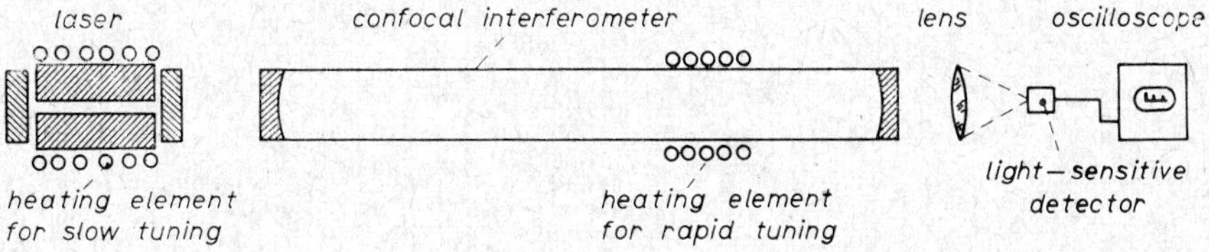

Fig. 9. – Experimental arrangement of the optical frequency analysis.

In Fig. 9 and 10 we show respectively the experimental arrangement and the simultaneous intensity variations of two modes shifting in frequency under the

(*) The theory of these mode phenomena has been studied by Dr. M. J. Offerhaus of this laboratory; his work will be published elsewhere.

Doppler width. The modes indicated by I_1 and I_2 have a frequency separation of 12 MHz.

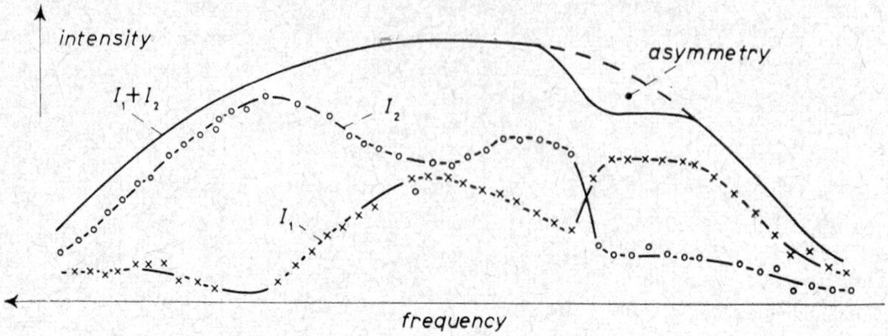

Fig. 10. – Intensity of two competing modes as well as their sum as a function of the frequency.

On account of the saturation condition [8], determined by the natural line-width (which is important because the frequency separation of the modes is smaller than the natural line-width of about 30 MHz), the measured intensity variations give information on the competition between the two modes and on the Doppler profile itself. The intensity of a single mode not influenced by others is proportional to the natural line-width times the energy available at frequency ν — neglecting hole-burning effect — as indicated in Fig. 11. When two or more

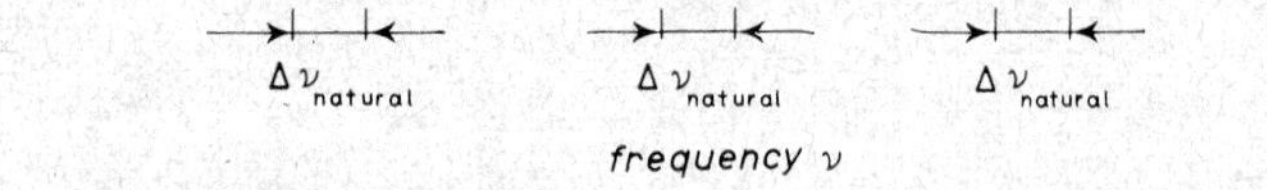

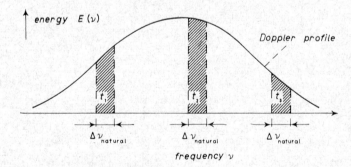

Fig. 11. – Energy under the Doppler profile as a function of the frequency in connection with the saturation condition at different moments t_n during the tuning. Saturation condition: $\sum I_m \propto \int_{\Delta\nu_{\text{nat}}} E(\nu)\,\mathrm{d}\nu$.

modes exist within the natural line-width the sum of the intensities should be subjected to the same saturation condition:

$$\sum_m I_m \propto \int_{\Delta\nu_{\text{nat}}} E(\nu)\,\mathrm{d}\nu\,.$$

Returning to Fig. 10, just before the centre of the Doppler profile, mode I_2 is seen to decrease and I_1 to increase. Beyond the centre I_2 first increases again while I_1 decreases, and then suddenly I_2 decreases, I_1 increases and becomes dominant. The sum of the intensities of the two modes I_1+I_2 in Fig. 10, reveals a small asymmetry in the profile at the sudden transition of the different mode intensity. An estimate of the frequency difference between the centre of the Doppler profile and the centre of the asymmetry gives a value of about 250 MHz, in agreement with the measurements of SZÖKE and JAVAN, who found an asymmetry at 260 MHz caused by isotope shift [7].

We hope to supplement the described optical analysis by making an electrical investigation of the change of the intensity of the beats and by looking into the possibility of a change in the beat frequency during the tuning experiment.

* * *

We acknowledge stimulating discussions with Prof. H. G. VAN BUEREN and Dr. M. J. OFFERHAUS and help in the optical work from Dr. H. DE LANG and Mr. G. BOUWHUIS. Mr. S. J. VAN HOPPE and Mr. O. E. SCHELTEMA have given technical assistence.

REFERENCES

[1] A. JAVAN, W. R. BENNETT jr. and D. R. HERRIOTT: *Phys. Rev. Lett.*, **6**, 106 (1961).
[2] H. G. VAN BUEREN, J. HAISMA and H. DE LANG: *Phys. Lett.*, **2**, 340 (1962).
[3] C. F. LUCK, R. A. PAANANEN and H. STATZ: *Proc. I.R.E.*, **49**, 1954 (1961).
[4] D. R. HERRIOTT: *Journ. Opt. Soc. Am.*, **52**, 31 (1962).
[5] J. KILLPATRICK, H. GUSTAFSON and L. WOLD: *Proc. I.R.E.*, **50**, 1521 (1962).
[6] J. HAISMA and H. DE LANG: *Phys. Lett.*, **3**, 240 (1963).
[7] A. SZÖKE and A. JAVAN: *Phys. Rev. Lett.*, **10**, 521 (1963).
[8] W. R. BENNETT jr.: *Applied Optics*, in *Supplement on Optical Masers* (1962), p. 24.

The Use of Terahertz Photobeats for Precise Velocity-of-Light Measurements.

Z. BAY and H. S. BOYNE

Atomic Physics Division, National Bureau of Standard - Washington, D. C.

1. – Introduction.

The coherent output from a continuous He-Ne gas laser [1] can be used as a radiation source for the development of long-range interferometry. Interferometer fringes have already been obtained for optical path differences up to 200 m [2]. The experimental results of Javan indicate that with sufficient mechanical and thermal isolation one can achieve linewidths of a few Hz, stability of the order 5 kHz and wavelength resettability of a part in 10^9 [3]. With such a source, the limitations of any interferometric study are instrumental.

Because of the coherence of the laser radiation it is possible to measure accurately the beat frequency between two laser lines using photomixing techniques [4]. Detailed calculations presented below show that by the use of a traveling-wave cathode-ray tube beat frequencies up to the order of 10^{12} Hz can be accurately measured. With the interferometric study of the corresponding wave-number difference a precision of one part in 10^8 for the velocity of light could be achieved with a path length of a few meters.

2. – General description.

The experimental involves measuring the wavelength of a stabilized He-Ne laser with respect to the wavelength standard, measuring the difference in wavelength between two laser lines, and measuring the difference in frequency between the same two laser lines. If we have two lines which are closely spaced, λ_1 and λ_2, the frequency and wavelength in vacuum are given by

$$\nu_1 = c/\lambda_1\,, \qquad \nu_2 = c/\lambda_2\,,$$

therefore

$$\nu_2 - \nu_1 = c\left[\frac{1}{\lambda_2} - \frac{1}{\lambda_1}\right] = \Delta\nu$$

or

$$\Delta\nu = c\,\frac{\Delta\lambda}{\lambda_1\lambda_2}$$

and

$$c = \frac{\Delta\nu}{\Delta\lambda}\,\lambda_1\lambda_2$$

or

$$c = \frac{\Delta\nu}{\Delta\lambda}\,\lambda_1(\lambda_1 - \Delta\lambda)\,. \tag{1}$$

This is the basic equation in which λ_1, $\Delta\lambda$, and $\Delta\nu$ are to be determined. It will be more convenient to express eq. (1) in terms of the beat frequency $\Delta\nu = \omega$ and the wave number separation $K = k_1 - k_2$ where $k = 1/\lambda$. Therefore,

$$c = \omega/K\,. \tag{2}$$

The uncertainty in the measurement of c is given by

$$\frac{\partial c}{c} = \frac{\partial\omega}{\omega} + \frac{\partial K}{K}\,.$$

The uncertainty of K is discussed in the next Section. The uncertainty with which one can measure ω will be discussed in Sect. **6**.

3. – Wavelength measurement.

We wish to consider an evacuated Fabry-Perot scanning interferometer for the measurement of K. The difference $\lambda_1 - \lambda_2$ would be measured with linear scanning techniques which have been used successfully in the measurements of isotope shifts and in the comparison of spectral lines with the krypton standard. The linear scan could be accomplished with magnetostrictive invar spacers, or by changing the index of refraction in a linear manner [5].

The uncertainty in the measurement of λ_1 with respect to the length standard depends, of course, on what is used as the wavelength standard. If λ_1 is determined with respect to the krypton standard, an uncertainty in the measurement of 1 part in 10^8 is expected [6]. The precision with which one can measure $\Delta\lambda = \lambda_1 - \lambda_2$ depends on the spectral range and the finesse of the interferometer.

The instrumental linewidth of a Fabry-Perot interferometer is given in cm^{-1} by $\Delta = 1/2LF$ where L is the spacer length and F is the finesse. If $\mathscr{E}$ represents that fraction of the linewidth which can be determined reproducibly, the uncertainty in determining K is $\delta K = \mathscr{E}\Delta$. Therefore

$$\frac{\delta K}{K} = \frac{\mathscr{E}}{2FLK} = c\,\frac{\mathscr{E}}{2FL\omega}\,. \tag{3}$$

One sees from eq. (3) that:

1) For given values of $\delta K/K$, F, and $\mathscr{E}$ the precision of the measurement is determined by the product $L\omega$. Therefore, the higher ω is, the smaller L has to be. For example, if $\delta K/K = 10^{-8}$, $F = 100$, and $\mathscr{E} = 0.01$ in the region from 1.0 μm to 1.2 μm [7], then for $\omega = 10^{10}$ Hz, L must be 150 meter whereas, for $\omega = 10^{12}$ Hz, $L = 1.5$ meter.

2) For given values of L, F, and $\mathscr{E}$ the precision of the c measurement increases in proportion to the beat frequency ω.

We shall therefore attempt to measure the highest beat frequencies possible (*i.e.* 10^{12} Hz). The laser lines of interest in the He-Ne system are listed in the following table [8]:

Laser lines (μm)	K (cm^{-1})	ω ($\cdot 10^{12}$ Hz)
1.207 1.199	58	1.66
1.084 1.080	40	1.2
1.118 1.115	28	0.83
1.141 1.139	14.4	0.43
1.161 1.160	9.3	0.28

4·1. *Frequency measurement.* – The measurement of a 10^{12} Hz beat frequency requires means exceeding common techniques. The frequency range is a factor 50 greater than frequencies which have been measured with photosurfaces to date [4] and is considerably beyond the present capabilities of microwave technology. We wish to examine in detail the possibility of measuring such frequencies using traveling-wave cathode-ray tube techniques.

Basically, the measurement is visualized in the following way. The two laser lines of interest with electric field strengths

$$E_1 = E_0 \cos(2\pi\nu_1 t + \varphi)\,,$$
$$E_2 = E_0 \cos(2\pi\nu_2 t)\,,$$

are focused on a photocathode. Since the photocathode is a square-law detector, the number of photoelectrons emitted per unit time is proportional to

$$E^2 = (E_1 + E_2)^2 = E_1^2 + E_2^2 + 2E_1\cdot E_2$$

or

$$E^2 = E_0^2\{\cos^2(2\pi\nu_1 t + \varphi) + \cos^2 2\pi\nu_2 t + \\ + \cos[2\pi(\nu_1 - \nu_2)t + \varphi] + \cos[2\pi(\nu_1 + \nu_2)t + \varphi]\}\,.$$

The optical frequencies ν_1 and ν_2 are $\sim 3\cdot 10^{14}$ Hz and the beat frequency $\nu_1 - \nu_2 \simeq 10^{12}$ Hz. If E^2 is time-averaged over an optical period then [9]

$$\overline{E^2} = E_0^2\{1 + \cos[2\pi(\nu_1 - \nu_2)t + \varphi]\} = E_0^2\{1 + \cos(2\pi\omega t + \varphi)\} \tag{4}$$

and $\overline{E^2}$ is 100% modulated (assuming equal amplitudes E_0 of electric fields E_1 and E_2). The modulated electron beam is now accelerated and enters into a traveling-wave deflection system operating at the driving frequency $\Omega \simeq 10^{10}$ Hz and is then focused on a fluorescent screen. Since the electron

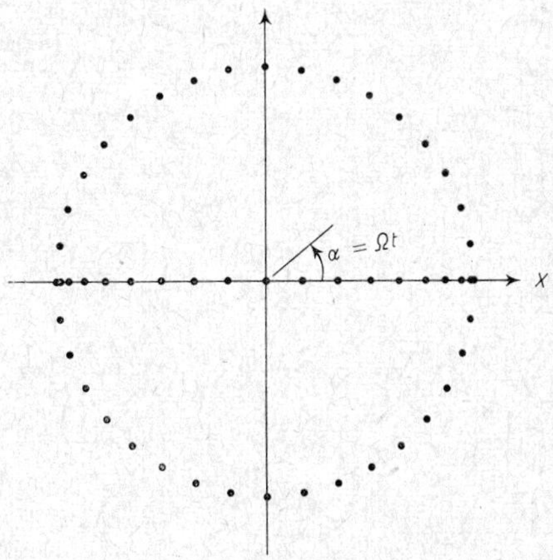

Fig. 1. – Schematic representation of the intensity-modulated cathode-ray spot. The dots along the x-axis represent the projection of the circular dot pattern.

beam is modulated at frequency ω and deflected at frequency Ω, the resultant display on the screen will be intensity modulated.

In the ideal case of appropriately phased simutaneous X and Y deflection, the cathode ray spot on the screen moves on a circle with frequency Ω (see Fig. 1). Because of the intensity modulation of the beam at frequency ω, there will be $\omega/\Omega = n$ light spots on the screen. If n is an integer the spot pattern is standing, otherwise it runs around the circle. Such a running pattern can be viewed through a mask which has n openings where n is an integer, say the nearest integer to ω/Ω. The number n will be referred to as the mask number.

Consider a mask made as a film with a transmission for light (from a fluorescent screen)

$$\varrho = \tfrac{1}{2}(1 + \cos n\alpha)\,, \tag{5}$$

where α is the polar angle around the center of the circle (Fig. 1). Such a mask will multiply the sweep frequency Ω by n. With no electron-beam modulation ($\omega = 0$), a photocell mounted to view the total fluorescent light intensity from the pattern through the mask would, in principle, have a response at the frequency $n\Omega$. When the electron beam is modulated according to eq. (4) the total light intensity seen through the mask is

$$\begin{aligned} I = \tfrac{1}{2} I_0[1 + \cos(2\pi\omega t + \varphi)][1 + \cos 2\pi n\Omega t] = \\ = \tfrac{1}{2} I_0\{1 + \cos(2\pi\omega t + \varphi) + \cos 2\pi n\Omega t + \\ + \tfrac{1}{2}\cos[2\pi(\omega + n\Omega)t + \varphi] + \tfrac{1}{2}\cos[2\pi(\omega - n\Omega)t + \varphi]\}\,. \end{aligned}$$

This expression must now be averaged over a time equal to the response time of the fluorescent screen which is much longer than the period $1/\omega$ but shorter than the period $1/(\omega - n\Omega)$. Therefore, all oscillatory terms except the last term will average to zero and

$$\bar{I} = \tfrac{1}{2} I_0\{1 + \tfrac{1}{2}\cos[2\pi(\omega - n\Omega)t + \varphi]\}\,. \tag{6}$$

If $\omega - n\Omega = 0$ the pattern is standing and the intensity can be anything between $\tfrac{1}{4}I_0$ and $\tfrac{3}{4}I_0$ depending on the value of the phase constant φ. If $\omega - n\Omega \neq 0$, $\bar{I}$ oscillates with a frequency

$$\pm\mu = \omega - n\Omega\,.$$

Since the mask number n is a fixed parameter chosen for the experiment, ω can be determined by measuring μ and Ω.

In the proposed measurement it is assumed that $\omega \sim 10^{12}$ Hz, $n = 100$, $\Omega \sim 10^{10}$ Hz can be varied over $\sim 1\%$ of its center frequency so that the frequency μ (*e.g.*, 10^4 Hz) can be fixed by applying a narrow band filter to the output of the photomultiplier. In this case there are two values of Ω for which the filter responds:

$$n\Omega_+ = \omega + \mu\,, \qquad n\Omega_- = \omega - \mu\,.$$

Therefore

(7) $$\omega = n\bar{\Omega} = n\left[\frac{\Omega_+ + \Omega_-}{2}\right]$$

and

(8) $$\Omega_+ - \Omega_- = 2\frac{\mu}{n}\,.$$

Measurement of Ω_+ and Ω_- for a fixed frequency μ determines ω unambigously.

It must be noted that the appearance of a unique doublet is bound to the conditions of the ideal experiment, that is, pure harmonic modulation of the beam and pure harmonic transparency of the mask. Departures from ideal conditions of modulation are discussed in the Appendix.

It is interesting to point out that in the measurement of the frequency μ the current of the photomultiplier is integrated over the response time of the low-frequency filter. This charge-accumulating feature of the experiment helps decisively in improving the signal-to-noise ratio appearing in the output, as compared to that existing in the photocurrent of the cathode-ray tube. For a photocurrent of 10^{10} electrons/s, there is on the average only 1 photoelectron appearing in the period of 100 beats while the relative fluctuation in the output current, with a filter bandwidth of $\sim 10^3$ Hz, is only ~ 3 parts in 10^4 (cf. Sect. **6**).

4·2. *Application to one-deflection system.* – In the proposed experiment the deflection will be restricted to one dimension (call it X) therefore the circular motion of the spot must be projected on the X axis (Fig. 1)

(9) $$X = R\cos\alpha\,, \qquad \alpha = \cos^{-1}\frac{X}{R}\,.$$

The mask is now aligned along the X axis and its transparency ϱ is a function of X

(10) $$\varrho = \frac{1}{2}\left[1 + \cos n\left\{\cos^{-1}\frac{X}{R}\right\}\right]$$

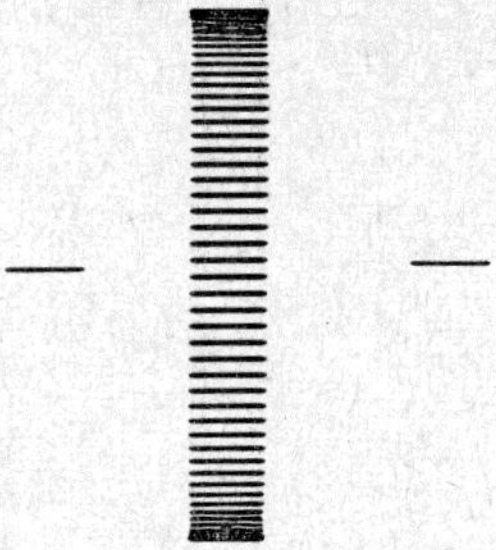

Fig. 2. – Mask used in the model experiment. The mask was made from a photograph of a standing-dot pattern by modulating the beam of a Tektronix Model 533 cathode-ray tube at the frequency $\omega = 10^5$ Hz and deflecting the beam at the frequency $\Omega = 10^3$ Hz. The mask number is $n = 100$.

representing a wave structure in which the waves are compressed at each end (Fig. 1 and 2). Since in a full sweep period (α changing from 0 to 2π) the beam spot passes twice along the mask, the number of waves in the mask is $n/2$. It is reasonable now to choose n as an even integer in order to avoid half-waves in the mask. It is also desirable to make the transparency function symmetric around the center of the mask. This condition is satisfied if the mask number n is a multiple of 4.

5. – Analysis of cathode-ray-tube response.

Thus far, we have assumed that the response of the photocathode of the tube is sufficiently fast to modulate the electron beam with frequencies up to 10^{12} Hz. We now wish to analyse this problem in detail.

5·1. *Correlation time of the electron-photon interaction.* – PERSHAN and BLOEMBERGEN [10] have estimated this interaction time in metals to be of order $\tau = 10^{-14}$ second at room temperature. This means that modulations (beats) in the light intensity can be detected up to $1/\tau = 10^{14}$ Hz. Corresponding interaction times are not known for composite photolayers (Ag-O-Cs cathode) but we shall assume them to be similar to the above figure for pure metals. Therefore we do not expect the electron-photon interaction time to be a limitation in this experiment.

5·2. *Transit-time spread in the photolayer.* – If there is no delay due to electron scattering within the lattice, the electron which absorbs 1 eV inside the layer must traverse a typical layer thickness for the photocathode of 150 Å in the time

$$t = \frac{X}{v} = \frac{150 \cdot 10^{-8}\ \text{cm}}{5 \cdot 10^{7}\ \text{cm/s}} \simeq 3 \cdot 10^{-14}\ \text{s}\,.$$

This transit time will have a spread since the electrons are not all traveling normal to the surface and not all electrons traverse the full thickness of the layer. However, the average spread can be expected to be less than 10^{-13} second which would represent an upper frequency limit in this measurement of 10^{13} Hz.

5·3. *Velocity spread of photoelectrons.* – There is an energy distribution of electrons emitted from the photocathode which causes a spread in the electron bunching and reduces the percentage modulation. We shall assume that the energy distribution of photoelectrons emerging from composite photocathodes is similar to the distribution for the alkali metals. Since we are interested in the normal energy distribution in the vicinity of maximum energy, we shall use the theory of DU BRIDGE [11] which applies to this situation for pure metals and is confirmed by precise experiments on potassium [12]. The maximum energy attainable is given by

$$\mathscr{E}_m = h\nu - \Phi e ,$$

where Φ is the work function. In our case $h\nu \sim 1$ eV and $\Phi \simeq \frac{3}{4}$ V [13] thus $\mathscr{E}_m \simeq \frac{1}{4}$ eV. We take the distribution of « normal energies » which is a linear curve at 0 °K with the peak at zero energy. At room temperature the maximum of the distribution is shifted to slightly higher energies (Fig. 3). Since the half width of the energy distribution curve is about the same at absolute zero and at room temperature the absolute-zero distribution will be used in order to facilitate calculations.

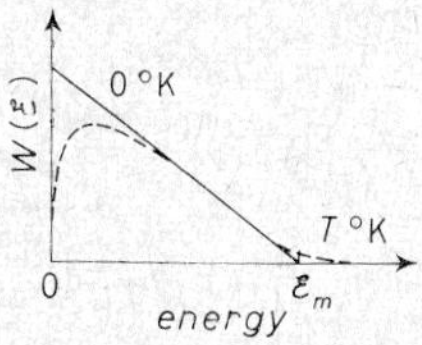

Fig. 3. – Normal energy distribution of emitted photoelectrons according to DuBridge's theory. The solid line represents the distribution at 0° K. The dashed line indicates the distribution at room temperature.

The linear energy distribution function is

$$W(\mathscr{E}) = \frac{2}{\mathscr{E}_m^2}\,(\mathscr{E}_m - \mathscr{E}) . \tag{11}$$

The velocity distribution is obtained from the energy distribution

$$\varphi(v)\,\mathrm{d}v = W(\mathscr{E})\,\mathrm{d}\mathscr{E}$$

and $\frac{1}{2}Mv^2 = \mathscr{E}$, where M is the electron mass:

$$\varphi(v) = 4/v_m^4[v_m^2 v - v^3] . \tag{12}$$

The problem of spread will now be analysed on the energy scale and the velocity scale.

1) Energy scale:

$$\bar{\mathscr{E}} = (2/\mathscr{E}_m^2)\int_0^{\mathscr{E}_m}(\mathscr{E}\mathscr{E}_m - \mathscr{E}^2)\,\mathrm{d}\mathscr{E} = 1/3\mathscr{E}_m , \tag{13}$$

(14) $$\overline{\mathscr{E}^2} = (2/\mathscr{E}_m^2)\int_0^{\mathscr{E}_m} (\mathscr{E}^2\mathscr{E}_m - \mathscr{E}^3)\,\mathrm{d}\mathscr{E} = 1/6\mathscr{E}_m^2\,,$$

(15) $$\overline{\Delta\mathscr{E}^2} = [\overline{\mathscr{E}^2} - (\overline{\mathscr{E}})^2] = (\tfrac{1}{6} - \tfrac{1}{9})\mathscr{E}_m^2 = \tfrac{1}{18}\mathscr{E}_m^2$$

and

(16) $$\text{r.m.s. } \Delta\mathscr{E} \simeq \tfrac{1}{4}\mathscr{E}_m\,.$$

2) Velocity scale:

(13a) $$\overline{v} = (4/v_m^4)\int_0^{v_m} (v_m^2 v^2 - v^4)\,\mathrm{d}v = 4(1/3 - 1/5)v_m = (8/15)\,v_m\,,$$

(14a) $$\overline{v^2} = (4/v_m^4)\int_0^{v_m} (v_m^2 v^3 - v^5)\,\mathrm{d}v = 4v_m^2(1/4 - 1/6) = (1/3)\,v_m^2\,,$$

(15a) $$\overline{\Delta v^2} = \overline{v^2} - \overline{v}^2 = v_m^2(\tfrac{1}{3} - 64/225) = (11/225)\,v_m^2 \simeq (1/20)\,v_m^2\,,$$

(16a) $$\text{r.m.s. } \Delta v \simeq (1/4.5)\,v_m\,.$$

For both the energy and velocity distribution the r.m.s. spread appears to be about $\frac{1}{4}$ of the maximum value. Thus the spread in the electron bunching corresponds to $2\times v_m/4 = v_m/2$ rather than v_m. The detailed calculations will now be applied to the geometry of the cathode-ray tube where the photoelectrons are accelerated over a short path L and fly over a long path through the deflection system with uniform velocity.

The time-of-flight spread caused by the initial velocity distribution will be calculated for a uniform acceleration over a distance L and an initial energy $\mathscr{E}$ for the electron. Then

(17) $$E = E_m X/L$$

where E_m is the maximum energy attained by the accelerating electron and

(18) $$v = \sqrt{\frac{2}{M}}\,(E + \mathscr{E})^{\frac{1}{2}}\,, \qquad \text{or} \qquad v = \sqrt{\frac{2}{M}}\,E_m^{\frac{1}{2}}\left(\frac{X}{L} + \frac{\mathscr{E}}{E_m}\right)^{\frac{1}{2}}.$$

The time of flight $T = \int_0^L \mathrm{d}x/v$ and

$$T = \left[\frac{M}{2E_m}\right]^{\frac{1}{2}}\int_0^L\left(\frac{X}{L} + \frac{\mathscr{E}}{E_m}\right)^{-\frac{1}{2}}\mathrm{d}x = \left[\frac{M}{2E_m}\right]^{\frac{1}{2}} 2L\left(\frac{X}{L} + \frac{\mathscr{E}}{E_m}\right)^{\frac{1}{2}}\Bigg|_0^L = T_0\left[\left(1 + \frac{\mathscr{E}}{E_m}\right)^{\frac{1}{2}} - \left(\frac{\mathscr{E}}{E_m}\right)^{\frac{1}{2}}\right]$$

and

$$T = T_0\left[1 + \frac{1}{2}\frac{\mathscr{E}}{E_m} - \sqrt{\frac{\mathscr{E}}{E_m}}\right], \tag{19}$$

where

$$T_0 = \frac{2L}{\sqrt{2E_m/M}} \tag{20}$$

is the time of flight for $\mathscr{E} = 0$.

For our case $\mathscr{E}_m = \frac{1}{4}$ eV and $E_m = 2.5 \cdot 10^4$ eV so that the term linear in $\mathscr{E}/E_m$ is negligible compared to the square root. Therefore

$$T \simeq T_0\left(1 - \sqrt{\frac{\mathscr{E}}{E_m}}\right) = T_0\left(1 - \frac{v}{V_m}\right), \tag{21}$$

where V_m is the speed corresponding to the energy E_m. The maximum value of the last term is

$$\left[\left(\frac{\mathscr{E}_m}{E_m}\right)\right]^{\frac{1}{2}} = \left[\frac{1}{4 \cdot 2.5 \cdot 10^4}\right]^{\frac{1}{2}} \simeq \frac{1}{3} \cdot 10^{-2} \tag{22}$$

and the maximum time spread during the acceleration is for $L = 1$ cm is

$$\Delta T_m = \frac{T_0}{3} \cdot 10^{-2} = \frac{2}{3} \cdot 10^{-12}\ \text{s}. \tag{23}$$

After the acceleration the electrons emerge with a velocity

$$V = \sqrt{\frac{2}{M}(E_m + \mathscr{E})} = V_m\left(1 + \frac{\mathscr{E}}{E_m}\right)^{\frac{1}{2}},$$
$$\simeq V_m\left(1 + \frac{1}{2}\frac{\mathscr{E}}{E_m}\right).$$

The time of flight over the distance D from the accelerating electrode to the screen is

$$T_D = \frac{D}{V} = \frac{D}{V_m}\left(1 - \frac{1}{2}\frac{\mathscr{E}}{E_m}\right). \tag{24}$$

The maximum deviation from the time of flight corresponding to $\mathscr{E} = 0$ is

$$\Delta T_D = \frac{1}{2}\frac{D}{V_m}\frac{\mathscr{E}}{E_m}.$$

For our case $D \sim 50$ cm, $V_m \sim 10^{10}$ cm/s, and $\mathscr{E}/E_m = 10^{-5}$;

$$\Delta T_D = 2.5 \cdot 10^{-14} \text{ s}$$

which is negligible when compared with eq. (23). We therefore conclude that only the time-of-flight spread brought about during the process of acceleration is of importance. This spread is (eq. (21))

$$\Delta T = T_0 \frac{v}{V_m} = \frac{2L}{V_m^2} v = M \frac{L}{E_m} v \,. \tag{21a}$$

For a given v this spread is proportional to L/E_m, *i.e.*, inversely proportional to the accelerating electric field strengths. Since E_m determines the final electron velocity and this has to be tuned to the propagation velocity in the traveling-wave deflecting system, there is probably not much choice in the value of E_m. One possibility of diminishing ΔT is to choose L as small as possible. Another possibility of decreasing the time-of-flight spread is given by the use of a nonuniform accelerating field, such that the electric field strength is made larger in the vicinity of the cathode. This can be achieved by the use of a curved (*e.g.*, spherically shaped) cathode. In the case mentioned above (distance between cathode and accelerating electrode $L = 1$ cm, $E_m = 25$ keV) a curvature of the cathode of 1 cm radius makes the field at the cathode twice the previous value, or 50 kV/cm. This field strength is still tolerable for field emission, which sets in above 100 kV/cm, and it is preferable with respect to break-down as compared to the uniform field with $L = \frac{1}{2}$ cm. The maximum time-of-flight spread would be $\frac{1}{3} \cdot 10^{-12}$ s in this case, permitting higher-frequency operation of the tube.

The influence of the time-of-flight spread on the modulation intensity will now be calculated. If $\mathscr{E} = 0$ the intensity is

$$I = I_0[1 + \cos 2\pi\omega t]$$

at the cathode and

$$I = I_0[1 + \cos 2\pi\omega(t - T_0)]$$

at the accelerating electrode. If $\mathscr{E} \neq 0$, $v \neq 0$, then

$$I = I_0 \left[1 + \cos 2\pi\omega \left\{t - T_0 \left(1 - \frac{v}{V_m}\right)\right\}\right] . \tag{25}$$

In the case of v variable, the cosine term must be integrated over the velocity distribution and

$$I(t) = I_0 \left[1 + \int_0^{v_m} \cos 2\pi\omega \left(t' + T_0 \frac{v}{V_m} \right) \varphi(v)\, \mathrm{d}v \right] ,$$

where $t' = t - T_0$. The second term within the bracket is

$$\int_0^{v_m} \varphi(v) \cos 2\pi\omega \left[t' + T_0 \frac{v}{V_m} \right] \mathrm{d}v = \cos \omega t' \int_0^{v_m} \varphi(v) \cos 2\pi\omega T_0 \frac{v}{V_m}\, \mathrm{d}v -$$

$$- \sin \omega t' \int_0^{v_m} \varphi(v) \sin 2\pi\omega T_0 \frac{v}{V_m}\, \mathrm{d}v = \alpha \cos 2\pi\omega t' - \beta \sin 2\pi\omega t' = \gamma \cos (2\pi\omega t' + \varphi) ,$$

where

(26) $$\alpha = \frac{4}{v_m^4} \int_0^{v_m} (v_m^2 v - v^3) \cos \omega T_0 \frac{v}{V_m}\, \mathrm{d}v ,$$

(27) $$\beta = \frac{4}{v_m^4} \int_0^{v_m} (v_m^2 v - v^3) \sin \omega T_0 \frac{v}{V_m}\, \mathrm{d}v$$

and

(28) $$\gamma = \sqrt{\alpha^2 + \beta^2}$$

is the amplitude of the modulation.

With the substitution

$$x = 2\pi \frac{v\omega T_0}{V_m} = 2\pi\omega\, \Delta T_m ,$$

$$\alpha = \frac{4}{x_m^2} \int_0^{x_m} x \cos x\, \mathrm{d}x - \frac{4}{x_m^4} \int_0^{x_m} x^3 \cos x\, \mathrm{d}x ,$$

$$\beta = \frac{4}{x_m^2} \int_0^{x_m} x \sin x\, \mathrm{d}x - \frac{4}{x_m^4} \int_0^{x_m} x^3 \sin x\, \mathrm{d}x .$$

After calculation of the integrals one obtains

$$\alpha = \frac{24}{x_m^3} \sin x_m + \left[\frac{24}{x_m^4} - \frac{8}{x_m^2} \right] \cos x_m - \left[\frac{4}{x_m^2} + \frac{24}{x_m^4} \right] ,$$

$$\beta = \left[\frac{24}{x_m^4} - \frac{8}{x_m^2} \right] \sin x_m - \frac{24}{x_m^3} \cos x_m .$$

The calculated values of α, β, and γ for several values of x are given in Table I. In Fig. 4 γ is plotted *vs.* x_m. The value $x_m = 2\pi$ corresponds to $\Delta T_m = \frac{2}{3} \cdot 10^{-12}$ s as given in eq. (23) and $\omega = 1.6 \cdot 10^{12}$ Hz.

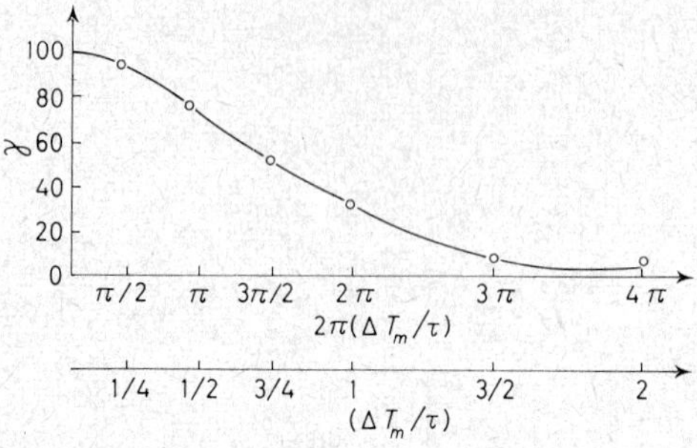

Fig. 4. – Percentage modulation of the electron beam *vs.* $x = 2\pi\Delta T_m/\tau$ where ΔT_m is the maximum time spread for the electrons and ω is the beat frequency.

TABLE I.

	0	$\pi/2$	π	$3\pi/2$	2π	3π	4π
α	1	+ 0.627	— 0.084	— 0.458	— 0.304	+ 0.039	— 0.076
β	0	+ 0.700	+ 0.774	+ 0.321	— 0.097	+ 0.029	— 0.01
γ%	100	93	78	55	31	5	7.6

5·4. *Writing speed limitation.* – The discussion and analysis of the characteristics of the image tube have been based on the performance characteristics of the EG & G Model KR-5 cathode-ray tube [14]. In a similar tube GOLDBERG has reported a writing speed of $3 \cdot 10^{12}$ spot diameter/s [15]. This speed is related to single shot experiments thus the beam intensity required to obtain a photograph in $\frac{1}{3} \cdot 10^{-12}$ s is involved. In our repetitive (current accumulating) experiment the upper limit of the « writing speed » is given by the time-of-flight spread of electrons within the electron focusing and deflecting system. This time-of-flight spread has to be added to the ones calculated in the present analysis for the photoelectron acceleration procedure.

Consider the path length from the accelerating grid to the fluorescent screen to be $D = 2l$ and that an electron can have a lateral displacement d within the aperture of the beam.

The path traversed by the elctron is then $2l'$ rather than $2l$ and the difference in path length will cause a time spread:

$$l' = (l^2 + d^2)^{\frac{1}{2}} = l\left(1 + \frac{d^2}{l^2}\right)^{\frac{1}{2}} \simeq l\left(1 + \frac{1}{2}\frac{d^2}{l^2}\right),$$

$$l' - l = \Delta l = \frac{1}{2}\frac{d^2}{l}$$

and

$$\Delta T = \frac{\Delta l}{V_m}.$$

For the EG&G tube $l \simeq 25$ cm and $d = 0.25$ cm, therefore $\Delta l = 1.25 \cdot 10^{-3}$ cm and

$$\Delta T = \frac{1.25 \cdot 10^{-3}\ \text{cm}}{10^{10}\ \text{cm/s}} = 1.25 \cdot 10^{-13}\ \text{s}\,.$$

This time spread is less than the time spread in the acceleration process of the photoelectrons (eq. (23)).

Conclusion: The analysis given in this Section shows that the upper frequency limit for the operation of the proposed tube is given by the initial velocity spread of the photoelectrons. If we require a beam modulation amplitude of 30% or greater, the upper frequency limit of operation is $\sim 1.5 \cdot 10^{12}$ Hz with an accelerating field (at the cathode) of 25 kV/cm and $\sim 3 \cdot 10^{12}$ Hz with a field of 50 kV/cm.

6. – Stability and noise in the frequency measurement.

The accuracy in the measurement of the frequency

$$\pm \mu = \omega - n\Omega$$

is limited by the fluctuations in ω, Ω, and by noise current.

Since the optical frequencies ν_1 and ν_2 are derived from two different oscillations (resulting from two different atomic transitions) of the same cavity, the fluctuations in ν_1 and ν_2 are correlated. By neglecting small nonlinear effects of mode pulling [16]

$$\nu_1 = n_1 \frac{c}{2L}$$

and

$$\nu_2 = n_2 \frac{c}{2L},$$

where n_1 and n_2 are integers. Therefore

$$\nu_1 - \nu_2 = \omega = (n_1 - n_2) \frac{c}{2L}$$

and for a small change δL

$$\frac{\delta \nu_1}{\nu_1} = \frac{\delta \nu_2}{\nu_2} = \frac{\delta \omega}{\omega} = \frac{\delta L}{L}$$

or

$$\delta\omega \simeq \frac{\omega}{\nu}\,\delta\nu\,, \tag{29}$$

where ν is either one of the optical frequencies. Thus, the fluctuation in ω is diminished in proportion to the ratio of the beat frequency and the optical frequency. Taking $\Delta\nu \sim \pm 5$ kHz (which appears to be the present long-term stability with lasers [17]) $\Delta\omega \sim \pm 15$ Hz for $\omega \sim 10^{12}$ Hz.

The stability of the driving frequency Ω can be made 1 Hz without great effort. Since Ω is frequency multiplied by the mask number n in the experiment and $n \sim 10^2$, the major fluctuation in μ is expected to come from the instability in Ω rather than from the laser. Both instabilities result in the precision of ω to about one part in 10^{10}.

The probability character of the photoelectron emission results in shot noise. It can be shown by a qualitative argument, that the frequency instability in the measurement of μ, caused by noise, is much lass than one part in 10^{10}.

In the frequency measurement, the output current I is a function of μ. The sensitivity of the measurement is proportional to the slope $S = \mathrm{d}I(\mu)/\mathrm{d}\mu$. Therefore, an uncertainty in the current δI results in an uncertainty

$$\delta\mu = \frac{\delta I(\mu)}{S}\,. \tag{30}$$

The bandwidth of the filter, $\Delta\mu_f$, must be larger than the bandwidth $\Delta\mu$ given by the frequency fluctuation of the input signal. A reasonable value for the filter bandwidth is

$$\Delta\mu_f \simeq 10\,\Delta\mu\,.$$

An upper limit for the slope S can be taken as

$$S = \frac{I(\mu)}{\Delta\mu_f}$$

and, from eq. (30),

$$\delta\mu = \frac{\delta I}{I}\,\Delta\mu_f\,. \tag{31}$$

Using the shot noise formula

$$\overline{\delta I^2} = 2eI\,\Delta\mu_f$$

we obtain

$$\delta\mu = \sqrt{\frac{2e(\Delta\mu f_f)^3}{I}}\,. \tag{32}$$

If we consider a 20 microwatt power output for each laser line and a photoefficiency of 10^{-4} at 1.1μ ($S1$ photosurface) then $I = 1.6 \cdot 10^{-9}$ A. With a filter bandwidth $\Delta\mu_f = 10^3$ Hz,

$$\delta\mu \simeq 0.5 \text{ Hz} ,$$

which is less than 1/100 of the fluctuation $\Delta\mu = 100$ Hz caused by the microwave frequency instability Ω.

7. – Summary.

It was shown in Sect. **3** that a measurement of the wave-number separation $K \simeq 40\ \text{cm}^{-1}$ could be made with a precision of one part in 10^8 using a Fabry-Perot interferometer of 1.5 meter length.

It was shown in Sect. **5** and **6** that the measurement of the beat frequency $\omega = 10^{12}$ Hz (corresponding to $K = 40\ \text{cm}^{-1}$) is feasible and its precision could be made one part in 10^{10}.

Therefore, a measurement of the velocity of light with a precision of one part in 10^8 could be done in a laboratory of conventional size.

* * *

It is a pleasure to thank P. L. Bender, R. D. Huntoon, K. G. Kessler, G. G. Luther, W. C. Martin, and W. G. Schweitzer for several illuminating discussions.

Appendix

Departures from the ideal conditions of modulation.

In the treatment of the beat experiment one has to take into account that:

1) the Z-modulation of the cathode-ray beam with the frequency ω is not pure harmonic;

2) the transparency function of the mask is not pure harmonic.

Such departures from the ideal case can easily be accounted for by replading the cosine terms in eqs. (4) and (5) by the Fourier expansions of the modulation functions. Then

$$I = I_0 \Big[\sum_{k=0}^{\infty} a_k \cos(2\pi k\omega t + \varphi_k)\Big] \Big[\sum_{l=0}^{\infty} a_l \cos(2\pi l\Omega t + \varphi_l)\Big] . \tag{A.1}$$

A general remark can be made about the amplitude a_k. Since it is planned to measure the very hyghest frequencies detectable in the experiment, the higher harmonics k of ω will not be well resolved. Thus beyond $k = 0$ and $k = 1$, the a_k amplitudes will rapidly decrease with increasing k.

There are several effects which would give rise to the anharmonicity of the transparency function. Such effects are, for example,

a) the wave structure of the mask is distorted,

b) the mask transparency may not be sinusoidal.

In using the mask in the high-frequency-beat experiment, errors appear if

c) the fluorescent screen illumination is not linear with beam intensity,

d) the beam deflection is not exactly centered around the center of the mask,

e) the amplitude of the beam deflection does not eactly match the size of the mask,

f) the photomultiplier does not give a uniform response to the full extension of the kask,

g) the X-deflection of the beam is not sinusoidal in time, etc.

It is important to point out that all the imperfections *a*), ..., *g*), and others, can only lead to a simple line spectrum given by the Fourier expansion of eq. (A.1) with the frequencies $l\Omega$ and amplitudes a_l. This can be seen in the following way. Let the transparency (as seen by the photomultiplier) be any function $F(x)$ of the position co-ordinate in the mask. Now the position co-ordinate of the moving beam spot will be a periodic function, say $\varphi(t)$, of the time, *i.e.*,

$$\varphi(t+T)=\varphi(t)\,,$$

where $T=1/\Omega$. Thus $F(x)=F[\varphi(t)]$ is a periodic function of the time with the period T.

Therefore, imperfections in the mask and in its use can be characterized by the statement that the mask number n splits up into a spectrum of integers l. The breadth of this spectrum depends on the imperfections, but certainly the values of l which are near n will be the most significant in the experiment. Therefore n, for which the mask is prepared, still retains its significance and will further be called the mask number.

In contrast to the single doublet of the ideal experiment, the harmonics in eq. (A.1) lead to a multiplicity of beats in the output of the phototube. They are characterised by the frequencies $k\omega-l\Omega$. In case the low-frequency filter μ is used, one obtains

$$k\omega-l\Omega=\pm\mu\,. \tag{A.2}$$

1) First the case $K=1$ is treated. For each value l a doublet

$$\Omega_{l+}=\frac{\omega+\mu}{l}\,,\qquad \Omega_{l-}=\frac{\omega-\mu}{l}\,, \tag{A.3}$$

is obtained with the center $\Omega_l=\omega/l$ and doublet separation $2\mu/l$. The centers of the l-th and $(l+1)$-th doublet are separated by

$$\Omega_l-\Omega_{l+1}=\Omega_l\frac{1}{l+1}=\Omega_{l+1}\frac{1}{l}\,,$$

consequently

$$l = \frac{\Omega_{l+1}}{\Omega_l - \Omega_{l+1}}$$

and also

(A.4) $$l = \frac{\Omega_{l-1}}{\Omega_{l-1} - \Omega_l}\,.$$

Thus eq. (A.4) gives means for the determination of the « order number » l of a doublet by measuring the frequencies of the doublet centers and using the « order separations », $\Omega_l - \Omega_{l+1}$ or $\Omega_{l-1} - \Omega_l$, of neighboring doublets.

The knowledge of the order number l determines the high frequency to be measured as

(A.5) $$\omega = l\Omega_l$$

without ambiguity.

The knowledge of the mask number n facilitates location of the doublets when arranging an experiment. For example if $n = 100$, the doublet separation is expected to be $\sim 1\%$ of 2μ and the order separation $\sim 1\%$ of Ω.

2) For $k > 1$ only the beats between $k\omega$ and $l' \sim kl\Omega$ can result in low frequencies equal to μ. For these

(A.6) $$\omega - l'\Omega = \pm \frac{\mu}{k}\,.$$

These lines appear *within* the doublets given generally by eq. (A.3) and represent lines which are at the distances $\pm\mu/2$, $\pm\mu/3$, $\pm\mu/4$, ... from the center. It is to be expected that their amplitudes decrease rapidly with increasing k. If they can be detected they can be utilized as additional information for the determination of the doublet centers.

Model experiments.

With the mask of Fig. 2 model experiments have been performed with

$$\omega = 10^7\ \text{Hz}\,, \qquad \mu = 2 \cdot 10^4\ \text{Hz}\,.$$

Ω was slowly varied around 10^5 Hz. The output of the filter was viewed on an oscilloscope and it also was introduced through a diode demodulator into a recorder. The frequency Ω was read on a frequency counter. The recorder output as a function of Ω is shown in Fig. 5. The doublets appear at the frequencies as expected. The separation in the doublets is

$$\sim \frac{2 \cdot 2 \cdot 10^4}{100} = 400\ \text{Hz}$$

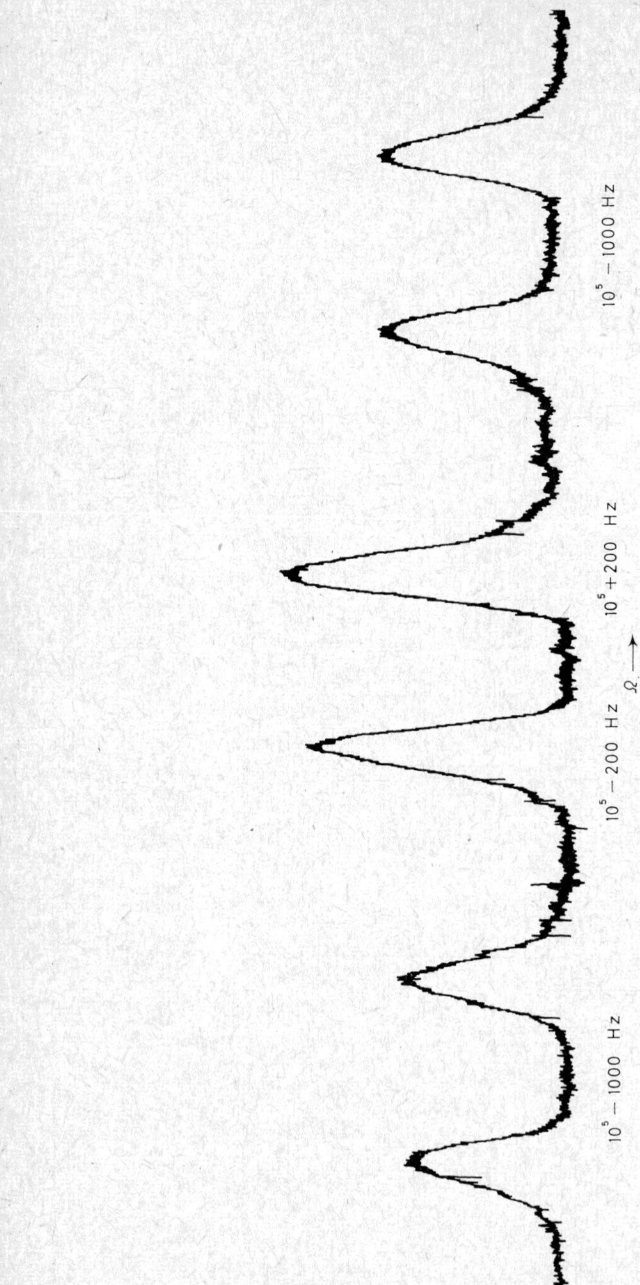

Fig. 5. – Recorder output as a function of Ω. Doublet separation is 400 Hz. Separation between neighboring doublets is 10^3 Hz.

and the separation between neighboring doublets is

$$\sim\frac{10^5}{100}=10^3\ \text{Hz}\,.$$

No additional lines within the doublets (corresponding to $k>1$) could be detected in the experiment.

REFERENCES

[1] A. JAVAN, W. R. BENNETT jr. and D. R. HERRIOT: *Phys. Rev. Lett.*, **6**, 106 (1961).

[2] K. F. NEFFLEN, T. MOROHUMA, T. KLUCHER and T. LAWRENCE: to be published.

[3] A. JAVAN: *Proc. of the Third International Conference on Quantum Electronics* (Paris, 1963); T. S. JASEJA, A. JAVAN and C. H. TOWNES: *Phys. Rev. Lett.*, **10**, 165 (1963).

[4] A. T. FORRESTER, R. A. GUDMUNDSEN and P. O. JOHNSON: *Phys. Rev.*, **99** 1691 (1955).

[5] See for example: P. JACQUINOT and C. DUFOUR: *Journ. Recherches C.N.R.S.*, **2**, 91 (1948); C. F. BRUCE and R. M. HILL: *Astral. Journ. Phys.*, **14**, 61 (1961).

[6] R. L. BARGER and K. G. KESSLER: *Journ. Opt. Soc. Am.*, **50**, 651 (1960); W. G. SCHWEITZER: to be published.

[7] R. A. PAANANEN (*Proc. I.R.E.*, **50**, 2115 (1962)) has measured the passive bandwidth of a one-meter laser interferometer to be 0.3 MHz. This measurement implies a finesse $\simeq 500$.

[8] The 1.207, 1.199, 1.161 and 1.118 μm lines were reported in ref. [1]. The 1.139, 1.084 and 1.080 μm lines were reported by R. A. McFARLANE, C. K. N. PATEL, W. R. BENNETT jr. and W. L. FAUST: *Proc. I.R.E.*, **50**, 2111 (1962). The 1.140 and 1.160 μm lines were reported by J. D. RIGDEN and A. D. WHITE: *Proc. of the Third International Conference on Quantum Electronics* (Paris, 1963) under the condition that the 6 328 Å line was used to suppress the 1.53 μm line which competes with the two above-mentioned transitions.

[9] This averaging is permissible since the optical frequencies ν_1 and ν_2 are washed out by the velocity spread of the photoelectrons discussed in Sect. **5.3**.

[10] P. S. PERSHAN and N. BLOEMBERGEN: *Appl. Phys. Lett.*, **2**, 117 (1963).

[11] L. A. DUBRIDGE: *Phys. Rev.*, **43**, 727 (1933).

[12] C. L. HENSHAW: *Phys. Rev.*, **52**, 854 (1937).

[13] There is some ambiguity as to the value of the work function Φ. We have taken $\Phi=\frac{3}{4}$ V as a lower limit representing the maximum possible spread in the electron energy distribution function.

[14] E. G. & G. Tech. Memo no. B-391 (October 1962).

[15] J. GOLDBERG: *Conference on Fast Pulse Techniques in Nuclear Counting* (Berkeley, Calif., 1959).

[16] W. R. BENNETT jr.: *Applied Optics Supplement on Optical Masers* (December 1962).

[17] T. S. JASEJA, A. JAVAN and C. H. TOWNES (*Phys. Rev. Lett.*, **10**, 165 (1963)) have demonstrated a short term (1 to 2 s) stability of this order using two free running lasers. P. RABINOWITZ, J. LA TOURETTE and G. GOULD (*Proc. I.E.E.E.*, **51**, 857 (1963)) have achieved a tracking accuracy of this order with two lasers using optical heterodyne detection.

Tipografia Compositori - Bologna - Italy